1988
Which?
Wine Guide

Edited by Roger Voss

Published by Consumers' Association
and Hodder & Stoughton

Which? Books are commissioned and researched by
The Association for Consumer Research and published by
Consumers' Association, 14 Buckingham Street, London WC2N 6DS and
Hodder & Stoughton, 47 Bedford Square, London WC1B 3DP

British Library Catologuing in Publication Data

Which? wine guide. – 1988 –
    1. Wine and wine making –Periodicals
    2. Wine and wine making – Great Britain – Directories
    I. Voss, Roger   II. Consumers' Association
    641.2'2'0294   TP544

ISBN 0-340-41362-X

Typography   Tim Higgins
Cover photograph   Trevor Melton
Cover design   Fox + Partners
Illustrations   Diana Durant

Cartography by GEOprojects (UK) Ltd
Henley-on-Thames, Oxfordshire

Typesetting by Rowland Phototypesetting Ltd
Bury St Edmunds, Suffolk

Printed and bound in Great Britain
by Collins, Glasgow

Diana Durant.

Contents

Part I Where to buy

Part II What to buy

Part III Wine away from home

Introduction

In last year's introduction, we commented on the wine retailing revolution that had led to the rapid increase of wine warehouses entering the pages of this Guide. They and the supermarkets, we felt, were squeezing the High Street off-licences out of the wine market.

With one or two honourable exceptions, this process has continued: the High Street multiples are being forced to decide willy-nilly whether to continue to sell a varied range of wines alongside beers, cigarettes, branded spirits and sweets, or whether to cut down their wine lists drastically, almost to the point of removing wine from their shelves altogether.

In a sense, we shouldn't be too concerned about their fate. They are – again with a few exceptions – part of large brewing empires. And just as most pubs still have to learn about wine because they are controlled by brewers, so most High Street off-licences are run according to policies essentially dictated by beer and spirits interests. The honourable exceptions are either not part of a brewing group, or are operated independently.

The small-is-beautiful merchant

But while one sector of wine retailing declines, another grows. We have become accustomed to supermarkets and wine warehouses as the source of often high quality bottles, nearly always offering good value for money. But the pages of the 1988 Guide record that you don't have to be big to survive in modern wine retailing.

More and more one-person-band wine merchants are starting up in business. Since this is the age of the specialist, it is appropriate that many should be concentrating on one wine area or one type of wine; or, seen from another stance, that they should not be aiming to cover the whole world with a seemingly random selection of wines, but should be offering careful selections, indicating that they have gone out and chosen the wines rather than simply finding them at big wine tastings in London.

There is terrific enthusiasm among these people. They organise wine tastings, lectures, even tours of vineyards. Many of their lists are full of helpful information and idiosyncratic notes which make buying wine from them fun.

Service on offer

They offer something else – service. The supermarkets and wine
warehouses are able to cut their costs to a minimum – and pass on the
benefit to the customer – by cutting down on service. Nobody expects a
supermarket to deliver wine, nor to organise a wine tasting for them
and their friends – and nobody is criticising them for not doing this. It's
not their business.

But there are wine buyers who want good value *and* service. A
surprising number of these one-person-bands offer both.

In all this, we mustn't forget the traditional wine merchants, those
who have been serving the gentry for generations. Some have fallen by
the wayside in this age of increasing wine consumption simply because
they were not offering the interesting and often better value range of
wines that were available from every other quarter. Sadly, others
survive entirely on their wine sales to restaurants – there is still an
amazing lack of interest in the quality of wine among a majority of
restaurateurs.

But others again survive and prosper. They do this by offering
top-class wines (which doesn't necessarily mean expensive wines)
combined with traditional service. It seems that they can still come to
terms with modern retailing – even opening wine warehouses and the
like – without compromising those two essentials.

Wine clubs – to join or not to join

There is yet another form of wine retailing in this country: wine clubs.
The clubs developed because of the difficulty of getting decent wine
away from the precincts of traditional wine merchants. They were –
and are – essentially mail order businesses. A few of the very best offer
stimulating programmes of tastings and visits to underline that they
are clubs or societies as well as wine merchants.

But there is a strong case for arguing that they now do no more than
the best wine merchants – those that win the awards in this Guide.
This is certainly the view of Robert Joseph, who contributes one half of
a dialogue on wine clubs and societies on page 21. He is opposed by
Tony Laithwaite, principal figure behind one of the most successful
wine clubs.

High and low technology

Other features in this year's Guide include a look at the effects of
technological advances on wine making. Although we are also
interested in the growth of the availability of organic wines in the UK
(see the list of specialist merchants who stock organic wines on page
532), we are also very much aware that without the use of much of the

equipment inside a modern winery, whole areas of the world would still be producing quite undrinkable plonk that would hardly travel to the nearest town, let alone to our shops.

And those wines are now flooding in from ever further afield. Every wine merchant seems to list Australian wines, which are excellent value at the moment, as well as being very enjoyable to drink. Italy, Spain and the French regions are all countries or areas from which more and more exciting wines are emerging, while the classic French areas of Bordeaux and Burgundy seem to be offering less and less value for money.

But whoever heard of Zimbabwe or Brazil as wine producing countries – or Texas, come to that? Well, they turn up in this 1988 Guide – just as India did in 1987. The one country that still makes no appearance is South Africa. The decision last year that it would be unsuitable to reintroduce that section in view of the political situation in that country still stands. We can only repeat our hope that future years will bring about a change which will allow us to return South Africa to the Guide.

On the other hand there are two countries whose representation is diminishing, not for political reasons but because their wines are less and less in demand. Germany, until so recently riding on the crest of a wave of Liebfraumilch, has allowed her image as a quality wine making country to suffer terrible harm. Merchants and importers who stock the top quality estate wines can make no headway when the wines are viewed against £1.99 Lieb or Piesporter. It is scarcely surprising that there are fewer of these top wines this year than last on merchants' lists – with no sign of the decline stopping.

Austria has suffered even more. In fact, wines from that country have virtually completely disappeared – and what there is seems to be ageing stock. A combination of factors is at work here: the 1985 diethylene glycol scandal; the fact that Austrian wines are seen to have a similarity to German wines and are therefore suffering from the general decline of interest in this style of wine; and an apparent reluctance on the part of Austrian producers to bother to export.

The Guide at your service

The Guide is at your service to tell you about the wines you can buy and where you can buy them. But we need your help, too. We continue to expand our inspections of wine merchants, but we would like your comments – good as well as bad – on any that appear in the book. We want to add even more to the number we consider each year – we now have getting on for 1,000 merchants on our lists – so if any merchant is not in the Guide that you consider worthy of inclusion, please let us know. You will find report forms at the end of the book.

Elsewhere in the Guide, we look at wine away from home. As last year, we present our top fifty selection of wine bars – some old favourites, a good number coming into the Guide for the first time. We also carry an analysis of the state of wine in restaurants, in which the few good boys continue to stand out against the many others.

We have updated our legal advice to take into account recent legislation to protect the consumer; and we have increased the selection of books in our Bookshelf pages. And we have an entirely new set of drawings to add to your enjoyment as – we hope, right through 1988 – you continue to consult *Which? Wine Guide*.

Acknowledgements

Our thanks go – as always – to the writers who have contributed the articles at the front of the Guide; to James Ainsworth for his feature on wine in restaurants; to Jeni McCallion for her legal contribution; to Diana Durant for her illustrations; and to Mary Redgate, who meticulously sorted out the stockists in the WHAT TO BUY section.

ROGER VOSS

How to use this Guide

Which? Wine Guide can be used both as a directory of merchants and as a guide to wines. You may want to find out the names of local wine merchants, or the Guide's views on a shop or chain of shops. Or you may want to know where to get hold of a particular wine – and what we think of it. Either way we can help you.

Directory of merchants

The first principal section of the Guide, the WHERE TO BUY section, is a directory of wine retailers. This includes individual wine merchants as well as high street off-licences, supermarkets and wine warehouses. They are there because the wines they sell are either exciting enough to warrant inclusion or because they offer good value – and generally because of a combination of both. We have investigated many more wine merchants than have finally gained an entry: some may have even slipped through our net (in which case we would be delighted to hear from readers about them – use the report forms at the back of the book if you like), but most merchants who are not in the Guide are not, in our opinion, good enough.

Directory entries

Before the main text, a directory entry will give you the following information:

1 Name of the firm – generally the name of the shop.

2 The address of the place where you can order or buy wine. For chains with a number of branches, we give the head office only – phone them for your nearest branch.

3 Any special awards that the merchant has won – see page 47.

4 Open and closed – the opening hours and the days on which the shop or order office is closed.

5 Credit cards – which ones are accepted; whether you can open a personal or business account. Most merchants operate on 30-day credit if you have an account – but always read the small print in their list or ask if you are planning to open an account. Some merchants now charge interest on overdue accounts.

6 Discounts – what discounts are offered (generally on unmixed cases). This information does not include any special offers a merchant may make.

7 Delivery – what delivery terms the merchant offers. It pays to read these closely, because even if a merchant seems expensive, free delivery can make quite a difference in the final bill.

8 Glass hire – information on what you need to spend on wine in order to hire glasses free of charge. Always ask for details about payment for breakages.

9 Tastings and talks – whether the wine merchant organises tastings or talks and at what charge. Details of some merchants' tastings and talks are in the FIND OUT MORE ABOUT WINE section (see page 588).

10 Cellerage – whether a merchant will look after your wine for you if your cellar is not big enough, and how much he will charge.

11 An indication of whether the shop sells wine by the single bottle or by the case only. Wholesalers are not allowed to sell wine by the single bottle – they are indicated by the symbol ■.

Guide to wines

The second principal reference section is a review of what's happening in the vineyards of the world, the WHAT TO BUY section. Each regional entry is organised like this:

1 An introductory section giving up-to-date information on new styles of wine, new trends and what to watch for over the coming year.

2 A glossary of terms used in that region to describe wines.

3 A directory of principal producers, merchants and estates in the region, with information about particular stockists in this country.

4 Best buys – our choice of the wines we would buy over the next year from that region.

5 Specialist stockists – wine merchants who specialise in the wines of the region. Unless the address is printed there, details of the merchants will be found in the WHERE TO BUY merchants directory.

More help?

Other sections of the Guide are also designed to help you bring a wine and a merchant together or find a merchant in your area.

1 WHO'S WHERE – the gazetteer on page 51 – lists all the merchants in the WHERE TO BUY merchants directory by town or village and by county. Use this if you want to find a good local wine merchant. The gazetteer cannot, however, include all the branches of chains, high street off-licences or supermarkets – you will need to contact the head office for this information (see page 56).

2 The index of wines – if you want to find where a wine is mentioned in the WHAT TO BUY section, turn to page 283.

The power of the supermarkets

Over half our retail purchases of wine – as distinct from those made in pubs and restaurants – are carried out in supermarkets. It means that the wine buyers at the supermarket groups have a huge power to influence what we, the consumers, toss into our shopping trolleys and take home to drink. ALICE KING *explains how they use that power.*

The enormous influence that supermarkets have on the country's wine buying is relatively recent. Until ten or so years ago the high street chains and off-licences had a dominant market share. They were the convenient corner stores where people popped in for a bottle of beer, spirits or cigarettes, and sometimes wines. But the advent of the 'one-store shop' has changed general shopping trends, and the buying of wine is no exception. The supermarket wine buyers realised that the millions of consumers walking through their doors represented a huge potential captive market. The problem was how to tap that market when they were selling the same big name branded wines as the off-licences.

Own-label – the new brands?

The breakthrough came with 'own-label' packaging. As Allan Cheeseman of Sainsbury's explains: 'Customers had faith in our baked beans and were therefore prepared to try our wines.' That philosophy, adopted by many of the supermarkets, paid off and now own-label sales (which include fine wines as well as everyday bottles) have eclipsed sales of the once dominant branded wines, especially over the past five years, according to Adrian Lane of Tesco. All Marks & Spencer's wines are own-label and over 90 per cent of both Sainsbury's and Tesco's wines. But Waitrose, Sainsbury's and Tesco are still happy to sell the brands while the demand is there.

It could be argued that supermarkets' own-label wines are merely a new way of creating brands. The onus of maintaining the public's awareness has been switched from the producer to the retailer, the latter reaping the benefits of increased profits.

Each supermarket approaches 'own-label' in a different way. While Sainsbury's and Marks & Spencer feature their names in large print, others, such as Tesco and Asda, keep a low profile, feeling that their customers may not like to broadcast the fact that the wine on their table is from a supermarket. And Waitrose is not at all keen on own-label wines, restricting them to a few bestsellers. They prefer the versatility of being able to change supplier and buy in small parcels of wine at will.

'If it sells, people must like it'

So how do the buyers decide which wines to put on their shelves? Is it what they assess their customers want or is it what they think their customers ought to drink?

It is clear from interviews with many of the main supermarket buyers that their market research does not actually involve asking their customers what they want. Rather, many gauge the popularity of a wine by its sales, assuming that if a wine is particularly bad customers will complain. Moreover, with the up-to-date computer control of companies like Sainsbury's and Tesco, they can quickly decide what is selling and what is staying on the shelf on a daily basis. 'Sometimes we take a risk with certain wines which we cannot know will sell. In the vast majority of cases we get it right. But customers will let you know by not coming back for more if they don't like a product,' says Allan Cheeseman.

I suspect that there are far more disappointing bottles than supermarket complaints departments ever know about, simply because few people can be bothered with all the hassle of taking a wine back. You may feel foolish, and wonder if it's your taste which is at fault, quite apart from having to remember to take along a half-open bottle on your next shopping trip and searching out the appropriate person, often after wading through a sea of uninterested check-out staff. The smaller independents with helpful, knowledgeable staff will always score here. Even so, 'with a big seller it's not worth the risk of offering an inferior wine because if customers have a disappointing bottle, they could start buying their wine elsewhere' (Allan Cheeseman again).

Perhaps more market research dealing directly with customers in the shop would avoid this and lead to the supermarkets having a greater understanding of what the customer wants. It is not good enough to say: if it sells, people must like it. That attitude led the big high street chains into the mess they now find themselves in.

The search for quality

Anyway, whether or not we are listened to as much as we might be, it's quite clear that the major supermarkets have identified a marketing opportunity and taken advantage of it. By and large it appears that they are providing us, the consumers, with what we want – at a basic level. If we want Liebfraumilch they will provide it, but the best buyers will make sure it's the best one possible.

Most supermarket buyers spend time abroad, searching out new wines, visiting producers and checking on quality control. But few wines are actually ordered on the spot in the vineyards. Samples are brought back to Britain and put into a tasting where the identities of the wines are kept secret until the verdicts are given. In addition, the buyers receive samples from UK-based agents and visit all the major wine fairs in search of new wines. Obviously the price is an important factor in the final decision, although as Allan Cheeseman points out: 'We don't always buy the cheapest. Quality and reliability are priorities. Rather than offering the cheapest Liebfraumilch around we will pay a few pence more to make sure it is decent.' They certainly have their work cut out – despite Sainsbury's huge sales, the team of buyers numbers only seven.

But quoting numbers of buyers can be misleading. Most supermarkets have a separate quality control department which visits suppliers and analyses all the wines to make sure they conform to EEC standards. And the administrative and accounting back-up is enormous, using systems that only such massive organisations could afford.

But being big does not automatically mean that supermarkets buy well. Because of their huge sales of standard wines they have to look to the larger suppliers to ensure continuity. Success can undermine quality, the original reason for that success. Some suppliers, such as Waitrose, prefer to deal with smaller suppliers in order to keep more eggs in more baskets, and others, such as Sainsbury's, have established 'fine wine sections', largely governed by the price of the wine (ie over £5 a bottle rather than the traditional definition of fine wine), in their bigger stores, where they can offer small quantities of growers' wines.

The importance of labelling

Supermarkets are very careful that the wording on their labels conforms to EEC rules. But they're also well aware of the power of certain words on the label. Terry Horton of Marks & Spencer gives an example: 'The Chardonnay grape is now so popular that it appears on many labels, whereas only a few years ago it would only have appeared in small print on the back label. In my opinion, the simpler the label, the more appealing it is. The days of the horrendous, indecipherable gothic script appear to be on the wane.'

Furthermore, any supermarket concerned with educating the customer will have shelf tickets describing the origin and flavour of a wine. The best have a helpful sweetness code for white wines and a code indicating the weight of a red wine (light, full-bodied etc). Presentation of the wines is important and the best supermarkets lay out their wines clearly, often by country or by style so that, for instance, all the sweet wines can be found together.

Individual approaches

Sainsbury's are thought to account for as much as 12 per cent of Britain's total wine sales, a staggering one million bottles a week. They believe it's their skill as buyers that results in their having a strong influence over what their customers drink. 'It would be wrong to say we lead them by the nose. If a wine tasted like vinegar our customers simply would not buy it. However, they trust in our name and we have the power to create a market simply by making sure we are aware of everything that's going on. Obviously we watch what's selling, watch the wine market and trade press as well as noting which countries are attempting an aggressive push of their wines.'

A good example of how they create a market can be seen from their sales of a once unknown wine, Aruda, from southern Portugal, now one of their bestsellers. 'If we'd simply labelled it Aruda, it would not have sold. But by adding our name, Sainsbury's, which people have been trusting for over 116 years, it sold because they have faith in us.' And of course a substantial advertising budget, as evidenced by numerous double page colour spreads in the Sunday supplements, probably helps reinforce that trust!

Tesco, the second biggest supermarket wine outlet, feel that influence is a two-way thing. They take note of the market research but also try to gauge what customers will like in the future. Head of the team, Adrian Lane, explains: 'Obviously all the traditional areas are covered but when we find wines from non-traditional areas such as Vin de Pays de Gascogne, we offer them to our customers because they are value for money. A few years ago that area was unheard of and now this wine's a bestseller.'

The Co-op, who have only recently started treating wine seriously, rely to a great extent on the advice of their market research department which pinpoints obvious gaps in their list, where either their sales or range does not tally with national figures. Individual Co-op shops are not obliged to buy their wine from the central wholesale division, so the marketing department spends a great deal of time talking to the shopkeepers in an attempt at ascertaining exactly what the customers want. Because many of the Co-op stores are small, the owners are involved directly with the shoppers, so the Co-op marketing men are able to get more direct feedback than can those at Sainsbury's, for instance.

Waitrose have a different approach again, aiming to provide as wide a range of wines as possible, typical of their kind. Their philosophy is to allow customers to choose rather than trying to force something down their throats. This enables them to list wines which do not have a huge turnover, such as the sparkling Clairette de Die or Jurançon from South-West France. They buy purely on the 'gut-feeling' and expertise of their buyers and, by having a particularly wide selection, are able to offer both basic and unusual wines.

This is the total opposite to Marks & Spencer's approach. Because their stores are sited in expensive central shopping areas, all products have to justify their shelf space: if any product is on the shelves for more than six weeks, it must be selling well. Terry Horton explains: 'We're influenced by customers and we influence them.' As an example he cites Chablis as a past good seller because people knew the name. Then they offered Montagny as they became aware that their customers liked the flavour of the Chardonnay grape, and then Mâcon which sold well once the words 'white Burgundy' appeared on the label.

Effective clout

Supermarkets have gone a long way towards offering the customers what they want, with plenty of choice at a basic level. The biggest risk is that, like the dinosaur, they will grow too big and become extinct, especially if they don't listen to what we want. But long may they flourish if they can keep one step ahead to use their clout effectively on our behalf.

Are wine clubs worth it?

Many people buy wines through wine clubs. They buy this way because they feel that wine clubs can offer something some wine merchants are unable to provide, like tastings and wine tours. They may also feel they are getting better wine bargains – just like book clubs. But are they? And do wine clubs offer a better service than top wine merchants who run a mail order business? We asked ROBERT JOSEPH, *who is suspicious of the value of wine clubs, to put the case against, and* TONY LAITHWAITE, *of Bordeaux Direct and The Wine Club, to put the case for.*

THE CASE AGAINST

As a wine drinker, the idea of joining a wine club has sometimes appealed to me. The only problem has been that the phrase 'wine club' has a number of completely different meanings.

There is the wine club which anyone with even a slightly literal mind might expect to find: a local club peopled by a diverse group whose common interest is wine. They may also take an interest in food, and meet to eat, drink and discuss. A local wine merchant may offer them discounts for buying in bulk as a group.

The second type are wine clubs of which the raison d'être is to sell wine, but which also offer their members the kind of social activities laid on by the local wine societies. With few exceptions, they are either tied to a wine merchant or act as a merchant themselves.

Then there is the commercial club, a wine merchant by any other name which has discovered that, by calling a part of its activities a club, it can persaude more of its customers to part with more of their money than they might do otherwise. They offer little in the way of social activities.

It is this last type of wine club which worries me. The genre could be compared with the book and record clubs so eagerly promoted in Sunday newspaper supplements. After all, the 'Nature Lovers', 'World War Two Enthusiasts' or 'Rampant Gourmets' who join their appropriate book clubs do so in order to obtain books at preferential prices. They don't invite members to gather together to discuss the subject or listen to readings. They are merely sales operations. The books are often identical (apart from a publishers' imprint) to the ones on sale throughout the country – but they are cheaper.

With the commercial wine clubs, the situation is different. In terms of prices – and often quality – few of the clubs would want their range of wines compared, bottle for bottle, with the contents on a good supermarket shelf – nor the list of many wine merchants. They might do better, but equally they might do worse. In the blind tastings run by wine magazines, no wine club comes out any better on average than any wine merchant in this Guide. In one sense, it would actually make more sense to describe the supermarkets themselves – with their enormous buying power – as the equivalent of the book or record clubs, rather than any of the wine clubs.

There is another major difference between book clubs and commercial wine clubs. The book clubs don't demand a membership fee. Nor, for that matter, do wine merchants who run mail order lists. If you don't buy, after a while they stop sending you the list, but no money has changed hands.

Wine clubs' membership fees are not negligable, either. Les Amis du Vin charge £15 a year, the Vintner Wine Club (the wine club of wine merchant Arthur Rackhams) £12 a year. In other words, it costs the price of a decent bottle of wine just to belong. What do you receive in the way of privileges?

There is certainly a discount on what you buy, but that's no different from the book club, which doesn't charge a membership fee. And if you bought regularly in reasonable quantity from any of Britain's better specialist wine merchants you would also find yourself at the receiving end of special offers and discounts – without paying for the privilege.

So we come back to the second type of wine club – the one that combines the commercial wine merchant with the benefits of a club. In this category, I would put The Wine Society, the Wine Club, possibly Les Amis du Vin, certainly Le Nez Rouge and probably a new wine club which is being set up this autumn, the London Wine Club.

Of these, two stand head and shoulders above the rest: The Wine

Society and The Wine Club. The former is, in one way, the closest to a club of any, because it exists truly for the benefit of its members rather than that of any owning wine merchant. The full name, International Co-operative Wine Society, tells it all: members are shareholders whose shares rise in value with the success of the society. And, as the entry for The Wine Society in the WHERE TO BUY section of this Guide indicates, the wines aren't bad either.

The Wine Club has built is reputation on the originality of its wines, pioneering Bulgarian wines at a time when Eastern European wines were thought to come in two styles; Laski Riesling and Bull's Blood. More recently, its forays into the South of France have introduced British drinkers to wines they would almost certainly never have tasted otherwise. They also hold tastings, hosted by wine luminaries such as their president Hugh Johnson, run trips abroad and issue a lively newsletter.

Les Amis du Vin do organise tastings, even if they do not put on tours, and carry a good range of New World wines. But their European selection is disappointing and expensive.

Lovers of more traditional European wines would be better off at Le Nez Rouge or at the Vintner Wine Club, or (I hope) the new London Wine Club which will draw on the wine talents of H Allen Smith for its range (see the WHERE TO BUY section).

Certainly all these clubs have something to offer, but I am still not sure why they are any better than some of the top non-club wine merchants. Not one of them produces a better list than, say, Adnams or Tanners. None runs better tastings than Lay & Wheeler or a number of other wine merchants. If you have an account card at Majestic Wine Warehouses, you can go and meet Rémy Krug of Krug Champagne or Gérard Jaboulet of Jaboulet Aîné – and you can't get better tastings than that.

It all depends on what you want a club to provide. If it is the chance to buy interesting wine at an advantageous price, I suspect few of Britain's commercial clubs – even those I've named above – come up with better goods than some of the top wine merchants. If you want the opportunity to meet like-minded souls, those wine merchants' tastings are as good a setting as any. Or you could pay the (inexpensive) membership fees to join clubs such as the International Wine and Food Society, the Zinfandel Club, the Wine and Dine Society, or other clubs whose addresses appear in the WINE CLUBS section of this Guide.

I don't mind buying some of the good things the wine clubs have to offer. I just don't see why I should pay for the privilege of buying from a wine merchant by any other name.

ROBERT JOSEPH

THE CASE FOR

I cannot really speak for all wine clubs, but I'll try and outline what a wine club can do for you, without necessarily implying that my own or any other particular wine club totally achieves that ideal.

Wine clubs sell wine plus information. Of course, everybody who sells wine sells information. A label on a bottle is information, but it is not much – any more than shelf cards in a supermarket give much information. And there is an absolutely insatiable demand for information.

Many wine drinkers get their information from articles in newspapers and magazines, and then go off to their local branch of Waitbury's to buy the latest bargain. There's nothing wrong with this system, except one little thing: most people just don't have the time.

They very much want to discover the wonder whizz new Eritrean Cabernet, and they definitely intend to get out and buy it. But, alas, if they find the time, they often forget just which Cabernet was the outstanding bargain of the high street this week.

And if, unbriefed, they walk up to the liquor shelves of Waitbury's, there's nobody to ask. It's no good asking the check-out girls, because they will ask a supervisor – and you can imagine how popular that will make you in the queue.

On the other hand, a wine club puts the information about a wine right next to the little box you tick: where it comes from, who makes it, roughly what it tastes like and why, how to serve it – and so on. Sounds just what you want? Tick the box, and in a couple of days the van driver should be at the door with your wine – and you won't have had to lug any bottles home.

That, I believe, is why people join wine clubs. And we proliferate and grow. We are, of course, subject to price comparisons: and often those comparisons with a supermarket don't look good. If you compare our Bergerac or Bulgarian Cabernet with the ones on Waitbury's shelves, they will probably be cheaper at Waitbury's.

Why? I don't think it's because of the buying power of the supermarkets, huge though that is. Our turnover is now into eight figures, and if any supermarket group has a wine turnover of more than eight figures, they haven't announced it. And differences in buying power between ten and fifty or sixty-plus million mean nothing in wholesale wine-buying prices, because of the unusually small size of most of the production units – the vineyards.

But consider Monsieur Petit-Vigneron and the six barrels of wine he wants to sell to Britain. Why should he give a better deal to Waitbury's than to Mr Tweed-Claret, country wine merchant for six generations? That's true of penniless peasants in the Midi, just as it's true of grands crus in Bordeaux. Even in the case of large estates or co-operatives – or state monopolies as in Bulgaria – the scales of production and purchase are such that no advantage can accrue to the supermarkets that cannot accrue to the big wine clubs.

It is in other ways – not buying power – that supermarkets save money. They don't sell quite the same wines, even though they may buy from the same producer. Nor do they make wine buying as easy or nice: they don't dish out free bottles to get people going, they don't deliver, they don't trumpet full refund guarantees (although they are obliged to refund if there is something wrong with the wine, how often do people complain?). They are not on the end of a phone for reassurance or advice, they don't take you to visit Monsieur Petit-Vigneron or bring him over to Britain to pour out samples for club members.

These are the extras (we consider them essentials) that cost money. That is where the price differences occur, and it's up to the public to choose what it wants. Supermarkets may be cheaper, but with the best will in the world they are rather boring.

When I became a wine merchant, I didn't just want to sell bottles, I wanted to sell the magic of wine as well. Of course, many specialist wine merchants like to sell the magic too. I do not deny that some wine merchants offer a club-like service – they all try to. But provided the membership fee is adequately compensated for with tangible benefits – genuine discounts, free bottles, magazines, free delivery, just the pleasure of belonging – a club is certainly best for most people.

On file in our offices, we have many letters making the same, (for us) bittersweet compliment: 'Thank you, Wine Club, for getting me started in wine. I'm off now to hunt for bargains on my own.' Whilst we see that as a little problem (and we're working on it), it shows, does it not, that we wine clubs can't be all that bad, can we?

Tony Laithwaite

Taking the hit and miss out of winemaking

High tech developments have revolutionised the way wine is made over the past two decades. They've meant that what we drink is consistent, reliable and much more attractive to consumers. But, argues MAUREEN ASHLEY, *Master of Wine, high tech can go too far in influencing the taste of the wine.*

It must have been a hit and miss affair, buying wine in the bad old days before winemakers had come across technology. It would have been all right for the fine wines, if you could afford them, bought from a traditional wine merchant who had selected with care after tasting. Otherwise, the lack of consistency between shipments, or even between bottles, would probably have been sufficient to explain why we remained a nation of beer drinkers.

It must have been pretty disheartening for the serious winemaker, too. Imagine seeing the results of a year's labours in the vineyards being ruined during vinification, knowing what was wrong, but not having the means to do anything about it.

It was in the immediate post-war years that winemaking really came to be regarded as a science instead of, or perhaps as well as, an art. It wasn't until the sixties, though, that the means of controlling the process began to catch up with the theoretical knowledge. Then, and in the seventies, the impact of the new methods resounded through the cellars, causing what has been called the technological explosion. Now, the people making wine with no recourse at all to post-war know-how are exceedingly few and far between.

With technology, styles of wines can be created that couldn't exist without it, but its great benefit and, surely, its main purpose are to enable the winemaker to produce the sorts of wines he is capable of *without* its help – but to produce them more often and more reliably.

As an example, one major area where technology has infiltrated winemaking is that of temperature control during fermentation. A certain amount of warmth is required to activate yeasts enough for a fermentation to start. Once going, a good deal of heat is created and the temperature of the must-becoming-wine can rise considerably. If the temperature really soars, the yeasts die off and the fermentation stops, but even if this limit isn't reached, too high a temperature makes for an unpleasant, coarse wine of reduced ageing potential.

In earlier times the only ways of controlling an excessive temperature rise in a vat were to open the cellar doors to let cold air enter (assuming that the ambient temperature was colder than that in the cellar) or to throw ice into the vat, with a resultant dilution of the wine. Both measures were sometimes more curative than preventative and by the time they had taken effect, often the damage was done.

These days temperature control can be dealt with automatically. A thermostat positioned inside a vat is set to trigger action at whatever temperature the winemaker reckons wise. Usually this is a couple of degrees below the maximum he is prepared to tolerate in order to allow the temperature to increase a little more while remedial action is being taken. In the more sophisticated systems this involves automatic cooling, either by water running down the walls of the vat (made of stainless steel) or by coolant passing through a serpentine inside the vat.

Power to control fermentation

So far, so good. Technology is giving the winemaker the power to control a fermentation so that it proceeds reliably every time, the way it would have done only occasionally in extremely lucky conditions. The wine can only taste better. Then the line of thought develops that if less hot is good, then even cooler must be better. So fermentation temperatures became steadily cooler and cooler, especially for white wines, which are particularly sensitive to the effects of heat through which they lose their fragrance and elegance. It almost developed into a challenge to see just how low the temperature could get. It didn't matter how slowly the yeasts worked, as long as they didn't stop altogether.

The results were some beautifully clean wines, fresh, lively and, well, vinous – but not much more. What had happened was that all the primary aromas had been carefully conserved but at the expense of the secondary aromas, which help give varietal character. These sorts of wines were the creations of technology. They could not have existed previously.

Sense has, thank goodness, returned and temperatures are now back up at a level that allows freshness, cleanliness, aroma and character all to be present. There's no doubt that this control has given us many more attractive, drinkable white wines than were imaginable twenty years ago.

Temptation to tinker

The temptation to tinker went on, though. Warmth is necessary to extract colour from reds. By macerating the must on the grape skins during fermentation the colour is extracted, but so are tannins and various other elements which give body, structure and keeping power. For more serious reds technology has just lent a helping hand. Instead of a labourer having to punch down each day the cap of skins and stalks that rises to the top of a fermenting mass, or instead of him having to pump, manually, wine from the bottom of each vat over the cap at the top to ensure that the colour is extracted, simple tech does it for him.

Light, easy-drinking reds can't undergo this treatment without losing their essential lightness. So they can suffer from a lack of colour – and customers seem to like good colour. Enter technology. By heating the must before it begins to ferment, a lot of colour can be extracted without much else. It can then be cooled, pressed and fermented away from the skins, like a white wine, so colour without tannin results. Apart from a tendency for their colour to drop out during fermentation, these wines are fine when very young but tire remarkably quickly. No doubt another technique will be developed to prevent this premature ageing but it does seem to make wine more a marketing man's ideal than a natural product.

Apart from these uses of wine science, it seems that the more technology one uses the more one is forced to use. For example, it is agreed that a clean must goes a long way towards producing a clean wine. Traditionally, pressed juice was allowed to rest for a few hours before fermenting to allow any bits and pieces to settle out. Now, in cellars of a certain size and wealth, a centrifuge looks after all that. It's very efficient, removing much more débris more quickly. It's so efficient, though, that it strips out the natural yeasts as well, making the use of an innoculated yeast culture imperative.

Some producers in fact prefer yeast cultures. They are more reliable, more controllable, and specific cultures can be selected to give certain desired characteristics. To have the choice is fine; to be compelled to have a slightly altered final product is debatable. For the type of yeast used does affect the taste of a wine. It's not as obvious as getting a

Burgundian taste by using a yeast from Burgundy, but subtle differences do result and much research work is still being done on yeast cultures.

The size of the cellars

The extent of technological ingress depends to a large extent on the size of the cellar, ie the volumes of wine being handled. Many cellars look pretty much the same as they did many years ago: there are lots of wooden casks, possibly the odd cement vat, not a sign of stainless steel; the walls are covered with fungus, the floor is basic; tubing, demi-johns and other rudimentary pieces of equipment are strewn around. The influence of technology seems minimal, yet the wine that issues forth is heavenly. So why all this need for innovation?

Firstly, the very fact that small quantities of wine are being handled removes much of the need for sophisticated temperature control schemes. A small container has a larger ratio of surface area to volume, so there's a natural air-cooling effect. However, if the cellar handles white wine, it will without doubt have at least one piece of modern equipment: the press. Modern horizontal presses, designed to extract the juice as gently as possible, with the minimum of pressure and the least damage to the grapes, have so proved their worth in the quality of the final wine that no one trying to make decent wine would even dream of not investing in one.

For reds, crushing by foot has been retained only in a few outposts, and much of that for tourists' benefit. Mechanical crushers, however basic, are the norm. Yet there's still a belief that the best way to crush grapes is by the gentle, consistent, rolling action of the human foot, so much so that a crusher has now been invented, at enormous expense, to replicate a foot's action.

A small artisan's cellar will contain wines made, to a certain extent, in much the same way as a place full of stainless steel and computer banks. There's less need for automation since one man, clucking over each of his precious wine containers like a mother hen, can know exactly the characteristics of each one, and can minister to each as and when necessary. This is impossible as volumes increase. However, without the technological advances of the last twenty years, he wouldn't necessarily have had the tools to do anything at all, but at least he can get away with things that bigger outfits can't.

Cutting out the crystals

For instance, they can't permit tartrates in their wines. These are small, harmless crystals of potassium tartrate which are formed quite naturally from the tartaric acid present in wine when it is kept cold. Unfortunately, they look like glass or sugar crystals and tend to put off potential drinkers. So the larger-scale producers have to invest in

29

expensive refrigeration equipment to precipitate out all the potential tartrates before the wine gets bottled. For the small winemaker this doesn't matter. He may well be keeping his wine a fair time before bottling in cool cellars so there's a lot of natural precipitation. Even if he doesn't, he's dealing in more expensive wines to a more sophisticated public which doesn't recoil at the sight of a crystal-encrusted cork.

His customers are probably not quite so fussy either about absolutely star-bright wine, so he doesn't have to indulge in the super-efficient filtration systems of his larger-scale fellows. He may not filter at all. Small volumes of wine kept in small containers for considerable times will fall bright naturally by precipitation. The larger the volume, the slower this process. He may just filter lightly, especially if he sells wine to the United States, whose drinkers are more particular about that sort of thing.

Filtering removes any minute particles from the wine, leaving it clear and limpid. There's a strong argument for saying that it strips flavour elements at the same time, so a filtered wine will always be the poorer for the process. What price, then, the large establishment whose wines may undergo three successive filtrations, the last so tight that anything bigger than 0.45 microns won't get through? That's smaller than the size of bacteria or yeasts so if the wine loses a little fine tuning in filtration, at least it's secure against microbiological spoilage, an important consideration.

More consistency, less spark

So technology may well be the reason why there's more consistency but less spark in some of our wines. It also tends to get blamed, less fairly, for the existence of additives and other chemicals in them. That is far more the role of the chemist who, having recently discovered a great deal about the structure of wine, has been able to advise on what substance to add to combat one defect or to disguise another. In fact, in one very important way, technology is a help much more than a hindrance: it can permit much lower levels of sulphur dioxide.

Sulphur dioxide (SO_2) is a necessary evil in wine. It has been used since time immemorial to stop wines oxidising and to protect them against the effects of harmful bacteria. No other anti-oxidant is as successful without itself being harmful. Too much SO_2, though, is bad news. It can combine with elements in wine to create sulphites, which some believe may be inadvisable for our health if ingested in huge quantities. More obviously, it is unpleasant: it attacks like spent matches, making the nose or throat itch, or the eyes and nose run, or the sufferer cough or sneeze. There's no way of doing without sulphur dioxide, so the aim of any conscientious winemaker must be to restrict its use to the minimum necessary to produce the desired effect.

The skill is to keep as high as possible a proportion of the SO_2 added active as an anti-oxidant and not combined with the wine. This can only be done with careful winemaking and with a number of the techniques that technology makes available. One of the arguments against reducing the legal limits for SO_2 was that it would then be impossible for many small, artisan winemakers to make wines in accordance with the law, since they were without the technological know-how and equipment necessary. This may be a slight exaggeration, but nevertheless if SO_2 levels come down it will be more because of technology than despite it.

The more one examines developments in wine technology the more one realises that it brings the security of producing a sound, reliable product. The major disadvantage, if the temptation to create new wine types using it is followed, is the loss of quirky brilliance from time to time. The moral for any winemaker is clear: the less he is prepared to gamble with a year's livelihood, the more he needs technology to serve him.

Changing attitudes to wine drinking

We drink more wine than ever before. But do we appreciate what we're drinking? Do we listen to the pundits who try and influence our taste? And should we be too worried anyway about what we drink? After all, the best thing we can do with wine, reckons CHRIS FOULKES, *is to sit back and enjoy it.*

One of the sad occasional accidents of an era of inflation is the discovery of old bills, odd scraps of paper bearing forgotten prices. 'Did we really only pay that for a meal out, or a gallon of petrol, or a new suit?' The other day an annotated bill surfaced in the corner I keep for wine notes. It gave me quite a shock. It was six years old, to the day, and it showed that in 1981 I was paying more or less exactly what I am paying now for everyday wine.

The 1981 cellar included a 1976 petit château at £2.49, a Loire Gamay at £1.97 and a Chilean Cabernet at £2.19. A branded Spanish red, probably a Valdepeñas, was £1.97. The Chilean was a relative bargain, for the same wine now sells at nearly £4. But in 1987 I can drink claret of much the same quality as that 1976 Ch Palanque for only pence more. Majestic lists Loire Gamay at £1.99 – a mere 2p dearer than in 1981. The equivalent of the Spanish wine is now actually cheaper.

The price factor

If you are going to change people's attitudes to something it helps enormously to change the relative price too. That wine is now cheaper than it was, relative to the price of other goods, especially beer and spirits and, crucially, to average income, is the biggest change in the field since I have been observing it.

I have heard it said by wine retailers that a key point came when the price of a four-pack of beer (going up) met the price of an ordinary bottle of wine (static, or more likely going down). Your ordinary shopper, casting his or her eye along the shelves of the corner off-licence is hard put to consider wine an elitist drink when it costs less than lager.

Britain is happily placed as the last consumer economy without a real wine-drinking habit. It may come as a surprise to some to realise how little we drink. The winemaking countries – France, Italy, Spain – are ahead by a factor of ten. Germany, which is only partly a wine country (most of it makes, and drinks, beer) is three times as thirsty. Holland and Belgium, perhaps the closest comparisons to us in terms of climate, culture and lack of home-grown wine, drink more than we do, and even America is well ahead.

Wine producers have spotted this and reasoned that if Britain's thirst can be increased they can sell us more wine – but there's an awful lot of wine out there to sell. We are living in an age of gluts: wine lakes and grain mountains occur all over the agricultural world, not just in maladministered Europe. The search for market share is getting a little frantic, as any British wine merchant will testify. This is why, in an inflationary world, the price of wine stays more or less static.

The socio-economic factor

The wine trade maintains that there has been a revolution in the British attitude to wine. Their evidence is the rapid growth in consumption and the widening of the wine market. This is an assumption I question. It is true that more people are drinking more wine, and it is also true that many of today's drinkers are far removed from the classic image of the gentleman with a fine taste in claret, but I am not convinced that attitudes to wine are changing as fast as the statistics.

Is the change in wine drinking an economic revolution or a social one? Try to disentangle the two, answer the economists, at the same time unravelling the complicating strand of greater awareness of health. Talk a little about increased travel and the consequent familiarity with foreign habits. If you are not careful, you stray into generalizations about the growth of the middle classes and the rise of the dinner-party culture. Note, furthermore, that wine books make it into the bestseller lists and that just about every periodical seems to have a wine writer.

All these considerations are true, all have their bearing on the way we use wine, the way it fits into our way of life. But then just spend a few minutes in a wine retailer and observe the people who buy. Confident assertions die on the lips. Here, in a London supermarket, is a family planning a party. The trolley is stacked high with cans of lager and bottles of white Lambrusco in equal numbers. A mile or so away a wine warehouse assistant is patiently counselling Henry and Caroline who are giving a barbecue. His diffident attempts to steer the couple away from the cheapest plonk in the place are construed, indignantly, as high-pressure sales talk. They leave with two cases of a wine better fit for marinating the steak than drinking with it.

Observe what other random consumers drink – not what they tell the market researchers they drink. A scrap-metal dealer in Essex gives a party and serves nothing but Dom Pérignon. A prison governor in South London anxiously quizzes me on the phone about the likely maturity of his stock of 1970 Grand Cru St-Emilions. A group of soberly suited science students puzzles long and hard over a particular Burgundy at a college wine tasting. Japanese managers on a course to fit them for working in Britain study the etiquette of the wine list and absorb the need for a different glass for each wine.

All are wine drinkers, all part of the statistical pattern but highly individual in their attitude and approach, but only one of those snapshot consumers is really interested in wine, the prison governor. The others are buying a social necessity or a piece of one-up-manship or part of the equipment required in the fight for a good job – there are as many motives as customers.

A nation of connoisseurs?

Connoisseurship is the minority motive. It is a fallacy that a growth in wine drinking has made us a nation of connoisseurs. Far more people drink wine than appreciate it. Is this an inevitable part of the widening of the habit, on the 'more means worse' principle? It seems unlikely. The truth is surely that the average Brit always did drink out of habit, social necessity and – let's be honest – to get drunk. Georgian three-bottle squires and Edwardian Champagne Charlies may have been concerned about the quality of their drink, but quantity came first. Wine was, with beer, a drink of known wholesomeness: unlike water it did not give you cholera (clean, reliable mains water was a mid-Victorian innovation). Wine may have lost this role, but it is as well to remember that it is, and always has been, a beverage before it is a hobby.

The extra factor today is availability, or, to be more precise, affordability. More people are able to afford wine than ever before, and moreover, since there is much better, inexpensive wine, and plonk no longer necessarily equals rot-gut, there's no reason why they should have to take it seriously before they buy it.

The sweetness factor

The extent to which wine buyers care about its taste and quality is unknown. Cynical wine experts will point to the success of certain branded, widely advertised wines and aver that taste and excellence have little to do with popularity. Yet who is out of step? If people buy wine for more reasons than to please their palates, who are the experts to argue? And is the accepted standard of taste in 'expert' circles the only one? It is noticeable that the leading mass-market wine stores sell more Liebfraumilch than anything else. When polled by a curious journalist, the chain stores listed their 'top ten'. None of the branded wines made it very high in the charts, and only one or two chains gave first place to a wine other than a cheap German. The public, voting with their cash and their credit cards, wants a drink that is soft, bland and slightly sweet.

Sweetness is, except in carefully defined circumstances, bad news to wine experts. But is the current public taste so different from those in the past? Port, after all, is sweet. Claret was until not so very long ago pepped up with sweet southern wines to fit it to the English taste. I know of elderly people who consider Sauternes the ideal meal-time drink and cannot understand this fashion for 'thin potations' like Sancerre and Muscadet. Are we self-conscious wine drinkers, in our search for authenticity in wine, out of touch with the mainstream of taste?

America has seen an erosion of the market for 'straight' wines since the fashion for coolers ripped across the country. Coolers are promoted as low in alcohol, but they are also sweeter than most white wines. Are American consumers turning away from oaky Chardonnays and austere Sauvignons, seduced by the fruity sweetness of the coolers? Or are different people drinking the two drinks? The American wine industry has a history of sweet wine-based drinks. Apple wine made millions for the Gallo Brothers before Napa Cabernet was born or thought of. Thunderbird, a heavily advertised, sweet, fortified wine drink – part of American folklore almost – is showing signs of taking off in London among the black community as well as among those other groups who habitually follow US fashions (however second-hand).

Even the French, held up by the British wine-appreciating classes as paragons of discernment, have some sweet-toothed habits. They drink sugary, immature port before meals (and by doing so enable British port shippers to indulge a taste for austere and gentlemanly tawnies). For every French aperitif with a sophisticated herby, dry tang there are two whose sweetness would appal even a British Liebfraumilch drinker.

A boom in reassurance

So: far more British people drink wine than appreciate it. More people want their wine unfashionably sweet than the experts like to think. Yet there is a wine boom, a boom in curiosity. Ask any retailer whose products have been recommended in a widely read wine column. Dramatic increases in sales follow. Being a day or two late in trying to buy a praised Champagne or claret is like buying a tipped share after it has been in the Sunday papers: you are lucky to find any left. So people *are* eager to be advised, and are prepared to follow that advice. One conclusion could be that wine drinkers are a lot less certain about the stuff than they would like to be. The search for reassurance sells wine books and prompts people to read the wine columns.

The wine world recognises this uncertainty and attempts to ease it by promoting their wares as safe and unquestionably correct. One advertisement shows a stiff French father being won over by a wine no real Frenchman ever drinks, another reveals aristocratic Germans letting us into the secret of their ancestral Moselle, made in reality at a factory down the autobahn. A Spanish bodega buys the right to a noble title by inviting a Marqués on to the board, then uses his name on the label.

British conservatism

But we are a conservative lot. Take labels, for instance, which are about the most archaic form of graphic design in retailing. Just about every other package in the supermarket, from soap to curry powder, has undergone the design treatment and come out smarter, cleaner, more modern. But with wine, we still like landscapes and gothic script, coats of arms and ancient titles. And whatever happened to wine boxes, those convenient packages with so many advantages over glass? Where are the tetrapaks, the cans? Australians buy half their wine in non-glass packaging. Why not us?

Wine boxes initially got a very bad press, mostly for the good reason that the wine inside them was poor stuff. But I worry that the dismissal of convenient packages and popular wines by commentators is out of touch with public taste and is simply helping to preserve that uncertainty. Much has been done to broaden wine journalism in the last ten years, but even among the younger writers there are too many whose personal preference for fine and esoteric wines colour their judgment. They are listened to – sales figures show that – but are they dealing with the wines people actually want to buy?

An end to history-mystery

One day, a wine will come along which is sold and bought as a fresh, modern, no-nonsense product. Marketeers will announce, and consumers accept, that it is a scientifically farmed and technologically produced blend, without wild quality fluctuations, and is guaranteed pure. Other sectors of commerce would consider any other approach to be commercial suicide. But not wine. Our attitude to wine is still stuck in the days of history-mystery.

When that modern brand does appear, we will know that the British have lost their suspicion of wine. They will be at home with their own preferences and not cowed by the experts and their 'correct' tastes.

Australia seems to have managed this transition and done so in a short space of time. Remarkably fine wine is still made and drunk there, but the mainstream of the market seems to have settled down into regular, unfussy buying of boxes (known as 'casks'). Partly this is due to its being very cheap: British wine prices may have dropped, relatively, but there is still a long way to go. The other reason for this swift (and it *was* swift: not that long ago you'd have caused a riot by asking for a poncy drink like wine in an Aussie bar) acceptance of wine is national pride. Alas for the factors that keep our own wine industry so small.

Australia, and California, and of course most of Europe, has that advantage over us. If wine is made nearby, perhaps by people you know, or friends of friends, it loses much of its mystery. Cellar-door sales bring wine-buying into the same category as picking your own raspberries at a fruit farm: a normal, human activity. We would be more at ease with wine if we had a bigger indigenous wine-growing industry, and perhaps one that could distance itself emotionally from the country crafts workshops and minor stately homes that it seems to have to compete with for summer afternoon visitors. English wine has passed the joke stage in the public consciousness, but has got stuck in a rather twee rut as something middle-class drop-outs do and then have to let coach parties gaze at to pay the bills.

A golden age of choice

The good news about wine in this country is that there is more of it, more variety among it, more chance of it being good, and it's cheaper – all of which are the good side of not having native suppliers to protect. The bad news is that this burgeoning of choice has swamped many consumers. So will the wine trade be able to go on selling the current vast variety of good wine in the face of the public's tentativeness about what it likes. The wine revolution has happened, but it is rather like the supposed revolution in shareholding. Millions of Sids had their punt on British Gas, but that doesn't make them investors. Millions have got the habit of an occasional bottle of wine, but that doesn't make them connoisseurs. Some over-optimistic merchants in both fields are going to have to take account of this. Winemakers all over the world have been forced into bankruptcy through competition, and in the USA, several of the biggest drinks companies have recently pulled out of the mainstream of wine, seeing no further growth in the market. Interestingly, they have stayed in the 'premium' wine business, the area where prices are higher. But the days of good-value everyday wine in America may be numbered. If that trend continues we may face less choice and higher prices.

If you like something a lot, you want other people to like it. People keen on vegetarianism, or model railways, or stamps, or matrimony, want others to join too. Wine lovers are not dissimilar. But it is worth reminding ourselves, those of us who find it worthwhile reading about wine and searching out new and better-value bottles, that we are a quirky minority. Even if a majority of the adult population enjoys a glass of wine – as the researchers tell us – that doesn't make every household a hotbed of connoisseurship, or every dinner table a debating forum for claret vintages. The best thing we can hope for is that we British emulate the Australians, cast aside our diffidence and accept wine as a healthy, enjoyable, easy-going drink. The minority to whom wine is a hobby will then be well catered for by a prosperous wine trade, buoyed up by a steady demand for everyday wine. If we fail to make the transition, then I fear we may look back on the Eighties as a golden age of choice, value and freedom. And we'll regret that the British disease of diffidence, snobbery and conservatism has let another opportunity slip by.

Just up from the country

Vins de pays are wines frequently offering terrific value from areas of France we hardly know about. Perhaps surprisingly, they're not necessarily from old traditions, but the creations of marketing men. GORDON BROWN *explains what they are, and whereabouts in France they come from.*

If 'vins de pays' gets translated at all, the English version is 'country wines'. Nothing is lost in the translation, indeed, there is a confusing gain: the English term has come to mean *all* French wines, controlled or otherwise, grand or simple, which come from outside the mainstream appellation contrôlée areas like Burgundy, Bordeaux and Champagne.

In France, 'vins de pays' refers specifically to a non-blended wine that is a step up from a usually blended vin de table but two steps below appellation contrôlée. However, in Britain the wine trade lumps proper but lesser known ACs, such as Bergerac, and VDQS wines (vins délimités de qualité supérieure, the next stage down) such as Côtes du Vivarais, together with vins de pays and vins de table because no one has ever heard of them, which makes them tough to sell. It means that as a 'country wine', the vin de pays gains in status by such lumping together.

The high-rise structure

When the French appellation contrôlée laws were established in 1935, wines were initially designated either as vins d'appellation contrôlée or vins de table. The latter tended to be a polite term for rustic wines which were knocked back in the fields, in sheds or on tractors. No one bothered carrying them as far as the dining table, probably because the container was too cumbersome.

In the fifty years since then, France's wine classification has developed into a high-rise structure, with VDQS wines (originally intended for the French domestic market and subject to slightly less stringent controls than AC wines), and, most recently, vins de pays filling in the area between the first two extremes.

However, France's famous wine names are all ACs, and over the years, consumers have picked up the fact that AC is some kind of badge of approval. Things went well for a while, but then, in the 1970s, as producers of the well-known ACs exercised what they believed to be their right to put up prices every year, France began losing out to Spanish and Italian wines.

It was then that the French government stepped in to promote the new idea of vins de pays, as cheaper and good value French wines. In the UK, a specimen price tag of £2.99 was first floated, and yet for such a sum one could still buy fine, mature vintages of Spanish Rioja, Portuguese Dão and Italian Chianti Classico, all of which were the broad equivalent of AC – not just one but two categories higher. The price had to come down before the UK consumer took the bait, but now sales of vins de pays have soared. France's falling share of our wine purchases has been restored and, indeed, has increased, but because of more modest wines rather than AC wines.

The French government's decrees have given a terrific impetus to producers of vins de pays with the result that wines are being much more tailored to consumers' demands than before: already wines are priced around the magic £2 mark; they are approachable and easy to drink; they cover the popular range with enough choice within each style to allow experimentation; and if consumers want to spend a little more, there are special bottles which offer character, more depth and some finesse – see 'Super vins de pays'.

New traditions

A promotion slogan for today's vins de pays reads '*Une Tradition Nouvelle*' – a new tradition indeed, energetically reinforced over a 17-month period from March 1981 when 96 vin de pays denominations were decreed, making a grand total of 129.

In fact, many good wine-making traditions were already there, scattered about the country, and all the new legislation did was formalise them and give them substance through documentation.

But in the South of France, with its widespread negative traditions stemming from producers' greed and tunnel-vision, the aim had previously been for quantity; nobody had faced up to the fact that their wines were impossible to sell. Some of the wines were so anaemic that they could scarcely reach the minimum natural alcoholic strength to qualify even for the name of wine.

However, the new vin de pays laws, and the positive response by many of the growers, have resulted in steadily improving standards in the Midi. The new denominations give a goal, recognition, a shop window and a marketing advantage to producers who want to make better wine.

Sorting out the regulations

Because EEC (as opposed to French) regulations distinguish only between quality wines (vins de qualité produits en régions déterminées) and simple wines (vins de table), vins de pays inevitably fall into the latter category, so that term must appear on the label.

Further, vins de pays must come from a single geographical area, with no blending from outside its boundaries. On labels, the production area must figure, such as 'Vin de Pays des Maures'. There are three geographical categories: *zones* (for instance, Vin de Pays de Retz), which are usually the smallest delimited areas and are subject to additional requirements such as specified (as opposed to recommended) grapes. Zone wines are most likely to offer some individualism. *Départements* (such as Vin de Pays du Cher) are French administrative 'counties'. They may each contain several zones. *Régions* (like Vin de Pays du Jardin de la France) are large units and may comprise two or more départements, often covering very big production areas. Part of their function is to give blending possibilities for similarly styled wines from within its boundaries when large volumes of a consistent regional identity are required.

For all categories of vins de pays there are recommendations and restrictions regarding the grapes used. Yields are limited, as are sulphur dosages and acidity levels. The minimum natural alcohol level must be 9 to 10 degrees by volume according to area and, in addition to laboratory analysis and tasting of the finished wines, the grower must declare his volume of production and the vine make-up of his vineyards.

The right to use your local delimited name (including AC) is not awarded or bestowed like an end-of-session school prize; it is simply applied for by the grower when he thinks he is producing according to the minimum requirements of the specific denomination for his area. In law, the peasant farmer is indistinguishable from the maker of a super vin de pays (see below) who will have looked at his soil, his micro-climate and the skills available to him, and will have decided he can make truly superior wine which goes unrecognised by the sole denomination available to him. About 10 per cent of the wines submitted each year for vin de pays status are turned down.

Grapes and vineyard areas

All eight broad vineyard areas which produce designated vins de pays abut, or lie within, better-known AC zones and tend to use the same grapes, plus other local varieties. The South of France – Languedoc–Roussillon, Provence, Rhône and Corsica – uses the Syrah/Grenache/Carignan/Cinsault clutch of vines which give quality, mellowness, robustness, volume and flavour in varying proportions, depending on how they are combined, the nature of the soil, and how industrial or otherwise the production philosophy is. Wines from the West and South-West – Garonne, Aquitaine and Charente – tend to be based on Bordeaux's Cabernet Sauvignon, Cabernet Franc, Merlot and Sémillon, plus Tannat, Cot, Syrah and Beaujolais's Gamay, while the Loire area strongly features the Sauvignon and Gamay grapes. The north-eastern stretches use Pinot Noir and Chardonnay from Champagne and Burgundy, the Gamay and Alsace's Pinot Gris.

In efforts to boost quality and character, Cabernet Sauvignon is being experimented with everywhere as a varietal or in blends, and Chardonnay and Merlot are almost as widespread.

Although 45 per cent of the wine drunk in the UK is white, only 10 per cent of vin de pays production is white, but the range of styles available easily meets mainstream demand here: dry reds, dry and medium-sweet whites and dry sparklers. There are few dessert wines and no pétillant equivalents to Lambrusco. Broadly speaking, vins de pays are for immediate drinking which means that there is a preponderance of fresh, lively, fruity wines, both red and white, best at only one or two years old. Some reds will last somewhat longer, and there is a growing trend in importing classy, domaine-bottled wines which are made to take some reasonable maturing.

Super vins de pays

There are some extremely notable (and expensive) exceptions to the general vin de pays rule, where growers have seen the potential in a particular area and/or particular grapes. One such is Mas de Daumas Gassac in the Hérault, an estate bought in 1973 for the express reason that it was the only outcrop of soil in the South of France identical to certain top vineyards in Burgundy. Perversely, one might think, the owner planted claret vines (70 per cent minimum Cabernet Sauvignon) and now produces a wine which is compared by the experts to Châteaux Lafite, Latour and others. The retail price of the 1985 is over £10, and the wine will not be ready to drink until about 1992. But it is still only classified as Vin de Pays de l'Hérault because of its location and the grapes used.

These 'Super Vins de Pays' are certainly around but they do not yet have the presence and renown of their counterparts in Italy, where the

Super Vini da Tavola are so good, so numerous and so famous that they have come to confuse the whole issue of whether or not wines should be denominated by area. Although the sumptuous AC dessert wines for which the Midi is famous – Muscat from Rivesaltes and Frontignan, and Grenache from Banyuls – do not have a vin de pays equivalent, there is, however, a growing availability of 'primeur' wines, local parallels to Beaujolais Nouveau, in which the second fermentation is dispensed with. This means that wines can be on the retailers' shelves within eight weeks of the grape harvest – very much in line with the *consommation courante* precepts of vins de pays.

If we do not make the mistake of regarding appellation contrôlée as offering a guarantee of quality, it becomes easier to accept the high quality to be found in lesser denominations.

Some pointers

With around 130 geographical denominations of vin de pays, keeping track is never going to be easy, and the two most practical ways of deciding which are the best areas are a) to taste, and b) to look for intelligent innovation. Vin de Pays de l'Hérault seems worth following. It includes the Mas de Daumas Gassac Super Vin de Pays, and also the attractive Cante-Cigale Cinsault-Syrah. Vin de pays du Jardin de la France is a large regional denomination in the Loire area, and some elegant examples of Chenin and Sauvignon are emerging there. Vin de Pays d'Oc Listel is doing similarly classy things with Sauvignon, and producers of Vin de Pays des Côtes de Gascogne have shown great faith in making a varietal Colombard, usually regarded in Europe as a bit of a wimp. In the Côteaux de l'Ardèche you'll find nudists frolicking in the famous river gorges as well as tasty wines. There is a lot of experimentation in that zone with Cabernet Sauvignon, Merlot and Syrah, and the eminent Louis Latour's Chardonnay Vin de Pays shows how impressive these developing wines can be.

One of the bonuses of the vin de pays category is the high incidence of single vineyard wines. Good examples we have come across are Vin de Pays de la Loire-Atlantique, Domaine de Cléray and Vin de Pays des Maures, Domaine de Peyrassel, plus a quite numerous presence from the Bouches-du-Rhône and the as yet small vin de pays production of the Côtes de Thau.

However, most of the 25 million people in the UK who are now sometime wine-drinkers are not interested in grape-types. This gives almost unlimited scope to vins de pays, with their myriad cépages, to prove themselves popular to our national palate, probably in much the same way that Rioja and the other non-French wines did when they were new arrivals here. An important aspect of vin de pays is just that variation of style and characteristics available in its ranks.

Everything's in a name

Some of the zone and département names are likely to be real
marketing stumbling-blocks, though. We are not a linguistically gifted
nation and it could be that, in the way that Germany's delicious
Pfaffen-Schwabenheimer Mandelbaum Beerenauslese has yet to make
its mark in the UK, terms like Vin de Pays d'Hauterive en Pays d'Aude
Cépage Malbec will be difficult to make stick in the mind. Oc (mostly
cheap and cheerful from a biggish area) should do better, and also
Côtes de Brian (good reds with Rhône overtones). Yes, names can
catch on for the silliest of reasons.

Part I

Where to buy

1988 Which? Wine Guide awards

Awards are made on the basis of the quality of the wines sold, the range of the list, the prices of the wines and the service offered. This year, we have four four-symbol and twelve three-symbol award winners – all achieving, in our view, the high standards we have set.

Key to symbols

🐷 **Low mark-up on wine** Awarded to merchants who are more modest than most in their pricing of lower and middle price ranges in particular (*not* to those who offer poor wines at cheap prices).

❀ **Wine quality** Awarded to merchants whose wines are of a consistently good quality across their range.

▱ **Wine range** Awarded to merchants with an unusually wide choice of good wines, whether from one country or the whole world.

☞ **Service** Awarded to merchants who give exceptional service.

	🐷	❀	▱	☞
Addison Avenue Wine Shop		❀		
Adnams		❀	▱	☞
James Aitken & Son			▱	
H Allen Smith		❀		
David Baillie Vintners				☞
Barnes Wine Shop		❀	▱	
Berry Bros & Rudd				☞
Bibendum	🐷	❀	▱	☞
Bin 89 Wine Warehouse	🐷			
Bordeaux Direct			▱	
Buckingham Wines		❀		
Anthony Byrne Fine Wines		❀		☞
D Byrne			▱	

	🐷	✹	🍾	☞
Champagne House		✹		
Chesterford Vintners				☞
City Cellars		✹		
Corney & Barrow		✹		☞
Croque-en-Bouche			🍾	
Curzon Wine Company		✹		☞
Davisons				☞
Discount Wine	🐷			
Domaine Direct		✹	🍾	
Peter Dominic	🐷		🍾	
Eldridge Pope			🍾	
Farr Vintners		✹		
Farthinghoe Fine Wine & Food				☞
Alex Findlater		✹	🍾	☞
Fine Vintage Wines		✹		
Friarwood		✹		
Andrew Gordon Wines			🍾	
Great American Wine Company			🍾	
Great Northern Wine Company			🍾	
Peter Green	🐷	✹	🍾	☞
Green's	🐷	✹		☞
Gerard Harris		✹		☞
Haynes Hanson & Clark		✹		☞
Hicks & Don	🐷	✹	🍾	☞
High Breck Vintners	🐷			
George Hill of Loughborough	🐷			
J E Hogg	🐷		🍾	
Hungerford Wine Company			🍾	☞
G Hush	🐷			
Ilkley Wine Cellars			🍾	
Ingletons Wines		✹		
S H Jones		✹	🍾	
Justerini & Brooks		✹		☞
Kurtz & Chan Wines		✹		
Lay & Wheeler		✹	🍾	☞
Laymont and Shaw		✹	🍾	

	Pig	Flower	Bottle	Hand
Laytons		✿		
Lockes	🐷			
O W Loeb		✿	▱	☞
Lorne House Vintners	🐷			
Majestic Wine Warehouses	🐷	✿	▱	☞
The Market		✿	▱	
Market Vintners			▱	
Marks & Spencer		✿		
Martinez Fine Wine			▱	☞
Master Cellar Wine Warehouse	🐷			
Andrew Mead Wines	🐷	✿		
Millevini			▱	
Moreno Wines			▱	
Philip Morgan	🐷			
Morris & Verdin		✿		
William Morrison	🐷			
Le Nez Rouge/Berkmann Wine Cellars		✿	▱	
Nickolls & Perks		✿		
Oddbins	🐷	✿	▱	
Ostlers		✿	▱	
Pavilion Wine Company		✿		
Peatling & Cawdron			▱	
Christopher Piper Wines			▱	☞
Stephen Porter Wines		✿		
Premier Wine Warehouse	🐷			
Arthur Rackhams			▱	
Raeburn Fine Wines and Foods		✿	▱	
Reid Wines		✿		
La Réserve		✿		
J Sainsbury	🐷		▱	
Paul Sanderson Wines	🐷		▱	
Seckford Wines		✿		
Selfridges			▱	
Edward Sheldon		✿		
Sherborne Vintners			▱	
Sookias and Bertaut			▱	☞

	🐷	❀	◁	☞
Stapylton Fletcher	🐷			
T & W Wines		❀		
Tanners Wines		❀	◁	☞
Taste Shops			◁	
Tesco	🐷			
Philip Tite Fine Wines		❀		
Henry Townsend		❀		
Ian & Madeleine Trehearne Wines				☞
Ubiquitous Chip Wine Shop	🐷			
Valvona & Crolla		❀		
Helen Verdcourt Wines			◁	☞
La Vigneronne		❀	◁	☞
Waitrose	🐷		◁	
Wapping Wine Warehouse	🐷			
Whynot Wine Warehouses	🐷		◁	
Windrush Wines		❀	◁	☞
Wine Case Place	🐷			
Winecellars	🐷	❀	◁	
Wine Society		❀	◁	☞
The Wine Spot	🐷			
Wizard Wine Warehouses	🐷			
Peter Wylie Fine Wines		❀		
Yapp Brothers		❀	◁	☞
Yorkshire Fine Wines				☞

Who's where

This is a gazetteer of individual wine stockists listed in the Guide. See also the directory of chains and supermarkets on page 56.

London

E1
Wapping Wine
 Warehouse 252

E2
Balls Brothers 72

E8
Italian Wine Centre 166

EC1
Cantina Augusto 100
Corney & Barrow 110
Market Vintners 178
Ostlers 197
Prestige Vintners 205

EC2
Corney & Barrow 110
Pavilion Wine
 Company 199

EC3
Bulls Head 267
Champagne and
 Caviar Shop 102
Green's 144
Russell & McIver 216

EC4
Bow Wine Vaults 88
Corney & Barrow 110
Reynier Wine Library
 213

N1
Bretzel Foods 259
The Market 178

N5
Alistair Cameron 99

N6
Bottle & Basket 87
The Market 178

N7
Le Nez Rouge/
 Berkmann Wine
 Cellars 192

N8
Heywood Wines 128

NW1
Bibendum 80
Laytons 173
Prestige Vintners 205

NW3
H Allen Smith 63
The Market 178
Le Provençal 178
Ian & Madeleine
 Trehearne Wines
 241

NW6
Kershaw's Wine
 Warehouse 169
Sherston Wine
 Company 227

NW8
Alex Findlater 131

NW10
Wine Growers
 Association 261

SE1
Davys of London 116
O W Loeb 174
Mayor Sworder 182

SE10
Wines Galore 266

SW1
Barwell & Jones 77
Berry Bros & Rudd 78
Ellis Son & Vidler 127
Farr Vintners 129

Fine Vintage Wines
 133
Green's 144
Harrods 148
John Harvey & Sons
 149
Justerini & Brooks 168
Kurtz & Chan Wines
 170
Morris & Verdin 189
André Simon 228
Stones of Belgravia
 233

SW3
H Allen Smith 63
Buckingham Wines
 93
College Cellar 108
La Réserve 212
André Simon 228
The Wine Gallery 90

SW5
Les Bons Vins
 Occitans 84
Buckingham Wines
 93

SW6
Friarwood 134
Haynes Hanson &
 Clark 151
The Market 178
Premier Wine
 Warehouse 204
Pugsons Food and
 Wine 206
Supergrape 233

SW7
L'Alsacien 247
Jeroboams 166
La Vigneronne 247

51

SW10
Brinkleys 90
Caves de la
    Madeleine 101
The Wine Gallery 90

SW11
Albert Wharf Wine
    Co 61
Goedhuis & Co 137

SW12
The Market 178

SW13
Barnes Wine Shop 74

SW15
Sookias and Bertaut
    230

SW17
Newman & Gilbey
    192

SW18
Bart's Cellars 76
Winecellars 259

W1
H Allen Smith 63
Les Amis du Vin 65
Buckingham Wines
    93
Christopher & Co 107
Curzon Wine
    Company 114
English Wine Centre
    128
Fortnum & Mason
    133
Selfridges 223
André Simon 228
The Wine Society 264

W2
Nigel Baring 74
The Champagne
    House 103
Continental Wine
    House 109
The Market 178
Moreno Wines 188
La Réserve 212

W4
Chiswick Wine Cellar
    106
Philip Tite Fine
    Wines 238

W8
Buckingham Wines
    93
La Gourmet Gascon
    139
Haynes Hanson &
    Clark 151
Tempest, Slinger &
    Co 105

W9
Moreno Wines 188
The Winery 65

W11
Addison Avenue
    Wine Shop 57
Buckingham Wines
    93
Corney & Barrow 110
The Wine Gallery 90

W14
Queens Club Wines
    206

WC1
H Allen Smith 63
Domaine Direct 121
Great American Wine
    Company 141

WC2
Findlater Mackie
    Todd 132

England

Avon

Bath
Sainsbury Bros 218
Sherston Wine
    Company 227

Batheaston
Luxembourg Wine
    Company 176

Bristol
Averys of Bristol 69
John Harvey & Sons
    149

Hallatrow
Reid Wines 211

Bedfordshire

Houghton Conquest
Bedford Fine Wines
    78

Lilley
Smedley Vintners 229

Berkshire

Goring Heath
Copyhold Farm Shop
    110

Hungerford
Hungerford Wine
    Company 161

Maidenhead
David Alexander 62
Helen Verdcourt
    Wines 246
Wines of Westhorpe
    268

Reading
Bordeaux Direct 85
Vintage Roots 249

Sunninghill
Marske Mill House 180

Buckinghamshire

Amersham
Demijohn Wines 118

Aston Clinton
Gerard Harris 147

Beaconsfield
Henry Townsend 240

Gerrards Cross
William Rush 215

Marlow
Marlow Wine Shop 57

Cambridgeshire

Cambridge
Barwell & Jones 77
Oxford & Cambridge
    Fine Wine 198
Joshua Taylor 210

Ramsey
Anthony Byrne Fine
    Wines 95

Sawston
Redpath and
    Thakray 210

Cheshire

Alderley Edge
Eaton Elliot
    Winebrokers 124

Bramhall
Whynot Wine
   Warehouses 255

Chester
George Dutton 256

Davenport
Whynot Wine
   Warehouses 255

Handforth
Whynot Wine
   Warehouses 255

Nantwich
Rodney Densem
   Wines 119

Stockport
Millevini 185

Cornwall

St Austell
Del Monico's Famous
   Wine Emporium 117

Truro
GM Vintners
Laymont and Shaw

Cumbria

Alston
Alston Wines 64

Burgh-by-Sands
BH Wines

Carlisle
Rattlers Wine
   Warehouse 209

Grange-over-Sands
A L Vose 250, 262

Kendal
Frank E Stainton 231

Penrith
Cumbrian Cellar 113

Derbyshire

Buxton
Mi Casa Fine Wines
   185

Devon

Bideford
Wickham & Co 72

Doddiscombsleigh
Nobody Inn 194

Exeter
David Baillie
   Vintners 71
City Cellars 107
Reynier Wine Library
   213
The White Hart
   Vaults 266

Marsh Barton
G M Vintners 136

Ottery St Mary
Christopher Piper
   Wines 201

Plymtree
Peter Wylie Fine
   Wines 270

Dorset

Bridport
Wessex Wines 254

Leigh
Sherborne Vintners
   255

Shillingstone
C C G Edwards 124

Wimborne Minster
Richard Harvey
   Wines 150

Durham

Durham
Alston Wines 64

Essex

Chelmsford
Welbeck Wine 253

Chigwell
Classic Wines 108

Coggeshall
Peter Watts Wines
   253

Colchester
Lay & Wheeler 170
Snipe Wine Cellars
   229

Maldon
Ingletons Wines 163

Saffron Walden
Chesterford Vintners
   105

Gloucestershire

Cirencester
Windrush Wines 257

Longlevens
Stephen Porter
   Wines 203

Greater Manchester

Altrincham
Whynot Wine
   Warehouses 255

Chadderton
Willoughbys 256

Hale
Cadwgan Fine Wines
   98

Heaton Chapel
The Wine Spot 265

Manchester
Willoughbys 256

Urmston
The Wine Spot 265

Hampshire

Basingstoke
Berry Bros & Rudd 78

Headley
High Breck Vintners
   155

Portsmouth
John Harvey & Sons
   149

Winchester
Lockes 173

Hereford & Worcester

Cleobury Mortimer
Hopton Wines 158

Hereford
Tanners Wines 235

Honeybourne
Arriba Kettle 66

Malvern Wells
Restaurant
   Croque-en-Bouche
   111

Worcester
The Wine Centre 260

Hertfordshire

Odsey
Pennyloaf Wines 201

St Albans
Discount Wines 120
Sherston Wine
  Company 227

Sawbridgeworth
Hedley Wright 152

Stevenage
The Wine Society 264

Ware
Sapsford Wines 220

Humberside

Hull
J Townend & Sons
  239

Kent

East Farleigh
Stapylton Fletcher
  232

Sevenoaks
Reid Wines 211

Staplehurst
A O L Grilli Wines 144

Lancashire

Clitheroe
D Byrne & Co 96

Lytham St Annes
Whynot Wine
  Warehouses 255

Preston
Borg Castel 86

Leicestershire

Ashby-de-la-Zouch
David's of Ashby 115

Leicester
G E Bromley & Sons
  92

Loughborough
George Hill of
  Loughborough 156

Lincolnshire

Spalding
J H Measures 92, 184

Merseyside

Birkdale
Oriel Wines 197

Liverpool
Thomas Baty 256
Hilbre Wine
  Company 156
David Scatchard 221

Middlesex

Eastcote
CC Enterprises 262

Norfolk

Elmham
Hicks & Don 154

Great Yarmouth
Sherston Wine
  Company 227

Harleston
Barwell & Jones 77

Norwich
Barwell & Jones 77

Thetford
T&W Wines 234

Weston Longville
Roger Harris Wines
  148

Northampton-
shire

Farthinghoe
Farthinghoe Fine
  Wine and Food 129

Titchmarsh
Ferrers le Mesurier
  130

Nottinghamshire

Askham
Askham Wines 69

Keyworth
Plumtree Wines 202

Newark
Ian G Howe 159

Oxfordshire

Banbury
S H Jones 167
Sherston Wine
  Company 227

Blewbury
Sebastopol Wines 221

Oxford
Fine Vintage Wines
  133
Grape Ideas Wine
  Warehouse 140
Oxford & Cambridge
  Fine Wine 198
Turl Wine Vaults 242

Shropshire

Bridgnorth
Tanners Wines 235

Shrewsbury
Tanners Wines 235

Somerset

Bishop's Lydeard
Châteaux Wines 105

Castle Cary
Sherston Wine
  Company 227

Shepton Mallet
Bowlish House Wine
  Shop 89

Suffolk

Felixstowe
The Grosvenor 77

Hadleigh
Hadleigh Wine
  Cellars 145

Halesworth
Alex Findlater 131

Ipswich
Barwell & Jones 77
Champagne de
  Villages 103
Wines of Interest 267

Martlesham Heath
Seckford Wines 222

Needham Market
Snipe Wine Cellars
  229

Southwold
Adnams 58

Woodbridge
The Cross Inn 77

Surrey

Buckland
Ben Ellis and
  Associates 126

Camberley
Hampshire Wine
  Company 146

Cranleigh
Lorne House
  Vintners 175

Croydon
Master Cellar Wine
  Warehouse 181
Wizard Wine
  Warehouses 269

Dorking
Andrew Gordon
  Wines 138

East Horsley
Upper Crust 244

**Kingston-upon-
  Thames**
Wizard Wine
  Warehouses 269

Richmond
Richmond Wine
  Warehouse 213

Sutton
The Market 178

Wallington
Sherston Wine
  Company 227

Sussex (East)

Alfriston
English Wine Centre
  128

Brighton
The Butlers Wine
  Cellar 94

Lewes
Cliff Cellars 127

Sussex (West)

Billingshurst
Charles Hennings 153

Haywards Heath
Rex Norris 195

Midhurst
Duras Direct 123

Petworth
Charles Hennings 153

Pulborough
Charles Hennings 153

Worthing
Chaplin & Son 104

Tyne & Wear

Newcastle upon Tyne
Dennhöfer Wines 118
Richard Granger 140

Warwickshire

Leamington Spa
Alastair's Grapevine
  60
Wine Case Place 258

Shipston-on-Stour
Edward Sheldon 224

Stratford upon Avon
C A Rookes 215

Warwick
Broad Street Wine
  Company 91
Alexander Robertson
  & Partners 214

West Midlands

Birmingham
Connolly's 109

Stourbridge
Greenwood & Co 193
Nickolls & Perks 193

Wiltshire

Mere
Yapp Brothers 271

Salisbury
Bamptons of
  Salisbury 73
Sherston Wine
  Company 227

Westbury
Hicks & Don 154

Yorkshire (North)

Harrogate
Martinez Fine Wine
  180

Nun Monkton
Yorkshire Fine Wine
  Company 272

York
Cachet Wines 97

Yorkshire (South)

Huddersfield
Pennine Wines 262

Rotherham
Bin Ends 82

Sheffield
Bin 89 Wine
  Warehouse 82
Michael Menzel
  Wines 184
The Wine Schoppen
  262

Stainforth
Wine Warehouse 262

Yorkshire (West)

Huddersfield
Grapehop 212

Ilkley
Ilkley Wine Cellars
  163
Martinez Fine Wine
  180

Leeds
Cairns & Hickey 98
Great Northern Wine
  Company 142
Martinez Fine Wine
  180
Vinceremos 249

Linthwaite
La Reserva Wines 212

Shipley
Whynot Wine
  Warehouses 255

Scotland

Ayr
Blakes & Co 83

Bridge of Allan
J E Hogg 157

Dundee
James Aitken & Son
  59

Edinburgh
Peter Green 143
J E Hogg 157
G Hush 162

Justerini & Brooks 168

Raeburn Fine Wines
and Foods 208

Paul Sanderson
Wines 219

Valvona & Crolla 245

Glasgow
Ubiquitous Chip Wine
Shop 242

Leith
Irvine Robertson
Wines 165
Wines from Paris 167

Moffat
Moffat Wine Shop 187

North Berwick
J E Hogg 157

Perth
Matthew Gloag &
Son 135

Stevenston
Premier Wines 204

Thurso
The Wine Shop 263

Wales

Cardiff
Philip Morgan &
Sons 189

Hawarden
Ashley Scott 68

Llanblethian
Ballantynes of
Cowbridge 72

Presteigne
Andrew Mead Wines
183

Welshpool
Tanners Wines 235

Channel Islands

St Brelade
Victor Hugo Wines
160
The Vintner 250

St Helier
Victor Hugo Wines
160

St Saviour
Victor Hugo Wines
160

Northern Ireland

Belfast
Direct Wine
Shipments 120

Coleraine
Direct Wine
Shipments 120

Downpatrick
Direct Wine
Shipments 120

Republic of Ireland

Dublin
Mitchell & Son 186

CHAINS AND SUPERMARKETS

Space does not permit us to list the addresses of all the branches of each chain, but details at the head of the entry include the address and telephone number of the company's head office, from whom you will be able to find out your nearest branch.

Agnew Stores 59
Asda 67
E H Booth 85
Cullens 112
Davisons 115
Peter Dominic 122
Eldridge Pope 125
Fuller, Smith & Turner
(Fullers) 135
Godrich & Petman
137
Gough Brothers 139

Haddows 145
House of Townend
159
Majestic Wine
Warehouses 176
Marks & Spencer 179
William Morrison 190
Morris's Wine Stores
191
Oddbins 196
Peatling & Cawdron
200

Arthur Rackhams 207
Roberts & Cooper 214
Safeway 217
J Sainsbury 218
Taste Shops 236
Tesco 237
Thresher 238
Unwins 243
Victoria Wine
Company 247
Waitrose 251

Specialist merchants, chains and supermarkets

Addison Avenue Wine Shop

8 Addison Avenue, London W11 8QS	TEL 01-603 6340/6334
The Marlow Wine Shop (Retail),	TEL (0628) 890001
Anglers Court, Spittal Street, Marlow,	
Buckinghamshire SL7 1DB	

OPEN Mon–Fri 10–7.30 Sat 10–6 CLOSED Sun, public holidays
CREDIT CARDS Access, Amex, Visa; personal and business accounts
DISCOUNTS 5% on 1 case DELIVERY Free in London/Marlow area (min 1 case);
elsewhere carriage at cost; mail order available GLASS HIRE Free with case
order TASTINGS AND TALKS Monthly in-store tastings; to groups on request
CELLARAGE Free; in bond charges at cost ■

A new entry to the Guide, these Holland Park vintners have already
put together a quality list, mainly concentrating on the classic areas of
France, but with sidesteps into other countries as well.

A short collection of French country wines includes an excellent
Faugères from Jules Gaston (£2.95) and the fresh rosé from Ch de
Fonscolombe (£3.55). Clarets go back to 1966 (Ch Beychevelle at
£49.50), but sensibly also include some petit château bottles of more
recent vintages (Ch Moulin de Landry, Côtes de Castillon 1982, £3.95;
Ch La Croix du Berny, Puisseguin St-Emilion 1982, £5.25).

Burgundy is dominated by wines from the firm of Chartron et
Trébuchet who produce good whites from Meursault, Corton and
Montrachet – at inevitably high prices. There are more whites from
Etienne Sauzet, while reds are less interesting. From the Rhône, a
good, simple Côtes du Rhône Villages from the Co-operative of
Rasteau (1985 at £3.99) and wines from the top Châteauneuf-du-Pape
estate of Ch de Beaucastel, and the associated Côtes du Ventoux of La
Vieille Ferme (1985 vintages at £3.55), all look attractive.

Beyond France, Italy supplies Chianti from Badia a Coltibuono, and
Spain offers Riojas from Bodegas Olarra and the superb Cabernet
Sauvignon from Marqués de Griñon (the 1983 vintage is £7.75). Look
also for the Muscat-based João Pires Branco 1985 from Portugal (£3.55),
Yalumba Cabernet Sauvignon 1984 from Australia (£3.75) and Delegats
Sauvignon Blanc 1986 from New Zealand (£4.99).

Best buys

Faugères, Jules Gaston, £2.95; Bourgogne Hautes Côtes de Nuits 1983, Georges Duboeuf, £4.99; Côtes du Ventoux La Vieille Ferme 1985, £3.55; Viña Albali 1982, Valdepeñas Felix Solas, £2.95; Ch Theulet 1983, Monbazillac £3.69

Adnams

The Crown, High Street, Southwold, Suffolk IP18 6DP	TEL (0502) 724222
The Wine Shop, South Green, Southwold, Suffolk IP18 6EW	TEL (0502) 722138

OPEN Mon–Fri 9–1, 2–4.30 (Wine Shop Mon–Sat 9.30–1, 2.15–7.30), Sat by appointment   CLOSED Sun, public holidays   CREDIT CARDS Access, Visa; business accounts   DISCOUNTS £1.15 per case on 5–10 cases, £1.85 per case on 11–20 cases, £2.30 per case on 21–50 cases, £2.99 per case on 50+ cases; single case surcharge £2.30   DELIVERY Free on UK mainland (min 2 cases); mail order available   GLASS HIRE Free with 1-case order (deposit required)   TASTINGS AND TALKS Regular monthly tastings at The Crown (Oct–May); to groups on request   CELLARAGE £2.99 per case per year

Adnams' is one of those lists – they're scattered appetisingly through the Guide – which you want to read as well as buy from. Simon Loftus, the wine buyer, writes essays at the beginning of each section to set the scene – as well as to parade a few prejudices.

Most of Adnams' business is by mail order (although a few stalwarts make the pilgrimage to the Suffolk coast to buy direct and probably have a meal in Adnams' restaurant at the Crown). So, in addition to the list, they keep up a constant flow of special offers, en primeur offers (although not for the 1986 clarets – Simon Loftus felt they were too expensive), and information on interesting new areas into which they have gone (such as the Reciotos from Valpolicella, a talking point last year).

The meat of the list is as impressive as it appears. Strengths continue to be in French country wines, Bordeaux, Burgundy, the Rhône, Italy and Germany, but the New World section is expanding, and the range of fortified wines – particularly the old Sherries – is as exciting as ever.

Simon Loftus writes in his introduction: 'What I look for in wine is the character of its maker, the vivid identity which sets it apart from the anonymous mediocrity of the mass-produced brand'. This philosophy certainly shows in the way estate-produced wines dominate the list – especially in areas where it matters, such as in Burgundy and Italy, with the smaller producers in the Veneto supplying the range of Reciotos (Valpolicella Recioto Amarone 1982 Monte Ca' Paletta of Quintarelli, £11.50, and many more); or the straight Valpolicella Classico Superiore 1980 of Serego Alghieri, £5.95. Similarly in Tuscany, pride of place goes to the top estate of Castello di

Volpaia, while wines from Gaja in Barbaresco are the cream from
Piedmont.

In France, look for the deliciously drinkable Côtes du Rhône Ch du
Grand Moulas of Marc Ryckwaert (1986 at £3.20), the northern Rhône
wines from Guigal and the Châteauneuf of Ch de Beaucastel. From the
Loire comes a fascinating selection of Vouvrays from Foreau at Clos
Naudin (1976 for £8.90 is a bargain). French country wines take one on
an inexpensive tour round the individualists of southern France (the
characterful red Domaine de Sainte-Eulalie 1985 in Minervois is £2.60,
for example).

From other countries, the estate wines from Germany, the Ridge and
Trefethen wines from California, the reds from Brown Brothers and
Petaluma in Australia (and also the selection of white Semillons – Moss
Wood 1985 is £6.20), and a good range of Tokays from Hungary all
appeal greatly.

Best buys

Côtes du Ventoux 1986, Domaine des Anges, £2.95; Valdadige 1986,
von Keller, £2.30; Côtes du Rhône Ch du Grand Moulas 1986, £3.20;
Bourgogne La Digoine 1984, A de Villaine, £4.95; Dolcetto d'Ovada
1985, Vigna Tronzo, Guiseppe Poggio, £5; Trittenheimer Altarchen
Riesling Kabinett 1985, Bishöfliches Priesterseminar, £4.10; Koombahla
Shiraz 1982, Brown Brothers, £4.05; Vinho Verde 1986, Casa de
Cabanelas, £3.10

Agnew Stores

HEAD OFFICE Hawthorn House, Cloberfield   TEL 041-956 2345
Industrial Estate, Milngavie, Glasgow G62 7LN
Over 70 branches in Scotland and Tyneside

OPEN (Hours may vary from store to store) Mon–Sat 9–10   Sun (Tyneside only)
12–2 7–9.30   CLOSED Sun (Scotland only)   CREDIT CARDS Access, Visa,
business accounts   DISCOUNTS 5% for 1 case; larger quantities negotiable
DELIVERY Free locally   GLASS HIRE Free   TASTINGS AND TALKS To groups
on request   CELLARAGE Not available

This chain of shops has a selection of wines from the Oddbins list (*qv*)
with some differences in prices.

James Aitken & Son

53 Perth Road, Dundee, Tayside DD1 4HY   TEL (0382) 21197
OPEN Mon–Fri 8.30–5.45   Sat 8.30–5   CLOSED Sun, public holidays and local
holidays   CREDIT CARDS None accepted; personal and business accounts
DISCOUNTS 5% on 1 case (unmixed) or 2 cases (mixed)   DELIVERY Free within
Dundee city boundary; 50p per case beyond; mail order available
GLASS HIRE Free   TASTINGS AND TALKS To groups on request
CELLARAGE Free for wine bought from James Aitken

Quality foods vie with the wines in this 100-year-old shop. Old-fashioned it may appear, but there has been no stopping the expansion of the wine list to countries that were unknown for wine-growing when the shop first opened.

The Australian selection, for instance, has grown over the past year. Now you can find wines from Rosemount Estate, plus some of the superb sweet Muscat wines from Brown Brothers (Dessert Muscat is £9.28), as well as their dry wines (Koombahla Cabernet Sauvignon 1982, £6.95).

However, the main strength of James Aitken's selection is in France. Vintages of claret go back to 1978 and are particularly strong in 1981 and 1983 – try Ch la Gurgue Margaux 1983 at £7.50 or Ch d'Angludet 1983 at £8.95. Over in Burgundy, many of the wines come from the négociant house of Faiveley, but wines from Tollot-Beaut (Aloxe-Corton 1982 is £11.95) and, in whites, from Etienne Sauzet, also make an appearance. Beaujolais is from Georges Duboeuf.

There's a small range of 1983 Alsace from Dopff and Irion (Muscat d'Alsace at £5.35 makes a delicious aperitif) and Dopff au Moulin. Rhône wines come entirely from Jaboulet Aîné.

Outside France, look for Chianti Classico Rocca delle Macie 1984 – one of the few to be recommended from that year – and the Brunello di Montalcino of Fattoria dei Barbi (the 1978 vintage is £9.31). Some good German estate wines are from Bürklin-Wolf and von Buhl in the Rheinpfalz and Bert Simon in the Mosel (Serriger Antoniusberg Riesling Spätlese 1983, £5.85). Riojas are from Faustino and La Rioja Alta.

And, of course, this being on a level with Highland Line, there's a wide range of malt whiskies to choose from.

Best buys
Señorio de los Llanos 1975, Valdepeñas, £3.88; Côtes de Buzet Cuvée Napoléon 1983, £4.15; Montepulciano d'Abruzzo Bianchi 1984, £2.80; Ch Castéra, Médoc 1982, £5.50

Alastair's Grapevine

2 Upper Grove Street, Leamington Spa,   TEL (0926) 39032
Warwickshire CV32 5AN

OPEN Mon–Fri 10–6.30 Sat 9.30–5.30 CLOSED Sun, public holidays CREDIT CARDS Access, Visa; business accounts DISCOUNTS Quantity discounts related to method of payment and distance DELIVERY Free within 30-mile radius of Leamington Spa (min 2 cases); elsewhere £3 per case, 6 cases free; mail order available GLASS HIRE Free (min £50 order)
TASTINGS AND TALKS In-house promotional tastings on Saturday mornings; spring and autumn major tastings; to groups on request CELLARAGE Not available

Alastair Macbrayne obviously likes the apt quotation where wine is concerned – his list is sprinkled with them. But it's also full of good things, which is why we welcome him to the Guide.

The greatest interest is in France, not least in a healthy section of country wines (from Bergerac, Jurançon – the wines of Jean Guirouilh – Côtes du Roussillon and Minervois). Look also for the Cahors-like Vin de Pays des Coteaux de Quercy, excellent value at £2.95.

In more classic areas, there's a well-balanced claret list, Burgundy mainly from Labouré-Roi, and Chablis from Jean Durup, Alsace promises well with wines from Louis Gisselbrecht, the Loire with a top-rate Pouilly Fumé from Domaine Thibault and the Rhône with wines that include the Côtes du Rhône of Domaine la Soumade (the 1985 vintage, £3.99) as well as the Gigondas of Hilarion Roux's sons. Champagne is from George Goulet, or you might choose an excellent Crémant de Bourgogne or Cadre Noir sparkling Saumur.

From the rest of Europe, we would recommend the German estate wines of von Buhl, and pretty well all the interesting Italian range (Brunello from Altesino; Nebbiolo and Spanna from Villadoria, and a white Lugana of Azienda Due Torri). The Spanish bottles number amongst them Riojas from Faustino, and the Portuguese ones a Bairrada from Caves Frei João. Australian wines are from Yalumba, Pewsey Vale and Renmano, plus the superb sweet Botrytis-affected Riesling from Petaluma. California is more limited with a few Mondavi wines. Offley Ports, Barbadillo Sherries and Rutherford and Miles Madeiras are further enticements.

Best buys

Cava Castellblanch Cristal, £4.30; Pinot d'Alsace 1985, Gisselbrecht, £3.99; Franciacorta Rosso 1985, Contessa Camilla Maggi Martinoni, £3.50; La Mancha, La Teja white and red, £2.49; Barbadillo Sherries

Albert Wharf Wine Co

80/100 Gwynne Road, London SW11 3UW   TEL 01-223 8283
OPEN Mon–Fri 10–8 Sat 10–7 CLOSED Sun, public holidays
CREDIT CARDS Access, Visa; personal and business accounts
DISCOUNTS Negotiable DELIVERY Free within London area (min 5 cases);
elsewhere by national carriers GLASS HIRE Free; free delivery with wine
order TASTINGS AND TALKS None CELLARAGE Not available   ∎

Prices are still competitive at this wine warehouse (case sales only) which is right by the river Thames between Battersea and Wandsworth Bridges.

France's regional wines and petit château Bordeaux are the strengths of the list. From the South-West of France the Côtes de Duras 1985 from the local co-operative is good value (£2.59), as is the white Vin de Pays des Côtes de Gascogne 1985 (£2.25). In the Rhône Valley, look for the attractive Côtes du Rhône Villages Beaumes de Venise 1983 (£3.59) and the Vin de Pays de l'Ardèche Cabernet Sauvignon (£2.39).

In Bordeaux, we would enjoy Ch Grand Canteloup 1983 (£3.45) or Ch la Fleur Canon 1983, Côtes de Fronsac (£4.75), as well as wines from neighbouring Bergerac. The Loire offers less interest, and the cost of white Burgundy has whittled the selection down to next-to-nothing.

From the brief list outside France, Italy may be getting better but still gives few producers' names, so it's difficult to tell. We would recommend the good Riojas from Campo Viejo (Reserva 1980 at £3.99).

Best buys

Cannonau del Parteola 1983, Sella e Mosca (Sardinia) £2.59; Campo Viejo Rioja Tinto 1983, £2.99; Vin de Pays de l'Ardèche Cabernet Sauvignon, £2.39; Sylvaner d'Alsace 1985, Co-opérative Divinal, £3.29

David Alexander

69 Queens Street, Maidenhead, Berkshire SL6 1LT   TEL (0628) 30295
OPEN Mon–Sat 10–8.30   Sun, Good Friday 12–2   CLOSED Public holidays (except Good Friday)   CREDIT CARDS All accepted; personal and business accounts   DISCOUNTS Negotiable: 'We will haggle on anything'
DELIVERY Free from Maidenhead to London along Thames Valley and within 10 miles of M4; elsewhere at cost; mail order available   GLASS HIRE Free with order   TASTINGS AND TALKS In-store tastings most Saturdays
CELLARAGE Limited

This Berkshire wine merchant's wide-ranging list takes in most parts of the world. In France he has assembled a big list of clarets, with some good value as well as a concentration of wines from the Cordier estates (Prieur de Meyney 1982 is £5.99; Ch Talbot 1980, £11). In other parts of Europe, look for German estate wines, some of the Italian super vini da tavola (Le Cane from Boscaini, for example, or the Taurasi of Mastroberardino) and a big selection of Riojas (including the whole range of CVNE wines, and wines from Faustino, Berberana, Campo Viejo and Olarra).

In Ports, David Alexander specialises in young vintages, with 1983 vintage Ports from all the major houses. Over in the New World, look for California wines from Firestone, Robert Mondavi, Jordan and Wente.

Best buys

Riojas; petit château clarets

Special awards

🐷 is for bargain prices   📋 is for a very good range of wines

🏵 is for high quality wines   ☞ is for exceptional service

H Allen Smith

24/25 Scala Street, London W1P 1LU   TEL 01-637 4767
29 Heath Street, London NW3 6TR   TEL 01-435 6845
56 Lamb's Conduit Street, London WC1N 3LW   TEL 01-405 3106
26 Old Church Street, London SW3 5BY   TEL 01-352 4114

OPEN Mon–Fri 9.30–6.30 (Heath Street Mon–Sat 10–8)   Sat 10–1
CLOSED Sun, public holidays   CREDIT CARDS All accepted; personal and business accounts   DISCOUNTS 5% for 1 case (min)   DELIVERY Free within Greater London (min 3 cases); elsewhere £6 for 1 case, £3.50 per case for 2–5 cases, £2.50 per case for 6–10 cases; mail order available   GLASS HIRE Free with 1-case order   TASTINGS AND TALKS Monthly/bimonthly promotions involve tastings; to groups on request   CELLARAGE £3.45 per case per year

This small group of shops is associated with the wine shipping firm of Ehrmanns, whose list has some very fine wines, including the Portuguese wines of José Maria da Fonseca, the wines from Tiefenbrunner in the Alto Adige of Italy, those from Thomas Hardy and Geoff Merrill in Australia, and from von Buhl in Germany – and other equally famous names.

But to start with France: there's a good range of country wines – try the Vin de Pays des Collines Rhodaniennes Pure Syrah 1984 at £2.95, for a taste of the Rhône at rock-bottom price; or the Cabernet-Sauvignon-based Vin de Pays de Mont Caume 1985 from the Bandol area at £4.50. Bordeaux is marked by some good value petit château wines as well as a judicious selection of classed growth names (Ch Marquis de Terme 1982 – a classed growth from Margaux – is £11.65). Vintages in Bordeaux are strong on 1982, 1979 and 1978.

The house Champagne is Jeanmaire (non-vintage, £11.95). In Burgundy, look for the good value white Mâcon from the co-operative of Buxy (1984 vintage at £4.25). There's a small Loire section – the Quincy Duc de Berri 1985 is £4.95 and gives a taste of Sancerre at below Sancerre prices.

And so to the agency lines. The Italian Alto Adige provides the top-class wines of Herbert Tiefenbrunner – the 1986 wines are full of character with delicious acidity. The Chardonnay comes either without wood or with some barrique-ageing – both are very good, and offer terrific value for this much sought-after grape. Aldo Conterno in Piedmont makes one of the best Barberas we have ever tasted (Barbera d'Alba 1985, £6.95). The Chiantis from Castello di San Polo in Rosso (and the super vino da tavola Centinaia 1981 at £9.60) are also well worth looking out for.

The wines of J M da Fonseca are generally regarded as some of the best in Portugal. H Allen Smith carries the largest range in this country (although not necessarily at the cheapest prices) – with a number of vintages of the Fonseca Periquita and Pasmados red wines. João Pires' white Moscato is clean, fresh and full of character (1986 vintage £3.50). Ports are from Churchill Graham. Spain produces the top-class

Cabernet Sauvignon wine from Marqués de Griñon in Rueda (1984 vintage is £7.95) as well as Riojas from Muga. There's a range of Sherries from Sanchez Romate.

The Australian range is big on the wines of Thomas Hardy (Nottage Hill Shiraz 1985 is £4.35; the Captain's Selection red and white are both £3.25). You can also find here wines from Geoff Merrill who is the winemaker at Château Reynella as well as owning his own vineyards.

Best buys

João Pires Branco, £3.50; Chianti Rufina Villa di Monte 1985, £2.95; Chardonnay 1986, Tiefenbrunner, £4.25; Vin de Pays de Vaucluse, Cellier de St-Siffrein red and white, £2.15; Periquita 1982, J M da Fonseca, £2.95; Hardy's Captain's Selection red and white, £3.25; Justice Walk Vintage Character Port, £5.95

L'Alsacien

See La Vigneronne.

Alston Wines

Front Street, Alston, Cumbria CA9 3HU   TEL (0498) 81800
Bluecoat Building, Claypath, Durham,   TEL (091) 384 3379
Co Durham DH1 1RF

OPEN (Durham) Mon–Sat 10–5.30; (Alston) Mon–Thur 9.30–5.30   Fri 9.30–7   Sat 9–7   public holidays 10–5.30   CLOSED Sun, Chr Day, Boxing Day, New Year's Day, Good Friday; public holidays (Durham only)
CREDIT CARDS Access, Amex, Diners; personal and business accounts
DISCOUNTS 5% on ½ unmixed case, 10% on 1 mixed case   DELIVERY Free within 3-mile radius of either shop (min ½ case) otherwise northern England and southern Scotland £1.50 per case; elsewhere on application; mail order available   GLASS HIRE Free with bottle order   TASTINGS AND TALKS To groups on request   CELLARAGE Not available

Expansion has been in the air at Alston Wines whose first shop is in the highest town in England: owner Mac Brown has branched out east to Durham, to 'improve the service' to his customers in that area.

What they are getting is a well-balanced, interesting range of wines, in a part of the country that is sadly lacking in good wine merchants. In Italy, for instance, well-chosen wines from right across the country give cause for enthusiasm: Chianti Classico Riserva 1979 from Pagliarese is a bargain at £5.45; the Bonarda Oltrepò Pavese 1984 of Fugazza (£4.45) is from one of the best producers in the area; and the Frascati of Villa Catone at £3.85 seems to be the only decent Frascati to be found in this country.

Australia, too, gets a good share of the interest with wines from Brown Brothers, Orlando, Taltarni and Rosemount. Clos du Val represents California.

Austria used to be Mr Brown's main focus, and his formerly large selection is now principally of older vintages, but still worth searching out if you want wines (a few reds as well as whites) from that country. The Spanish Rioja range comes mainly from CVNE, but with some from the Agramont range representing Navarra; Palacio de León red is good value at £2.70.

On the French shelves, there's a short, sensible selection of clarets (Ch Caronne Ste-Gemme 1979 at £7.30 and Ch Duplessis 1979 at £6.40 are both good value). Burgundy is from Mazilly, Beaujolais from Bouchard Père et Fils. Rhône wines include the enjoyable Côtes du Rhône Ch de l'Estagnol 1983 at £5.05, and amongst an interesting few bottles from the Loire Bonnezeaux Domaine de la Croix de Mission 1984 (£6.20) will be delicious in ten years' time. As a fascinating curiosity, Mac Brown offers a range of Jurançon wines from Jean Guirouilh, who makes his dry wine taste as good as his superb sweet.

Best buys

Orlando RF Chardonnay, 1985, Austria, £4.60; Chianti Putto 1985, Fattoria dell'Ugo, £3.50; Serradayres 1980 red, Portugal, £3; Freixenet Cordon Negro, £5.50

Les Amis du Vin

MAIL ORDER CLUB 19 Charlotte Street, London W1P 1HB	TEL 01-636 4020
SHOPS 51 Chiltern Street, London W1M 1HQ	TEL 01-487 3419
The Winery, 4 Clifton Road, Maida Vale, London W9 1SS	TEL 01-286 6475

OPEN Mon–Fri 10.30–7 (Winery 10.30–8.30)   Sat 10.30–5 (Winery 10.30–6.30) CLOSED Sun, public holidays   CREDIT CARDS All accepted; personal and business accounts   DISCOUNTS 10% per case for club members, 12½% for 10+ cases   DELIVERY Free on UK mainland (min 2 cases or orders over £75); elsewhere £3 charge; mail order available (Wine Club)   GLASS HIRE Free TASTINGS AND TALKS Occasional in-store tastings; regular tutored tastings CELLARAGE £4.83 per case per year

Les Amis operate at two levels: one as a mail order wine club, the other through shops – which include a newly acquired shop at The Winery in Maida Vale, London. If you are a member of the club, you can buy at reduced prices, but the ones we quote here are shop prices.

In fact, the list is only a part of the activities of the club, which also goes in for special offers of wines of the month (including a recent one of wines from Domaine de la Romanée-Conti in Burgundy) and en primeur claret promotions. It also supplies members and customers on the mailing list with a range of general information. In the basic range of house wines, we would recommend the red and white Burgundy (red at £4.19, white at £5.25), the house claret (£3.29) and the red and white California (both at £2.79).

Les Amis du Vin wines come from all over the world, but strengths lie in New World wines (especially California) and in Bordeaux, which is taken seriously. Les Amis make regular en primeur offers, but much of the current interest lies in the selection of wines from vintages of the early 1980s (Domaine la Grave de Bertin 1983 at £3.75; Ch Maucaillou 1982 at £12; Ch Haut Canteloup 1978 at £10.95).

The selection of Loire and Alsace wines is short and rather dull, but more encouragingly some good domaine-bottled Burgundy and Rhône wines from Jaboulet Aîné and Ch de Beaucastel in Châteauneuf boost the French pages. The Italian range is expanding, and we were pleased to see some Barolo and Barbaresco from Borgogno (Barolo 1979 Riserva at £5.59 is good value).

And so to California. Robert Mondavi is the big star, but other famous names include Trefethen, Firestone, Clos du Bois, Heitz, Ridge and Mark West. Most of these wines are available elsewhere, sometimes at lower prices, but the selection is probably more comprehensive here. In the past three years, Les Amis has participated in an en primeur California offer.

We have been told of complaints about the changing conditions for members of the club – requirements for regular purchases, the cost of the organised tastings and, more recently, the difficulty of storing wine purchased although originally Les Amis had undertaken to store it until required. So while the list remains worth investigating, anybody who wishes to join the club should read the small print carefully.

Best buys

Côtes du Marmandais 1986, Cave de Cocumont red and white, £2.75; Côtes du Ventoux La Vieille Ferme 1985, £2.45; Les Amis claret, £3.29; Marqués de Murrieta Ygay 1982 white Rioja, £4.95; Geoffrey Roberts California white and red, £2.79

Arriba Kettle

MAIL ORDER Catalogue from   TEL (0386) 833024
Buckle Street, Honeybourne, Nr Evesham,
Hereford & Worcester WR11 5QB

OPEN Office hours; answering machine operative when closed
CREDIT CARDS None accepted   DISCOUNTS £1 per case (min 4 cases), £1.75 per case for 7–10 cases, £2.50 per case for 11+ cases; further £1 per case when collected personally   DELIVERY Free on UK mainland (min 2 cases); elsewhere negotiable   GLASS HIRE Free in West Midlands, north Cotswolds and central London   TASTINGS AND TALKS Tastings for customers in Birmingham and north Cotswolds in November; to groups on request   CELLARAGE Not available

Spain is the raison d'être of this list, which operates through mail order only. The range is wide, and many of the wines are not available from other sources.

The list centres around Rioja, with wines from Bodegas Alavesas, Viña Salceda (the 1982 vintage is £3.97), Martinez Bujanda (Conde de Valdemar 1976 at £6.52 is a fine, big wine at a good price, considering its age), and Castillo de Cuzcurrita, whose Conde de Alacha 1973 is still full of quite youthful fruit (£8.68). Other bodegas listed include Cáceres, Muga, Bilbainas, La Rioja Alta and CVNE.

Elsewhere in Spain, wines from Torres, Manuel Sancho and Masía Bach in Penedès are in the company of Bodegas los Llanos in Valdepeñas (Señorio de los Llanos 1975 Gran Reserva is a terrific bargain at £3.85) and wines from Peñafiel in Ribera del Duero (Peñafiel 5th year, £5.15). Almacenista Sherries are from Lustau, and other Sherries come from Orleans Borbon and Garvey. Sparkling wine is the Cava of Manuel Sancho under the Mont Marçal brand.

Best buys

Señorio de los Llanos Gran Reserva 1975, £3.85; Atardi Rioja white and red, £3.23; Mont Marçal Cava Brut, £4.99; Viña Salceda Rioja 1982, £3.97; Conde de Valdemar 1980, £4.16

Asda

HEAD OFFICE Asda House, Britannia Road,   TEL (0532) 539141
Morley, Leeds, West Yorkshire LS27 0BT
108 licensed branches nationwide (but mainly in the North of England)
OPEN Generally Mon–Sat 9–8 (may be regional variations)
CREDIT CARDS Access, Visa DISCOUNTS, DELIVERY, GLASS HIRE Not available TASTINGS AND TALKS Regular monthly in-store tastings; to groups on request CELLARAGE Not available

There have been big changes for the better at Asda, and we are delighted to welcome this group of supermarkets – mainly in the North of England – back to the Guide.

In August 1986 Asda introduced a range of 76 wines into about three-quarters of the stores. The list includes own-label wines and fine wines. One of the most striking aspects is a good range of vins de pays – look for the white from the Côtes de Gascogne (£1.99) and the red and white from Vaucluse (£1.89). Asda's own-label Champagne is particularly good value at £7.45; the rosé version is £8.45. In the sparkling wines, we would recommend the Crémant de Bourgogne at £4.99.

While other countries are less well represented in the Asda own-label selection, the fine wine list is more exciting. Apart from some well-chosen clarets (Ch la Cardonne 1983, £4.99), the Châteauneuf du Pape 1984 of Domaine du Mont Redon is worth trying (£6.99), as are the good value Barolo 1980 of Borgogno (£4.49) and Franciacorta 1982 of Longhi-de Carli (£2.99).

From Spain, we would recommend the Rioja Gran Reserva 1978

from Faustino (£4.99), the Torres Coronas 1982 £3.49) and Marqués de Murrieta white Rioja 1984 (£4.19).

Best buys

Ch la Cardonne 1983, £4.99; Rioja Gran Reserva 1978 Faustino, £4.99; Franciacorta 1982 Longhi-de Carli, £2.99; Chardonnay di Appiano 1985, £2.99; Asda Champagne £7.45

Ashley Scott

PO Box 28, The Highway, Hawarden,   TEL (0244) 520655
Deeside, Clwyd CH5 3RY

OPEN Mon–Sat 8.30–6; customers may telephone at any reasonable time – answering service available on (0244) 520655   CREDIT CARDS None accepted; personal and business accounts   DISCOUNTS 5% (min 1 unmixed case)   DELIVERY Free in North Wales, Cheshire and Lancashire (min 1 case); elsewhere current carrier rates; mail order available   GLASS HIRE Free with 1-case order; delivery available   TASTINGS AND TALKS Annual tasting in November for customers; local groups on request   CELLARAGE Available   ■

An all-round expansion in their range brings a welcome return to the Guide for this merchant in an area where wine shops of any sort are sparse.

Italy and Burgundy have strengthened in particular, and this year wines from Australia (Wyndham Estate and Yalumba) and New Zealand (Cooks) have been brought in. Portugal, too, has looked up, with the interesting Torre Velha Reserva Tinto 1982 at £4.35, as well as a small range of Ports and Madeiras from Henriques. Sherries from Delgado Zuleta are worth trying.

Italy, then, has a sound range of wines. Of particular interest are the Recioto Amarone of Quintarelli (£12.79) and, at the other end of the price spectrum, the deliciously honeyed Moscato del Piemonte 1981 of Paola Colla (£2.99). Chianti from Cassiano and Rosso di Montalcino from Tenuta Il Poggione also provide interest.

In France, the Burgundy list takes in a mix of négociant wines from Chanson and domaine wines. Beaujolais from Thorin and Alsace from Muré are good news. A small Bordeaux selection includes some sensibly priced petit château wines, and the Rhône produces Châteauneuf-du-Pape from Chante-Cigale.

Best buys

Fitou 1982, Terre Natale, £2.95; Rosso di Montalcino 1983, Tenuta Il Poggione, £3.95; Ch Mayne de Bernard 1985, Côtes de Bourg, £3.65; Alsace wines

---

Prices are correct to the best of our knowledge in summer 1987.

Askham Wines

Askham, via Newark, Nottinghamshire NG22 0RP   TEL   (077 783) 659
OPEN Mon–Fri 9–7   Sat 9–12 noon   CLOSED Sun, public holidays
CREDIT CARDS None accepted; personal and business accounts
DISCOUNTS To trade customers by arrangement   DELIVERY Free within
50-mile radius (min 1 case); otherwise £3 per case, 5+ cases free; mail order
available   GLASS HIRE Free   TASTINGS AND TALKS Tastings held in local
hotel every 4 months; to groups on request   CELLARAGE Not available ■

Andrew Brownridge continues to find unusual wines for stocking his
shop, either looking to the world's lesser wine areas or by delving
more deeply into the byways of more familiar parts of the
wine-growing world.

For example, he has gone strongly for Portugal in addition to his
most recent range. Bairrada wines from Caves Aliança (their excellent
Garrafeira Particular 1976 at £4.70 is a typical red Portuguese bargain)
vie with the smooth red of the Tinto da Anfora of João Pires (1982
vintage at £3.95). The deliciously sweet Moscato de Setúbal 1982 (£5.60)
is also a find.

France gets its due attention: particular bottles that drew our
attention were the top-class Côtes du Rhône of Roger Combe at £4.10 –
we hope the 1985 vintage is on its way – and some well-priced clarets
such as St-Emilion Ch le Tertre Rôteboeuf 1983 at £6.50. Beaujolais is
from Loron (as is the house wine) and Sylvain Fessy. Then there's the
red and white from Ch Val-Joanis in the Côtes du Luberon, and
Champagne from Billecart-Salmon.

California is likewise well treated, with wines from Hawk Crest,
Conn Creek and Cuvaison. A small selection of wines from the Pacific
North-West, including Alpine Vineyards Chardonnay 1983 from
Oregon at £7.75, is an added bonus.

Best buys

Dry Muscat Palmela João Pires, £3.75; Viña Alberdi 1983, Rioja, £3.85;
Ch du Palanquay 1982, Côtes de Castillon, £4.45; Bairrada Reserva
1980, Caves Aliança, £2.95

Astral Wines

See Morris's Wine Stores.

Averys of Bristol

7 Park Street, Bristol, Avon   TEL   (0272) 214141
OPEN Mon–Sat 9–6   CLOSED Sun, public holidays   CREDIT CARDS Access,
Visa; personal and business accounts   DISCOUNTS Trade discounts
negotiable   DELIVERY Free within 5-mile radius of Bristol (min 1 case), UK
mainland (min 2 cases) and Northern Ireland (min 10 cases); smaller quantities

charged £5.50 extra (£5 for Northern Ireland); mail order available
GLASS HIRE Free   TASTINGS AND TALKS In-store tastings on Thur and Fri;
major annual tasting in April; to groups on request   CELLARAGE £2.50 per
case/part case per year, payable in advance either in bond or duty paid

This merchant established a reputation for venturing to Australia and
New Zealand long before most other British wine retailers had realised
they even made wine there. Today, though, many merchants have
overtaken Averys, and it is as much for wines from traditional areas in
France that they now merit inclusion in the Guide.

The range of clarets – especially from the 1983 and 1982 vintages –
is long and takes in some reasonable value petit château wines as
well as more famous names (Ch Reverdi Listrac 1983, £4.74; Ch Haut-
Sociondo Côtes de Blaye 1982, £5.09, Ch de Cadillac Bordeaux 1979,
£4.63). Vintages go back to 1966. Burgundy, while dominated by wines
from the négociant firm of Remoissenet and by bottlings specially for
Averys, also boasts a few older vintages which are well priced
(Pommard Rugiens 1967, Remoissenet, £16.24). Additional white
Burgundies come from Domaine Henri Clerc.

Rhône wines are dominated by Salavert, Beaujolais by Loron
(Beaujolais Villages 1986, £4.05). The Loire has some Sancerres from
Vacheron – but at prices which are high even for these pricey wines.
We would recommend, however, the red St-Nicolas de Bourgueil 1983
of Domaine du Fondis (£3.97), and the crisp, white St-Pourçain 1985
(£4.74). Alsace comes from the Ribeauvillé co-operative and Hugel –
although, as with other parts of the list, Averys are sometimes
strangely reticent about who makes their wines. The rest of France
might almost not exist.

A short German range displays some good Kabinett wines from the
1983 and 1985 vintages (Deidesheimer Kieselberg 1983 von Buhl at
£5.60; Hochheimer Holle Riesling Kabinett Aschrott at £6.18). Italy's
offerings include three vintages of Sassicaia – 1981, 1982, 1983 – and
some generic wines like Bardolino, Valpolicella and Soave whose
provenance is unknown.

Australia is dominated by three famous names – Wolf Blass
(Although recent changes may mean these wines will disappear from
this list), Tyrrells (Long Flat White and Red both at £3.88 are good
value), and Rouge Homme. From New Zealand come the wines of
Nick Nobilo, one of the top producers of reds in a country better
known for its whites (Cabernet Sauvignon 1983, £7.22).

Best buys

Investiture Finest Vintage Reserve Port, £7.79; Côtes de Duras
Sauvignon 1986, £3.59; Ch du Juge 1983, Bordeaux Supérieur, £4.92;
Bourgogne Passe-tout-Grains 1983, Averys, £5.03; Vin de Pays de
l'Aude, Domaine de Laurens Chardonnay 1984, £4.17; Tyrrells Long
Flat Red and White, £3.88

David Baillie Vintners ☞

At the Sign of the Lucky Horseshoe,   TEL (0392) 221345
Longbrook Street, Exeter, Devon EX4 6AP

OPEN Mon–Sat 9–6 CLOSED Sun, public holidays CREDIT CARDS All
accepted; personal and business accounts DISCOUNTS 5% for 1 case, 7½% for
10+ cases DELIVERY Free throughout UK (min 2 cases, £1.20 for 1 case); mail
order available GLASS HIRE Free TASTINGS AND TALKS Up to 6 tastings
annually; wine courses; talks to groups on request CELLARAGE £1.44 per case
per year

This continues to be a range full of pleasures and enthusiasms. It
shows not only in the list, but in the newsletter which goes out to
regular customers and in the special offers – such as the rare Early
Landed Vintage Cognac from Hine. David Baillie Vintners also run a
school of wine.

Areas of obvious interest are Burgundy and the Rhône, but
increasingly sights are set much further afield – on Australia and New
Zealand. But to France first. There are some good nuggets in Bordeaux
– Ch Labégorce-Zédé 1982 (£9.14) and Ch les Deux Moulins 1978,
Médoc (£5.01), for instance, with more famous châteaux's names there
as well. House claret is from Nathaniel Johnston (£3.48).

The Burgundy list is inevitably more pricey than it used to be, but the
range is still as good, with wines from Tollot-Beaut, Jacques Germain,
Bruno Clair, Louis Trappet, Henri Clerc and Jean-Claude Monnier. On
the Rhône, Jaboulet Aîné dominates (Côtes du Rhône 1983 Parallèle 45
is £4.14), while on the Loire, good names include Sancerre from
Vincent Delaporte and Sylvain Bailly. Further west the sweet Quarts
de Chaume from Joseph Renou (1981 vintage at £7.27) would be a treat.
Alsace wines come from Hoen.

Elsewhere in Europe, while Germany and Italy seem a mite
neglected, the Spanish range from Torres in Penedès and CVNE in Rioja
(Rioja Tinto 1983 at £3.43) and the Portuguese wines of J M da Fonseca
revive the interest. Look also for the Lustau almacenista sherries and
Cossart Gordon Good Company Madeiras.

The Australian selection is now much larger, with wines from
Rosemount (Chardonnay 1985, £4.92), Brown Brothers (Shiraz 1983,
also at £4.92) and Rothbury Estate, plus the outstanding Semillon 1984
from Quelltaler (£7.38). Two wines from Cooks in New Zealand are
likewise new to the list.

Best buys

David Baillie Claret, £3.48; Jean de Lacorte Cava Brut, £4.34; Quarts de
Chaume 1981, Joseph Renou, £7.27; Chinon 1985, Le Pressoir, £3.82;
Le Prince Pirate Rouge, £2.81; Periquita 1978, J M da Fonseca, £3.51

Most wine merchants will supply wine for parties on a sale or return basis.

Ballantynes of Cowbridge

Stallcourt House, Llanblethian, Cowbridge, TEL (04463) 3044
South Glamorgan CF7 7JU

OPEN Mon–Fri 9–6 Sat answering service CLOSED Sun, public holidays
CREDIT CARDS None accepted; personal and business accounts
DISCOUNTS Not available DELIVERY Free in UK mainland (min 5 cases); 1–4
cases £4 supplement; mail order available GLASS HIRE Not available
TASTINGS AND TALKS Regular in-store tastings CELLARAGE £2.30 per year ■

Burgundy forms the heart of this list, and the wines from this
notoriously difficult region are chosen with great care, but the Rhône
and Bordeaux also provide interest. Many of the wines listed are
imported in small parcels, so it is advisable to be on the mailing list for
regular fine wine lists.

Recent mail shots have included the opening offer for 1985
Burgundy – with names like Domaine Varoilles, Georges Clerget,
Domaine Ponsot, Machard du Gramont, Pousse d'Or and Henri Jayer
mingling with less familiar names like Gros Frères et Soeur in
Vosne-Romanée and Ch de Maltroye in Chassagne. Prices reflect the
scarcity of the wine and the demand.

Early in 1987 Ballantynes floated a Rhône opening offer for 1985s
from Joseph Jamet in Côte Rôtie, Bernard Faurie in Hermitage and
Robert Michel in Cornas, and a short list of en primeur 1986 Bordeaux
included the unknown, but potentially exciting Ch Tour Haut-Caussan
in the northern Médoc (ex cellars £36 a case) as well as more familiar
names.

Best buys
Domaine-bottled Burgundy

Balls Brothers

313 Cambridge Heath Road, London E2 9LQ TEL 01-739 1642/6466
ASSOCIATED WITH Wickham and Co, New Road, TEL (02373) 73292
Bideford, Devon EX39 2AQ

OPEN Mon–Sat 10–6 CLOSED Sun, public holidays CREDIT CARDS Access,
Visa DISCOUNTS Not available DELIVERY Free in UK mainland (min 2
cases); mail order available GLASS HIRE Free; delivery free with wine order
TASTINGS AND TALKS Regular tastings in Wine Centre; annual tasting of new
list; to groups on request CELLARAGE £1.30 per case per year

While Balls Brothers are probably more familiar to lunchtime City
workers as operators of wine bars (see more about those in our wine
bars section on page 540), they also run a large Wine Centre in the East
End. There is an associated branch in Bideford, Devon – Wickham and
Co.

Bordeaux and Burgundy – inevitably along with Champagne – are the mainstays of this essentially traditional list from which they also supply directors' dining rooms. So there are clarets mainly from the 1983 vintage (Ch La Tour St-Bonnet 1983 is £5.10; Ch Cissac is £6.70), plus a few older wines, going back to 1976. House St-Emilion is from J-P Moueix, the famous Pétrus house.

The Burgundy selection contains some good names – Nicolas Servant, Jean Germain, Machard de Gramont and some négociant wines from Faiveley and Chanson Père. Beaujolais is from Robert Sarrau. Loire wines include Sancerres from Vincent Delaporte and Bernard Reverdy.

There's additional interest on the Rhône, with Côtes du Rhône from Ch du Grand Moulas (1986 vintage at £3.90) and Châteauneuf-du-Pape from Domaine du Mont Redon, with Côte Rôtie from Guigal. The Vin de Pays de l'Hérault white Ch de Gourgazaud is in the modern style but has some character (£2.87).

Best buys

Sancerre Les Monts Damnés 1985, Delaporte, £6.73; Ch la Garenne 1983, Lussac St-Emilion, £5; Coteaux Varois Domaine de St-Estève £2.76; Chianti Riserva 1981, Castello di Nipozzano, £5.52

Bamptons of Salisbury

21 Queen Street, Market Square,   TEL (0722) 332038
Salisbury, Wiltshire SP1 1EY

OPEN Mon–Fri 10–6.30   Sat 9.30–6.30   CLOSED Sun, public holidays
CREDIT CARDS Access, Amex, Visa; personal and business accounts
DISCOUNTS 5% for 1 case; quantity discounts negotiable   DELIVERY Free
locally; elsewhere at cost; mail order available   GLASS HIRE Free
TASTINGS AND TALKS Wines always available for tasting in-store; to groups on
request   CELLARAGE Available; charges on application

Under new ownership (and with a name change as the Bamptons took over from the Brandons), this shop is now in its second year in what used to be an ordinary branch of a High Street off-licence chain. It comes into the Guide on the wide-ranging quality of its list, even though prices are not cheap.

In Bordeaux, the Bamptons have put together a reasonable range of petit château wines, but there's also an interesting featuring of two châteaux: Ch Cissac in the Médoc and Ch Le Tertre Rôteboeuf in St-Emilion. Try the Private Reserve 1983, the second wine of Ch Kirwan, at £6.88. Both Burgundy and Beaujolais show a good mix of producers – with the Beaujolais especially strong. Less interesting is the Loire, but the excellent Champagnes are from Billecart-Salmon. Wines from Guigal and Jaboulet Aîné on the Rhône look good. The country wine section offers some good prices.

Germany provides a few estate wines – from Von Hövel and J J Prüm on the Mosel – and England wines from Chalkhill and Fonthill. Further

73

south we would recommend the Soave Classico of Rizzardi and the Gattinara Riserva of Nervi among the Italian wines, where you can also find the top-price Barbaresco of Gaja. Spain comes up with a decent selection of Riojas, and a good Sherry list – including wines from Valdespino, Garvey and Williams and Humbert, as well as old Sherries from Gonzalez Byass.

To the New World: Brown Brothers and Knappstein wines represent Australia, with California wines coming from a number of top wineries.

A fine wine and bin end list changes regularly.

Best buys

Côtes du Roussillon 1983, Ch d'Avallrich, £2.97; Cava Castellblanch Brut Zero, £4.44; Commanderie of St John, Cyprus dessert wine, £3.43

Nigel Baring

11 Stanhope Place, London W2 2HH   TEL 01-724 0836

OPEN Mon–Fri 9–5   CLOSED Sat, Sun   CREDIT CARDS None accepted; personal and business accounts   DISCOUNTS Not available   DELIVERY Free in London (min 8 cases); otherwise £1 charge in London and £2.50 outside; mail order available   GLASS HIRE Not available   TASTINGS AND TALKS Two annual tastings – free to existing customers   CELLARAGE £2.87 per case per year (in bond only)   ■

This firm operates primarily as a stockholder of fine claret. They buy and sell en primeur – and what is not sold in this way forms the stock. Thus their current list includes wines from recent vintages – 1985, 1984, 1983, 1982, 1981, plus a few wines from older vintages back to 1966. Most of the wines are available in bond.

They also hold a small selection of northern Rhône wines from Guigal, Bernard Faurie and Rostaing, plus Burgundy from Louis Jadot, some of which are exclusive to them.

Best buys
Classed growth clarets

Barnes Wine Shop

51 Barnes High Street, London SW13 9LN   TEL 01-878 8643

OPEN Mon–Sat 9.30–8.30   Sun 12 noon–2   CLOSED Public holidays
CREDIT CARDS Access, Visa; personal and business accounts   DISCOUNTS 5% on 1 case; larger discounts negotiable   DELIVERY Free in London (min 1 case); elsewhere at cost; mail order available   GLASS HIRE Free with 1-case order
TASTINGS AND TALKS Daily tastings; to groups on request   CELLARAGE £2.75 per case per year

This merchant has had plenty of publicity in the past year, most of it well deserved. For what is a comparatively small shop, the range is enormous, with every wine justifying its place on the shelves.

One of the aspects that sets their printed list apart is that wines are coded for their suitability with different types of food as well as their dryness (for white wines) or their body (for reds).

The list is also one of the few which is arranged in the way most people buy wine – by colour. So, you start off with whites wines, going straight into Australia – the selection includes wines from Brown Brothers and de Bortoli, and from small wineries like Richard Hamilton, Peter Lehmann and Peterson. Red Australians take in the superb Cabernet Sauvignons from Yarra Yering and Cape Mentelle as well as more familiar names such as Hardy's and Brown Brothers.

New Zealand is equally well served: whites include the Montana Chardonnay (1986 vintage at £4.15) and the interesting Sauvignon/Semillon blend from Selaks (1986 vintage at £6.95). The range from California takes in some good names: Dry Creek, Ch St Jean, Mark West, Mondavi, Cuvaison, Firestone and Clos du Val among them. From the Lebanon, look for old vintages of Ch Musar (1961 at £12.95) and some magnums.

In Europe, Spain has wines from Raimat and Torres in Penedès, Olarra in Rioja, and the Marqués de Griñon Cabernet Sauvignon wine (the 1983 is £7.50). Sherries come from Don Zoilo and Barbadillo, and Madeiras from Cossart, Gordon. In Italy, the interest centres on the excellent Verdicchio of Bianchi and the same producer's Rosso Cònero San Lorenzo (1981 vintage, £3.95), Chianti from Badia a Coltibuono, the Black Label Venegazzù della Casa of Loredan Gasparini.

In France, Alsace is from Trimbach and the Turckheim co-operative, and house Champagne from Bricout (non-vintage Carte Noire is £9.95). There are small selections from Bordeaux and Burgundy on the standard list and more on the fine wine list.

One of the specialities here is sweet pudding wines. Sauternes and Barsac appear on the fine wine list, but wines from most other parts of the world are very attractive: Orange Muscat and Flora from Brown Brothers in Australia (the 1985 is £4.25); de Bortoli's Late Harvest Botrytised Semillon 1982 at £9.95 for a half-bottle; and Solera Scholtz Málaga 1885 (yes, that's right) at £6.25.

Best buys

Domaine du Tariquet 1986, Vin de Pays des Côtes de Gascogne, £2.75; Champagne Bricout Carte Noire NV, £9.95; Chardonnay 1985 Cousiño Macul, Chile, £3.95; Bardolino Classico Ca Bordenis 1984, £3.59; Ch Musar 1961, £12.95; Sauvignon Blanc 1986, Montana, £4.15

Bart's Cellars

19 Enterprise Way, Osiers Road,   TEL 01-871 2044
London SW18 1NL   (24-hour answering machine)
OPEN Mon–Fri 8.30–6.30   CLOSED Sat, Sun, public holidays
CREDIT CARDS None accepted; personal and business accounts
DISCOUNTS Negotiable   DELIVERY Free in central London (min 3 cases);
elsewhere at cost   GLASS HIRE Free with 3-case order
TASTINGS AND TALKS Annual in-store tasting in Dec; to groups on request
CELLARAGE £2.88 per case per year   ■

Various companies are associated with Barts Cellars, including
Jeroboams in South Kensington (see separate entry) and George
Vesselle Champagne.

The list is essentially that of a fine wine merchant, offering French
wines only. A strong rank of clarets stretches back to 1923 (a jeroboam
of Ch Margaux would be £1046 – prices on the list do not include VAT,
but we have added it here). More realistically, there are in-bond offers
of younger vintages (1985, 1984, 1983) as well as duty-paid offers for
more mature wines. A speciality is the Graves property of Ch Rahoul
(the 1982 vintage is £5.33).

Burgundy is dominated by the reds of Domaine de la
Romanée-Conti and the whites of Louis Latour. There are vintages of
Ch de Beaucastel in Châteauneuf-du-Pape, and a full range of
Champagne from Georges Vesselle (non-vintage is £131 a case),
including one of the better Bouzy Rouge still wines from the
Champagne area.

Louis Gisselbrecht is behind the Alsace wines, and there's some of
the Cabernet-Sauvignon-based Mas de Daumas Gassac (the 1983 is
£6.13). Sauvignon de Touraine and Sancerre from Paul Buisse are
suggestions from the Loire.

Best buys

Ch Rahoul 1982, £5.33; Côtes du Luberon La Vieille Ferme, £2.83;
Bourgogne Rouge 1983, Chanson Père et Fils, £4.22

Most wine merchants will hire out glasses free of charge, provided they are
collected and returned clean, and that you are buying enough wine to fill
them! In most cases, it's first come, first served, so get your order in early to
ensure supply.

We have tried to make the *1988 Which? Wine Guide* as comprehensive as
possible, but we should love to hear from you about any other wine
merchants you feel deserve an entry, or your comments on existing entries.
Write to us either by letter or using the report forms supplied at the back of
the book.

Barwell & Jones

24 Fare Street, Ipswich, Suffolk IP4 1JU	TEL (0473) 56751
94 Jermyn Street, London SW1Y 6JL	TEL 01-839 2287

MANAGED HOUSE WITH OFF-LICENCE

The Cross Inn, 2 Church Street, Woodbridge, Suffolk IP12 1DH	TEL (03943) 3288
The Grosvenor, 25/29 Ranelagh Road, Felixstowe, Suffolk IP11 7HA	TEL (0394) 284137

MANAGED OFF-LICENCES

118 Sprowston Road, Norwich, Norfolk NR3 4QH	TEL (0603) 484966
70 Trumpington Street, Cambridge, Cambridgeshire CB2 1RJ	TEL (0223) 354431
WHOLESALE 3 Radenhall Road, Harleston, Norfolk IP20 9EN	TEL (0379) 852243
94 Rushmere Road, Ipswich, Suffolk IP4 4JL	TEL (0473) 77426

OPEN Hours vary from branch to branch   CREDIT CARDS Access, Visa; personal and business accounts   DISCOUNTS Negotiable   DELIVERY Free in East Anglia (min 2 cases); mail order available   GLASS HIRE Free TASTINGS AND TALKS Occasional tastings; to groups on request CELLARAGE Charges minimal

The south of France and Italy continue to be the strongest points in the list of this small group of off-licences. Be warned that only the main Ipswich shop carries the full range.

From the south of France, we have enjoyed the Coteaux d'Aix-en-Provence wines of Commanderie de la Bargemone (the 1983 red is £3.99). From Bandol, you could try the Moulin des Costes Rouge 1980 (£5.86), while we would also recommend the Ch d'Avallrich Rouge 1983 from Côtes du Roussillon (£2.99).

Italy is well served with Soave, Valpolicella and Bardolino from one of the top firms in the area – Guerrieri-Rizzardi – plus Piedmont wines from Bruno Giacosa (look for the Barbera d'Alba 1983 at £5.47).

An extensive range of clarets mainly covers vintages after 1978 (especially 1982 and 1983). Burgundies from Jaboulet-Vercherre and Coron Père, Alsace wines from Pierre Sparr, and good house Champagne from Barancourt (non-vintage Réserve Brut at £12.34) are further attractions.

Best buys

Coteaux d'Aix-en-Provence, Commanderie de la Bargemone 1983, £3.99; Montecillo Cumbrero 1982, Rioja, £3.80; Rosso di Montalcino 1983 Col d'Orcia, £4.28; Pinot Blanc 1985, Pierre Sparr, £4.15

Thomas Baty & Sons

See Willoughbys.

Bedford Fine Wines

The Knife and Cleaver, Houghton Conquest,   TEL (0234) 740387
Bedford, Bedfordshire MK45 3LA

OPEN Mon–Fri 9–3, 6–10   Sat 9–2, 6–10   Sun and public holidays by
appointment   CREDIT CARDS Access, Visa; personal and business accounts
DISCOUNTS 5% unmixed cases, 3% mixed cases   DELIVERY Free within 15
miles of Bedford, Luton, St Albans and north and central London; elsewhere
£4.50 per case; over £200 order free; mail order available   GLASS HIRE Free with
1-case order   TASTINGS AND TALKS Weekly (Wed) from Oct–April; to groups
on request   CELLARAGE Not available

Bedford Fine Wines have what they call 'a special interest' in Bordeaux
but do not neglect other wine areas. For instance, from a good selection
of French country wines, Louis Latour's Chardonnay from the
Ardèche is good value (£4.76) compared with the same producer's
white Burgundies. Reds are from Faugères in the south of France
(Cuvée Jules Gaston 1984, £2.60) and Corsica (Domaine de Torraccia
1983, £2.85), and Alsace wines from Dopff et Irion. On the Loire,
Savennières La Roche aux Moines from Soulez and Quarts de Chaume
from Jean Baumard (the 1980 vintage at £8.20) took our eye.

Other countries have small selections: Frescobaldi wines from
Tuscany; Torres wines from Spain; Schloss Groenesteyn from the
Rheingau of Germany (Rüdesheimer Berg Rotland Riesling Spätlese
1983 at £7.95); Sherries from Bardillo and Lustau; Madeira from
Rutherford and Miles.

In the focal point of Bordeaux, there's a good balance between top
class growths and more approachable wines. In 1983, for instance, look
out for Ch Sénéjac in the Haut-Médoc for £5.65, and the superb
Domaine de Chevalier from the Graves at £18 – with plenty in
between.

Best buys

Vin de Pays des Côtes de Gascogne, £2.09; Ch de Pouzols 1985,
Minervois, £2.58; Ch Timberlay 1982, Bordeaux, £4.50; Domaine de
Torraccia 1983, Vin Corse de Porto Vecchio, £2.85; Galestro 1984,
Fresobaldi, £3.70

Berkmann Wine Cellars

See Le Nez Rouge.

Berry Bros & Rudd   ☞

3 St James's Street, London SW1A 1EG   TEL 01-839 9033
    (answering machine 01-930 1888)
The Wine Shop, Houndmills, Basingstoke,   TEL (0256) 463759
Hampshire RG21 2YH

OPEN (London) Mon–Fri 9.30–5; (Basingstoke) Mon–Fri 9–5   Sat 9–1
CLOSED Sat (London), public holidays   CREDIT CARDS Access, Diners, Visa;
personal and business accounts   DISCOUNTS 3% on 1–5 cases, 5% on 5–10
cases, 7½% on 10+ cases   DELIVERY Free throughout UK mainland (min 1
case); elsewhere £1 per case; mail order available   GLASS HIRE Free with wine
order   TASTINGS AND TALKS 2 annual tastings at Basingstoke; to groups on
request   CELLARAGE £3.18 per case per year

Tradition lives at Berry Bros (never, you notice, Brothers). It lives in the panelled splendour of the shop itself and in the bias towards the classic wine regions. It also lives in the fact that Berry Bros are one of the few remaining wine merchants to bottle wine in this country (and very well they do it, too).

Tradition, of course, isn't cheap. We would hardly recommend Berry Bros for their competitive prices: neither, though, are they too high. But they do offer service. They also issue regular newsletters to customers on their mailing list, and produce the smallest list of any wine merchant – not, we hasten to add, in terms of number of wines, but in its pocket size.

Anybody who has drunk Berry Bros wine will probably have tasted their Good Ordinary Claret, which is bottled in London and is good value at £3.05 (they ought to do a house claret well, though, because a major strength of the list is clarets). They usually run an en primeur offer, and are currently offering for sale wines from vintages between 1983 and 1967 (plus a good selection of half-bottles and magnums, too). Strong vintages are 1981 and 1978, but we would suggest you avoid the 1972s still listed.

Burgundy is mainly from négociants like Prosper Maufoux and Moillard, but there are domaine wines as well. Interesting old red Burgundies include Chambolle-Musigny 1969, Doudet-Naudin at £29.30 a bottle. More practically, Berry's Own Bourgogne Pinot Noir is stylish at £4.25.

Other French areas are still under-rated on these premises, although the country wine section is improving. The Loire selection is short and dull. The Rhône is better, dominated by wines from Chapoutier; Alsace is supplied by Kuentz-Bas and Trimbach. The list shows a traditional interest in good German wines with a good choice of the fabulous 1976, 1975 and 1971 wines. New to the list in 1987 were Charta Riesling wines from some of the top Rheingau estates – 1983 Rüdesheimer Berg Roseneck Riesling Kabinett of Scholl & Hillebrand at £6.29. Sadly, Italy still needs to be appreciated here.

But then there's Australia. So Berry Bros are not so traditional after all – they've bought a good clutch of wines from Brown Brothers, Rosemount, Quelltaler, Penfolds and Tyrrells – and are selling them at prices that make some of the French wines look ridiculous.

The Berry Bros vintage Ports, their excellent house Champagne (£9.95) and the range of sample cases are other notable features.

Best buys

Good Ordinary Claret, £3.05; Berry Bros UK Champagne, £9.95;
Bourgogne Pinot Noir, £4.25; Prestige d'Automne 1982, Jurançon
moelleux (sweet), £5.45

B H Wines

Boustead Hill House, Boustead Hill,   TEL (022 876) 711
Burgh-by-Sands, Carlisle, Cumbria CA5 6AA

OPEN All hours (24-hour answering machine)   CREDIT CARDS None accepted;
business accounts   DISCOUNTS Negotiable on large/regular orders
DELIVERY Free locally (min 1 mixed case); elsewhere charges by negotiation;
mail order available locally   GLASS HIRE Free with 1-case order
TASTINGS AND TALKS Min of 2 annual tastings; to groups on request
CELLARAGE Not available   ■

Not great quantity but sensible buying bring this merchant back into
the Guide. The wine list is divided by wine style rather than by country
– a practice which pits Bulgarian wines against Bordeaux. In fact, most
of the Bulgarian wines available in this country figure somewhere in
this list at their usual amazingly good prices.

From Bordeaux come a few petit château wines, from the Rhône
Domaine des Anges Côtes du Ventoux and Châteauneuf from Chante
Cigale. A few French country wines are available at good prices –
Minervois 1982, Domaine Maris Cuvée Spéciale (£3.05). Interesting
Italian bottles include Barolo from Borgogno and Chardonnays from
the Alto Adige. There are plenty of Australian wines – Leasingham,
Tyrrells, Orlando Jacob's Creek, McWilliams – with Riojas from CVNE,
Sherries from Garvey and a dry Vinho Verde from Portugal (Cinco
Cicades 1985 at £2.71).

Best buys

Orlando RF Cabernet Sauvignon 1982, £3.79; Montana Sauvignon
Blanc 1985, £3.89; Spanna 1983, Agostino Brugo, £3.03; Spring Gulley
Riesling 1984, Leasingham Bin 75, £3.25

Bibendum

113 Regents Park Road, London NW1 8UR   TEL 01-586 9761
OPEN Mon–Sat 10–8   Sun 11–6   CLOSED Public holidays
CREDIT CARDS Access, Visa; business accounts   DISCOUNTS 5% for 1 unmixed
case   DELIVERY Free within London postal districts; elsewhere £3.45 per
delivery; mail order available   GLASS HIRE Free with 1-case order
TASTINGS AND TALKS Various wines always available for tasting; specialist
tastings of direct shipment offers 4/5 times a year; new list launch tastings twice a
year; to groups on request   CELLARAGE £2.76 per case per year   ■

BIBENDUM

Bibendum has been described as an up-market wine warehouse. It's certainly in a posh part of London, and it does have an enormous range of fine wines – enticingly laid out in their wooden boxes piled high off the floor. But it has an equally interesting range of everyday drinking wines from round the world.

To start with France. This year, the country wine list has been lengthened and strengthened. Almost at random, we could pick out the red Vin de Pays du Gard of Domaine de Valescure (£2.67) which proves what good quality is coming from the south of France. Or the really tasty organic Muscadet of Guy Bossard (£3.93). Or the red Domaine Sarda-Malet of Max Malet in Côtes du Roussillon (£3.40). Or the rare taste of the white Pacherenc de Vic-Bilh of Alain Brumont (£4.70). Or many more . . .

From more classic areas, there's no shortage of attractions either and at some keen prices. The extensive fine wine list goes back to the 1953 claret vintage (Ch La Mission Haut Brion, £69 for a half-bottle). Petit château claret is regularly available, joined annually by en primeur claret offers. Burgundy and Rhône wines are also available this way.

If you're impatient, there are plenty of wines to drink now. Guigal, Albert Dervieux, Gilles Barges, Guy de Barjac and others represent the northern Rhône, with the wines of Ch de Beaucastel and Clos de Papes in Châteauneuf-du-Pape highlights in the southern Rhône. For Burgundy, Bibendum has built up an extensive list of domaine-bottled wines, often available only in limited quantities.

From the rest of France, Alsace wines are from Rolly Gassmann (Pinot Blanc 1985 at £4.64) with Réserve Personnelle wines from Hugel. Loire wines include a range of fascinating Coteaux du Layon sweet wines from Philippe Leblanc.

Italian wines cover the Barolos of Aldo Conterno and the Barbaresco of Castello di Nieve as well as Chianti from Volpaia and Badia a Coltibuono. From Germany, a small range of top estate wines looks inviting.

And so on down the range. The Australian selection has grown again this year, reflecting the current interest in this country, and besides familiar names, some small estates put in an appearance: Primo in South Australia (Sauvignon Blanc 1986 at £6.95); the Robson Vineyard in New South Wales (Chardonnay 1986, £10.29); and the wines from Moss Wood in Western Australia and Geoff Merrill in South Australia.

Other areas to scrutinise are vintage Ports, the range of Champagnes (Albert Beerens Réserve is the house Champagne at £8.88), or the Portuguese wines of Montez-Champalimaud in the Douro.

Bibendum has recently bought Green's (*qv*).

Best buys

La Vieille Ferme, Côtes du Ventoux 1985, £2.98; Ch Court-les-Mûts 1985, Saussignac, £3.94; Ménétou-Salon 1986, Jacky Rat, £4.38; Côtes du Rhône 1983, Guigal, £4.92; Bourgogne Rouge 1985, Domaine de la Combe, Michel Lafarge, £4.98; Albert Beerens Champagne (NV), £8.88; Bardolino 1986, Fraterna Portalupi, £3.48

Bin 89 Wine Warehouse

89 Trippet Lane, Sheffield S1 4EL   TEL (0742) 755889

OPEN Tue–Fri 11–6   Sat 10–5   CLOSED Mon, Sun, public holidays
CREDIT CARDS None accepted; personal and business accounts
DISCOUNTS 5% on 5+ cases   DELIVERY Free in Sheffield and parts of
Derbyshire (min 2 cases); elsewhere at cost   GLASS HIRE Free with 2-case
order   TASTINGS AND TALKS Two annual tastings by invitation only; to groups
on request   CELLARAGE Not available   ∎

The range of wines at this warehouse has been expanded enormously and encouragingly since last year – hence their entry in the Guide for the first time. Prices are keen, too.

France is well represented by the wines of Listel from the south (Domaine de Villeroy 1985 is £3.25), the attractive Côtes du Rhône 1985 of Celliers du Dauphin (£3.25) and wines from the Pfaffenheim co-operative in Alsace and Thorin in Burgundy. The selection of clarets ranges from Ch Puy Barbe 1979 at £2.75 (drink it now) to Ch Fourcas-Hosten 1979 at £19.50.

Fizz comes in the form of Granier Champagne, Marqués de Monistrol Cava and the less usual Windsor Brut from Australia (£6.75). Spanish still wines are mainly from Torres plus some Viña Albina Riojas. There are short selections from Portugal and Italy, a range of Bulgarian wines (Merlot 1981 at £2.20) and McWilliams, Taltarni and Orlando wines from Australia.

Best buys

Lancorta Rioja 1981, £3.25; Coonawarra Shiraz 1982, Mildara, £3.95; Montpeyroux le Souverain 1983, £2.20; Ruster Beerenauslese 1979, £4.95; Sylvaner d'Alsace 1983, Hugel, £3.35

Bin Ends

83–85 Badsley Moor Lane, Rotherham,   TEL (0709) 367771
South Yorkshire S65 2PH

OPEN Mon–Fri 10–5.30   Sat 9.30–1   CLOSED Sun; public holidays
CREDIT CARDS None accepted; personal and business accounts
DISCOUNTS 5% on unmixed cases, 7½% on 3+ mixed cases   DELIVERY Free
within 15-mile radius (min 1 case); elsewhere by negotiation   GLASS HIRE Free
with 1-case order   TASTINGS AND TALKS Three annual in-store tastings; to
groups on request   CELLARAGE £2 per case per year

Here is a solid list, with strengths in unexpected areas – like Beaujolais and Italy – plus several attractive wines from classic areas and the promise of some attention to the New World. Sadly, a certain amount of detective work is necessary to discover who actually produces some of the wines.

There's a good range of Beaujolais grands crus from Paul Sapin, with some 1983 and 1985 wines still in stock. Wines such as the Chénas and Juliénas represent good value when compared with other grands crus – Fleurie, for instance. Burgundy proper consists of wines from Pierre Ponnelle. Chablis is expensive – inevitably – but good, with wines from Henri Laroche.

From an attractive range of clarets, with vintages going back to 1978 (Ch Fonplégade, St-Emilion at £11.60), Ch Canteloup 1982, St-Emilion (£4.30) and Ch Reynier 1983 (£4.25) are both good value. Alsace wines come from Dopff au Moulin and the house Champagne is André Simon (£8.99).

In the Italian range, wines have obviously been bought with care: try Le Cane, the super vino da tavola of Boscaini (1978 vintage at £4.95); Taurasi 1982 of Mastroberardino (£7.15); or, more simply, the Bianco di Custoza 1984 of Tedeschi at £2.65. Spanish wines include the single vineyard Riojas of Contino. Fortified wines have Ports from Fonseca and Kopke and Sherries from Garvey among their number.

Best buys

Cabernet Vino da Tavola NV, £2.60; Syrah Vin de Pays d'Oc 1984, £2.99; Chardonnay Vin de Pays de l'Ardèche, 1984, Louis Latour, £5.75; Monopole Rioja 1983, CVNE, £3.99

Blakes & Co

24 York Street, Ayr, Strathclyde KA8 8AN   TEL (0292) 264880

OPEN Mon–Sat 9.30–5.30   CLOSED Sun   CREDIT CARDS All accepted; personal and business accounts   DISCOUNTS 8% on case orders DELIVERY Free within 40-mile radius (min 1 case); elsewhere £3 charge; mail order available   GLASS HIRE Free   TASTINGS AND TALKS Occasional in-store tastings; to groups on request   CELLARAGE £3 per case per year

A short list, but with some nuggets to justify inclusion in the Guide. There is a strong emphasis on wines from Beaujolais and Burgundy.

Beaujolais from Georges Duboeuf, for a start: the selection includes some of the special cuvées from this top négociant: Morgon Jean Descombes, Saint-Amour des Sablons, Brouilly Ch du Prieuré (1984 vintage for £5.26).

Burgundies feature wines from Labouré-Roi, and we would recommend the Pinot Noir Clos du Roi 1983 at £4.77 as typical of the best type of négociant wine. It would also be worth trying the few domaine-bottled wines from Chantal Lescure and René Manuel.

In Italy, Chianti and Brunello come from the giant Villa Banfi estate (Chianti Classico Riserva 1981, £4.29), Valpolicella from Masi (including the single vineyard Serego Alighieri), Barbaresco from Gaja and Barolo from Oddero.

Best buys

Cuvée Labouré-Roi red and white, £2.51; Brouilly 1984, Georges Duboeuf, £5.26; Soave Classico Superiore 1985, Masi, £3

Les Bons Vins Occitans and Les Bons Vins Biologiques

19A Wetherby Gardens, London SW5 0JP   TEL 01-370 6529

OPEN Mon–Fri 9–1, 2–5   Sat 9–12 noon   CLOSED Sun, public holidays
CREDIT CARDS Access, Visa; personal and business accounts
DISCOUNTS Negotiable   DELIVERY Free in central London (min 1 case); £1.15 charge for Greater London; mail order available   GLASS HIRE Free with 1-case order   TASTINGS AND TALKS Monthly tastings at Institute of Directors; tutored tastings on organically produced wines and wines of the Midi
CELLARAGE Not available   ■

The big attraction of this list of wines from France is that nearly all are organically produced.

Thus from the south you get the excellent Coteaux des Baux en Provence wines of Mas de Gourgonnier (Réserve du Mas 1985, £4.33), Terres Blanches (Rouge 1985, £4.33, Ugni Blanc 1986, £4.11) and Domaine de Trévallon. Further temptations are the Châteauneuf-du-Pape from Pierre André (the 1983 vintage is £6.66), and the deliciously sweet sparkling Clairette de Die Tradition of Vincent Achard (£4.57).

Further north, the wines of Ch le Barradis in Bergerac and Monbazillac, Ch du Moulin de Peyronin in Bordeaux (1985 vintage at £3.66), Muscadet from Buy Bossard and Alsace from E Meyer all provide interest.

New wines are being discovered all the time – recent finds include a white wine from the Clairette de Bellegarde area near Nîmes, and a Faugères from the local co-operative.

Best buys

Mas de Gourgonnier, Réserve du Mas 1985, £4.33; Ch le Barradis Bergerac Sauvignon 1985, £3.55; Muscadet sur Lie 1985, Guy Bossard, £3.93; Faugères 1984, Cave Co-opérative, £2.54

Find the best new wine bargains all year round with our newsletter, *Which? Wine Monthly*, available for just £15 a year from: Dept WG88, Consumers' Association, FREEPOST, Hertford SG14 1YB – no stamp is needed if posted within the UK.

E H Booth

HEAD OFFICE 4–6 Fishergate, Preston,   TEL (0772) 51701
Lancashire PR1 3LJ
(20 branches in Lancashire)

OPEN Variable opening hours   CREDIT CARDS Access, Visa
DISCOUNTS Negotiable   DELIVERY At cost; mail order available
GLASS HIRE Free   TASTINGS AND TALKS Regular in-store tastings; to groups
on request   CELLARAGE Not available

Booths stores run two tiers of wines: a standard range which is available in all branches; and a fine wine list available on order and at the Fishergate store in Preston. Although the standard list is acceptable enough, it is for the fine wines that Booths make it into the Guide.

Here you will find a good range of mature clarets, from vintages back to 1973 and up to 1984. Some wines are very reasonably priced (Ch Rausan-Ségla 1976 at £11.65 and Ch Giscours 1978 at £13.50, for example), and with the more recent vintages there are a number of petit château wines. Burgundy offers a good number of domaine-bottled wines and some mature reds from the superb 1978 vintage, again with some bargains (in Burgundian terms, that is).

While the other French fine wine areas get less attention, Germany does very well, with plenty of estate wines (including 1976s and 1979s and a lot of 1983s). Italy has some mature Barolos and Brunellos and more recent vintages of classic wines such as Pieropan's Soave Classico 1985 (£4.85).

The other part of the world to show well on this fine wine list is Australia. There are a couple of Californians, too, and a good range of vintage Ports from old vintages.

The standard list has far fewer attractions. But in the middle of too many branded wines, we spotted areas of interest: vintage Ports, Raimat wines from Spain, Champagne and some white Italian wines.

Best buys

Asti Spumante Martini, £4.19; Cooks New Zealand wines; Raimat Chardonnay sparkling, £3.35; Booths Champagne, £8.49; Côtes du Marmandais red and white, £2.39; Gigondas 1982, E H Booth, £4.49

Bordeaux Direct

HEAD OFFICE New Aquitaine House, Paddock   TEL (0734) 481718
Road, Reading, Berkshire RG4 0JY (Mail order only)

CREDIT CARDS All accepted; personal and business accounts   DISCOUNTS On
special offers only   DELIVERY Free on UK mainland (min £50 order)
GLASS HIRE, TASTINGS AND TALKS Not available   CELLARAGE On request ■

Bordeaux Direct continues as a mail order outfit, while the Taste Shops (*qv*), which used to operate the same list, are now run separately (see also The Wine Club in the WINE CLUBS section). The policy of discovering new wines from lesser-known areas and then offering them at very fair prices hasn't changed.

The list is divided by wine style rather than geographical origin, so you get light dry whites and full dry whites followed by light reds and full reds. The choice in each section ranges widely: you might find wines from Bulgaria, Coteaux du Languedoc, Bergerac, Graves, Washington State, Muscadet, Burgundy and Sancerre all within a few inches of each other. Special offers – including mixed cases of half-bottles – highlight wines the club management thinks are good value.

Bordeaux Direct has a penchant for wines from the south and south-west of France and from Spain and Italy. They import everyday drinking wines from Friuli, and their luncheon red is a Navarra wine from Spain. From the south of France, they offer a Sablet Côtes du Rhône-Villages as well as a lighter Côtes du Rhône from the Caves de Chusclan. From the Midi, the wines of Jean Demolombe at Domaine de l'Abbaye de Valfernière in the La Clape region of Coteaux du Languedoc look interesting.

For a greater outlay, Jekel wines from California feature, as does a small range of petit château clarets (finer clarets appear on a fine wine list), and Burgundy from some well-known domaines.

Best buys

Vin de Pays des Côtes de Pérignan 1986 red, Cave de St-Exupéry, £2.98; Marcillac 1986, Cave de Valady, £3.35; Coteaux du Languedoc La Clape 1985, Domaine du Pech-Redon, £3.65; Côtes du Forez 1986, Cuvée Lys de Martagon, £3.65; The Wine Club's Tocai Grave del Friuli, £3.14

Borg Castel

Samlesbury Mill, Goosefoot Lane,   TEL (025 485) 2128
Samlesbury Bottoms, Preston, Lancashire PR5 0RN

OPEN Mon–Fri 10–5   Thur 7 pm–9.30 pm   Sat by appointment only   1st Sun of each month 12–4   CLOSED Sat, Sun (except 1st Sun in the month), last 2 weeks of Jan   CREDIT CARDS None accepted; personal and business accounts DISCOUNTS According to quantity   DELIVERY Free within 30-mile radius (min 1 case), otherwise at cost; mail order available   GLASS HIRE Free with order TASTINGS AND TALKS In-store tastings every Thur evening and first Sun each month; spring and summer tastings; to organised groups on request CELLARAGE Not available

Bordeaux and Germany are the highlights of this list which ranges quite widely within the classic areas; Borg Castel also produce a fine wine list.

The Bordeaux wines on the standard list are mainly of recent vintages: Ch Beaugérit 1983, Côtes de Bourg (£4.31) at one end, Ch

Chasse-Spleen 1982 (£12.61) at the other. The Burgundy list has wines from Salavert and Vallet Frères, Pasquier-Desvignes and Mommessin, with the occasional domaine-bottled wine as a bonus. Alsace wines come from Hugel and the co-operative at Turckheim.

On the Rhône, look for the Côtes du Rhône from the co-operative of Rasteau (Cuvée de Maître 1985, £3.46) and Châteauneuf du Pape from Chante Cigale (the 1982 vintage is £7.13). The Loire is less interesting (although try the Vouvray Clos du Bourg of Gaston Huet at £6.17). House wines unusually come from Henri Maire in the Jura.

German estate wines include examples from Deinhard in the Rheinpfalz and von Plettenberg in the Nahe, and although Italy's wines are dull, Spain's wines come from CVNE (Viña Real 1981 is £3.61), and Australia's from Orlando.

Best buys

Bonchalaz, Henri Maire red, white and rosé, £2.87; Marcilly Sélection NV, Burgundy, £3.39; Côtes du Rhône 1985, Cuvée de Maître, Co-opérative de Rasteau, £3.46; Muscat de Rivesaltes Vin Doux Naturel, £4.87; Viña Real 1981, CVNE, £3.61

Bottle & Basket

15 Highgate High Street, Highgate Village, London N6 5JT	TEL 01-341 7018

OPEN Mon–Fri 11–3, 5–9   Sat 11–9   Chr Day 12–1   Other religious holidays 12–2, 7–9   Public holidays 11–3, 5–9   CREDIT CARDS Access, Visa
DISCOUNTS 5% for 1 case   DELIVERY Free locally (min 1 case); delivery elsewhere not available   GLASS HIRE Free with reasonable order
TASTINGS AND TALKS Occasional in-store tastings   CELLARAGE Not available

The small bow-fronted window of this four-year-old shop in London's Highgate Village belies an enormous range of wines. Even if some areas are more successful than others, and prices are on the high side, pretty well everywhere are to be found pockets of interest. There is a tendency with Bordeaux and Burgundy – and on the Loire and Rhône – to rely on négociants, but that does turn up some good clarets from estates handled by Alexis Lichine and, in Burgundy, some of the domaine wines of Bouchard Aîné. In Alsace, the wines come from Dopff au Moulin and Willm.

Italian wines come mainly from Ruffino and Antinori in Tuscany, Pio Cesare in Piedmont and Santa Margherita in the Veneto (Merlot di Pramaggiore 1984, £4), but occasional excursions from these names reveal such finds as the red Cannonau 1982 from Sella e Mosca in Sardinia (£3.90). The Spanish list is long and has a super range of Reserva and Gran Reserva Riojas, most of which are ready to drink, alongside other top wines such as Vega Sicilia from Ribera del Duero and Torres wines, plus a wide choice of sparkling Cavas and Sherries.

Best buys

Navarra 1982 red, Señorio de Sarria, £2.25; Spanish Gran Reserva
Riojas; Alsace Pinot Blanc 1985, Willm, £4.50

Bottoms Up Superstores

See Peter Dominic.

Bow Wine Vaults

10 Bow Churchyard, London EC4M 9DQ   TEL 01-248 1121

OPEN Mon–Fri 9–6 (closed daily 3.15–4.15)   CLOSED Sat, Sun, public
holidays   CREDIT CARDS Access, Diners; personal and business accounts
DISCOUNTS 5% for 1 case   DELIVERY Free in mainland UK (min 2 cases); mail
order available   GLASS HIRE Free with any case order
TASTINGS AND TALKS Annual autumn tastings; monthly tastings/promotions in
the shop, bars and restaurants; to groups on request   CELLARAGE £4 per case
per year

Beware if you go shopping at this wine merchant and wine bar at
lunchtime – the place will be packed with City folk consuming hot food
or sandwiches. On the other hand, it's a good way of giving yourself a
chance to try the wines before you buy. (More details can be found in
the WINE BARS section.)

The shop is at the front, facing out on to narrow Bow Churchyard.
As befits a merchant in the City (even post Big Bang), there's a great
emphasis on wines suitable for directors' dining-rooms, so you will
find a good range of clarets, mainly of recent vintages. Sauternes from
Ch Gilette, the château that keeps its wine for years before releasing it
(the 1959 is the most recent vintage at £49.50 a bottle) would be a rare
treat. The Burgundy line-up comes from a mix of négociants
(Mommessin, Louis Latour, Prosper Maufoux) and domaines (Claude
and Michelle Joubert, Louis Bersan, Georges Verret).

Loire wines take in Quincy from Pierre Mardon (1986 vintage at
£5.35) and Savennières Clos du Papillon of Yves Soulez (1983 vintage at
£6.50), plus Muscadet from Jean Mace. On the Rhône, Côtes du Rhône
of Guigal and Cru du Coudoulet rub shoulders with Guigal's Côte
Rôtie and Châteauneuf from Domaine du Vieux Télégraphe. In the
Midi, look for vintages of the Cabernet Sauvignon star, Mas de
Daumas Gassac in the Hérault. Alsace is represented by Trimbach and
Kuentz-Bas. House Champagne is good – it has to be in the City – and
consumed in vast quantities (non-vintage is £9.95).

There's a pocket of German estate wines, Spanish Riojas from Olarra
and Berberana, and Sherries from Hidalgo, with Australian wines from
Balgownie (Cabernet Sauvignon 1982, £7.80).

Best buys

Jurançon Sec 1985, Jean Guirouilh, £4.75; Domaine du Paradis 1986, Domaines Fonscolombe, white and red, £3.85; Ch du Petit Thouars 1985, Loire, £4.25; Fino Hidalgo, £3.70

Bowlish House Wine Shop

Bowlish House, Wells Road, Shepton Mallet, Somerset BA4 5JD
TEL (0749) 2022

OPEN Mon–Sat and public holidays 'all hours' CLOSED Sun 10–4, 4 days at Christmas CREDIT CARDS None accepted DISCOUNTS Negotiable DELIVERY Will deliver within 25-mile radius of Shepton Mallet; elsewhere if in the area; mainly cash and carry GLASS HIRE Available
TASTINGS AND TALKS To groups on request CELLARAGE Free to customers

'We feel our role as a wine merchant is to make available some of the gems that exist outside the classic growing areas,' writes owner Brian Jordan at the beginning of his list. Good as his word, he omits most of Bordeaux and Burgundy, but includes Champagne, because, he says, there is no substitute.

Instead we are presented with a short range of wines from around the world. Australia is represented by wines from McWilliams (Inheritance red and dry Semillon at £3.30), Rosemount and Penfold. From New Zealand, we find Montana wines (Cabernet Sauvignon/Pinotage at £2.90).

The French choice is eclectic: Sauvignon du Haut-Poitou 1986 (£3.55) and the Chardonnay 1986 from the same region (£3.75); the Cahors 1983 of Domaine du Colombie (£3.55); the ripe, fruity Vacqueyras 1983, Domaine du Couroulou (£5.35); Beaujolais from Georges Duboeuf and Alsace wines from Louis Gisselbrecht.

In Italy, look for wines from Masi in the Veneto, Barolo from Oddero, Chianti from Castellare and the Tignanello of Antinori. A rarity is the white Tocai Breganza di Breganza 1984 of Maculan (£4.65) from hills north of Vicenza.

The pudding wines look appetising – after all, the wine shop is associated with Bowlish House restaurant, where you can buy wines from the mammoth 400-bin list. Sherries are from Barbadillo, there's Rioja from La Rioja Alta and other Spanish wines from Torres (Viña Sol 1985 at £3.65), plus the Gran Reserva Señorio de los Llanos 1978 (£3.90). Portugal's range is short, but includes the Colares wines from Chitas (1970 vintage at £5.50).

Best buys

McWilliams Inheritance red and Semillon, £3.30; Bairrada Garrafeira Particular 1979, Caves de Barrocão, £3.95; Winemakers Selection Cabernet Sauvignon/Pinotage, Montana, £2.90; Barbadillo Manzanilla, £3.60

Brinkley's Wines

51 Hollywood Road, London SW10 9HX	TEL 01-351 6711
ASSOCIATED OUTLETS Brinkley's Restaurant, 47 Hollywood Road, London SW10 9HX	TEL 01-351 1683
The Wine Gallery, 49 Hollywood Road, London SW10 9HX	TEL 01-352 7572
The Wine Gallery, 294 Westbourne Grove, London W11 2PS	TEL 01-229 1877
The Wine Gallery, 232 Brompton Road, London SW3 2BB	TEL 01-584 3493

OPEN Mon–Sat 10–10   Sun 12–2   CLOSED Public holidays
CREDIT CARDS Access, Visa; personal and business accounts
DISCOUNTS 10% (min 1 case)   DELIVERY Free locally; elsewhere
discretionary GLASS HIRE Free with 1-case order TASTINGS AND TALKS,
CELLARAGE Not available

There's expansion in the air at Brinkleys. In the same row of shops in Hollywood Road they run a wine bar, a restaurant and a wine shop. They have opened two more wine shops (wine galleries, they call them) in other parts of West London – and more are planned.

To stock these shops, Brinkleys have put together a fairly up-market range of wines. They're not, they say, able to compete on price with the major groups (although if they open a few more shops, they might try). So don't expect bargains: what you will find are well-chosen wines from most parts of the world.

A range of clarets covers mainly recent vintages. They have 1982s and 1983s, and have bought into top wines of the 1980 vintage – on the basis, we assume, that for this vintage the top growths are not too expensive (Ch Cos d'Estournel 1980 is £13.50; Ch Mouton Rothschild 1980 is £32). Burgundies are roughly half from négociants, half from growers, and Georges Duboeuf supplies the Beaujolais. The Champagne selection covers quite a few of the famous names; house Champagne is £8.50.

Other parts of France have only short representation. Look for the Vieille Ferme wines from the Côtes du Ventoux and Côtes du Luberon. The Italian and Spanish choices are distinctly unadventurous.

Outside Europe, there's California from Mondavi, Phelps, Trefethen and Firestone, Australian wine from McWilliams, Yalumba, Berri Estates (Cabernet Sauvignon 1981 at £4.60) and Rothbury; New Zealand wine from Cooks; and Chilean from Concha y Toro.

Best buys

Berri Estates Cabernet Sauvignon 1981, £4.60; Brinkley's Champagne (NV), £8.50; La Vieille Ferme red and white, £3.95; Californian Reserve, Geoffrey Roberts red and white, £3.30

Broad Street Wine Company

The Holloway, Market Place, Warwick,   TEL (0926) 493951
Warwickshire CV34 4SJ

OPEN Mon–Sat 9–6   CLOSED Sun, public holidays   CREDIT CARDS Access,
Visa; personal and business accounts   DISCOUNTS 4% for 1+ mixed case; 60p
per case collection allowance   DELIVERY Prices include 60p per case delivery
charge for Warwickshire, Hereford & Worcester, West Midlands, Staffordshire,
Oxfordshire, Buckinghamshire and Northamptonshire (min 3 cases); elsewhere
additional £1; mail order available   GLASS HIRE Free
TASTINGS AND TALKS Wines for tasting always available in-store for customers;
to groups on request   CELLARAGE Not available ∎

Apart from vintage Ports, this merchant stays very firmly in France.
Maybe there's something about their premises in 17th-century cellars
in the centre of Warwick that keeps them firmly along traditional lines.
Most pockets are catered for.

There's a strong showing of Loire wines: we would recommend the
Muscadet from Ch des Gautronnières (£2.57), the Pouilly Fumé of
Serge Dagueneau (1985 vintage, £4.62), or the Vouvrays of Gaston
Huet (for a special treat try the superb Vouvray le Mont Moelleux 1961
at a bargain £12.42). You might instead be lured by Coteaux du Layon
from Moulin Touchais.

One feature of the list is a long run of Alsace wines, all from the giant
co-operative of Turckheim, which has a reputation for producing
excellently clean, fruity wines (try the Pinot Blanc 1985 at £2.40).
Beaujolais is from Quinson and Champagne from Bricout (Carte Noire
non-vintage at £7.29).

And so to Burgundy and a mouth-watering range of wines, almost
entirely from estates. Wines from Vallet Frères and Tollot-Beaut vie
with Domaine du Duc de Magenta and Machard de Gramont or
Domaine des Varoilles. On the Rhône, we see wines from the top
co-operative of the Côtes du Rhône-Villages at Rasteau, and
Châteauneuf-du-Pape from Chante Cigale (the 1982 vintage is £4.98).
A sensible selection of Bordeaux goes back to 1978.

Best buys

Bourgogne Pinot Noir 1984, Vallet Frères, £4.75; Ch des Gautronnières
Muscadet de Sèvre et Maine 1985, £2.57; Côte du Ventoux 1985,
Domaine des Anges, £2.05; Pinot Blanc 1985, Cave Co-opérative de
Turckheim, £2.40; Ch Tourteau Chollet 1983, Graves, £4.05

Prices were correct to the best of our knowledge as we went to press. They,
and ranges of wines stock, are likely to change during the course of 1988,
and are intended only as a rough indication of an establishment's range
and prices.

G E Bromley & Sons

London Street, Leicester, Leicestershire LE5 3RH   TEL (0533) 768471
271 Leicester Road, Wigston Fields, Leicester,   TEL (0533) 882057
Leicestershire LE8 1JW
ASSOCIATED WITH J H Measures & Sons,   TEL (0775) 2676
The Crescent, Spalding, Lincolnshire PE11 1AF

OPEN (*London Street*) Tue–Sat 10–1, 5–9.30 (Tue–Thur), 5–10 (Fri), 6–10 (Sat)
Sun 12–2, 7–9.30   (*Wigston Fields*) Mon–Sat 10–1, 5–10   Sun 12–1.30, 7–10
(*J H Measures*) Mon–Sat 9–6   CLOSED (*London Street*) Mon; (*J H Measures*) most
public holidays   CREDIT CARDS Access, Visa; personal and business
accounts   DISCOUNTS 2½% on 5 cases, 5% on 12+ cases   DELIVERY Free in
Lincoln, Boston, Holbeach, Peterborough, Wellingborough, Rugby, Nuneaton,
Ashby, Derby, Nottingham and Newark (min 3 cases); 1 case £3.45, 2 cases
£2.30; elsewhere at cost; mail order available   GLASS HIRE Free with 1-case
order; delivery with wine order to Leicester city only
TASTINGS AND TALKS Regular in-store tastings; to groups on request
CELLARAGE £2.40 per case per year (in advance)

While France and Germany still dominate this list, there's interest in
Italy and a passing nod at the New World.

Germany, in fact, comes in for a very good showing. On the
Rheingau, wines from Schloss Vollrads and Langwerth von Simmern
(Eltviller Sonnenberg Riesling Kabinett 1983 at £4.99, for instance) look
attractive. The Nahe is well represented by wines from the State
Domaine at Niederhausen, the Zentralkellerei of the Nahe, and von
Plettenberg. In the Rheinpfalz, the range from Bürklin-Wolf and
Bassermann-Jordan would be worth exploring. The Mosel takes in
wine from Rudolf Müller, from the Bischöfliches Priesterseminar and
from von Kesselstatt, as well as Ruwer wines from von Schubert.

In France, we would recommend some of the country wines: the
Coteaux d'Aix-en-Provence wines of Ch de Fonscolombe (red, white
and rosé at £2.98); the Cépage Colombard white from the Plaimont
co-operative in Gascony (£2.58); and the Domaine Ste-Eulalie 1985,
Minervois at £3.12.

In Bordeaux, of the plenty of petit château wines we would suggest
the Domaine de Zauzet 1982, Canon Fronsac at £3.99, or Ch Ruat Petit
Poujeaux 1982, Moulis at £4.69. Older wines go back to the 1970
vintage. Burgundy has domaine wines from producers like Antonin
Rodet and Machard de Gramont as well as négociant wines from
Chanson.

On the Rhône, we were attracted by the range of Châteauneuf
wines, particularly Ch de Beaucastel, Domaine du Vieux Télégraphe.
Also look for the Gigondas 1981, L'Oustau Fauquet of Roger Combe at
£5.32. With the Loire, the main interest centres on the Sancerre of Guy
Saget and Pouilly Fumé of Ch de Tracy. Alsace is from Blanck, and
house Champagne from Baron de Beaupré (£8.69).

The Italian section contains Alto Adige wine from Tiefenbrunner,

Barolo from Pio Cesare and Fontanafredda and Chianti from
Frescobaldi and Ruffino, and Lungarotti's Riserva 1977 Vigna
Monticchio from Torgiano in Umbria.

Best buys

German estate wines; Domaine Ste-Eulalie 1985, Minervois, £3.12; Ch
de Fonscolombe red, white and rosé, £2.98; Chianti Rufina 1983, Villa
Vetrice, £2.89

Buckingham Wines

157 Great Portland Street, London W1N 5FB	TEL 01-580 1622
71 Abingdon Road, London W8 6AW	TEL 01-937 3996
6 Fulham Road, London SW3 6HG	TEL 01-584 1450
98 Holland Park Avenue, London W11 3RB	TEL 01-727 5148
282 Old Brompton Road, London SW5 9HR	TEL 01-370 4402

OPEN Mon–Sat 10–7.30 (9.30 Fulham, Old Brompton Road and Holland Park;
10.30–8.30 Abingdon Road) Sun 12–2 (Holland Park Avenue), 7–9 (Fulham),
12–2 and 7–9 (Old Brompton Road) CLOSED Sun, public holidays (Fulham and
Holland Park open but reduced hours) CREDIT CARDS Access, Visa; personal
and business accounts DISCOUNTS 5% on 1–5 cases, 7½% on 6–9 cases, 10%
on 10+ cases DELIVERY Free within 1-mile radius of each store and central
London; elsewhere variable; mail order on request GLASS HIRE Free with
appropriate case order TASTINGS AND TALKS 2–3 in-store tastings per month
for customers; to groups on request CELLARAGE Available; charge minimal

'London's finest wine merchant,' they claim modestly above their
newly refurbished shops. Well, that's a difficult claim to prove – but
they are pretty good, especially when dealing with the classic areas.

One source of pride is a good list of clarets, with plenty of wines
from the left bank of the Gironde to allow for current drinking, some
classed growths from recent vintages for laying down and, for those
who want to splash out, some older vintages back to 1961. Talking of
splashing out, their Champagne list is dominated by some of the big
names in non-vintage and special cuvées.

In Burgundy, Buckinghams have gone for a mix of domaines (mainly
in the reds) and négociant wines, mainly from recent vintages (except
for the occasional red from the 1960s). In Alsace, they've followed
Trimbach and Schoech, and on the Loire, they have roped in some top
names in Sancerre and Pouilly Fumé. Rhône wines are mainly from
Chapoutier.

French country wines are well treated – and there's a special
emphasis on wines from Savoie – maybe something to do with all the
skiers who patronise their shops. But they seem to have a blank spot
with Italy, recovering with Spanish wines (an attractive range of
Riojas). Plenty of vintage Ports grace the shelves but fewer Sherries.

New World wines take in Cooks from New Zealand and Hardys and Wynns from Australia. Here you see Concha y Toro wines from Chile, but California is neglected.

Regular special offers and sales complement the standard list.

Best buys

Non-vintage Champagnes; vintage Ports; Chilean wines from Concha y Toro

---

The Butlers Wine Cellar

247 Queens Park Road, Brighton BN2 2XJ   TEL (0273) 698724

OPEN Mon–Sat 9–5.30   Sat 9–1   CLOSED Sun, public holidays, Chr Day–5 Jan   CREDIT CARDS Visa; business accounts   DISCOUNTS Not available   DELIVERY Free within 15-mile radius (min 1 case) and nationally (min 3 cases); otherwise 1 bottle £2.75, 2–3 bottles £4.50, 4–12 bottles £5.75, 13–35 bottles £7.50   GLASS HIRE Free with 1-case order; delivery available   TASTINGS AND TALKS, CELLERAGE Not available

---

Old wine is the theme here – the older the better, according to owner Geoffrey Butler, who has put together a rapidly changing list of fine wines, with interest inevitably centring on Bordeaux, Burgundy and the Rhône.

So, in a recent list, we found claret right back to 1926, with strong showings of vintages in the 1960s (including a mouth-watering range of 1961s), and 1970 and 1978 both coming along nicely. From the current Sauternes and Barsac bottles the oldest is Ch de Peyrat Cérons 1924 (£32.50). The Burgundies tend to be younger, but there are 1978s in the reds, and plenty of 1983s in the whites.

From the Loire, it's the sweet wines of Moulin Touchais in Anjou and Vouvray that compete in the age stakes (1947 Vouvray, Marc Brédif, £40). And from the Rhône, Hermitage 1971 (from Bellicard at £14.95) and Côte Rôtie 1969 (from Chapoutier at £18) would appeal to any Rhône buff.

German prizes are wines from the 1975 and 1976 vintages. And watch out for the oddments corner at the back of the list which can contain anything at all.

Best buys

Old vintages of claret

Special awards

🐷 is for bargain prices   ▭ is for a very good range of wines

✳ is for high quality wines   ▱ is for exceptional service

Anthony Byrne Fine Wines

SALES OFFICE Kingscote House, Biggin Lane, Ramsey, Cambridgeshire PE17 1NB
WAREHOUSE/CASH AND CARRY 88 High Street, Ramsey, Cambridgeshire PE17 1BS

TEL (0487) 814555 (for both addresses)

OPEN Mon–Sat 9–5.30 CLOSED Sun, public holidays
CREDIT CARDS Access, Visa; personal and business accounts DISCOUNTS 5% on 1 case DELIVERY Free throughout the UK (min 2 cases); mail order available GLASS HIRE Free with 2-case order TASTINGS AND TALKS Wines always available in-store to taste; to groups on request CELLARAGE £1.95 per case per year

The heart of this excellent list is Burgundy. The list of domaine-bottled wines reads like a roll-call of the great and the good: Bernard Bachelet in Chassagne-Montrachet, Lucien Denizot in the Côte Chalonnaise (Bourgogne Blanc 1983, £5.55), Domaine Gagnard Delagrange in Montrachet, Domaine Leflaive in Puligny Montrachet, Jean Grivot in Vosne-Romanée, Pousse d'Or in Volnay (Volnay Caillerets 1983 at £16.13). And many more. Inevitably, they're expensive, but fair considering the cost price of the wines.

New agencies this year have taken Anthony Byrne to the New World. We have enjoyed his choice of wines from Delatite in Australia (the Rhine Riesling 1986 at £7.05 is stunning, as is the Pinot Noir 1985 at £7.05 – a rare example of the grape actually working Down Under). From California, the Cuvaison Winery has supplied a Cabernet Sauvignon and Chardonnay (both at £7.57).

Back in France, Georges Duboeuf is behind the Beaujolais, and is the only négociant in the sea of growers of Burgundy on this list. In fact, Anthony Byrne carries the widest range of Duboeuf wines in the UK, including many special cuvées which aren't normally seen here.

If other areas seem neglected, it's only by comparison with Burgundy. Treats turn up in most parts: the organic wines of Domaine des Terres Blanches in Coteaux des Baux en Provence, Alsace wines from Zind-Humbrecht and the Co-operative of Pfaffenheim, Pouilly Fumé from one of the great originals – Didier Dagueneau (try his barrique-aged Les Silex 1986 at £10.14), Madiran from Alain Brumont. You could also try the old vintages of Ch Gilette in Sauternes or lay down some younger vintages of Churchill's Port.

Anthony Byrne runs a regular programme of tastings to keep his customers up to date, and has developed a computer programme designed to help choose wines to go with a dinner party.

Best buys

Domaine-bottled Burgundy; Beaujolais 1986, Duboeuf, £3.43; Madiran 1979, Alain Brumont, £4.62; Pinot Blanc 1985, Cave Co-opérative Pfaffenheim, £3.24; Champagne les Impitoyables (NV), £9.78

D Byrne & Co

12 King Street, Clitheroe, Lancashire BB7 2EP   TEL (0200) 23152
OPEN Mon, Wed, Sat 9–6   Thur, Fri 9–8   Tue 8.30–6   CLOSED Sun, public
holidays   CREDIT CARDS None accepted; personal and business accounts
DISCOUNTS £1 on mixed case, £1.20 on unmixed case, 5% on orders over £500
DELIVERY Free within 50-mile radius of Clitheroe; elsewhere 1 case £4, 2 cases
£3.50 per case, 3 cases free; mail order available   GLASS HIRE Free with 1-case
order   TASTINGS AND TALKS Annual customer tasting, monthly in-store
tastings; to small groups on request   CELLARAGE Free

The printed version of this list is a mess. Names crop up in apparently
random order, with no information about what the wines taste like or
where they come from (apart from regional headings). Some wines –
like Alsace – turn up under French country wines as well as under the
heading Alsace.

It's a great pity, because the wines themselves – when you can sort
them all out – cover an amazing amount of ground. A big range of
clarets goes back to 1978, with many petits châteaux as well as classed
growths (look for Ch Fourcas-Hosten 1978 at a bargain £8.39; also Ch
Caronne Ste-Gemme 1980 at £5.49 for current drinking). 1985 clarets
are now ready to buy.

In Burgundy, while Chanson features largely, plenty of wine from
domaines (and Chablis from Henri Laroche) pop up. On the Rhône,
there's a good range of Châteauneuf (Ch Fortia 1981 is £7.75 and Clos
l'Oratoire 1981, £7.49). We would also recommend the Côtes du Rhône
Ch de l'Estagnol 1984 at £4.05. Beaujolais comes from Georges
Duboeuf. Loire wines are less interesting, but there's a huge range of
Alsace from Jérôme Lorentz, Louis Gisselbrecht, Hugel, Trimbach,
Dopff et Irion and Dopff au Moulin. Bargain French country wines
abound.

Outside France, estate-bottled German wines put in a strong
showing, with plenty from the State domaines, from von Schönborn
on the Rheingau, from von Buhl and Bürklin-Wolf in the Rheinpfalz,
from von Schubert in the Ruwer, from Bergweiler Prüm in the Mosel.
There are plenty of treats in Italy, too: Chianti from Frescobaldi, Badia
a Coltibuono, Antinori, Ruffino, Rocca delle Macie, and Veneto wines
from Masi.

The Australian list is now beginning to read like a *Who's who*: Brown
Brothers, Rosemount, Orlando, de Bortoli, Taltarni, Wolf Blass, Geoff
Merrill, Lindemans, Hardy – just a few of the names. California is a bit
less illustrious but even so comes up with a pretty good roll-call.

How they keep all these wines in one shop, we can't imagine. The
list has the air of being thrown together: perhaps if they took more
trouble with its content and presentation, we could give them more
awards than we have done.

Best buys

Australian wines; Pure Syrah 1983, Domaine de Vallouit, £2.99; Ch de
la Jaubertie 1984, Blanc Sec, £3.09; German estate wines; Valpolicella
Castello d'Illasi 1984, Santi, £3.15; Alsace 1983 vintage wines

Cachet Wines

61/65 Heworth Road, York,   TEL (0904) 425853
North Yorkshire YO3 0AA

OPEN Mon, Tue, Thur, Fri 12–6   Sat 10–6   CLOSED Wed, Sun, public
holidays   CREDIT CARDS None accepted; personal and business accounts
DISCOUNTS 5% on 1 unmixed case   DELIVERY Free within 30-mile radius (min
1 case); elsewhere in Yorkshire £3   GLASS HIRE Free
TASTINGS AND TALKS Regular tastings in local wine bar   CELLARAGE £1.50
per case per year

'Quality and affordability' are his aims, says Terry Herbert of Cachet
Wines. Certainly, his range is sensible and well priced, with few duff
bottles, so he seems to be on the right track.

While France accounts for most of the list, expansion has been going
on beyond. We were pleased to see Italian wines from Friuli (Ca
Bolani's Tocai Friuliano di Aquileia 1986 at £3.63 is still good value),
from Bigi in Orvieto, from Oddero in Barolo. The smooth red
Portuguese Tinto da Anfora 1982 comes at another good price – £3.59.
Port is from Ramos Pinto. A short selection of Riojas from CVNE and
Torres wines forms the Spanish section. Mr Herbert has now brought
in some California wines (Geoffrey Roberts Reserve red and white at
£2.95), and wines from Rosemount, Jacob's Creek and Orlando to
represent Australia.

The Rhône Valley and the south generate the most interest in the
French section. Look for the varietal Vin de Pays Coteaux Flaviens
(Cabernet Sauvignon and Merlot at £2.79), the Côtes du Rhône, Cru du
Coudoulet 1985 (£4.99), the red from the Côtes du Vivarais, and the
sweet Muscat de Rivesaltes (also £4.99).

The South-West, Alsace (Willy Gisselbrecht) and the Loire (the
excellent varietal wines of the Confrérie des Vignerons d'Oisly et
Thésée in Touraine) all offer a few nice contributions, complemented
by well-balanced ranges from Bordeaux and Burgundy.

Best buys

Ch Bonnet 1983, Bordeaux, £3.68; Sauvignon de Touraine Maistre
Claude 1986, £3.35; Merlot 1986, Domaine de la Baume, Vin de Pays
des Coteaux Flaviens, £2.79; Domaine de Monestier Blanc 1985,
Bergerac, £2.99; Jacob's Creek red 1984, £3.39

Cadwgan Fine Wines

152A Ashley Road, Hale, Altrincham,   TEL 061-928 0357
Greater Manchester WA15 9SA

OPEN Mon–Fri 11–9 Sat 9–9 Sun open only in Dec public holidays 12–2,
7–9 CLOSED Sun except Dec CREDIT CARDS Access, Visa DISCOUNTS 5%
for 1 case DELIVERY Free within 10-mile radius (min 1 case); elsewhere £5 for 1
case, £3 for 2–5 cases, £2 for 6–9 cases, £1.20 for 10+ cases; mail order available
GLASS HIRE Free TASTINGS AND TALKS To groups on request
CELLARAGE Not available

An attractively produced list starts out with a series of food and wine
matches, setting the tone for the helpful notes throughout.

The range of wines still concentrates on France, and in a sensible
way, with some attractive house wines from Pierre Frain vying with
up-market offerings. Loire wines are from Huet in Vouvray (Clos du
Bourg Demi-Sec 1982 at £5.65) and Ch des Gautronnières in Muscadet,
and Champagne is from Bricout at the least expensive end (£9.65 for
the non-vintage) and Krug at the other (1976 vintage, £38.60).

In Burgundy, the emphasis is on domaine wines: look for Chablis
from Michel Remon, red Burgundy from Tollot-Beaut as well as Vallet
Frères and Beaujolais from J Dépagneux. There's a short range of
clarets, from 1982 and 1983 (Ch Beaugérit 1982, Côtes de Bourg, £3.85;
Ch les Ormes de Pez 1983, £9.89), and a good selection of Alsace wines
from the co-operative at Turckheim.

Stars on the Rhône include the Châteauneuf of Chante Cigale and
the Côtes du Rhône of the Rasteau co-operative. Estate German wines
are all from Deinhard. The Spanish and Italian contingents are short
but turn up Riojas from CVNE and the Verdicchio dei Castelli di Jesi
from Bianchi. Smith Woodhouse supplies the basic Ports, but there are
some vintages from other houses.

Best buys

Côtes du Ventoux 1985, Domaine des Anges, £2.78; Pinot Blanc 1986;
Cave Co-opérative of Turckheim, £3.20; Ch Beaugérit 1982, Côtes de
Bourg, £3.85; Chardonnay, Venegazzù della Casa 1984, £3.40

Cairns & Hickey

17 Blenheim Terrace, Woodhouse Lane, Leeds,   TEL (0532) 459501
West Yorkshire LS2 9HN

OPEN Mon–Fri 9–6 Sat 9–1 (extended hours over Chr period) CLOSED Sun,
public holidays CREDIT CARDS None accepted; personal and business
accounts DISCOUNTS 5% on cases of wine for payment at time of purchase
DELIVERY Free within 25-mile radius of Leeds; elsewhere at cost; mail order
available GLASS HIRE Free with suitable wine order
TASTINGS AND TALKS Wine available for tasting in-store for customers; to
groups on request CELLARAGE £1.50 per case per year

A few excitements among a rather dull middle-of-the-road range are enough to keep Cairns & Hickey in the Guide this year.

They offer a good selection of mature clarets, going back to 1961 and 1952. 1982 has a nice line in different bottle sizes of Ch Malescot St-Exupéry and Ch Rausan-Ségla, while good value is to be had in 1978s (Ch Cantemerle, £9.95; Ch Chasse-Spleen, £9.95).

Burgundy is dull, with négociant wines predominating, and the Rhône has likewise little to offer, but the Loire offers Ménétou-Salon 1985 from Henri Pellé (£5.25) and Sancerre from Paul Millerioux (1985 vintage at £5.70). A short selection from Hugel and Dopff et Irion accounts for the Alsace part of the list.

It's impossible to tell about most of the German wines – the list lacks producers, although some Deinhard estate wines are lurking there. Spain is better served, with Riojas from Faustino and Campo Viejo, plus some decent Sherries from Valdespino and Lustau; the range of vintage Ports is good, and watch for bin-end lists.

Best buys

Rhine Riesling 1986, Old Triangle Vineyard, £3.45; Sauvignon de St-Bris 1984, £3.95; Campo Viejo Rioja, £2.85; Ch Filhot 1981, Sauternes, £4.35 (half-bottles)

Alistair Cameron

6 Stradbroke Road, London N5 2PZ   TEL 01-354 1391
(24-hour answering machine)

OPEN Telephone and mail order service only – no shop   CREDIT CARDS None accepted; business accounts   DISCOUNTS Not available   DELIVERY Free within M25 area (min 1 case London postal districts, min 2 cases within M25); otherwise £3 for 1 case; elsewhere £5 for 1 case, £2.50 per case for 2 cases, £2 per case for 3–5 cases, 5+ cases free   GLASS HIRE Free with appropriate case order   TASTINGS AND TALKS Three tastings annually in central London; occasional tastings in Surrey; to groups in London and Home Counties on request   CELLARAGE £2.50 per case per year   ■

This one-man band was started in 1986, too late for inclusion in the 1987 Guide. Alistair Cameron operates a mail order service from a sensibly balanced, well-produced list.

He's particularly strong on French wines, but in keeping with contemporary wine budgets, it's the non-classic regions which get most of the space. For instance, in white French country wines, he offers the Côtes du Luberon of Cellier de Marrenon, and the Sauvignon and Chardonnay from Haut-Poitou. Reds include good, straightforward Minervois Ch de Villerambert 1985 (£2.25) and an unusual Gamay wine from the upper Loire, the Côtes Roannaises 1985 (£4.20). House wines are from Georges Duboeuf (Cuvée Duboeuf red and white at £2.69).

The Loire comes up with yet more interesting bottles: Chinon 1985 from Paul Buisse (£4.10) and a classic Touraine Sauvignon 1986 at £2.65, among others. Beaujolais is from Georges Duboeuf and Alsace from Boeckel (Pinot Blanc 1986 at £4.15). In Bordeaux, look for the oak-aged white Graves Ch Cabannieux 1984 (£6.25), and an excellent red Fronsac, Ch Hervé Laroc 1983 (£5.45).

Elsewhere in France, Burgundy is supplied by a mix of négociants and estates, while the Rhône wines come principally from Pascal. Hector Richemont house Champagne is a bargain £7.95.

Spain's range is equally sensible: Torres wines, Señorio de Sarria Navarra wines and Cáceres Rioja. Mr Cameron has picked the good Chianti Classico from Serristori (Machiavelli Riserva 1982, £4.25) and Barolo from Ceretto (Zonchera 1982, £8.25). New World wines are from Clos du Bois and Joseph Phelps in California, and McWilliams and Lindeman in Australia. Look also for the most vintage-like of Late Bottled Vintage Ports – those from Smith Woodhouse and Warre.

Best buys

McWilliams Inheritance red and white, £3.25; Bourgogne Rouge 1983, Claudine Deschamps, £5.25; Champagne (NV) Hector Richemont, £7.95; Minervois Ch de Villerambert 1985, £2.25; Touraine Sauvignon 1986, Compagnie de la Vallée de la Loire, £2.65

Cantina Augusto

91–95 Clerkenwell Road, London EC1R 5BX   TEL 01-242 3246

OPEN Mon–Thur 9–6   Fri 9–6.30   Sat mornings in Dec   CLOSED Sat (except mornings in Dec), Sun, public holidays   CREDIT CARDS None accepted; personal and business accounts   DISCOUNTS Approx 10% on 1+ cases
DELIVERY Free in London (min order £100), £2 charge for orders under £50, £1 charge for orders £50–£100; elsewhere at cost; mail order if requested
GLASS HIRE Free with order (£5 deposit per dozen)
TASTINGS AND TALKS Regular in-store tastings; to groups on request
CELLARAGE Not available

In the days when newspaper journalists still worked in the Fleet Street area, this shop and its wine bar below ground were a popular haunt. Times have changed, but still Italian wines are the reason for this merchant's inclusion in the Guide, although they also stock wines from France, Germany, Spain and Portugal.

White wines include Alto Adige wines from Niedermayer, and the Tocai and Pinot Grigio from Angoris in Friuli. In Piedmont, Gavi's Fontanafredda (1985 vintage for £4.60) and the same firm's delicious sparkling Moscato d'Asti (£3.85) are alluring. Look also for the Vin Santo, Tuscan dessert wine, from Antinori (£6.10).

The reds range widely across Italy: Chianti from Ruffino and Rocco delle Macie, vini da tavola like Terricci 1983 from Guarnieri (£7.95), the top-class Rosso Cònero 1982 Vigneto San Lorenzo from the Marches (£3.80), and Lungarotti's Rubesco di Torgiano (1980 vintage at £5.40).

Look for Barolos from Prunotto, Pio Cesare, and the marvellously named Inferno 1982 from Negri (£4). From further south, the Aglianico del Vulture of Fratelli d'Angelo (1982 vintage at £6.25) and Taurasi 1981 of Mastroberardino (£8.60) are both examples of wine made from the ancient Aglianico grape.

Best buys

Chardonnay 1985, Niedermayer, £3.55; Chianti Classico Ruffino 1985, £3.70; Vino Nobile di Montepulciano Riserva 1982, Bigi, £4.90; Spanna 1979, Antoniolo, £3.45

Caves de la Madeleine

301 Fulham Road, London SW10 9QH   TEL 01-351 5863

OPEN Mon–Sat 9–8   CLOSED Sun, public holidays   CREDIT CARDS Access, Visa; personal and business accounts   DISCOUNTS Negotiable
DELIVERY Free in London (min 2 cases); elsewhere at cost; mail order available
GLASS HIRE Free with case order   TASTINGS AND TALKS Occasional in-store tastings by invitation; to groups on request   CELLARAGE £5 per case per year

This range of wines sticks strongly to the classic areas of France, providing a service for local Sloanes who may care less about the price than the name of the wine.

Nevertheless, Caves de la Madeleine choose well within their self-imposed confines, and display obvious enthusiasm in the tasting notes on their printed list. They also acknowledge the existence of French country wines, with an attractive range from the south and south-west: Cabernet Sauvignon Vin de Pays de l'Aude is £3.10; red Côtes du Marmandais 1985 from the Cave du Cucumont is £3.35; the white Cuvée Cézanne, Côtes du Luberon, 100 per cent Chardonnay, is £3.75.

The Bordeaux section is sensibly divided into wines for drinking and those for laying down. In the first, there are plenty of decent petit château wines, although prices tend to be a little high while the second goes in for classed growths. A fine wine list covers older vintages of classed growth claret.

Burgundy has some négociant wines – from Chartron et Trébuchet as well as Louis Latour – and some domaine wines. Northern Rhône wines are from Guigal and Jaboulet Aîné, and are cheaper elsewhere; the southern Rhône holds some excellent Côtes du Rhône-Villages. On the Loire, look for the Sancerre of Jean Vacheron, and the sweet Coteaux du Layon of Ch du Breuil. Alsace is from Zind-Humbrecht, Champagne from the small quality firm of Deutz.

The only wines to come from outside France are the fine Sherries of Valdespino, some of the old solera Sandeman Sherries, and a small selection of vintage Ports.

Best buys

Valdespino Pale Dry Fino, £3.65; Blanquette de Limoux 1981, £5.95; Mâcon Rouge 1985, Roger Lasserat, £4.50; Chardonnay Vin de Pays d'Oc 1985, £3.50; Cabernet Sauvignon Vin de Pays de l'Aude 1984, £3.10

C C Enterprises

See the Wine Schoppen.

Champagne and Caviar Shop

18 Leadenhall Market, London EC3V 1LR   TEL 01-626 4912
OPEN Mon–Fri 10–6   CLOSED Sat, Sun, public holidays
CREDIT CARDS Access, Amex, Visa; personal and business accounts
DISCOUNTS 5% for 1 case   DELIVERY Free within City of London; elsewhere
£3.50 for single bottle anywhere in UK; mail order available   GLASS HIRE Free
TASTINGS AND TALKS Lunchtime Champagne tastings 2–4 days each month
CELLARAGE Not available

Perhaps, like workers in chocolate factories, the owners get tired of eating caviar and drinking Champagne, but to us less fortunate mortals it does seem a pretty good combination to be selling.

The wine list has exactly Champagne – and no more. But the range from nearly all the grande marque houses and others is comprehensive, with a non-vintage, rosé, vintage and de luxe wine from most producers. The selection of magnums and jeroboams is also very good. Prices are not cheap, mind you, even for Champagne – with Mercier non-vintage at £10 the cheapest – but no doubt the City location means a few pounds here and there don't matter.

The Champagne House

15 Dawson Place, London W2 4TH   TEL 01-221 5538

OPEN Mon–Thur 9.30–6 CLOSED Fri, Sat, Sun, public holidays, September
CREDIT CARDS None accepted DISCOUNTS Negotiable (min 3 cases)
DELIVERY Free in Kensington, Chelsea, Westminster, City of London (min 1
case); elsewhere at cost; mail order available GLASS HIRE Free with 1-case
order TASTINGS AND TALKS Tutored tastings for established customers; to
selected groups on request CELLARAGE Not available ■

As stylish as the wine, the list from this merchant (who specialises
exclusively in wine from the Champagne region) has wines from small
growers as well as the more famous names.

So next to Bollinger (£14.77) on the non-vintage Champagne list, you
have Albert Le Brun's Cuvée Réserve at £9.78, Robert Driant's Extra
Brut Special at £11.40, and the top quality Seconde Prévoteau Brut at
£13.19. More famous marques to appear include Laurent-Perrier,
Gosset, Krug, Perrier-Jouët, Pol Roger and Roederer.

In vintage wines, there are plenty from 1979 – currently, we feel, the
most attractive vintage to drink – such as Perrier-Jouët at £15.40 or
Seconde Prévoteau at £14.70. Some of the prestige cuvées like
Perrier-Jouët Cuvée Belle Epoque or Dom Pérignon (1980 vintage at
£35.18) are here, too – and at prices which owe as much to their
packaging and image as the wines themselves.

A few still Coteaux Champenois wines and Ratafia and Marc de
Champagne are also listed.

Best buys

Albert Le Brun, NV, £9.78; Mumm Cordon Vert, NV, £12.89;
Larmandier Blanc de Blancs, £12.17; Roederer 1979, £17.69

Champagne de Villages

Park House, 29 Fonnereau Road, Ipswich,   TEL (0473) 56922
Suffolk IP1 3JR

OPEN Mon–Fri 9–5 CLOSED Sat, Sun, public holidays
CREDIT CARDS Access; personal and business accounts
DISCOUNTS Negotiable DELIVERY Free to UK mainland (min 1 case within
20-mile radius, 5 cases elsewhere); elsewhere £4 per case; mail order available
GLASS HIRE Free with 1-case order TASTINGS AND TALKS Regular tastings for
customers; on request to local institutes CELLARAGE £4 per case per year ■

Champagne, it says in the name, but not everything here is from that
region, what with Bordeaux, Burgundy, Loire and Alsace as well as a
smattering of wines from the south of France.

But Champagne is the most interesting part of the list. Growers
rather than the Champagne houses are the suppliers: Jean-Paul Arvois
in Chavot, Michel Labbé and Gilbert Bertrand in Chaméry, Pierre
Arnould in Verzenay, Raymond Devilliers in Villedommange, Georges

Lilbert in Cramant, Jacques Copinet in Montgenost and Alexandre Bonnet in Les Riceys. Many of these producers also make still Coteaux Champenois wines which are available here.

Bordeaux offers a short selection, particularly in Graves (Domaine du Chevalier, Ch Carbonnieux, Ch Larrivet-Haut-Brion) and Barsac (Ch Caillou). Burgundy is a mixture of domaine wines and wines from the négociant firm of B & J M Delaunay. Loires come from the eastern (Sauvignon) end of the river at Pouilly Fumé, Rully and Quincy. The small group of southern French wines includes Castel Roubine Côtes de Provence and a Cahors from Pelvillain et Fils.

Best buys

Vieille Réserve Brut Champagne, Jean-Paul Arvois, £9.89; Blanc de Blancs Extra Dry Champagne, Jacques Copinet, £9.83; Cru du Clocher 1981, Bordeaux, £5.52; Cahors 1983, Pelvillain et Fils, £4.37

Chaplin & Son

35 Rowlands Road, Worthing, West Sussex BN11 3JJ TEL (0903) 35888
(24-hour answering machine)

OPEN Mon–Sat 8.45–1.15, 2.15–5.30 (Fri open to 6) CLOSED Sun, public holidays CREDIT CARDS Access, Visa; business accounts DISCOUNTS 5% on 1 mixed case; trade and quantity discounts may be greater by arrangement DELIVERY Free within 7-mile radius (min 1 mixed case); greater distance for larger orders; mail order available GLASS HIRE Free with appropriate wine order TASTINGS AND TALKS Regular in-store tastings; to groups on request CELLARAGE Not available

This is a sound list, covering a lot of ground, and producing interesting wines from most areas. Don't expect in-depth coverage of any one wine region, though.

Working through the list, we came across Almacenista Sherries as well as Chaplin's own shipment Sherry, Tio Carlos. Sparkling Saumur wines come from Ackerman-Laurance (1811 brand, £5.19). Clarets show a sensible interest in petit château wines for current drinking as well as classed growths from recent vintages. Burgundy is mainly by courtesy of négociants – Loron, Antonin Rodet, Labouré-Roi, Chanson. From the south of France, look for the good value, organic wines of Listel (Domaine de Villeroy Blanc de Blancs, £3.11).

Outside France, there are a few German estate wines, and in Italy wines from Masi in the Veneto, and the delicious Cabernet Sauvignon/Merlot Venegazzù 1982 at £4.99. Spanish wines are from Paternina and Lopez de Heredia in Rioja and Torres in Penedès. The 1979 vintage of Ch Musar from the Lebanon can be had for £4.79.

The Australian selection is expanding – mainly Penfolds wines, but also some from Rosemount and Brown Brothers. New Zealand's contribution is by Cooks and Montana. For those who are keen on malt whisky, the choice is very wide.

Best buys

Vin de Pays du Jardin de la France, Sauvignon, £2.49; Champagne
Charles Balachat (NV), £8.35; Ch Haut Canteloup 1981, Médoc, £4.95;
wines from Listel; Paternina Rioja 1983, Banda Azul, £2.75; Bulgarian
Cabernet Sauvignon, £1.99

Châteaux Wines

11 Church Street, Bishop's Lydeard,   TEL (0454) 613959
Somerset TA4 3AT

OPEN Mon–Fri 9–5.30   Sat mornings until 12.30 (please phone before calling)
CLOSED Sun, public holidays   CREDIT CARDS Access, Visa; personal and
business accounts   DISCOUNTS Negotiable   DELIVERY Free on mainland UK
(min 10 cases); otherwise £3.80 for 1 case, £1.60 per case for 2–9 cases; mail order
available   GLASS HIRE Not available   TASTINGS AND TALKS To groups on
request   CELLARAGE £4 per case per year or part for wines purchased from the
premises   ■

This is a short list of estate-bottled wines, mainly from France with the
emphasis on Burgundy. A number of good Burgundian names include
Robert and Michel Ampeau, Armand Rousseau, Ramonet-Prudhon,
Claude Simmonet and Edouard Delaunay. A short selection of wines
from the Domaine de la Romanée-Conti commands typically
Romanée-Conti prices (La Tâche 1983, £118.83 a bottle).

There is a much shorter range of Bordeaux, from vintages after 1979,
including the attractive Ch Cheret-Pitres from the Graves (1982 vintage
at £6.45, 1981 at £5.20). A few wines from the Loire and the Rhône, and
some vintages of Ch Musar in the Lebanon, put in an appearance.

California wines are Clos du Val – a big selection from this estate –
while Australia picks out Rosemount wines, not least the Chardonnay
Brut méthode champenoise sparkling wine at £9.93. Champagne is
from Laurent-Perrier – in large bottles for those with bigger thirsts.

Best buys

Proprietors Reserve Burgundy red and white, £5.97; Juliénas 1985, Les
Envaux, £4.99; Côtes du Rhône 1984, Domaine des Garrigues, £3.02

Chesterford Vintners   ☞

The Old Greyhound, Great Chesterford,   TEL (0799) 30088
Saffron Walden, Essex CB10 1NY
ASSOCIATED OUTLET
Tempest, Slinger & Co, 34 Hornton Street,   TEL 01-937 0303
London W8 4NR

OPEN Mon–Wed 9.30–5.30   Thur–Fri 9.30–7.30   Sat 9–5 (Old Greyhound)
CLOSED Sun, public holidays   CREDIT CARDS Access, Visa; personal and
business accounts   DISCOUNTS 3% for 3–4 cases, 5% for 5+ cases
DELIVERY Free within 25-mile radius and central London (min 2 cases);

elsewhere up to 1 case £4.80, 2–4 cases £2.80 per case, 5–9 cases 96p per case, 10+ cases free; mail order available   GLASS HIRE Free with order
TASTINGS AND TALKS Three to four tastings annually; to groups on request
CELLARAGE £5 per case per year

Despite the presence of wines from Italy, Spain and the New World, this is really a French list, offering plenty of choice.

But the very first wine is English – Fonthill 1985 from Wiltshire, a blend of Müller-Thurgau, Seyval Blanc and Reichensteiner – and very good it is too (£3.98). Before moving on to France, we can recommend the Sherries from Delgado Zuleta, a specialist Manzanilla producer.

And so to the hub of the list. House Champagnes are by Alex de Saint-Ives and J-P Husson, both growers, and still Coteaux Champenois wines come from Denois Père et Fils. A sensible selection of Bordeaux, looking more to petit château wines than the big names, has been evolved. The red and white Coteaux du Lyonnais, from an area just south of the Beaujolais, might be interesting (£4.20 each).

Quite a few of the Loire wines are made by Cazin in Cheverny, a sub-district of Touraine – a Sauvignon, a Chardonnay, a Gamay and a Pinot Noir. Sancerre from Pierre and Gérard Thirot is matched by the Ménétou-Salon of Jean-Max Roger (1985 vintage at £5.08). There are more varietal wines from Châtillon-en-Diois in the Alps, and more Alpine wines from the Savoy region.

We would recommend many of the wines in the Rhône range, including the Côtes du Rhône of Ch des Vallonnières (1984 vintage at £3.87) and Châteauneuf les Cailloux of Brunel.

Everything else seems a bit of an afterthought. However, a few German estate wines are joined by a limited but well-chosen range of Italians: from Antinori, Villa Banfi and Serrestori in Tuscany, Lageder in the Alto Adige and Oddero in Barolo.

Best buys

Aligoté de Châtillon, Cellier Hannibal, £3.52; Zuleta Manzanilla, £3.79; Cahors 1983, Cuvée Jules Gaston, £3.64; Chardonnay de Cheverny, Bernard & François Cazin, £3.98; Coteaux des Baux en Provence 1983, Mas de la Dame, £3.83; Chianti Classico 1983, Machiavelli, £3.52

Chiswick Wine Cellar

84 Chiswick High Street, London W4 1SY   TEL 01-994 7989

OPEN Mon–Sat 10–10   Sun 12–2   CLOSED Chr Day, Easter Day
CREDIT CARDS None accepted; personal and business accounts
DISCOUNTS Negotiable   DELIVERY Free within 5-mile radius of shop (min 1 case); elsewhere at cost   GLASS HIRE Free   TASTINGS AND TALKS Monthly new product tastings in-store   CELLARAGE Not available

A well-run specialist Italian wine merchant. More reports, please.

Christopher & Co

19 Charlotte Street, London W1P 1HB   TEL 01-636 4020/01-637 1932
(24-hour answering machine)

OPEN Mail order only   CREDIT CARDS All accepted; personal and business
accounts   DISCOUNTS 6% for 1 unmixed case   DELIVERY Free in London and
Home Counties (min 2 cases); elsewhere at cost   GLASS HIRE Available
TASTINGS AND TALKS Occasional talks/tastings held in London; to groups on
request   CELLARAGE Not available

This firm is now part of the Les Amis du Vin empire, but still operates
from a separate list. They've retained some of their star lines, such as
the Frescobaldi Chiantis and other Tuscan wines and the Duca d'Asti
wines from Piedmont, and also their interest in Dow's Ports.

In France, although the range is now more restricted, their former
strength in clarets continues – best are the 1982 and 1983 vintages, with
a smaller choice in 1981 and 1979, but over most areas of the Bordeaux
spectrum. Burgundy tends to be dominated by négociant wines from
Ropiteau and Mommessin, although more domaine wines are
apparent than in the past. Other interesting bottles are a few French
country wines and Alsace wines from Willm.

Also worth looking for are Tyrrells wines from Australia and the
Cousiño Macul wines from Chile.

Best buys

Frescobaldi wines; Alsace wines from Willm

City Cellars

3 Upper Paul Street, Exeter, Devon EX4 3NB   TEL (0392) 214565

OPEN Tue–Sat 10–6   CLOSED Sun, Mon, public holidays
CREDIT CARDS Access, Visa; business accounts   DISCOUNTS 5% on 1 case
DELIVERY Free in southern England and London (min 1 case) and elsewhere if
delivery is combined with a wholesale delivery; otherwise at cost
GLASS HIRE Free with 1-case order   TASTINGS AND TALKS Regular customer
tastings; to groups on request (on estate-bottled German wine)
CELLARAGE Not available

This list – although not long – continues to be one of the best sources
for German estate wines in the country, in which Alastair Crosby
specialises exclusively. There are wines from Franconia (Fürstlich
Castell'sches Domänenamt), from Württemberg, and from Baden as
well as the more familiar areas, where particular interest lies in the
Nahe, Mosel and Rheingau.

Best buys

German estate wines from the Nahe and Mosel

Classic Wines

181 High Road, Chigwell, Essex IG7 6NU   TEL 01-500 7614

OPEN Mon–Fri 9–6   CLOSED Sat, Sun, public holidays   CREDIT CARDS None
accepted; personal and business accounts   DISCOUNTS Negotiable
DELIVERY Free nationwide (min 6 cases); mail order available
GLASS HIRE Not available   TASTINGS AND TALKS In-store tastings by
appointment; to groups on request   CELLARAGE Not available

Classic means just that. This is a range of fine clarets, vintage Port and
Burgundy, which inevitably changes as limited stocks become
exhausted, but which always seems to provide plenty of interest.

A recent list offered vintages of first growth claret back to 1961,
Burgundy from Domaine de la Romanée-Conti, as well as négociants
like Louis Latour, Joseph Drouhin and Bouchard Père et Fils, plenty of
Sauternes from Ch d'Yquem, and vintage Ports from as far back as
1945.

Cliff Cellars

See Ellis Son & Vidler.

College Cellar

56 Walton Street, London SW3 1RB   TEL 01-584 9855

OPEN Mon, Tue 10–7   Wed 9.30–8   Thur, Fri 9.30–7   Sat 9.30–5.30
CLOSED Sun, public holidays   CREDIT CARDS Access, Visa; personal and
business accounts   DISCOUNTS 10% for 1 case of house wines, 5% for 1 case of
other wines   DELIVERY Free in central London (min 1 case)   GLASS HIRE Free
with order   TASTINGS AND TALKS Tutored tastings; to groups on request
CELLARAGE Not available

The fine wine side of La Réserve (*qv*) carries an enormous and
changing range of fine wines. The best areas, inevitably, are Bordeaux
(where they often stock as many as 200 wines, sometimes going back in
vintage to 1924); Burgundy, with examples from Domaine de la
Romanée-Conti and Domaine Albert Morot, among plenty of other
domaine wines; vintage Port (vintages again back to 1924); vintage
Champagne; and the Rhône. Their sweet white Bordeaux are equally
enticing.

Best buys

Old vintages of claret and Port

> Wine in bag-in-box ages and spoils quicker than in bottle. If you buy boxes,
> buy and drink up one box before you buy the next. Boxes in the
> store-cupboard will lose their freshness. Used or unopened, a wine box will
> keep better if you store it tap downwards, keeping wine, not air, in the
> valve.

Connolly's

110 Edmund Street, Birmingham B3 2ES   TEL 021-236 9269

OPEN Mon–Fri 9–5.30   Sat 9–5.30 (but phone to check)   CLOSED Sun, public
holidays   CREDIT CARDS Access; personal and business accounts
DISCOUNTS 5%; negotiable on large orders   DELIVERY Free in Greater
Birmingham (min 1 case); elsewhere at cost; mail order available
GLASS HIRE Free with 1-case order   TASTINGS AND TALKS In-store tastings in
May and October; to groups on request   CELLARAGE Limited

If they could stop calling their list the Book of Bacchus – and stop
writing appalling doggerel to go inside it – we might be able to take the
wines themselves a little more seriously. Underneath the padding,
although it's by no means a wide range of wines, there is plenty of
interest.

In France, claret vintages go back ten years, while Burgundy offers
négociant wines from Faiveley, Drouhin and Boisset, plus a few
domaine wines. The Rhône list is short, but does include the Côtes du
Rhône-Villages from Rasteau (1984 vintage at £4.43 – quite pricey for
this wine). Other pockets of interest are Val-Joanis wines from the
Côtes du Luberon, and Pouilly Fumé from de Ladoucette.

Beyond France, there are some attractive German estate wines from
Deinhard, Bert Simon, Graf von Schönborn. Connolly's have
obviously not got to grips with Italy, but the Brunello di Montalcino of
Casale del Bosco shows that they are trying. Torres dominates the
Spanish list. House Champagne is Philipponnat, and there's a good
range of vintage Ports.

Hill Smith and Brown Brothers are the stars of the short Australian
selection, while – if you are in time – Cloudy Bay Sauvignon Blanc from
New Zealand is available here.

Best buys

Champagne Philipponnat (NV), £9.49; Bairrada Reserva 1982, £2.88;
Verduzzo del Veneto, £2.42; Ch Val-Joanis Côtes du Luberon red and
rosé, £3

Continental Wine House

25 Edgware Road, London W2 2JE   TEL 01-262 2126

OPEN Mon–Sat 10–10.30   Sun, public holidays 12–2, 7–10   CLOSED Chr
Day   CREDIT CARDS All accepted; business accounts   DISCOUNTS 5% for 1+
cases (unmixed and COD only)   DELIVERY Nominal charge of £1 within 3-mile
radius of Marble Arch; free for orders of £500   GLASS HIRE £1 per glass deposit,
refundable   TASTINGS AND TALKS Occasional in-store tastings
CELLARAGE Not available

Italy is the reason for the merchant's inclusion in the Guide. They carry
plenty of wines from France and some from Germany, Spain, Hungary

(a good selection of these), plus Rosemount wines from Australia, but the Italian list has the real interest.

In a very democratic manner, the wines are listed by regions alphabetically, starting with the Abruzzo. There are quite a few wines from the south of Italy – the rosé Cerasuolo from the Abruzzo, Aglianico del Vulture of di Angelo in Basilicata (£5.70), the formidable Taurasi from Campania (£5.95), and a clutch of Sardinian wines.

In the more classic areas, there is excellent Barbaresco and Barolo from Villadoria (£4.45), Chianti from Badia a Coltibuono, a big range of Veneto wines (including the white vino da tavola Masianco) and the red Venegazzù. Alto Adige wines are mainly from Lageder. Some beefy reds with intriguing names muscle in from Lombardy (Sassella, Grumello, Inferno).

A major problem through all this, though, is that the list is singularly lacking in producers' names and vintages – rather like a wine list in an Italian restaurant, in fact.

Best buys

Taurasi, £5.95; Chianti Classico Machiavelli, £3.10; Masianco, £3.60; Cerasuolo d'Abruzzo, £2.45; Cannonau, £2.90

Copyhold Farm Shop

Goring Heath, nr Reading, Berkshire RG8 7RT   TEL (073 57) 4720

OPEN Tue–Sat 9.30–1, 2–5   CLOSED Sun, public holidays
CREDIT CARDS None accepted   DISCOUNTS Available (min 1 case)
DELIVERY Not available   GLASS HIRE Free with 1-case order
TASTINGS AND TALKS Occasional in-store tastings   CELLARAGE Not available

See Goedhuis and Co.

Corney & Barrow   ✺ ☞

12 Helmet Row, London EC1V 3QJ	TEL 01-251 4051
118 Moorgate, London EC2M 6UR	TEL 01-638 3125
44 Cannon Steet, London EC4N 6JJ	TEL 01-248 1700
Coates Café, 45 London Wall, London EC2M 5TE	TEL 01-256 5148
190 Kensington Park Road, London W11 2ES	TEL 01-221 5122

OPEN Mon–Fri 9–7 (Kensington Park Road 10.30–8; Sat 9.30–8)   CLOSED Sat, Sun, public holidays   CREDIT CARDS Access, Visa; personal and business accounts   DISCOUNTS Negotiable   DELIVERY Free in London (min 2 cases) and UK mainland (min 3 cases); less than 2 cases London £5.75, less than 3 cases outside London: 1 bottle £5.75, 2 bottles £6.90, 3–35 bottles £8.05 per case   GLASS HIRE Free with 3-case order; delivery free with wine order   TASTINGS AND TALKS In-house tastings daily on request   CELLARAGE £3.91 per case per year or part year

If you want the definition of a serious wine list, look no further than Corney & Barrow. And you can look in more places this year, with the opening of a new shop in Kensington, and more restaurants in the City. (The Kensington shop offers a separate selection from the ones in the City.)

This is the firm that brings you Ch Pétrus, the wines of the top Pomerol producer and négociant, J-P Moueix, and bottles from some of the finest estates in Burgundy. That Corney & Barrow have ventured into Spain and Italy shows how good wines from these countries now are.

But claret and Burgundy form the heart of the list. The range of clarets, from nearly every vintage between 1985 and 1961, is one of the largest in the country. It is difficult to pick out any one area as better than any other, though, perhaps it is worth pointing to Fronsac and Canon-Fronsac where J-P Moueix have an interest – their wines offer very good value at the moment. The satellite villages of Pomerol, like Lalande de Pomerol, and the equivalents in St-Emilion – Montagne St-Emilion, for example – also offer good alternatives to the more pricey real thing. Don't forget the range of Sauternes.

The Burgundian list does just as well, sporting wines from many of the big named estates – Joseph Roty in Chambertin, Marquis d'Angerville in Volnay, Trapet, Dujac, Daniel Senard, Matrot, Leflaive, Newman (an American from New Orleans who makes Bonnes Mares), Mazis-Chambertin and Latricières Chambertin. Beaujolais and Mâconnais wines from Marc Dudet complete this fascinating section.

While the Loire and Rhône selections are much shorter by comparison, Germany continues to offer treats in its range of estate wines. The Mosel–Saar–Ruwer is the speciality here – look for wines from Friedrich Wilhelm Gymnasium and J J Prüm, for example, on the Mosel, von Hövel on the Saar, von Schubert on the Ruwer.

Spain offers the fascinating Cabernet-Sauvignon-based Marqués de Griñon, while for Italy, it's the wines of Antinori in Tuscany and Gaja in Barbaresco that take centre stage. Wines from Simi in California and Hungerford Hill in Australia are two further interesting choices.

Best buys

Wines from Fronsac; German estate wines; Marquis de Saporta, Coteaux d'Aix-en-Provence 1985, £3.56; Valdepeñas 1975, Señorio de los Llanos Gran Reserva, £4.48

Restaurant Croque-en-Bouche

221 Wells Road, Malvern Wells,   TEL (068 45) 65612
Hereford & Worcester WR14 4HF

OPEN Any reasonable time, by appointment CREDIT CARDS Access, Visa
DISCOUNTS Not available DELIVERY Free within 10-mile radius (min 2 cases);
elsewhere £4 per case, 5+ cases free; mail order available GLASS HIRE,
TASTINGS AND TALKS Not available CELLARAGE Free   ■

This restaurant, perched precipitously on the slopes of the Malvern Hills, has one of the biggest restaurant wine lists in the country. A smaller selection is also available on a retail basis, or you can buy from the main list at a £3 a bottle discount.

The main list ranges widely, with few areas left untouched. But the principal focuses of interest – owner Robin Jones calls them a 'passion' – are the Rhône and the Loire, especially the Rhône.

While the restaurant list is arranged conventionally by area, the retail list follows the new fashion – of which we approve – of listing wines by style and colour. So, for instance, under light, dry white wines, there are wines from Valencia, Haut-Poitou, Muscadet and other Loire vineyards, from Chablis and Burgundy, from Alsace and some New World vineyards (Rosemount in Australia, Clos du Val and Joseph Phelps in California). A similar catholic approach covers sweeter white wines (look for the Sauternes 1980, Ch les Justices at £7.30), and red wines, which are divided into light, medium and full-bodied.

Treats burst out all the way along, but we were particularly attracted to Robin Jones's passion. While he has gathered many wines from Jaboulet Aîné, there are other smaller growers, such as Guigal and Jasmin in Côte Rôtie, Chave in Hermitage, Clape in Cornas, Jean-Louis Grippat in St-Joseph. In the southern Rhône, there is a good range from top Châteauneuf-du-Pape estates (Ch de Beaucastel, Fortia, Rayas among them), and the rare red wines from Châteauneuf-du-Gadagne (the Réserve 1979 at £7.90 is a bargain). Gigondas from Roger Combe, Pascal and Hilarion Roux complete this superb range.

Best buys

Rhône wines; Lirac 1982, Domaine Castel-Oualou, £4.60; Pedroncelli Cabernet Sauvignon 1979, £4.60; Sauvignon du Haut-Poitou 1985, £3.20

Cullens

HEAD OFFICE Chantrey Court, Church Street,   TEL (0932) 59133
Weybridge, Surrey KT13 8DP
60 licensed stores in London and the South-East

OPEN Mon–Sat (hours vary from store to store)   Sun 12–2, 7–9
CREDIT CARDS Access, Visa; personal and business accounts   DISCOUNTS 5% on mixed case, 10% on unmixed case   TASTINGS AND TALKS In-store tastings during promotions   DELIVERY, GLASS HIRE, CELLARAGE Not available

---

The nature of these stores has changed over the past two years and the wine list has changed with it – and is not a patch on what it was. The short list of about 80 wines is now bought by Les Amis du Vin (*qv*), and within the self-imposed constraints of stores which stock a wide range of goods in a relatively small space at least performs an adequate job.

But expect neither excitement nor particularly good value. In fact, the best value is to be found in the house wines: the California red and white (£2.99), the Beaujolais 1986 (£3.99), the red Burgundy (£4.35) and the excellent house claret (£3.49). All these house wines are labelled under the Les Amis du Vin name.

Apart from these, look for the Australian and California wines (Merlot 1984 from Clos du Bois at £4.99) or the Rothbury Estate Semillon 1986 (£4.99). Other points of interest include Marqués de Murrieta Riojas and Montana wines from New Zealand.

Best buys

Claret Les Amis du Vin, £3.49; Ch la Gacherie 1985, Bordeaux, £2.99; California Les Amis du Vin red and white, £2.99; Pewsey Vale Cabernet Sauvignon 1984, £4.45

Cumbrian Cellar

1 St Andrew's Square, Penrith, Cumbria CA11 7AN   TEL (0768) 63664

OPEN Mon–Sat 9–5.30   CLOSED Sun, Chr Day, Boxing Day, Good Friday
CREDIT CARDS Access, Amex, Visa; personal and business accounts
DISCOUNTS 5% on 1 case   DELIVERY Free in Cumbria (min 1 case); mail order available   GLASS HIRE Free with 1-case order
TASTINGS AND TALKS Occasional in-store promotions; to groups on request
CELLARAGE £3 per case per year

Quite wisely, the Cumbrian Cellar excels in areas which a high street off-licence is less likely to reach. So Italy, Greece, Australia and Sherries are strong points, while other areas are not neglected.

In France, likewise, it's the non-classic areas which are best served. So Alsace has the wines from Muré (Tokay Pinot Gris 1983 at £4.10), the Loire has the occasional treat like the Ménétou-Salon of Henri Pellé (1982 vintage – drink it up fast – at £5.45), and in the south of France, there are vins de pays from the Tarn, the Hérault and the Gard, as well as the excellent Cahors Domaine des Acacias, and sweet Jurançon from Jean Girouilh (1982 vintage at £4.80).

Outside France, Italy does very well, with Barolo from Fontanafredda, Brunello di Montalcino Castelgiocondo, Chianti Classico of Rocca delle Macie, Vicchiomaggio, Gabbiano and Brolio; whites are less interesting. Greek wines include the quality Ch Carras as well as more familiar Greek restaurant wine names.

From Australia come wines from Mildara, Lindemans, Rosemount, Tisdall and Eden Valley (appropriate because Penrith is at the end of the Eden Valley in Cumbria). Sherries are from Osborne, Valdespino and Findlaters, vintage Port from Kopke. Skip the Russian wines unless you're curious.

Best buys

Domaine de la Caumette Vin de Pays 1983, £2.70; Barbera d'Alba 1983, Fontanafredda, £3.45; Chianti Classico 1985, Rocca delle Macie, £3.90; Ch Carras Côtes de Meliton 1980 red, £3.99; sherries from Osborne and Valdespino

Curzon Wine Company

11 Curzon Street, London W1Y 7FJ   TEL 01-499 3327

OPEN Mon–Fri 10–7   Sat 10–6   CLOSED Sun, public holidays
CREDIT CARDS None accepted; personal and business accounts
DISCOUNTS 5% for 1+ cases; further discounts by negotiation   DELIVERY Free
within central London (min 1 case); elsewhere at cost; mail order available
GLASS HIRE Not available   TASTINGS AND TALKS To account customers at
regular intervals; to groups on request (min 10 people)   CELLARAGE Charges
vary depending on value of goods

There is a list that gets better every year. Though prices are not cheap (how could they be with this address?), it's possible to find something noteworthy in most price brackets.

While Bordeaux and Burgundy have the biggest share, the range is eclectic, and includes such rarities as wines from Oregon in the United States (Tualatin Chardonnay 1983 at £10.81 is one of the best Chardonnays made in the States). California makes a small presentation of wines. Down Under, look for the Tasmanian wines of Heemskirk (Cabernet Sauvignon 1984 is £8.27) and from the Te Mata estate in New Zealand.

Back in Europe, the clarets cover vintages back to 1945 (Ch Sénéjac, £49.26), but concentrate on vintages of the 1960s and 1970s. As well as en primeur offers of claret, the Curzon Wine Company now also run en primeur offers of Burgundy, and these accord with the excellent range of domaine-bottled Burgundies, with reds back to the 1955 vintage.

Further south, look for the star Coteaux d'Aix-en-Provence wines of Ch Vignelaure (1980 vintage at £7.45) and Cahors from Ch de Haute Serre (1982 at £6.25), as well as a delicious Sauvignon Vin de Pays du Jardin de la France from Guy Saget, who also makes Pouilly Fumé. The full range of Léon Beyer Alsace wines is stocked.

The Italian prospect still needs broadening out, but the good value Riojas from Berberana and wines from Torres make Spain look good. There's also a good selection of English wines and of vintage Ports. Lebanon wines from Ch Musar come in still superb old vintages (1964 at £22.85).

Best buys

Côtes du Rhône 1981, Rasteau, £4.10; Sauvignon Vin de Pays du Jardin de la France, Guy Saget, £3.15; Carta de Plata Rioja 1983, £3.44; Côtes du Ventoux 1985, Jaboulet Aîné, £3.75

David's of Ashby

1–3 Mill Lane Mews, Ashby-de-la-Zouch,   TEL (0530) 415704
Leicestershire LE6 5HB

OPEN Mon, Tue, Thur, Fri 9–5   Wed 9–1   Sat 8.30–5   CLOSED Sun, Wed afternoons, public holidays   CREDIT CARDS Not accepted; personal and business accounts   DISCOUNTS 5% (min 1 case)   DELIVERY Free within 15-mile radius (min 1 case); elsewhere 1–8 cases £10, 8+ cases free   GLASS HIRE Free with 1-case order; delivery free   TASTINGS AND TALKS In-store tastings with new wines and promotions; talks and tastings on request   CELLARAGE £1 per case plus insurance

The few surprises in this list nevertheless justify the inclusion of this merchant in the Guide for the first time. David's would be wise, however, to get rid of the habit of split vintages – perhaps they shouldn't print the list so smartly.

Italy provides one such surprise: a range of the Barolos of Pio Cesare and the top Riserva Ducale Chianti Classico of Ruffino (1979 Gold Label at £7.65). There's little from Germany, though – and an annoying absence of producers' names. Spain produces a good range of Faustino Riojas, while Portugal offers some old vintages of Barrocão Dãos, and the unusual Colares 1970 of Chitas (£5.94) from vineyards in the sand dunes of the Atlantic. Vintage Ports are from Niepoort.

In France, more nuggets appear, the Mas de la Dame organic wines from Coteaux des Baux en Provence (1983 Special Réserve at £4.75), for example. Bordeaux is sensibly divided into petits châteaux and classed growths – although prices would anyway probably give the game away. There's some decent Beaujolais from Thorin, and some magnums of Moulin-à-Vent. Champagnes from Granier and Leclerc Briant join Pol Roger.

Best buys

Fitou Terre Natale 1982, £2.79; Coteaux des Baux en Provence 1982, Mas de la Dame, £4.75; Colares Chitas 1970, £5.94; Vin de Pays d'Oc Chardonnay, £2.99

Davisons   ☞

HEAD OFFICE 7 Aberdeen Road, Croydon,   TEL 01-681 3222
Surrey CR0 1EQ
76 branches throughout the Home Counties

OPEN Mon–Sat 10–2, 5–10   Sun 12–2, 7–9   CREDIT CARDS Access, Amex (some branches), Visa; personal and business accounts   DISCOUNTS 8½% for 1 case   DELIVERY Free locally; mail order from Master Cellar Wine Warehouse   GLASS HIRE Free   TASTINGS AND TALKS Occasional in-store tastings   CELLARAGE Not available

This chain of shops stays firmly with its excellent range of wines from the classic areas of France, while still seeming half-hearted about the rest of the world.

But if you want a remarkably good range from Bordeaux and Burgundy from a High Street off-licence, this is the place to come. They have plenty of mature wines, too, thanks to their enlightened policy of buying wine and maturing it in their own cellars before putting it in the shops. This also means that prices of some top wines are very good: for instance, £10.95 for Ch Batailley 1975 is the current auction price, as is the price for Ch Latour 1970 (£69). At less rarefied levels, there are plenty of decent petit château wines as well.

The Burgundian range is equally good, with a few good basic Burgundies and wines from lesser-known communes at affordable prices before we get on to the big names. Beaujolais is from Georges Duboeuf.

It's strange that, as we commented last year, the list falters after these two star areas. The Rhône comes up with the occasional treat, and Champagne can be had for generally acceptable prices (Champagne Ellner at £8.49). In Spain Torres wines, Marqués de Murrieta Rioja, and a good range of Sherry boost the shelves. But Italian wines are on the whole dull, and from Portugal the only attraction is the vintage Ports.

For a wider range of wines – especially Burgundy and Bordeaux – see Master Cellar Wine Warehouse.

Best buys

Cuvée Georges Duboeuf red and white, £2.49; Ch La Tour St-Bonnet 1978, £4.19; Inheritance Cabernet Shiraz 1983, McWilliams, £2.99; Alsace Pinot Blanc 1985, Cave Ingersheim, £3.35

Davys of London

151 Borough High Street, London SE1 1HR   TEL 01-407 1484

OPEN Mon–Fri 10–6   CLOSED Sat, Sun, public holidays
CREDIT CARDS Access, Diners, Visa, Davys of London; personal and business accounts   DISCOUNTS 5–12½% (min 1 case)   DELIVERY Free in Central London (min 1 case in City and SE1, min 2 cases in rest of London); elsewhere at cost; mail order available   GLASS HIRE Free (deposit required)
TASTINGS AND TALKS 4 tastings annually; to groups on request
CELLARAGE Not available

This is the retail side of Davys of London, which operates the chain of wine bars in London and Exeter (see the WINE BARS section). An associated company also operates the Wines Galore shops (*qv*), but the two lists are different.

Davys of London's retail shop list could hardly be described as adventurous, but as an extension of the wine bar list it provides some well-chosen, utterly reliable bottles.

The house wines are the most appealing because of their quality: Davys' Claret (NV) at £3.25 is one of the best house clarets around, and their Sauvignon 1985 at £3.25 is classic, straightforward Touraine Sauvignon, while the Rioja 1983 is good value at £3.35.

They have more serious claret, including classed growths, and Burgundy (mainly from négociants), but most of these wines could be bought more cheaply elsewhere. Champagne is a good value, though, as befits a firm with City wine bars – Veuve Clicquot at £11.95 and Piper Heidsieck at £10.40 are both very good prices. Look also for vintage Ports and Madeiras.

Best buys

Davys' Best Sauvignon 1985, £3.25; Davys' Claret (NV), £3.25; Davys' Rioja 1983, £3.35; Champagne (NV), Piper Heidseick, £10.40

The Delicatessen (North Berwick)

See J E Hogg.

Del Monico's Famous Wine Emporium

23 South Street, St Austell, Cornwall PL25 5BH   TEL (0726) 73593

OPEN Mon–Sat 9–6   Sun 12–2 (Aug only)   CLOSED Sun (except Aug), some public holidays   CREDIT CARDS Access, Visa; personal and business accounts   DISCOUNTS Negotiable   DELIVERY Free within 20–25 mile radius from St Austell (min ½ case)   GLASS HIRE Free
TASTINGS AND TALKS Occasional in-store tastings; to groups on request
CELLARAGE Free

You come to Del Monico's for its liveliness and competitive prices, certainly not for the information on its list, which tells you very little about the producers of the wines. The place carries a larger range of fine wines than before, while still keeping a good selection of less expensive wines.

France is the strength, with bargains from Bordeaux: Ch Bel-Air 1982 at £3.59, Ch la Tour de By 1983 at £4.89, Ch Monbousquet 1981, St-Emilion at £5.98. There are plenty of wines from the Rhône and Beaujolais, along with a few from the South-West.

Other areas of interest include Riojas from Campo Viejo, Olarra, Beronia and CVNE, a selection of fine German dessert wines, Sherries from Osborne and Garvey, and vintage Ports.

Best buys

Osborne Fino Manzanilla, £2.79; Bulgarian Cabernet Sauvignon, £1.95; Ch Toutigeac 1984, £2.89; Marqués de Monistrol Cava, £3.89

Demijohn Wines

Penn Street, Nr Amersham,   TEL (0494) 715376
Buckinghamshire HP7 0PX

OPEN Tue–Fri 12–7   Sat 11–7   CLOSED Mon, Sun, public holidays
CREDIT CARDS None accepted; personal and business accounts
DISCOUNTS 5% on 5 cases   DELIVERY Free within 5-mile radius (min 1 case);
elsewhere at cost; mail order available   GLASS HIRE Free with 1-case order
TASTINGS AND TALKS Wines available in-store daily; periodical theme tastings;
to groups on request   CELLARAGE Not available   ∎

While Italy happily continues to dominate this list, a few more French
wines and a couple of Spanish bottles have infiltrated to provide a
contrast.

But it's inevitably to Italy that attention will turn. Prices are attractive
and the range is wide. In reds, for example, the choice goes from the
excellent basic house red from Settesoli in Sicily (£2.53 – there's a white
at the same price) up to Barolo from the fine 1978 vintage (Marchesi di
Barolo Riserva at £7.79).

In between come Chianti Classico from some top estates – Badia a
Coltibuono, Aiola, Riecine, San Polo in Rosso – and wines from
Umbria (Torgiano Rubesco of Lungarotti 1980 at £4.75), from
Lombardy (Oltrepò Pavese 1983 of Montelio at £3.74) and the good
Barolo alternative of Spanna (1983 vintage from Nervi at £4.18).
Piedmont and Tuscany continue to be the strongest areas.

With whites, we would particularly enjoy the Tiefenbrunner wines
from the Alto Adige (Chardonnay 1984 at £4.69), the Verdicchio of
Umani Ronchi (1985 vintage at £3.49), and the sparkling Prosecco di
Conegliano (non-vintage) of Collalto (£3.69). Try also the sweet
Moscato Passito from Pellegrino in Sicily (£4.18).

Best buys

Settesoli red and white, £2.53; Montepulciano d'Abruzzo 1985,
Cornacchia, £3.57; Corvo Columba Platino 1984, £3.69; Chianti Classico
1978, Poggiarello Vecchio, £5.29

Dennhöfer Wines

47 Bath Lane, Newcastle upon Tyne,   TEL 091-232 7342
Tyne & Wear NE4 5SP

OPEN Mon–Fri 8.30–6.30   Sat 10.30–12.30   CLOSED Sun, public holidays
CREDIT CARDS Access, Amex, Visa; personal and business accounts
DISCOUNTS 5–12% (min 1 case)   DELIVERY Free in North-East (min 1 case);
elsewhere approximately £3.50 per case; mail order available   GLASS HIRE Free
with 2-case order   TASTINGS AND TALKS Regular tastings in warehouse and
restaurant   CELLARAGE Free when wine purchased from the premises

Germany continues to provide good value for money on this short list,
with wines from the 1985 vintage, and one of the few top-class Riesling

Sekts from Fürst von Metternich (£6.95). Dennhöfers have just introduced their own range of classic varietal wines at excellent prices (Classic Riesling 1986 at £2.61).

Good value is also to be found in the Alsace wines of Ringenbach-Moser, and in some of the Spanish wines (the Plandenas Reserva 1981 from Navarra at £2.95, for example). House Champagne is from Yves Pascal (£8.95).

In last year's Guide we commented that the list lacks information on producers. We regret to report that the situation hasn't improved.

Best buys

Corbières 1985, Ch St-Jean, £2.98; Dennhöfer Classic Riesling, £2.61; Bourgogne Blanc 1985, Labouré-Roi, £4.15; Alsace wines from Ringenbach-Moser

Rodney Densem Wines

OFFICE AND WHOLESALE Stapeley Bank,   TEL (0270) 623665
London Road, Nantwich, Cheshire CW5 7JW   (for both addresses)
RETAIL 4 Pillory Street, Nantwich, Cheshire CW5 5BD

OPEN Mon–Fri 10–6 (closed Wed pm in Winter) Sat 9–5.30 CLOSED Sun, public holidays CREDIT CARDS Access, Visa; personal and business accounts DISCOUNTS 5% for 1 case DELIVERY Free within 25-mile radius (min 1 case); elsewhere approx £4 per case; mail order available GLASS HIRE Free with 1-case order TASTINGS AND TALKS Occasional in-store tastings; to groups on request CELLARAGE Not available

This is not exactly the most exciting range of wines, but every section has a few wines which would make a visit to this wine merchant worthwhile. Prices on the list do not include VAT, but we have added it here.

While Bordeaux is expensive, there's more of affordable interest in Burgundy with some good wines from Joseph Drouhin (who also supplies the Beaujolais) and Faiveley. The basic red Burgundy from Labouré-Roi (1985 vintage, £4.24) and their Bourgogne Blanc 1985 (£4.93) are both good value.

Other French wines worth considering are the Châteauneuf-du-Pape of Louis Mousset and the rather pricey Hugel Alsace wines. Look also for wines from Listel in the Midi.

The German section really comes to life only with wines from Schloss Johannisberg, but Spain contains some interest in the shape of Torres and Berberana Riojas. In the New World, Rosemount and Brown Brothers represent Australia, and California introduces a couple of Blush wines (rosé to us Europeans).

Best buys

Listel wines; Bourgogne Rouge 1985, Labouré-Roi, £4.24; Champagne (NV), Heidsieck Monopole, £8.58

Direct Wine Shipments

5/7 Corporation Square, Belfast, Co Antrim BT1 3AJ	TEL (0232) 238700/243906
18 Abbey Street, Coleraine, Co Londonderry BT56 8LL	TEL (0265) 2113/4031
Duncairn Wines, 555 Antrim Road, Belfast, Co Antrim BT15 3BU	TEL (0232) 370694
Duncairn Wines, Unit 6, Downtown Shopping Centre, Downpatrick, Co Down BT30 6LZ	TEL (0396) 3392

OPEN Mon–Fri (main outlet) 9.30–5.30 Sat 10–1 CLOSED Sun, 3 days at Chr, Easter Mon and Tue, July 12, 13 CREDIT CARDS Access, Visa; personal and business accounts DISCOUNTS 5% for 1 unopened case DELIVERY Free in Northern Ireland (min 1 case); otherwise single cases £2, 6+ cases free; mail order available GLASS HIRE Not available TASTINGS AND TALKS Frequent in-store talks and tastings; to groups on request CELLARAGE Free

A broadly based list from the wine merchant acting as the focus of Northern Ireland's vinous life. They are particularly good on Bordeaux, Burgundy, Spain and Bulgaria.

Bordeaux has a well-balanced list, with a range up from petit château Canon Fronsac through bourgeois wines to classed growths from some old vintages (back to 1964). In Burgundy, wines tend to come from négociants – but we would recommend many of the wines from Loron in Beaujolais, Michel Laroche in Chablis and Chanson's domaine wines. The Alsace wines of Hugel and Gustave Lorentz also look good, and further south the Domaine de Paradis Coteaux d'Aix-en-Provence wines are good value at £2.99.

Spain gets considerable attention: a full range of wines from Torres and Riojas from Marqués de Cáceres, plus wines from Ribera del Duero (Protos red 1976 at £5.80 is good value) and sparkling Cava from Castellblanch. Fewer stars shine in Italy, but the Frascati of Colli de Catone and the Cirò wines from Calabria would all be enjoyable. A full range of Bulgarian wines is available from the basic Mehana brand to the fine Sakar Mountain Cabernet Sauvignon (£3.30). As a curiosity, Direct Wine Shipments have hit on Canadian wines from Inniskillin.

Best buys

Torres wines; Bulgarian wines; Coteaux d'Aix-en-Provence, Domaine du Paradis red, white and rosé, £2.99

Discount Wine

2 Canberra House, London Road, St Albans, Hertfordshire AL1 1LE	TEL (0727) 30322

OPEN Tue–Thur 10–7 Fri 10–8 Sat 9–8 Sun 12 noon–2 CLOSED Mon, public holidays CREDIT CARDS Access; personal and business accounts DISCOUNTS 7½% for 1 case; 10% for 5 cases DELIVERY Free in Radlett/

St Albans area (min 1 case)   GLASS HIRE Free with order
TASTINGS AND TALKS Weekly in-store tastings (Sat am); spring, summer,
autumn tastings in local hotel; to groups on request   CELLARAGE Not available

French vins de pays, Beaujolais and Alsace as well as Spain and
Australia get the best treatment on this list. Prices are good right
through, but especially in these areas.

To start with France and a very good range of vins de Pays. They
come from Domaine de la Condamine l'Evêque in Languedoc – look for
the varietal wines – and Domaine de la Serre. Côtes du Marmandais
red and white might be other choices.

While the small range of clarets is good value, more interest is
evident in the Beaujolais from some individual producers
(Moulin-à-Vent, Le Vivier 1986 at £5.45, Chénas 1985, Ch de Chénas at
£4.75). The Alsace wines come from Louis Gisselbrecht.

In Spain, we would enjoy the single estate Rioja Contino 1978 at
£4.95 (excellent value) and other wines from CVNE and La Rioja Alta, as
well as the Raimat Abadía Reserva 1982 (£3.95). With Australia,
interest centres on the Rosemount wines and the new addition of the
Redgate wines from Margaret River in Western Australia. New
Zealand is not forgotten, with a couple of whites from Montana.

Best buys

Wines from Domaine Condamine l'Evêque; Raimat Chardonnay 1985,
£3.65; Cabernet Sauvignon 1984, Orlando, £3.99; old Sherries from
Gonzalez Byass

Domaine Direct

29 Wilmington Square, London WC1X 0EG   TEL 01-837 3521/1142
OPEN Mon–Fri 9–6   Sat 9–1   CLOSED Sun, public holidays
CREDIT CARDS None accepted; personal and business accounts
DISCOUNTS Not available   DELIVERY Free in Central London (min 1 case) and
UK mainland (min 3 cases); otherwise £5.75 for 1 case, £8 for 2 cases; mail order
available   GLASS HIRE Free   TASTINGS AND TALKS Major annual tasting;
regular twice yearly tastings for private customers; to groups on request
CELLARAGE £3.45 per case per year   ∎

Despite price rises, Domaine Direct continues to offer a mouth-
watering list of Burgundies, some at very attractive prices. As their
name suggests, they buy direct from individual domaines rather than
going through middlemen.

The list ranges widely in price. At the less expensive end, it starts
with wines from the Côte Chalonnaise (Bourgogne Passe-tout-grain
1985, Domaine de la Folie, £5.46) in reds; and in whites Bourgogne
Aligoté Bouzeron 1984, André Lhéritier (£5.69). (Prices on the list do
not include VAT, but we have added it here.)

At a more exalted level, reds concentrate on the Côte de Beaune, with wines from Savigny-lès-Beaune, Santenay and Volnay prominent, but with other communes represented as well. Wines come from Pousse d'Or, Simon Bize, Tollot-Beaut, Guy Roulot, Domaine de Montille. In the Côte de Nuits, look for the Nuits St-Georges wines of Alain Michelot.

For the whites, Chablis is from Jean Durup and René Dauvissat (among others), plus more wines from the Côte Chalonnaise (Mercurey 1985, Michel Juillot at £9.20), the Mâconnais and the Côte de Beaune (a galaxy of famous names). The white selection is shorter than the red, reflecting the currently greater difficulty in obtaining supplies of white Burgundy.

A series of tastings is arranged for regular customers.

Best buys

Bourgogne Irancy 1983, Léon Bienvenu, £4.89; Bourgogne Passe-tout-grain 1985, Domaine Direct Selection, £4.54; Bourgogne Aligoté 1985, Domaine Direct Selection, £4.54; Givry 1984, J P Ragot, £6.04

Peter Dominic

HEAD OFFICE Vintner House, River Way,   TEL (0279) 26801
Harlow, Essex CM20 2EA

OPEN Varies from store to store; majority open 10–9, 7 days a week
CREDIT CARDS Access, Amex, Diners, Visa, Grand Metropolitan; personal and business accounts   DISCOUNTS 5% on cases   DELIVERY Free nationally (min £25 order); mail order available via Wine Mine Club   GLASS HIRE Free with order   TASTINGS AND TALKS Regular tastings in Superstores (Fri, Sat); to groups on request   CELLARAGE £3.50 per case per year or part year

---

This group of shops has expanded dramatically in the past year with the takeover of the Roberts & Cooper chain, giving them 1,100 branches, the largest number of any chain in the country. Roberts & Cooper shops are gradually being integrated with the Peter Dominic branches.

Despite their huge size, Peter Dominic seem to have got their act together very satisfactorily. If there is a future for High Street off-licences, this is the shape it will take. They have gone for a greater range of finer wines, looking round the world for the value which is not always available in France. They run an energetic Wine Mine Club (see WINE CLUBS) and publish a glossy magazine twice a year which is available through the shops.

The list is long, and while some dull wines are in evidence, there's plenty of interest. In France, we have enjoyed the varietal Vin de Pays des Coteaux de l'Ardèche Cabernet Sauvignon and Merlot (£2.49), the Côtes du Roussillon of Coteaux Catalans at the same price, the Muscadet of Ch de la Galissonnière 1985 (£2.99) and the Lirac Domaine du Moulin Blanc 1985 (£3.89). Burgundy is mainly from Bouchard Père, Alsace from Hugel.

In Bordeaux, Peter Dominic specialise in wines from Domaine Rothschild (look for Ch la Cardonne 1983 at £4.95), the wines of Ch de Pez, and most vintages of Ch Greysac (1982 vintage at £6.95).

The German section has some top estate wines from Deinhard. The Italian range has expanded – with wines from Carmignano (Villa di Capezzana 1984, £5.25) and Brunello di Montalcino from Argiano. The basic Chianti Rossini (£2.29) is good value. Look for the good range of Riojas, and Bulgarian wines at £1.99.

Outside Europe, Mondavi and Firestone wines come from California, while more Australians now fill the shelves, including Rosemount, Brown Brothers, Berri Estates (Cabernet Sauvignon/Shiraz at £3.75) and Tollana.

Best buys

Chianti Rossini 1985, £2.29; Vin de Pays des Coteaux de l'Ardèche Cabernet Sauvignon, £2.49; Murray River Cabernet Sauvignon/Shiraz, £2.59; Bulgarian varietal wines, £1.99; Bandol 1983, Cave de la Roque, £3.99

Duncairn Wines

See Direct Wine Shipments.

Duras Direct

61 Elmleigh, Midhurst, West Sussex GU29 9HA   TEL (073 081) 4150

OPEN Mon–Sat 9–7 Sun 10–12 noon CLOSED Public holidays
CREDIT CARDS None accepted; personal and business accounts
DISCOUNTS Quantity discounts negotiable DELIVERY Free within 10-mile
radius (min 1 case); elsewhere charges negotiable GLASS HIRE Not available
TASTINGS AND TALKS Wine tasting evenings held twice a year; other tastings
on request CELLARAGE Not available   ∎

A short list, with wines – as the name would suggest – from the Côtes de Duras region next to Bordeaux, plus a few wines from the Loire – and one from Cahors.

The Duras wines include in the white Sauvignon-based Domaine de Ferrant 1986 (£3.65), and the red Domaine las Brugues-Mau Michau 1982 (£3.60). We would also recommend the Cahors Domaines de Fages 1985 (£3.74) – for drinking in five years' time.

Loire wines are mainly from Sancerre and Pouilly Fumé (Sancerre 1986, André Neveu, £5.90; Pouilly Fumé 1985, Roland Chollet, £5.90).

Best buys

Côtes de Duras white, Domaine de Ferrant Sauvignon 1986, £3.65;
Côtes de Duras red, Domaine las Brugues-Mau Michau 1982, £3.60

George Dutton & Son

See Willoughbys.

Eaton Elliot Winebrokers

15 London Road, Alderley Edge, Cheshire SK9 7JT   TEL (0625) 582354
OPEN Mon–Fri 9–6 Sat 9–5.30 CLOSED Sun, public holidays
CREDIT CARDS All accepted; personal and business accounts DISCOUNTS 5%
on 1 case   DELIVERY Free within 25-mile radius of Alderley Edge (min 1 case);
elsewhere 1–5 cases £8.63 min charge, 6+ cases free; mail order available
GLASS HIRE Free with 1-case order TASTINGS AND TALKS Regular monthly
in-store tastings; wine for tastings in-store daily; to groups on request
CELLARAGE £2.95 per case per year

This Cheshire firm has honed down their list since last year, but the
quality of what is left remains high.

So, in France, look for wines from Domaine Corsin in Pouilly-Fuissé
(St-Véran 1985 is £7.22), from the co-operative in Buxy (good value
Bourgogne Pinot Noir 1985 at £4.47), and the Jura wines of Ch d'Arlay
(especially the rare Sherry-like Vin Jaune 1978 at £7.72). Loire wines
include Bourgueil from Caslot-Galbrun and Sancerre from Jean
Vacheron.

The other area of strength is Italy, with Barolo and Barbaresco from
Granduca d'Asti; Soave and Valpolicella from Santa Sofia (also try the
Bianco di Custoza 1986 at £3.29), and Chianti from Castello di Volpaia.
New arrivals to the list are a California Chardonnay and a Pinot Noir
from Walter Schug Cellars in Napa Valley.

Best buys
Vin de Pays des Côtes de Gascogne 1986, Domaine du Tariquet, £2.52;
Christophe Tatham Monopole Blanc, £4.23; Bianco di Custoza 1986,
Santa Sofia, £3.29; Côtes du Rhône 1986, Domaine Mistral, £2.82

C C G Edwards

Burlton, Shillingstone, Dorset DT11 0SP   TEL (0258) 860641
OPEN Any time, but telephone first CLOSED August CREDIT CARDS None
accepted DISCOUNTS Shippers' price (collected); up to £1.50 per case quantity
discount (delivered) DELIVERY Free locally (min 1 case); elsewhere £3 per case;
up to 10 cases £12 the consignment, £1.50 per case for 11+ cases; mail order
available GLASS HIRE Available TASTINGS AND TALKS Annual in-store
tasting; other tastings on demand CELLARAGE Not available   ■

This is a short list of European organic wines, with a strong showing of
the two organic vineyards of the Coteaux des Baux en Provence area:
Domaine des Terres Blanches and Mas de Gourgonnier. Mr Edwards
also sells organic honey and fruit juices from the same area. He has
tracked down a Beaujolais from Domaine Bosse-Platière (1985 at £4.80),

and from Franconia in Germany, wines from the Weingut Christ. England is not forgotten with the wine of the Avalon Vineyard.

Best buys
Vin de Pays Domaine de Gressac red and white, £3.50

Eldridge Pope ✉

HEAD OFFICE Weymouth Avenue, Dorchester,   TEL (0305) 251251
Dorset DT1 1QT
10 branches (called Godrich & Petman) and 2 Reynier Wine Libraries
OPEN Mon–Fri 9–1, 2–5.30 Sat 9–1, 2–5 CLOSED Sun, public holidays
CREDIT CARDS Access, Visa; personal and business accounts
DISCOUNTS Available DELIVERY Free within 20-mile radius of each branch
(min £20 order); under £20 there is a £1 charge; mail order available
GLASS HIRE Free with order TASTINGS AND TALKS In-store tastings; tutored
tastings held at Wine Libraries; to groups on request CELLARAGE £1.75 per
case per year

France and Germany form the cornerstones of this list. Classic wines are there in abundance, but complemented by a welcome interest in French regional wines to provide a balance. Ports and Madeiras are another strength, including a range of vintage Ports going back to 1917 (Graham) and several old solera Madeiras (Terrantez 1899 at £90.97 a bottle is an intensely sweet curiosity).

In fact, the interest in sweet wines, which we noted last year, continues. The Sauternes pages of the list are some of the best in the country, boosted by plenty of sweet Loire and Alsace wines, and, from Germany, some old Beerenauslesen of the 1976 and 1971 vintages.

But back to Bordeaux and the serious matter of clarets. Eldridge Pope has bought most of the recent vintages en primeur (apart from the 1986 vintage, which they believed did not represent good value), and wines from 1983 and vintages back from there show that they bought well. The oldest vintage currently listed is 1949. They have made a specialisation of some châteaux – Ch Cissac and Ch Gruaud-Larose, for example, but also offer a good choice of petit château wines of more recent vintages.

In Burgundy, Eldridge Pope are regular buyers at the Hospices de Beaune sales each year, but also buy wines from a number of domaines (Henri Clerc, Armand Rousseau, Marcel Vincent, among others). They stock many 1983 reds and 1986 whites.

Alsace wines, from Dopff et Irion, are generally good value, whether the basic blended Crustaces d'Alsace (1983, £3.59) or some great Sélections des Grains Nobles (Riesling 1983, £20.70). The Loire is similarly well covered: sweet Quarts de Chaume and Coteaux du Layon from Jean Baumard (also his Savennières Clos du Papillon), Pouilly Fumé from Michel Redde and a large number of vintages of

Moulin Touchais sweet Anjou. Laurent Perrier is the featured grande marque Champagne.

With Germany, Eldridge Pope are agents for Schloss Vollrads wines on the Rheingau, but also ship wines from von Buhl in the Rheinpfalz and a good range of Mosel estate wines. Italy, we feel, needs more attention, and Spain hardly exists. California is represented by the rather dull bottles from Gundlach Bundschu and the much more exciting wines from Grgich Hills. Australian wines come from Seppelt.

Best buys

Petit château clarets; German estate wines; Alsace wines; Pécharmant 1982, £3.52; Seppelt Chardonnay 1986, £4.67; Coteaux du Tricastin 1978, Cru de Meynas, £3.69

Ben Ellis and Associates

The Harvesters, Lawrence Lane, Buckland,   TEL (073 784) 2160
Betchworth, Surrey RH3 7BE

OPEN 'All hours' – 24-hour answering machine   CREDIT CARDS None accepted; personal and business accounts   DISCOUNTS By arrangement DELIVERY Free within 20-mile radius of Reigate and London area (min 2 cases or by arrangement, 1 case locally); elsewhere £5–£18 for 5 cases   GLASS HIRE Free with 1-case order   TASTINGS AND TALKS Two in-store tastings annually; other tastings by arrangement; to groups on request   CELLARAGE £2.42 per case per year (plus insurance)   ■

Two lists operate at this merchant. It would be worth getting on to the fine wine list as it is constantly changing. The standard list covers a range of good value mainly European wines.

Both lists offer extensive ranges of Bordeaux, classed growths on the fine wine list, and a good selection of petit château wines and crus bourgeois on the standard one. From the latter we would pick out Ch Segonzac 1983, Côtes de Blaye (£4.57) and Ch St-Jacques 1981, Bordeaux Supérieur (£3.63) as typical examples. Vintages go back to 1978. A few Rhônes and some Alsace wines from Muré are other French attractions.

Spain is covered well, with Riojas from Marqués de Cáceres, Olarra (Gran Reserva 1975 at £5.10), and good value wines from Palacio de León (£2.38). Madeiras from Henriques and Henriques join the Moscatel de Setúbal and Churchill Ports as Portugal's offering to post-prandial enjoyment.

Best buys

Alsace Pinot Blanc 1985, Muré, £3.34; Ch St-Jacques 1981, Bordeaux Supérieur, £3.63; Coteaux du Tricastin 1984, Domaine de Grangeneuve, £3.10; Ramona Gran Reserva Rioja 1978, £4.48

Ellis, Son & Vidler

57 Cambridge Street, London SW1V 4PS   TEL 01-834 4101
Cliff Cellars, 12/13 Cliff Estate, Lewes,   TEL (0273) 480235
East Sussex BN8 6JL

OPEN Mon–Fri 9–5   CLOSED Sat, Sun, public holidays
CREDIT CARDS Access, Visa; personal and business accounts
DISCOUNTS Variable   DELIVERY Free within 30 miles of Lewes office and 8–10 miles of London office (min 3 cases); elsewhere 1 case £6.77, 2 cases £3.50 per case; 3–5 cases £2.40 per case, 6–10 cases £1.55 per case, 10+ cases free; mail order available   GLASS HIRE Free with any case order
TASTINGS AND TALKS Autumn and spring tastings; to groups on request
CELLARAGE £3.17 per case per year (£4.69 per case per year for wines bought elsewhere)

Despite token nods in the direction of the New World, this essentially remains a range of wines from the traditional regions. Bordeaux is at the heart, fortified wines follow close behind.

There has been some serious buying of recent vintages of claret from 1978 onwards, the 1982s and 1983s being particularly good. Some 1984s, a generally disregarded vintage, can be good value when judiciously chosen – as here. There's also a short but attractive selection of Sauternes from the classic 1983 vintage.

While the Loire remains uninteresting, the Burgundy section of the list has expanded, with some good domaine wines, especially from the 1983 vintage (plus a few 1978s) in reds, and the 1985 and 1983 vintages in whites. In Alsace, the wines of René Schmidt continue to show well. On the Rhône, the same is true of Jaboulet Aîné (Crozes-Hermitage 1984, Domaine de Thalabert, £5.75). We also enjoy the house Champagne from Dagonet et Fils (non-vintage, £8.87).

One other area worth looking for is that of fortified wines, where you will find some almacenista Sherries, a good range of vintage Ports, and plenty of Madeira from the associated company of Cossart Gordon. Old vintage Madeiras (1910 vintage at £59.80 a bottle) and the Duo Centenary blends (Sercial at £16.17 a bottle) are especially inviting.

For those keen on local produce, Ellis Son & Vidler list a number of English wines made in Sussex.

Best buys

Madeiras from Cossart Gordon; Claret, Ellis Son and Vidler, £3; Bourgogne Pinot Noir 1985, Fûts de Chêne, Cave Co-opérative de Buxy, £4.26; Ch de Pitray 1983, Côtes de Castillon, £3.91; almacenista Sherries; Reichensteiner 1984, Carr Taylor, £3.96

Prices are only a rough indication, and were current in summer 1987.

English Wine Centre

Drusilla's Corner, Alfriston, East Sussex BN26 5QS   TEL (0323) 870532
OPEN Every day (including most public holidays) 10.30–5   CLOSED 24–26 Dec,
1 Jan   CREDIT CARDS Access, Amex, Visa; personal and business accounts
DISCOUNTS Variable   DELIVERY Free within 15-mile radius (min 1 case) and
London (min 5 cases); elsewhere £7.59 for 1 case, £4.25 per case for 2 cases; £3.16
per case for 3–5 cases, £2.12 per case for 6–10 cases; mail order available
GLASS HIRE Free with 1-case order   TASTINGS AND TALKS Occasional
promotional tastings; to groups on request   CELLARAGE Available (limited)

Not surprisingly, this merchant concentrates on English wines from
Sussex and neighbouring Kent, so you get, in Sussex, vineyards like
Breaky Bottom, Berwick Glebe, Carr Taylor and Cuckmere. Kentish
wines come from vineyards such as Staple St James and Biddenden.
Other vineyards covered are Wootton (Somerset), Three Choirs
(Gloucestershire) and Bruisyard St Peter (Suffolk). Blended wines
under the regional names of Sussex County and Kent County are
produced here.

Best buys

Sussex County 1985, £3.65; Cuckmere Müller-Thurgau 1984, £4.34;
Biddenden Ortega 1984, £4.15; Kent County 1983, £3.75

English Wine Shop

SHOP 3 Harcourt Street, London W1H 1DS   TEL 01-724 5009
HEAD OFFICE Heywood Wines,   TEL 01-340 9635
9 Montenotte Road, London N8 8RL

OPEN Tue–Fri 11.30–6.30   Sat 10–3   CLOSED Sun, Mon, public holidays
CREDIT CARDS Access; personal and business accounts   DISCOUNTS 10% on 1
case (min)   DELIVERY Free in Central London (min 3 cases); UK mainland 1
case £6, 2 cases £3.50 per case, 3 cases £2.50 per case, 4 cases free; mail order
available   GLASS HIRE Free with 1-case order
TASTINGS AND TALKS Monthly in-store tastings; to groups on request
CELLARAGE Not available

This Marylebone shop has probably the widest range of English wines
available anywhere, and the Aikmans, who own it, have become
recognised specialists in the field. Prices are as competitive as English
wine prices can be.

Wines we particularly like include those from Michaelmas House,
Stocks, New Hall, Felstar and Abbey Knight – but almost anything in
the shop would be of interest, including the wine from the Aikmans'
own vineyard, Heywood in Norfolk. Look out also for the Carr Taylor
sparkling wine, made by the Champagne method (£7.95 a bottle).

Best buys

English wines

Farr Vintners

154 Tachbrook Street, London SW1V 2NE   TEL 01-630 5348

OPEN Mon–Fri 9–6   CLOSED Sat, Sun, public holidays   CREDIT CARDS None
accepted; personal and business accounts   DISCOUNTS Not available
DELIVERY 6+ cases free; otherwise at cost; mail order available
GLASS HIRE Not available   TASTINGS AND TALKS Regular tastings; tastings
can be arranged at other venues   CELLARAGE £2.50 per case per year   ■

It's fine wine all the way at Farr Vintners, and with four lists coming
out each year – plus supplementary ones – you need to contact them to
find out exactly what they have available at the time.

As appetisers, though, a recent list contained such gems as vintages
of Ch Pétrus back to 1924, Ch Cheval Blanc back to 1921, Ch Lafite to
1806, Ch Latour to 1881 – and that's only the first couple of pages.
While Bordeaux is the principal attraction, bargain hunters might like
to look among the Burgundies (old vintages never increase in price as
much as claret) and in the Rhône. Vintage Champagne and Vintage
Port complete this list of the rare and the great.

Best buys
Fine wines of old vintages

Farthinghoe Fine Wine and Food   ☞

The Old Rectory, Farthinghoe, Brackley,   TEL (0295) 710018
Northamptonshire NN13 5NZ

OPEN Mon–Fri 9–5   Sat, Sun, public holidays by arrangement
CREDIT CARDS None accepted; personal and business accounts
DISCOUNTS Depend on quantity (min 2 cases)   DELIVERY Free throughout UK
mainland and offshore islands (min 1 case); mail order available
GLASS HIRE £2 per box of 48 with 1-case wine order
TASTINGS AND TALKS 6–8 tastings annually; to groups on request
CELLARAGE £2.50 + VAT per case per year plus insurance (in bond only)

Food and wine are indeed firmly linked here: the Coxes, who run the
firm from an old rectory, offer cookery courses as well as wine tastings
to their customers, and have obviously chosen their wines with food in
mind.

That is why one of their most interesting sections is Alsace – wines
from one of the top gastronomic areas of France. They carry a wide
range: from Louis Gisselbrecht, Trimbach, Théo Faller, Rolly
Gassmann and Hugel, mainly of the 1983 and 1985 vintages.

Other areas of France which shine in this list include the Rhône
(wines from Jaboulet Aîné in the northern Rhône, and some top flight
Châteauneuf from further south), Champagne (a big range of Louis
Krémer and George Goulet) and a well-chosen section of claret – not
too long but well balanced between those for current drinking and
those for laying down. Again with a food connection in mind, look at

their list of pudding wines – Sauternes, Barsac and Quarts de Chaume.

Beyond France, the Coxes offer German estate wines from Deinhard and von Schubert, a good selection of Ports (they were offering 1985 vintage in bond during 1987) and Garvey Sherries. New World wines are strong in the California section – with some boutique wineries like Philip Togni and Sonoma-Cutrer, plus Trefethen, Stag's Leap Vineyard and Firestone.

Best buys

Alsace wines; Champagne, Louis Krémer White Label (NV), £9.99; Côtes du Rhône 1985, Domaine Bel-Air, £3.89; California Cabernet Sauvignon 1984, Hamilton and Tuttle, £4.99; Quarts de Chaume 1983, Domaine Baumard, £8.71

Ferrers Le Mesurier

Turnsloe, North Street, Titchmarsh,   TEL (080 12) 2660
Kettering, Northamptonshire NN14 3DH

OPEN All hours, but telephone first   CREDIT CARDS None accepted; business accounts DISCOUNTS Quantity discounts by arrangement DELIVERY Free within 50-mile radius of Titchmarsh, Cambridge area and Central London (min 1 case); elsewhere at cost GLASS HIRE Not available
TASTINGS AND TALKS Annual tastings at Cambridge University; other tastings by special arrangement CELLARAGE Free of charge for 2 years if wine purchased from premises   ■

The Burgundy section is still the pride and joy of this list. From a good collection of domaines come various 1985 whites: Guy Roulot, Clos de France of Lasserat, Rousset. In red Burgundy, they've bought more 1983s, so there are some very attractive wines to drink now from estates such as Dubreuil Fontaine, Truchot-Martin and Caillerets.

Estate wines run as a theme right through the list, so you find an excellent value Lirac 1985, Ch de Clary (£3.25), and wines from Peloux in Châteauneuf and Gigondas. On the Loire, Vouvray from Gaston Huet, and J P Balland's Sancerre le Grand Chemarin (1986 vintage at £5.29) would be worth considering. Alsace wines come from Louis Gisselbrecht and Champagne from George Goulet.

A new section covers wines from Australia (Wirra Wirra Chardonnay and St Leonard's Chardonnay), and New Zealand (Selaks Sauvignon 1986 at £6.90).

Best buys

Sauvignon de St-Bris 1985, £4.54; Côtes de Provence 1985, Ch de Puget red, £2.87; Lirac 1985, Ch de Clary, £3.73; Bourgogne Pinot 1983, Domaine Parent, £6.67

Alex Findlater

77 Abbey Road, London NW8 0AE   TEL 01-624 7311
Heveningham High House, Halesworth,   TEL (0986 83) 274
Suffolk IP19 0EA (wholesale only)

OPEN (Abbey Road) Mon–Fri 10–1, 2–9   Sat 10–9   (Heveningham High
House by appointment)   CLOSED Sun, public holidays
CREDIT CARDS Access, Visa; personal and business accounts
DISCOUNTS Approx 5% on 1 case   DELIVERY Free in Central London and
locally to Heveningham (min 1 case) and nationwide (min 3 cases); elsewhere 1
case £5, 2 cases £8; mail order available   GLASS HIRE Free with suitable case
order   TASTINGS AND TALKS 3 sessions per year; to groups on request
CELLARAGE £3.45 per case per year

This continues to be one of the yardstick lists in the Guide.
Considering the small size of the shop in Abbey Road, it's a wonder
that so many treats are to be found right through the range.

Alex Findlater is one of the few merchants to produce two
completely separate lists *and* a fine wine list. He has a standard list, and
– almost as long – an Australasian one. This is certainly the biggest
range of Australian and New Zealand wines in the country, with wines
from the big boys as well as the tiny boutique wineries. A quick glance
at the wineries listed in the Australian part of the WHAT TO BUY section
will give you an idea of how many are stocked here – and even where
they are not mentioned, Alex Findlater may well stock them anyway.
New Zealand is similarly well treated.

Despite this plethora of wines from the other side of the world,
there's still room for European and other wines on the mammoth
standard list. In the past year, expansion has taken place in some key
areas. In Germany, for example, more estates have been added to the
already large range. Featured estates include Langwerth in the
Rheingau, and Loosen Burgweiler Prüm in the Mosel.

In France, the number of petit château clarets has gone up, as has the
complement of French regional wines. Alsace continues to star, the
Loire has a good few reds from Chinon and Bourgueil, and Burgundy's
list is long, dominated by domaine wines (look for the Clos des
Lambrays reds from Domaine Cosson – vintages back to 1938).

Italian and Spanish wines continue to offer many treats and the
Italian list gets better and better. Portugal now shows off the Douro
table wines and Ports from Champalimaud at Quinta do Cotto.
Barbadillo Sherries include some delicious old dry amontillados.

Best buys

Australasian wines; old Sherries; German estate wines; wines from Ch
la Coste in Coteaux d'Aix-en-Provence; Barco Reale, Tenuta di
Capezzana 1982, £3.90; Quinta do Cotto Tinto 1982, Champalimaud,
£3.90

Findlater Mackie Todd

Findlater House, 22 Great Queen Street,
London WC2B 5BB

TEL 01-831 7158

OPEN Mon–Fri 9–6   Sat only during December (may extend to all year round)
CLOSED Sun, public holidays   CREDIT CARDS All accepted; personal and
business accounts   DISCOUNTS 7½% for 10 cases   DELIVERY Free in UK
mainland (min 1 case); surcharge of £3.50 per case for Northern Ireland and
off-shore; mail order available   GLASS HIRE Available
TASTINGS AND TALKS Special offer wines available in Findlater House; to
groups on request   CELLARAGE £3.50 per case per year

There has been a management buy-out since last year, and a move
from the familiar old shop in Wigmore Street to new premises in Great
Queen Street (due to open in April 1988).

The change in ownership has led to some changes in the list as well.
There are now fewer of the Italian wines we praised last year (although
Ruffino Chiantis and Pio Cesare Barolos are still worth looking for), but
France has plenty to consider: regional wines, such as the Syrah-based
Vin de Pays des Collines Rhodaniennes (1984 vintage at £2.85) or the
red from Ch Val-Joanis in the Côtes du Luberon (1984 vintage at £3.13);
a fine list of claret from recent vintages (back to 1982); Hugel wines
from Alsace, and on the Loire, the Ménétou-Salon Domaine Chatenoy
(£4.43); in Burgundy the domaine wines rather than the négociant
bottles; and finally the house Champagne, Duc de Marne (£8.28), or a
big range from Charles Heidsieck.

The German list shows off a good number of estate wines (Forster
Ungeheuer Riesling Kabinett 1983 from Basserman-Jordan at £4.60;
Graacher Himmelreich Spätlese 1983 of J J Prüm at £6.90). From other
parts, though, there is little to report, apart, of course, from Findlater's
own Sherries (Dry Fly Amontillado, £3.36).

Special offers and an Inner Cellar list of fine wines give an extra
dimenson to this wine merchant's standard list.

Best buys

Rioja Reserva 1982, Faustino V, £3.67; Chianti Classico 1985 Aziano,
Ruffino, £3.44; Syrah Vin de Pays des Collines Rhodaniennes, £2.85;
Ch Latour St-Bonnet 1981, Médoc, £5.51

The Wine Standards Board is the trade's disciplinary department and wine
watchdog. Their inspectors are responsible for rooting out any
malpractices – but they are concerned largely with labelling irregularities. If
you have genuine reason to suspect that the wine in a bottle is not what the
label claims it is, contact the Board at: 68½ Upper Thames Street, London
EC4V 3BJ; TEL 01-236 9512 or contact your local Trading Standards Officer.

Fine Vintage Wines

OFFICE & MAIL ORDER 140 Sloane Street, TEL 01-730 6588
London SW1X 9AY

SHOP 3/5 Hythe Bridge Street, Oxford, TEL (0865) 724866
Oxfordshire OX1 2EW

OPEN Mon–Sat 10–8 Sun 11–7 CLOSED Public holidays
CREDIT CARDS Access, Visa; business accounts DISCOUNTS Not available
DELIVERY Free on UK mainland (min 5 cases); elsewhere subject to quote; mail
order available GLASS HIRE Free with case order
TASTINGS AND TALKS Available CELLARAGE £3.45 per case per year

The name of these merchants is absolutely correct. They deal only in
top wines from Bordeaux, Burgundy, Germany and vintage
Champagne, Ports and Madeiras, with occasional visits to areas such
as the Rhône and Alsace. They also list wines from the Preston
Vineyards in California.

The list changes constantly, so you need either to pay them a visit at
their shop in Oxford (which is a shop within the Grape Ideas Wine
Warehouse – *qv*) or obtain their mail order list from the London
address. A typical recent list had vintages of claret back to 1947, with
considerable numbers of wines from 1970, 1978, 1982, 1983 and 1985.
There was a good range of mature Burgundy, much of it from
domaines, and a smaller amount of Rhône wines, principally from
Jaboulet Aîné. In fortified wines, the vintage Ports go back to 1948.
Fine Vintage Wines act as agents for the Madeiras of Power Drury.

Best buys

Fine clarets; vintage Madeiras

Fortnum & Mason

181 Piccadilly, London W1A 1ER TEL 01-734 8040

OPEN Mon–Sat 9–5.30 CLOSED Sun, public holidays CREDIT CARDS All
accepted; personal and business accounts DISCOUNTS 5% for 1–4 cases
(unmixed), 7½% for 5–9 cases (unmixed), 10% for 10+ cases (unmixed)
DELIVERY Free in London postal districts (except Eastern area); elsewhere 1
bottle £2.50, 2 bottles £3.95, 3 bottles £4.50, 4 bottles £4.95, 5 bottles £5.35, 6
bottles £6.40, 12 bottles £7.95; mail order available GLASS HIRE Not available
TASTINGS AND TALKS Champagne tastings in May/June CELLARAGE Not
available

This is still essentially a traditional list, but now many more wines from
the New World, and areas like French country wines and Italy, are
getting a chance. Prices are by no means cheap.

Claret and Champagne have always been mainstays here. Classed
growths dominate with only the occasional petit château wine.
Fortnums excel themselves with a superb range of grande marque

Champagnes, plus a house Champagne (£11.35) for anyone more modest in their aspirations; if you're feeling flush, look for large bottles of Champagne. Burgundy is getting a domaine look to it, which is encouraging.

Alsace is another area to come in for good treatment: Trimbach, Léon Beyer, Dopff et Irion, Kuentz Bas, Hugel, all jostle for a place on the shelves. From the Loire, there's a Sancerre from Vacheron; from Jura the Vin Gris of Henri Maire; from Provence the Cabernet Sauvignon Ch Vignelaure (1980 vintage, £8.40).

Outside France are a few German estate wines, Torres wines from Spain, Chianti Classico of Badia a Coltibuono and Castello Vicchiomaggio from Italy, not to mention Jordan wines from California, a good range of vintage Ports, and a fair number of English wines, too.

Best buys

Côtes de Duras 1985, Union Production Diffusion, £3.25; Chardonnay 1985, Ch d'Avrile, £4.30; Krug Collection Champagne

Friarwood

26 New Kings Road, London SW6 4ST   TEL 01-736 2628
OPEN Mon–Fri 9–6   Sat 9.30–6   CLOSED Sun, public holidays
CREDIT CARDS Access, Visa; personal and business accounts   DISCOUNTS Not available   DELIVERY Free in London (min 3 cases); elsewhere at cost; mail order available   GLASS HIRE Free with 1-case order   TASTINGS AND TALKS Tastings held most Sats; annual tasting; to groups on request   CELLARAGE Nine pence per case per year   ■

Friarwood's new shop now rather poshly calls itself a Vinothèque. The wines kept in the basement cellar continue to be dominated by Bordeaux and Burgundy, with occasional concessions to those with smaller bank balances.

The vintages of claret roll out from 1985 back to 1970. Few wines cost under about £5 a bottle, but essentially this is a fabulous list. 1985 wines are available ex-château, 1983 and back are available here.

Burgundy takes in some fine domaine wines (Roger Dupaquier, Domaine Engel, Domaine Pothier-Rieusset, Patrick Javillier, Domaine Fontaine-Gagnard, Domaine Pierre André). There are a few wines from the Loire, four from Alsace, and a couple from Bergerac. House Champagne is £8.24, plus a big range of Laurent-Perrier.

Beyond that, the list virtually stops. Look, though, for California wines from Franciscan Vineyards, and a small selection of vintage Ports.

Best buys

Domaine-bottled Burgundy; Ch Millet 1981, Graves, £6.52

Fuller, Smith & Turner (Fullers)

HEAD OFFICE Griffin Brewery, Chiswick,   TEL 01-994 3691
London W4 2QB
55 shops in West London and the Home Counties
OPEN Generally Mon–Sat, public holidays 10–2, 4–9   Sun 12–2, 7–9
CLOSED Chr Day   CREDIT CARDS Access, Visa; personal and business
accounts   DISCOUNTS Variable   DELIVERY Free in London (min 5 cases);
otherwise £1.60 per case   GLASS HIRE Free with reasonable case order
TASTINGS AND TALKS Regular tastings in larger stores; 2 major annual tastings
at Griffin Brewery; to groups on request   CELLARAGE Not available

The choice continues to improve at this chain of off-licences (mainly in West London). Most shops carry the full list. The buying policy seems to be to avoid branded wines, a decision we applaud.

We would recommend the increased range of petit château clarets from the 1982, 1983 and 1985 vintages – look for Ch Grand Mazerolles 1985, Premières Côtes de Blaye, or Ch Macquin St-Georges 1983 in St-Georges St-Emilion. There are a few classed growths and bourgeois growths as well. Burgundy, by comparison, needs a facelift, although a few domaine wines are now putting in an appearance.

Fullers have been specialising in a decent range of French country wines, and these continue to be interesting. We have enjoyed the range of Listel wines from the Vin de Pays des Sables du Golfe du Lion, the Ch la Coste red from Provence, or the Côtes du Roussillon 1984, Caramany.

Outside France, some good Rioja from Muga and Domecq Domain has now been brought in, as well as Torres wines from Penedès. There's a good value Bairrada from Portugal, and the Bulgarian wines continue to be amazing bargains. From the New World, William Wheeler is the winery from California, Rosemount from Australia.

Best buys

Alsace Pinot Blanc 1985, St-Odile, £2.99; Cépage Gamay and Cépage Cabernet Sauvignon, Vin de Pays de l'Ardèche, £2.25; petit château clarets

Matthew Gloag & Son

Bordeaux House, 33 Kinnoull Street, Perth,   TEL (0738) 21101
Perthshire PH1 5EU
OPEN Mon–Fri 9–5   CLOSED Sat, Sun, some public holidays
CREDIT CARDS Access; personal and business accounts   DISCOUNTS Not
available   DELIVERY Free on mainland Scotland (min 1 case); otherwise
England and Scottish Islands £2.20 per case, Ireland £8.05 per case; mail order
available   GLASS HIRE Free with 10-case order   TASTINGS AND TALKS Group
tastings   CELLARAGE £3.45 per case per year (min 6 cases)

Big changes have taken place at Matthew Gloag in the past year. Regular mail order customers will have noticed how the list has shrunk, both physically and in the numbers of wines it contains. Most sections are shorter, some – California, for example – have disappeared altogether.

Which is a pity, because we thought the list was getting better all the time, and were hoping for further improvements this year.

But making do with what we have we find a selection of clarets from recent vintages. As last year, though, we have to comment on the high prices of even the petit château wines. Burgundy continues to be rather dull, although the occasional domaine wine creeps in. The Loire is effectively non-existent, but the Rhône is now much better: good Châteauneuf from Domaine Font de Michelle, Ch de Beaucastel, plus wines from Jaboulet Aîné. The French country wine section still has a few decent wines from the South-West.

Outside France, German estate wines come mainly from Deinhard, while in Italy the star is the Brunello di Montalcino of Argiano (1979 vintage at £9.65). Australia weighs in with Orlando and Hardy wines. The Sherries from Barbadillo have largely disappeared but stocks of vintage Port have been kept up.

Best buys

Côtes du Roussillon 1984, Domaine de Mas Sibade, £2.90; Dão 1982, Terras Altas, £3.75; Jacob's Creek Australian red and white, £3.60

G M Vintners

7 Wellington Terrace, Truro, Cornwall TR1 3JA	TEL (0872) 79680
3 Alphin Brook Road, Marsh Barton, Exeter, Devon EX2 8RG	TEL (0392) 218186
Market Wine Stores, Lemon Street Market, Truro, Cornwall TR1 1QD	TEL (0872) 41446

OPEN Mon–Sat 9–5   CLOSED Sun, public holidays   CREDIT CARDS None accepted; personal and business accounts   DISCOUNTS Quantity discounts   DELIVERY Free in South-West England (min 1 case) and nationally (min 5 cases); otherwise £5 per delivery; mail order available   GLASS HIRE Free in South-West delivery area   TASTINGS AND TALKS Weekly in-store tastings during holiday season; to groups on request   CELLARAGE 3p per case per week (plus VAT)

G M Vintners is the name for the two wholesale wine warehouses in a group which also includes the Market Wine Stores in Truro. Prices quoted here are for the G M Vintners side, but include VAT which is lacking from the price list.

For what is in many respects a fairly standard list, there are interesting star turns. One such are the wines of Listel in the Salins du Midi, of which a range is featured (Domaine du Bosquet 1983 is £3.16). Another is Australia, where G M Vintners have brought in a good selection of wines from Penfold's, including Grange Hermitage (1980 vintage is £23), but also taking in some good value like the Dalwood Shiraz/Cabernet 1983 at £3.70 and the classic buttery Seaview Chardonnay 1986 at £4.41.

In France, the choice is between some well-priced Bordeaux petit château wines – with a couple of good value Fronsacs (Ch Mayne-Vieil 1982 at £5.25) – and a few more expensive classed growths. Burgundy continues to be dull, although a few more domaine wines than last year have appeared. There's plenty of good Beaujolais from Loron, and Laurent Perrier and Perrier-Jouët are the featured Champagne houses.

As last year, the Loire offers a good selection: Savennières from Ch d'Epire, Sancerre from Jean Vacheron, the excellent Chinon of Domaine de la Bellonière, and the Ménétou-Salon of Domaine de Chatenoy (1985 vintage at £4.11).

It is possible to find a few decent wines in their rather standard view of Italy – wines from Bolla in the Veneto, Regaleali from Sicily, and some of the Melini Chiantis are worth looking for. Spain offers Riojas from Lopez de Heredia and Marqués de Cáceres as well as Valdespino Sherries.

Best buys

Sylvaner 1985, Cave Vinicole de Pfaffenheim, £3.69; Penfold's Hunter Valley Semillon 1982, £4.40; Ménétou-Salon 1985, Domaine de Chatenoy £4.11; Listel wines; Loron Beaujolais

Godrich & Petman

9A Parchment Street, Winchester,   TEL (0962) 53081
Hampshire SO23 8AT
9 branches in the South and South-West

OPEN Mon–Fri 9–5.30   Sat 9–5   CLOSED Sun, public holidays
CREDIT CARDS Access, Visa; personal and business accounts
DISCOUNTS Variable   DELIVERY Free in Andover, Basingstoke, Portsmouth, Southampton area (min £20 order)   GLASS HIRE Free with appropriate order
TASTINGS AND TALKS Tasting of wines on offer in-store; to groups on request
CELLARAGE Not available

These shops are part of the Eldridge Pope group (qv).

Goedhuis & Co

101 Albert Bridge Road, London SW11 4PF   TEL 01-223 6057

OPEN Mon–Fr 9.30–6.30   CLOSED Sat, Sun, public holidays
CREDIT CARDS Access, Visa; personal and business accounts   DISCOUNTS 5% for 5 cases   DELIVERY Free within UK (min 3 cases); otherwise £2.50 per case for 1–2 cases; mail order available   GLASS HIRE Free
TASTINGS AND TALKS 3 major tastings at the Turf Club; to groups on request
CELLARAGE £2.90 per case per year   ■

Here you will find Rhône wines (Châteauneuf from Ch de Beaucastel and Côte Rôtie from Guigal), wines from Rolly Gassmann in Alsace and from Rioja and Penedès (Torres), plus Rosemount and Rothbury in Australia. Good though they are, however, they seem sideshows to the two classic areas of the list.

Clarets are a good balance between petit château wines, plus a few older classed growths which are ready for drinking now, and a big section of wines from recent vintages for laying down. In Burgundy, Goedhuis have laid in plenty of domaine wines, with a wider range in reds than whites. Vintages go back to 1980.

Best buys

Bourgogne Passe-tout-grain 1983, Domaine Roulot, £4.50; Côtes du Ventoux 1985, La Vieille Ferme, £3.20; Rioja Reserva 1981, Anares, £4.35; Sauvignon du Haut-Poitou 1985, £3.25

Andrew Gordon Wines

Andrew Gordon's Wine Warehouse, Glebelands,   TEL (0306) 885711
Vincent Lane, Dorking, Surrey RH4 3YZ

OPEN Mon–Fri 9–6   Sat 9–4   CLOSED Sun, public holidays
CREDIT CARDS Access; personal and business accounts   DISCOUNTS By arrangement for quantity   DELIVERY Free locally and in Central London (min 1 case); mail order service of 1–11 cases £1.25 per case (min charge £7.50), 12–21 cases £1 per case, 21+ cases free   GLASS HIRE Free with order; delivery with wine free   TASTINGS AND TALKS Two open house days annually by invitation only; educational tutored tastings throughout the year   CELLARAGE £2.50 per case (min 10 cases) ■

Since last year there has been some exciting expansion to the range of wines offered here: New World wines, for example, and the splendid Sherries of Barbadillo. The list of French country wines has also grown, and so has the selection of petit château clarets. So, come to that, has the Italian section. It looks as though Mr Gordon has been busy.

The French country section has a good showing from the South-West: wines from Duras, Bergerac, Tursan, Gaillac, Fitou and Cahors are all there. From other parts of France are the wines of Savoie (Apremont white and Mondeuse red), and a big, beefy Côtes du Roussillon Ch de Rey 1981 at £2.99.

From Bordeaux, we would recommend some of the petit château wines: Ch Moulin de Landry 1983, Côtes de Castillon at £3.24 is a bargain, as is Ch de Beychade 1982, Côtes de Bourg at £3.69. Superior wines flow in plenty. The Burgundy range offers some good domaine wines as well as some better value wines from the co-operatives. Rhône wines are from négociants – unusual in an area with so many good estates.

Italy has blossomed: look for the varietal wines from the Trentino (Merlot and Cabernet del Trentino, both at £2.67), or Santi's Cabernet

Sauvignon from the same area (£3.66). Chianti is from Rocca delle Macie, Barolo from Fontanafredda.

The increase in New World wines brings Rosemount in Australia and Clos du Val in California. There's Tunisian wine – if you feel strong enough – and the fine Ch Carras red from Greece, besides a good range of vintage Port and some well-chosen dessert wines.

Best buys

Vin de Pays Charentais, £1.99; Ch Ferrasses 1982, Côtes de Castillon, £3.67; Ch de Rey 1981, Côtes du Roussillon, £2.99; Quincy 1985, Domaine de la Maison Blanche, £3.50; Chianti Classico 1985, Rocca delle Macie, £3.34; Barbadillo Sherries

Gough Brothers

The 120 branches of Gough Brothers in London and the Home Counties are run by Oddbins (*qv*); prices of some wines are different.

Le Gourmet Gascon

3 Hillgate Street, London W8 7SL   TEL 01-221 4131

OPEN Mon–Fri 9.30–7.30 Sat 9.30–6.30 CLOSED Sun, public holidays
CREDIT CARDS Access, Diners, Visa; personal and business accounts
DISCOUNTS 5% for 1 case   DELIVERY Free in London, W8 (min 5 cases);
otherwise £5 per order; mail order available GLASS HIRE Available
TASTINGS AND TALKS Occasional tastings; to groups on request
CELLARAGE Not available

Le Gourmet Gascon specialises in organic wines, with quite a wide-ranging list not just from France, but also from England and Italy.

While well-known organic wines like those of Listel in the Midi can be bought here, Le Gourmet has also sought out lesser-known wines from Bordeaux (Ch Chavrignac 1984 at £4.86), Alsace (wines from Paul Frick) and Sancerre (Dauny, vintage 1983 at £5.14). They also sell the organic Muscadet from Robert Bossard.

English wines come from the Avalon vineyard (alongside country wines made from Apples). From Italy, the wines are mainly from the Veneto, with a number of Bardolinos, Soaves and Valpolicellas, including an Amarone (£7.89), and single vineyard wines from the same areas.

Best buys

Listel wines; Bianco San Pietro, vino da tavola, £3.70; Castello Guerrieri Rosso vino da tavola, £6.46; La Vieille Ferme white Côtes du Luberon, £3.55, and red Côtes du Ventoux, £3.85

Richard Granger

West Jesmond Station, Lyndhurst Avenue,　　　　TEL (091) 281 5000
Newcastle upon Tyne, Tyne & Wear NE2 3HH

OPEN Mon–Fri 8.30–6.30　Sat 8.30–2　CLOSED Sun, public holidays
CREDIT CARDS Access, Visa; personal and business accounrs　DISCOUNTS Not
available　DELIVERY Free in Newcastle and surrounding area (min 1 case);
charges elsewhere negotiable; mail order available for small orders
GLASS HIRE Available　TASTINGS AND TALKS Monthly fine wine tastings by
invitation; to customers on request　CELLARAGE Free to customers but limited
availability　　　　　　　　　　　　　　　　　　　　　　　　　　■

This is a short but select range of wines with particular strengths in
France. For instance, Richard Granger has marshalled a sensible range
of clarets, moving from House Claret at £2.86 to first growths (Ch
Mouton Rothschild 1980 at £26), but with the emphasis on the less
expensive end, and in Burgundy, he has picked out a few wines from
négociants. In the Rhône look for the Lirac Domaine de Castel Oualou
1982 at £4.75. Beaujolais from Georges Duboeuf and Hugel Alsace
wines (good prices for these) sit next to collection of Loire wines which
include the Pouilly Fumé of Paul Figeat (1984 was £4.54) and house
Champagne at £9.54.

Of wines from other countries, there are a few attractive German
estate wines from Deinhard and Schloss Vollrads, and Australian
wines from Leasingham and the Stanley Wine Co. Torres wines from
Spain join almacenista Sherries and Graham's Tawny Ports as the
Iberian contribution.

Best buys
Sélection de la Gare (litre) red and white, £2.87; Cooks New Zealand
Chardonnay 1986, £4.25; Vouvray 1985, £3.27; Hugel Alsace wines

Grapehop

See La Reserva Wines.

Grape Ideas Wine Warehouse

3/5 Hythe Bridge Street, Oxford,　　　　TEL (0865) 722137
Oxfordshire OX1 2EW

OPEN Mon–Sat 10–8　Sun 11–4　CLOSED Public holidays
CREDIT CARDS Access, Visa; personal and business accounts
DISCOUNTS Dependent on size of order (min 6 cases)　DELIVERY Free within
20-mile radius (min 1 case); £2.50 per case elsewhere on UK mainland; mail order
available　GLASS HIRE Free with 1-case order; delivery free with wine
purchase　TASTINGS AND TALKS Two major tastings annually and on
request　CELLARAGE 5p per case per week

There are two shops in one here: the wine warehouse – covered by this entry – and Fine Vintage Wines, for those who want to buy up-market (see their separate entry).

The two operations work in tandem. What you get at Grape Ideas is a wide range of wines for everyday drinking, with only a few sections that head for the stratosphere (inevitably Burgundy – never cheap – is one). A good selection of French country wines offers, for instance, Domaine de Plaisance 1985, Bergerac red at £2.75, and the white at £2.95. Claret names are Fronsac, Côtes de Bourg and Côtes de Castillon, and from Alsace come good value wines from Ziegler. Rhône wines from Jaboulet Aîné are a little more pricey (Crozes-Hermitage 1983 at £4.60), but the Muscadet from the Loire, Domaine de la Bretonnière 1985 at £2.99, is well worth the money.

Spain's contribution is with wines from Torres, and with Riojas from Campo Viejo and Marqués de Cáceres. The German selection is dull. Italy is enlivened by the Veneto wines of Santa Sofia (Soave Costalta 1985 at £3.90), and Portugal brings in the Grão Vasco Dão and Garrafeira as well as the attractive Gazela Vinho Verde.

Interesting bottles from further afield include the occasional Argentine wine, Australian wines from Lindemans, Ch Musar from the Lebanon and Shafer Winery wines from California.

Best buys

Fitou 1983, Cuvée d'Or, £2.49; Vin de Pays des Côtes de Gascogne 1986, £2.49; Ch Arnauton 1982, Fronsac, £4.95; Coronas 1983, Torres, £3.39; Cabernet Sauvignon 1983, Viña Linderos, Chile, £3.45

Great American Wine Company

BCM, Box 150, London WC1N 3XX   TEL 01-407 0502

OPEN Mon–Fri 9–5   CLOSED Sat, Sun, public holidays   CREDIT CARDS None accepted; personal and business accounts   DISCOUNTS Available
DELIVERY Free; mail order available   GLASS HIRE Not available
TASTINGS AND TALKS Tastings offered to customers; occasionally to groups on request   CELLARAGE Not available   ■

This all-American mail order company carries wines from California, Oregon and Washington State and, on the east coast, New York State.

It's a big range with wines from a mix of large and small (boutique) wineries. Bottles from the North-West have been stepped up – with Pinot Noirs from Amity Vineyards, Rex Hill, Bethel Heights and Yamhill Valley joining the just more familiar Knudsen Erath as the Oregon contingent – Oregon is often regarded as a better source of Pinot Noir than California. Another new signing is Hogue Cellars in Washington State, which has come in with a Sauvignon Blanc. In California, La Jota in Napa Valley provides a Cabernet Sauvignon 1982.

These wines join established wineries on the list: Fetzer, Mendocino

Estate, Tjisseling, ZD, J P Dore, Bel Arbres, Pine Ridge, Acacia and Louis Martini – among many more. What is especially attractive about this range is that prices go from the very good value (Fetzer and Dore wines in particular) right to the top quality, pricey star wines.

While this merchant handles wines only on a wholesale basis, every item can be bought by the single bottle at Ostlers Wine Merchants (see below).

Best buys

Fetzer Premium red and white, £2.99; J P Dore Négociant Reserve red and white, £2.99; Fetzer Lake County Cabernet Sauvignon 1984, £4.75

Great Northern Wine Company

Unit 5, The Dark Arches,   TEL (0532) 461200/461209
Leeds Canal Basin, Leeds, West Yorkshire LS1 4BR

OPEN Mon–Fri 9–6.30   Sat, public holidays 10–5.30   CLOSED Sun, 25 & 26 Dec, 1 Jan   CREDIT CARDS Access, Visa; personal and business accounts DISCOUNTS Variable (min 1 case)   DELIVERY Free within 30-mile radius of Leeds (min 1 case); otherwise 1–5 cases £7.50, 6–10 cases £1.50 per case, 11+ cases free; mail order available   GLASS HIRE Free with 1-case order TASTINGS AND TALKS Occasional tastings for customers; monthly tutored tastings; to groups on request   CELLARAGE Not available

---

This new company has already developed a well-balanced list with plenty of interest from most parts of the wine world.

They are especially strong in Australia, with wines from Peter Lehmann, Montrose, Brokenwood and Tisdall in addition to the larger producers such as Orlando and Rosemount. They also have the top quality Selaks wines from New Zealand (Sauvignon Blanc 1986 is £6.79).

The French collection includes country wines from Listel in the Midi (Cabernet 1983, Vin de Pays d'Oc is £3.38) as well as the Jura wines from Ch d'Arlay and the excellent Cahors 1983, Ch St-Didier Parnac (£4.25). Rhône wines have amongst their number the lovely, elegant Côtes du Rhône-Villages Beaumes de Venise of Nativelle (1985 vintage at £4.85). On the Loire, the Vouvray from Ch Moncontour is a top quality wine from a large estate (1985 vintage at £5.25). Louis Sipp provides Alsace wines, and while Burgundy has wines from Antonin Rodet as well as Chanson, the Bordeaux selection dwells principally on classed growths.

A small but good range of Riojas from Berberana and CVNE and a couple of good, beefy Portuguese reds make up the Iberian section. Italy offers more with the fine Chianti Riserva from Pagliarese (1979 vintage at £4.99) and the fresh Rocca della Macie Chianti Classico 1985 at £3.69. Look also for the Amarone from Boscaini. From the eastern Mediterranean come the 1979 vintage of Ch Musar from the Lebanon

(£5.15) and the Israeli wines from the Golan Heights. Valdespino and Don Zoilo come up with the Sherries, Souza and Ramos-Pinto with the Ports. There's a growing selection of half-bottles.

Best buys

Côtes du Luberon, La Vieille Ferme, £3.30; Champagne Laurent Perrier (NV), £10.95; Crozes-Hermitage 1983, Jaboulet-Vercherre, £3.85; Côtes du Rhône-Villages 1985, Cellier des Dauphins, £3.35

Peter Green

37A/B Warrender Park Road, Edinburgh EH9 1HJ   TEL 031-229 5925
OPEN Mon–Fri 9.30–6.30   Sat 9.30–7   CLOSED Sun, public holidays
CREDIT CARDS None accepted; personal and business accounts
DISCOUNTS 5% on unmixed cases   DELIVERY 50p per order in Edinburgh; mail
order available   GLASS HIRE Free   TASTINGS AND TALKS Annual tasting for
invited customers; to groups on request   CELLARAGE Not available

In 1987, one of our three top wine merchants in the last edition, Peter Green, celebrated 40 years as a family wine merchant. Their range of wines, one of the most interesting and varied in the Guide, has grown since last year – we wouldn't have thought it possible.

What is so interesting about the list is the way that expansion has taken place away from the classic French areas both into the byways of France and other countries. It's comparatively easy, we feel, to buy claret – provided you have the money. It's much harder to explore elsewhere and break new ground often enough to give variety and value for money to wine drinkers.

With such a wealth of wines, we can only pick out areas which have expanded in the past year and urge readers to get Peter Green's full list. In France, Alsace gets better and better – the 1985 wines in particular are listed at very good prices. The Loire has delicious sweet attractions from Quarts de Chaume and Bonnezeaux, but look also at the range of Sancerres and Pouilly Fumés. There's a growing range of French country wines, with special interest in the South-West and Provence.

In Germany, the range is superb, although we suspect sales must be slow, to judge by the number of 1976 wines still available – Germany is not all Liebfraumilch. Buy the 1983 wines as well – the Kabinetts are just right to drink now.

Italy is a treasure chest. Strong points are Barolos (from Fontanafredda and Giacomo Borgogno), Chiantis from a whole range of top estates, Brunello di Montalcino from Colombini, Amarone della Valpolicella from top producers, Taurasi from Mastroberardino . . .

Portugal and Spain are both well represented. Portugal has the wines of J M da Fonseca (Periquita, Pasmados and Camarate from various vintages), and the fine Douro wine, Quinta de Cotto, of Montez-Champalimaud (1982 vintage at £3.69). There are now around

40 Riojas as well as wines from Torres, Jean León and Conde de Caralt in Penedès. Peter Green is one of the few merchants we know with wines from Galicia. From Greece, look for the surprisingly elegant Calliga Ruby (£4.39) as well as Ch Carras.

Australia and California have both been boosted, and Oregon and Texas (yes, they now make wine there) have appeared on the list. There are plenty of Madeiras, including some old vintages, and a big range of Sherries.

Best buys

Côtes de Gascogne, £1.89; California Pinot Noir 1982, Firestone, £4.49; Cava, Segura Viudas, £4.19; Chardonnay di Appiano 1983, Viticoltori Alto-Adige, £3.29; Saumur Ch de Florent 1986, £3.65; Sherries and Madeiras

Green's

34 Royal Exchange, London EC3V 3LP   TEL 01-236 7077
36 Duke Street, St James's, London SW1Y 6DF   TEL 01-930 4566

OPEN Mon–Fri 9–5   CLOSED Sat, Sun, public holidays   CREDIT CARDS None accepted (Access, Visa accepted only on special offers when mailed to customers); personal and business accounts   DISCOUNTS 2½% for 12–59 bottles, 5% for 60 bottles   DELIVERY Free delivery in central London (min 1 case); elsewhere 1–23 bottles £6.33, 2–10 cases £4.03 per case, 11+ cases £2.88 per case; mail order available   GLASS HIRE £1.73 per dozen, supplied with wine order; no delivery outside Central London   TASTINGS AND TALKS Regular tastings in cellars and offices; also on request   CELLARAGE £4.49 per case

Greens was bought by Bibendum (*qv*) during 1987, and currently operates off the Bibendum list with a few of the Green's lines being retained (such as the house Floquet Champagne and German estate wines from Max Ferd Richter). There are plans to incorporate more of these specials into both the new-look Green's list and into Bibendum's – this is likely to happen during the winter of 1987/88. In the meantime, regular Green's customers can delight in a significant reduction in the profit margins that the new management adopts (Floquet Champagne, for example, was £10.58 and is now £9.96).

A O L Grilli Wines

Little Knox Bridge, Cranbrook Road, Staplehurst,   TEL (0580) 891472
Kent TN12 0EU

OPEN All week, but telephone to arrange first   CREDIT CARDS None accepted; personal and business accounts   DISCOUNTS Quantity discounts (min 1 case) DELIVERY Free on UK mainland (min 1 case); elsewhere at cost; mail order available   GLASS HIRE Free with wine order   TASTINGS AND TALKS On request; to groups on request   CELLARAGE No charge at present (end 1987) ∎

Portuguese wines continue to be the reason for this firm's inclusion in the Guide. Other areas, however, do provide some interest.

The new wines stick firmly to the Iberian peninsula with a much bigger range of Sherries, and more Riojas, as well as Jean Perico sparkling Cava.

In Portugal, a good range of vintage Ports goes back to 1963. For the table wines, the list still manages to contain some old vintages of reds – the Garrafeira 1974 of Carvalho, Ribeiro and Ferreira is £5.27, as well as Dãos from Caves São João (1975 Porta dos Cavaleiros at £5.49). Also look for the Colares red 1976 of Real Vinícola at £4.43; and the wines from J M da Fonseca for those who like a little less Portuguese character to their wines. In the whites, there's the good value dry Vinho Verde Casalinho.

Best buys

Dão Porta dos Cavaleiros 1980, £3.26; Vinho Verde Casalinho Extra Dry, £3.11; Cava Jean Perico, £4.77

Haddows

HEAD OFFICE Brook House, Chertsey Road, Woking, TEL (04862) 5066 Surrey GU21 5BE
96 branches throughout Scotland

OPEN Mon–Sat 10–10   CLOSED Sun, public holidays   CREDIT CARDS Access, Amex, Visa   DISCOUNTS 5% for 1 case   DELIVERY At branch manager's discretion only   GLASS HIRE Free with order   TASTINGS AND TALKS, CELLARAGE Not available

This chain of shops operates off a selection of wines from the Victoria Wine Co List (*qv*), and has access to that group's Cellar Selection of fine wines.

Hadleigh Wine Cellars

The Maltings, Duke Street, Hadleigh,   TEL (0473) 827670
Suffolk IP7 5DP

OPEN Mon–Fri 9–1, 2–5.30   Sat 9–2.30   Good Friday 9–1   CLOSED Sun, public holidays   CREDIT CARDS Access; personal and business accounts
DISCOUNTS 8% on 1 mixed case   DELIVERY Free in Hadleigh and surrounding area (min 1 mixed case), London area included for quantity orders; elsewhere at cost; mail order available   GLASS HIRE Free with order
TASTINGS AND TALKS 2 annual tastings held in the cellars; to interested groups on request   CELLARAGE Not available

A good, sensible list, which sticks mainly to France, offering plenty of good value as well as more expensive wines.

The latter category is made up mainly of clarets. Vintages go back to 1961, but in the younger wines, there are some attractive petit château

wines: Ch Trinité-Valrose 1985 is £3.85, Ch Patache d'Aux, 1985,
Médoc is £3.51; Ch Tiffray 1983, Lussac St-Emilion is £5.25.

There's a short range of Burgundy, and Beaujolais from Loron.
Rhône wines come from Jaboulet Aîné, but the Loire selection is dull.
With the smaller French regions, things look up again: the varietal
wines from the Vin de Pays de l'Ardèche are £2.85; the Côtes du
Vivarais in the south of France and Fitou and Jurançon in the
South-West provide some interesting wines, along with a couple of
Alsace wines from Muré.

A few German estate wines, a handful of Italians (Chianti Classico
1983, Castello Vicchiomaggio is £4.15), Rioja from Bodegas Artacho,
and a good, rich Bairrada Garrafeira from Portugal complete Europe. In
the New World, Orlando and Jacob's Creek wines speak for Australia,
and Selaks Sauvignon Blanc for New Zealand.

Best buys

Côtes du Vivarais 1986 red, Les Caves de la Cévenne Ardéchoise,
£2.70; varietal wines from the Vin de Pays de l'Ardèche, £2.85; Ch
Trinité-Valrose 1985, £3.85; Ch St-Martin-Berlans 1983, £3.42

Hampshire Wine Company

The Granary, Unit 2, Portesbury Road, Camberley,   TEL (0276) 62349
Surrey GU15 3SY

OPEN Tue–Fri 11–6 Sat 10–6 CLOSED Mon, Sun, some public holidays
CREDIT CARDS Access, Visa; personal and business accounts DISCOUNTS 2%
for 5 cases DELIVERY Within 20-mile radius of Camberley free with £50+
order, £2.50 charge for orders under £50; elsewhere charges approx £5 per case;
mail order available GLASS HIRE Free TASTINGS AND TALKS Wines
available for tasting at the warehouse; regular tastings organised for Club
Members; to groups on request CELLARAGE Not available   ∎

The Hampshire Wine Company describe themselves as Loire
specialists, with a wide-ranging selection from most of the major areas
along that river.

They start in Muscadet with wines from Guy Charpentier who also
produces Gros Plant and red Vin de Pays from the Cabernet Franc and
Gamay grapes. In Anjou, they go in for some of the superb sweet
white wines of Quarts de Chaume and Bonnezeaux (the Bonnezeaux of

---

If your favourite wine merchant is not in this section, write and tell us
about him or her. There are report forms at the back of the book.

Find the best new wine bargains all year round with our newsletter, *Which?*
Wine Monthly, available for just £15 a year from: Dept WG88, Consumers'
Association, FREEPOST, Hertford SG14 1YB – no stamp is needed if posted
within the UK.

Jean Godineau is especially good). Saumur wines come from Joseph Subileau, with a speciality of Saumur-Champigny wines (1986 Domaine des Rogelins is £4). Then there are Vins de Pays du Jardin de la France – the Vin de Pays which covers the whole river – and a big range of wines from négociant Rémy Pannier. Look also for the Reuilly wines of Jean-Michel Sorbe.

Wines from other areas of France come from Les Maîtres Goustiers, which is an association of winegrowers, and include some good value Burgundy, and Champagne from Antoine Nowack (Brut 1985, £10.55).

Best buys

Bonnezeaux 1983, Jean Godineau, £5.14; Saumur Champigny 1985, Domaine Rebeilleau, £3.65; Saumur Brut 1985, Subileau, £4.55; Reuilly 1985, Jean-Michel Sorbe, £3.66

Gerard Harris

2 Green End Street, Aston Clinton,   TEL (0296) 631041
Buckinghamshire HP22 5HP

OPEN Mon–Sat 9.30–8   CLOSED Sun, public holidays
CREDIT CARDS Access, Visa, Bell Card; personal and business accounts
DISCOUNTS 10% for 1 case (except fine clarets, older Burgundies and vintage Ports)   DELIVERY Free within 20-mile radius (min 1 case); otherwise £3.75 per consignment; mail order available   GLASS HIRE Free with 1-case order
TASTINGS AND TALKS Occasional in-store tastings; 3 major tastings annually; to groups on request   CELLARAGE £3.75 per case per year

This list continues to delight and, although Bordeaux and Germany are still the star areas, other parts of the world are coming along well.

That's particularly true of the Rhône, which now boasts a big selection of Jaboulet Aîné wines, with the occasional Guigal and Chapoutier wine thrown in for good measure. The good value Côtes du Rhône of Charavin (1985 vintage at £3.76) and Châteauneuf-du-Pape Domaine du Vieux Télégraphe keep up the excitement.

Other regions of France are being equally well treated: Provence with wines from Coteaux des Baux en Provence, Arbois from the Jura (the Vin Jaune of Henri Maire) and a big range of Alsace wines from Hugel.

Italy is merely ticking over, but it does include Chianti from Badia a Coltibuono and Chardonnay from Tiefenbrunner. There are CVNE Riojas and – new arrivals to the list – an increasing range of Australian wines from Rosemount and Brown Brothers and a range of Californian wines.

And so to Germany. Plenty of estate wines – from J J Prüm, the Friedrich Wilhelm Gymnasium and von Schubert in the Mosel–Saar–Ruwer, Deinhard, Bürklin-Wolf, von Knyphausen and many others on the Rhine – make this a very strong list.

Similar strength shows itself in Bordeaux, with a big range of clarets from vintages back to the great 1961, chiefly of bourgeois or classed growths, but with a good number of magnums for parties or special occasions. Burgundy, by comparison, is much more limited, but Champagne – as befits a wine merchant associated with a restaurant (the Bell Inn at Aston Clinton) – is good.

Best buys

Claret from vintages of the 1960s; estate-bottled German wines; Sauvignon de St-Bris 1985, Tabit, £5.19; Rioja 1981, Remelluri, £4.80

Roger Harris Wines

Loke Farm, Weston Longville, Norfolk NR9 5LG   TEL (0603) 880171

OPEN Mon–Fri 9–5   CLOSED Sat, Sun, public holidays
CREDIT CARDS Access, Amex, Diners, Visa; personal and business accounts
DISCOUNTS 2 cases £1 per case, 5+ cases £1.50 per case   DELIVERY (Included in price) UK mainland (min 1 case); mail order available   GLASS HIRE Not available   TASTINGS AND TALKS On request; to groups on request
CELLARAGE Not available   ∎

Specialist Beaujolais shipper is how Roger Harris describes himself, and his list demonstrates his enthusiasm. It makes for enjoyable reading, and is full of information about the wines, the different crus and about the Beaujolais in general.

Roger Harris goes in for growers' wines rather than those of négociants, and he covers the whole spectrum of Beaujolais from the simple Co-opérative Beaujolais, Cellier des Samsons (the 1986 vintage was £4.10), through the unusual Beaujolais Supérieur and Beaujolais rosé, to Beaujolais-Villages and the nine cru villages. Wines from 1985 still appear among the crus, but 1986s are following on soon – sadly, with increased prices. A few wines from the Mâconnais provide a white contrast to the predominating reds of the Beaujolais.

Best buys

Beaujolais 1986, Ch de Tanay, £3.59; Juliénas 1985 Henri Lespinasse, £5.44; Beaujolais-Villages 1986, Co-opérative des Producteurs, £4.28; crus Beaujolais from St-Amour, Chénas and Juliénas

Harrods

Knightsbridge, London SW1X 7XL   TEL 01-730 1234

OPEN Mon, Tue, Thur–Sat 9–6   Wed 9.30–7   most public holiday Mons
CLOSED Sun, public holidays except as above   CREDIT CARDS All accepted, House of Fraser Card; Harrods account   DISCOUNTS Full case of 12 bottles priced as 11 bottles (not vintage Ports, vermouth etc)   DELIVERY Free within 20-mile radius of Harrods; otherwise parcel post charges; mail order available   GLASS HIRE Not available   TASTINGS AND TALKS In-store promotional tastings most weeks   CELLARAGE Not available

It's in the unexpected areas that Harrods' list always pleasurably surprises: in Spanish table wines, for instance – hardly an area normally associated with such a smart wine department. But they've managed to prove – quite rightly – that Spain makes top wines as well as, say, France; and they've come up with some of the top names in Rioja, Torres and Jean León wines from Penedès, the unusual Aniversario 125 of Julián Chivite (£8), Vega Sicilia and the second wine, Valbuena, plus, of course, a good range of Sherries.

Clarets and other classic wines nevertheless continue to be the mainstay of the list, but Harrods have taken an interest in the Midi (Mas de Daumas Gassac 1984 at £8) and a good range of Jaboulet Aîné and Vidal-Fleury wines from the Rhône. The Loire is still relatively uninteresting, but Champagne does extremely well, as one might expect.

Other sections which are well treated are German estate wines, a good range from Tuscany, the oddity of some Swiss wines (at gnomic prices) and Israeli wines. Plus, of course, a wide range of Ports and a smaller one of Madeiras.

All this apart, Harrods need to look hard at their prices if they are to retain their traditional discriminating clientele.

Best buys

Periquita 1982, J M da Fonseca, £3.70; Spanish wines; Côtes du Roussillon 1981, Ch Montesquiou, £3.40; Madeiras

John Harvey & Sons

HEAD OFFICE Harvey House, Whitchurch Lane, Bristol, Avon BS14 0JZ — TEL (0272) 836161
27 Pall Mall, London SW1V 5LP — TEL 01-839 4695
12 Denmark Street, Bristol, Avon BS1 5DQ — TEL (0272) 273759
Portsmouth Area Order Office – Harvey House, 16 The Hard, Portsmouth, Hampshire PO1 3DT — TEL (0705) 825567

OPEN Mon–Fri 9.30–5.30 CLOSED Sat, Sun, public holidays
CREDIT CARDS All accepted; personal and business accounts
DISCOUNTS Quantity discounts DELIVERY Free on UK mainland (min 1 case); mail order available GLASS HIRE Free in own van delivery areas (London and Bristol) TASTINGS AND TALKS Regular in-store tastings; regular spring and autumn tastings in Bristol and London; to groups on request
CELLARAGE £2.64 per case per year

By far the most important section of this list is the range of clarets. At the head, inevitably, is a full set of vintages of first growth Ch Latour and its second wine Les Forts de Latour, for which Harveys are British agents. They also carry plenty of other clarets from vintages back to 1975, and while prices are not cheap, the quality of the wines is good.

Elsewhere, though, it is the occasional flash of interest rather than the overall quality of the list that is relevant – for instance, some decent

Rhône wines (Côtes du Rhône-Villages, Domaines Ste-Anne is one, the Lirac from Domaine Maby another). The French regional section contains some fairly priced wines, with a Faugères 1984 and Cahors 1982, Ch St-Didier Parnac (£3.54 – prices on the list do not include VAT, but we have added it here). On the Loire, there's the Pouilly Fumé of Gérard Coulbois and the Quincy of Domaine de la Maison Blanche (£4.27).

Look also for the Cockburn Ports (which include some crusted Ports like the Quinta da Eira Velha, bottled 1985 at £7.24 and 10- and 20-year-old tawnies), plus a big range of vintage Ports. Harveys Sherries take in the new top flight 1796 range and some old bottled Sherries.

Best buys

Les Forts de Latour 1980, £13; Harveys No 1 Claret, £3.37; Cockburns 10-year-old tawny Port, £7.02; Champagne Pirrot (NV), £8.53

Richard Harvey Wines

The Old Court House, 37 West Borough,   TEL (0202) 881111
Wimborne Minster, Dorset BH21 1LT

OPEN Mon, Tue, Thur, Fri 9.30–5.30   Wed, Sat 9.30–1   CLOSED Sun, public holidays   CREDIT CARDS Visa; personal and business accounts DISCOUNTS 2½% for 1 unmixed case, 5% on 6 unmixed cases; larger quantities negotiable   DELIVERY Free on UK mainland – Avon, Dorset, Somerset, Wiltshire, Berkshire, Hampshire and Central London (min 3 cases), rest of UK mainland (min 6 cases); otherwise £3.45 per case for 1–2 cases in own delivery area, £5.75 per case for 1–2 cases and £3.45 per case for 3–5 cases elsewhere; mail order available   GLASS HIRE Free with reasonable order TASTINGS AND TALKS 2 major tastings annually; to groups on request CELLARAGE £4.60 per case per year plus insurance at 75p per £100 of original purchase price ■

We continue to be impressed with this wine merchant who is confident enough to start off his list with an attractive range of French regional wines. Richard Harvey has also moved from what he calls 'a cold warehouse' to 'a warm shop' – coming in from the cold, you might say.

As well as supplying the house red, those regional wines include Cahors from Rigal (Carte Noire 1983 at £3.70), Jurançon Cru Lamouroux from Jean Chigé and the Gaillac Rouge from the Caves des Coteaux de Gaillac; and, in the Rhône Valley, the Côtes du Ventoux, Domaine des Anges (1984 vintage at £3.25).

Convention returns with clarets appearing next – a reasonable selection from recent vintages. Burgundy produces some good domaine names – Henri Jayer, Henri Prudhon, Michel Colin, Lafarge and Domaine Vincent. There are a couple of attractive Beaujolais. Further south, the Rhône provides some top names as well: Jaboulet Aîné, Desmeure, Guigal and, in Côtes du Rhône, the Domaine Bel-Air

(1985 vintage at £3.75). Treats crop up on the Loire, too, with Pouilly Fumé from Jean-Pierre Bailly and Touraine wines from Henri Marionnet. Look also for Alsace wines from Rolly-Gassmann.

Once outside France, the selection gets shorter, but good things can be bought from Italy (Chiantis from Volpaia and Badia a Coltibuono, Veneto wines from Ca' del Monte) and Germany (estate wines from Balthasar Ress).

In Iberia, we find Riojas from CVNE and a dry Vinho Verde, Solar das Boucas (£3.85). Sherry from Barbadillo and Churchill's Ports are highly regarded. In the New World, look for Australian wines from Brown Brothers and New Zealand wines from Selaks.

Best buys

Vinho Verde, Solar das Boucas, £3.85; English Bacchus/Reichensteiner 1985, Wake Court, £2.95; House Red, Rigal et Fils, £2.30; Gaillac Rouge, Les Carmes, £2.95; Côtes du Rhône 1985, Domaine Bel-Air, £3.75; Soave Classico 1985, Gini Olinto, £3.40

Haynes Hanson & Clark

HEAD OFFICE AND WHOLESALE WAREHOUSE	TEL 01-736 7878
17 Lettice Street, London SW6 4EH	
SHOP 36 Kensington Church Street,	TEL 01-937 4650
London W8 4BX	

OPEN Mon–Sat 9.30–7 (Lettice Street Mon–Fri 9.15–7) CLOSED Sun, public holidays CREDIT CARDS None accepted; personal and business accounts DISCOUNTS Approx 10% on 1 unmixed case DELIVERY Free in Central London, Thames Valley, Wiltshire, Gloucestershire, East Anglia (up to Norwich) and A1/M1 (up to Rutland/Nottinghamshire) (min 1 case); elsewhere 1 case £3.40, 2 cases £2.40 per case, 3–4 cases 90p per case, 5+ cases free; mail order available GLASS HIRE Free with order TASTINGS AND TALKS Regular in-store tastings in selected shops; for customers by invitation; to groups on request CELLARAGE Can arrange on customers' behalf

Burgundy producers are probably trembling in their shoes in the knowledge that Anthony Hanson, who wrote the definitive, and knowledgeably critical, work on the region, is revising and updating it. It follows, therefore, that this merchant's choice of Burgundies is worth paying particular attention to.

Virtually all the wines are from domaines: in reds, Luc Sorin in Irancy (Bourgogne Irancy 1985, £6.25), Philippe Rossignol, Hubert Lamy, Jean Maréchal, Simon Bize, Jean Grivot, Olivier Leflaive and the superb wines of Jacqueline Jayer. In whites, look for Domaine du Prieuré, Claude Laroche, François Jobard. Chablis is from Jean Durup.

But it's not all Burgundy. The claret range is strong as well, often at extremely good prices. The firm buys from good petit château areas like Canon-Fronsac, Fronsac, Lalande-de-Pomerol, and some excellent value 1983 wines are currently listed (Ch Moulin-Haut-Laroque 1983,

151

Fronsac at £7.25). Vintages go back to 1978. The Sauternes are a
handsome collection.

Elsewhere, you can find Rhône from Jaboulet Aîné and Domaine de
Bel-Air, plus Guigal in Côte Rôtie. Good Alsace from Jean-Pierre
Dirler, and the house Champagne Pierre Vaudon, an unusual Blanc de
Noirs (£9.80), continue to attract admirers. After the wealth from
France, other countries seem to have slowed down a bit, but the lists
from Spain and Italy are well chosen, and some good Australians from
Moss Wood and Petaluma have now appeared. Vintage Ports and
Valdespino Sherries complete this satisfying list.

Best buys

Domaine Burgundies; Champagne Pierre Vaudon, £9.80; Bordeaux
Rouge Pierre Coste, £3.75; Cépage Colombard Vin de Pays de
Gascogne, £2.85

Hedley Wright

The Old Maltings, Sawbridgeworth,   TEL (0279) 723344
Hertfordshire CM21 9JX

OPEN Mon–Fri 9–5 Sat 9.30–5 CLOSED Sun, public holidays
CREDIT CARDS Access, Visa; personal and business accounts
DISCOUNTS Available by arrangement DELIVERY Free within 20-mile radius
of Sawbridgeworth and Central London (min 1 case); otherwise £2 per case; 5+
cases free; mail order available, also for members of the Country Gentlemen's
Association GLASS HIRE Free with 1+ case order
TASTINGS AND TALKS Regular in-store tastings on Saturday mornings; 2 major
tastings annually; to groups on request CELLARAGE £3.39 per case

A traditionally based list that seems slightly ill-at-ease when it leaves
France – and which ignores Italy and the New World completely. But
on home ground, the wines are an attractive range. Plans are afoot to
open a new warehouse in Bishops Stortford to speed up distribution.

Bordeaux is an especially good part of the list. Wines come from
three major names on the Bordeaux scene – Nathaniel Johnston (who
supplies the house claret, £3.40), Peter Sichel and J-P Moueix. A good
range of petit château wines has been assembled, with a number of
wines between £4 and £5. Vintages of claret start with 1985 and go back
to a few wines from 1970.

The Burgundy section specialises in wines from a partnership
between Jean-Louis Fougeray and Bernard Clair-Daü (their Bourgogne
Pinot Noir 1985 is £5.60), with Chablis from Raoul Gautherin.
Beaujolais is from Demurget Lafarge and Geoffray. The Rhône has
wines from Jaboulet Aîné and also Châteauneuf from Domaine
Chambellan (1980 vintage at £8.80), while Alsace wines are provided
by Louis Gisselbrecht. De Castellane supply the Champagne.

The only area outside France to receive much attention is Spain, with Riojas from Campo Viejo and Penedès wines from Torres. Look also for the house Sherries, from Manuel de Argueso.

Best buys

Bulgarian Cabernet Sauvignon, £1.85; Ch Pitray 1984, Côtes de Castillon, £3.50; Mâcon-Lugny 1986, Producta, Charnay £4.25; Réserve Claret (NV), Nathaniel Johnston, £3.40

Charles Hennings

London House, Pulborough,   TEL (079 82) 2485/3909
West Sussex RH20 2BW
10 Jenger's Mead, Billingshurst,   TEL (040 381) 3187
West Sussex RH14 9TB
Golden Square, Petworth, West Sussex GU28 0AP   TEL (0798) 43021
OPEN Mon–Thur, Sat 9–6   Fri 9–7.30   CLOSED Sun, public holidays
CREDIT CARDS Access, Visa; personal and business accounts   DISCOUNTS 5%
for 1 case   DELIVERY Free in West Sussex (min 3 cases); elsewhere at cost
GLASS HIRE Free with corresponding case order
TASTINGS AND TALKS Monthly in-store tastings; annual Christmas tasting;
occasionally to groups on request   CELLARAGE Not available

From a useful rather than exciting list, we would recommend as worth considering the French regional wines, Bordeaux – especially the generic wines from Nathaniel Johnston (Médoc non-vintage at £3.99) – Spain, California and Australia. There's plenty of Champagne, too.

From a well-priced range of wines from the South and South-West of France, look for the Cahors 1983, Domaine de Colombie at £3.95, the delicious Muscat from José Sala at £2.89 and the Côtes de Provence Rosé from Les Maîtres Vignerons de St-Tropez at £4.39.

In Bordeaux, the generic wines are part of short list which moves up the scale to a few classed growths. Prices seem to rise more quickly than the quality of the wines. Elsewhere in France, there are a few Alsace wines from Trimbach and Muré, and Loron Beaujolais. Burgundy itself is dominated by négociant wines.

Spain offers a short section of interest with wines from Faustino and Marqués de Cáceres in Rioja and the Valdepeñas Reserva 1978, Señorio de los Llanos at £3.35, plus a couple of sparkling Cavas.

In the New World, there are Almadén wines from California, and Mildara and Penfolds wines from Australia.

Best buys

Mildara Church Hill Chardonnay 1986, £3.99; Cahors 1983, Domaine de Colombie, £3.95; Médoc (NV), Nathaniel Johnston, £3.99

Hicks & Don

4 The Market Place, Westbury, Wiltshire BA13 3EA TEL (0373) 864 723
Park House, Elmham, Dereham, Norfolk NR20 5AB TEL (0362) 81571

OPEN Mon–Fri 9–5.30 Sat by appointment 9–1 CLOSED Sun, public
holidays CREDIT CARDS None accepted; personal and business accounts
DISCOUNTS £2 off per case for 3+ cases DELIVERY Free on UK mainland (min
1 mixed case) and Northern Ireland (min 5 cases); mail order available
GLASS HIRE Free with 1-case order TASTINGS AND TALKS To groups on
request CELLARAGE £1.60 per case per year

This continues to be one of the strongest lists in the Guide. It's also
extremely well balanced, so that every part of the world gets a fair
share without any one section being top-heavy. A rare and difficult
achievement.

One area, in fact, could be considered an exception to that rule –
French regional wines. Here is a long and thorough list, full of good
value: varietal wines from the Vin de Pays du Jardin de la France
(Chardonnay at £3.25), and Côtes du Marmandais red and white
(£2.93). Cahors from Domaine Eugénie is next door to an excellent
Faugères (Cuvée Collection, £3.58).

Alsace is similarly well treated – lots of 1985 wines (plus some 1983s)
from a number of producers. Burgundy has expanded, while the Loire
provides some treats – especially a still white Saumur Ch de Villeneuve
(£6.03) which should keep for years, and a good Bourgueil. In
Bordeaux, the main list contains a good number of petit château wines
from recent vintages, plus the promise of classed growths for laying
down. The Rhône is full of exciting bottles: look for Guigal's Côtes du
Rhône 1983 (£5) and the Vacqueyras 1984, Domaine la Garrigue (£4.84).

Although the Italian sector has been trimmed a little, you could still
go for the Vinattieri Bianco 1985 at £4.50 if you can't afford Chablis.
Spain brings wines from the Penedès by Cavas Hill (Blanc Cru 1985 at
£3.72), Jean León and Torres, plus Olarra Rioja.

Via Greek wines (Calliga and Ch Carras) and wines from Portugal
and Chile, you arrive in a roundabout way at Australia. Plenty of
interest here, with Mountadam Rhine Riesling and Chardonnay, plus
wines from Tyrrells and Rosemount.

Back home, Hicks & Don – besides making their own Elmham Wine
in Norfolk – have an array of English wines from other East Anglia
estates.

Best buys

Côtes du Marmandais red and white, £2.93; Ch Haut-Peyruguet 1981,
Bordeaux, £3.98; Bourgogne Clos de la Fortune 1983, £4.97; Vinattieri
Bianco 1985, £4.50; varietal Vins de Pays du Jardin de la France

High Breck Vintners   🐷

High Breck, Spats Lane, Headley, Nr Bordon,   TEL (0428) 713689
Hampshire GU35 8SY
ASSOCIATED OUTLETS
Nalders Wine Agency, Reading, Berkshire   TEL (0734) 332312
Harbottle Wines, London SW6   TEL 01-731 1972
Beeston Hall Cellars, Wroxham, Norfolk   TEL (0692) 630771
Col. G P Peese, Pangbourne, Berkshire   TEL (07357) 2624
J Dudley, Rudgwick, West Sussex   TEL (9672) 2357
A G Barnett, Sussex   TEL (0902) 32629

OPEN Mon–Fri 9.30–6   Sat 9.30–12.30   Sun and public holidays by
arrangement only   CLOSED Chr Day   CREDIT CARDS None accepted;
personal and business accounts   DISCOUNTS 2½% for 10 cases or £600 per
year, 3¾% for 20 cases or £1,200 per year, 5% for £2,000+ per year; larger orders
negotiable   DELIVERY Free to UK mainland and Isle of Wight (min 3 cases
except within 10-mile radius); elsewhere £4.60 per case, £2.30 on each of 2 cases;
mail order available   GLASS HIRE Free with 4+ case order; delivery available
TASTINGS AND TALKS Approx 6 in-store tastings per year; also on request
CELLARAGE Not available   ■

Did you know that steeping hot peppers in white Port for a few weeks
produces a 'marvellous additive to meaty soups'? We didn't, but Tom
Johnson's chatty list tells us in connection with Taylor's white Port,
Chip Dry (£6.17). The list's also sensibly organised into styles – dry
white, sweet wine, etc – with the regions of secondary importance.

Among Mr Johnson's dry whites, we would happily start – as he has
done – with almacenista Sherries, plus Lustau's standard range, and
the excellent La Guita Manzanilla (£4.98). Sparkling wines include a
good non-vintage Champagne from Lamiable Frères at £9.20, and Nick
Ryman's Blanc de Blancs from Ch la Jaubertie (£5.85) (Mr Ryman's still
Bergerac wines are also featured). Other interesting finds are the
splendid Alsace wines of Wiederhirn, a small grower who is Mayor of
Riquewihr (his wines have a remarkable ageing ability), and a range of
single vineyard Sancerres and Pouilly Fumés from Gitton Père et Fils.
Sweet white wines include more treats from the Loire – this time from
Coteaux du Layon and Bonnezeaux.

In reds, things get serious, with a well-balanced list of clarets (petit
château wines as well as classed growths) from 1981 onwards. There
are a few négociant Burgundies, and Beaujolais from the Eventail
Producteurs de Corcelles, a co-operative of producers, whose wines
are bottled individually. A few wines from the South, South-West and
the Rhône complete a good value list.

Best buys

Champagne (NV), Lamiable Frères, £9.20; St-Chinian, Rouanet, £2.64;
Bourgueil 1985, Domaine des Raguenières, £4.60; Coteaux du Layon
Chaume 1985, Jean-Paul Tijou, £4.12; Alsace wines from Wiederhirn

Hilbre Wine Company

Gibraltar Row, Pier Head, Liverpool L3 7HJ   TEL 051-236 8800

OPEN Mon–Fri 8.30–5.30   Sat 9.30–12.30   CLOSED Sun, public holidays
CREDIT CARDS None accepted; personal and business accounts
DISCOUNTS Available   DELIVERY Free in Cumbria, Cheshire, Greater
Manchester, Lancashire, Merseyside, North Wales (min 1 case); elsewhere at
National Carrier rates; mail order available   GLASS HIRE Free
TASTINGS AND TALKS Annual 2-day tasting; wines available for tasting in the
warehouse from time to time   CELLARAGE By arrangement with the Liverpool
Warehousing Co

This sensible and traditional list covers French ground well and is
beginning to offer a few nuggets elsewhere.

Bordeaux and Burgundy are the best sections, Bordeaux being well
represented by petit château clarets, especially from the 1983 and 1981
vintages: Ch la Barde 1983, Côtes de Bourg, £4.28; Ch les Tours de
Bayard 1981, Montagne St-Emilion, £4.13; Ch la Clare 1980, Médoc,
£4.59. Pricier classed growth claret is there as well.

In Burgundy, improvements since last year include more domaine
wines – from Christine Ponsot, Ch de Meursault, Armand Rousseau,
with Chablis from Henri Laroche. Négociant wines are mainly from
Patriarche. Champagne is wide-ranging and good, but the Loire is
dull. Alsace is short (good wines from Dopff et Irion, though), and the
French regions might as well not exist.

Things look up again in Germany, with Rheingau wines from
Schloss Vollrads and Schloss Johannisberg. Campo Viejo and Marqués
de Murrieta supply good Rioja (white 1982 at £5.04 is a star). Italy
seems to have got caught in the days of party bottles. Australia has
come along strongly with Lindemans, matches in California by the fine
Clos du Bois Merlot 1985 (£4.95).

Best buys

Cabernet Sauvignon 1984, Lindemans, £3.90; Campo Viejo Tinto 1982,
Rioja, £2.86; wines from Schloss Johannisberg; Bourgogne Rouge 1983,
Domaine Boisset Deschamps, £4.72; petit château clarets

George Hill of Loughborough   🐷

The Wine Shop, 59 Wards End, Loughborough,   TEL (0509) 212717
Leicestershire LE11 3HB

OPEN Mon–Sat 9–6   CLOSED Sun, public holidays   CREDIT CARDS All
accepted; personal and business accounts   DISCOUNTS 10% for 1 case
DELIVERY Free within 50-mile radius (min 2 cases); mail order available
GLASS HIRE Free with case order   TASTINGS AND TALKS Occasional in-store
tastings; regular tastings at other venues; to groups on request
CELLARAGE £1.50–£1.75 per case per year

Here is a merchant who is strong on France and Germany, but who is obviously paying much more attention to what is happening elsewhere in the vinous world.

For instance, an excellent range of Riojas has been assembled – Siglo Saco (forget about the silly sacking around the bottle, the wine is good), Domecq Domain, CVNE, Marqués de Murrieta, Bilbainas, with Torres wines and Navarra wines to complement them. Italy, too, is looking good, and we're delighted to see that producers' names are now included in the list. New Zealand, Australia and California are all present, if limited.

The Bordeaux choice is sensibly short and well chosen – and as last year, there are some petit château bargains to be had (Ch Bel-Air 1985, Bordeaux, £3.40; Ch Haut-Peyroguet 1982, Bordeaux, £4). Beaujolais and Burgundy – mainly from négociants – are less interesting, but the Loire has a couple of stars (Coulée de Serrant 1982, Ch de la Roche aux Moines at £10.20, a bargain even at that price). Gabriel Meffre is the originator of some good Rhône wines. The selection of French country wines includes the Domaines des Terres Blanches in Coteaux des Baux en Provence (red 1984 is £4.99), the unusual white Pacherenc du Vic Bilh from the South-West and Listel Gris de Gris rosé.

The German list remains sound, with plenty of wines from 1983 and 1985 – and a 1976 Trockenbeerenauslese and a 1971 Beerenauslese at what are still good prices. Sherries include wines from Lustau and Valdespino, next to Madeiras from Blandys and Rutherford and Miles.

Best buys

German estate wines; Côtes du Rhône 1984, Ch de Ruth, £3.97; Spanish sparkling Cava; Chianti Classico 1983, Machiavelli, £3.35; Barossa Valley red and white, £2.89

J E Hogg

61 Cumberland Street, Edinburgh EH9 6RA TEL 031-556 4025
The Delicatessen, 71 The High Street, North Berwick, TEL (0620) 2854
East Lothian EH39 5DS
The Wholefood Shop, 28 Henderson Street, TEL (0786) 833903
Bridge of Allan, Central FK9 4HP

OPEN Mon, Tue, Thur, Fri 9–1, 2.30–6 Wed, Sat 9–1 CLOSED Sun, local holidays CREDIT CARDS None accepted DISCOUNTS Not available DELIVERY Free in Edinburgh (min 6 bottles); otherwise 50p for under 6 bottles in Edinburgh; elsewhere in UK £3.60 per case; mail order available GLASS HIRE Free with appropriate order TASTINGS AND TALKS Occasional tastings for customers; to groups on request CELLARAGE Not available

If you disagree with us, please tell us why. You will find report forms at the back of the book.

James Hogg has been out empire-building in the past year. Understandably, his list has attracted attention from Scots who don't live in Edinburgh, so to help them out, he has appointed agents to handle a limited selection of his wines. The first two – the Delicatessen in North Berwick and Clive Ramsay in Bridge of Allan – are operating and more may follow. Prices are not quite as competitive as Mr Hogg's own, but the wines are just as good.

The multi-coloured list is divided up by wine style. Under dry white wines (on white paper, naturally), we find an enormous range of Alsace wines from a number of top producers, alongside the amazing value of the Settesoli Bianco from Sicily at £1.89 (the red is the same price). The Loire pitches in with the sweet Quarts de Chaume of Jean Baumard (1982 vintage at £7.90) and Pouilly Fumé and Sancerre from some big names. Big names abound in Burgundy, too, especially in reds (on red paper) where growers' wines include Marquis d'Angerville, Armand Rousseau and Dominique Guyon.

Clarets go back to 1971, and in vintages like 1982 and 1983 there's plenty to choose from. Prices remain good (Ch Ramage la Batisse 1983 at £5.83; Ch la Tour St-Bonnet 1983 at £5.22; Ch Lestage 1981 at £4.73). The Rhône is full of Jaboulet Aîné wines.

With Italy, a range of serious wines impresses, especially from Piedmont with Barolos and Barbarescos. In Tuscany, some top Chiantis, super vini da tavola and Brunello di Montalcino can all be bought. There's a small but well-chosen Rioja collection – and don't forget the big range of Sherries. Germany is full of estate wines.

Australia comes up with wines from Penfolds, Sefton's Idyll Vineyard, Pewsey Vale and many others (Krondorf Cabernet/Shiraz 1979 at £4.92). California offers Firestone and Mondavi.

Best buys

Rioja Gran Reserva 1976, Domecq Domain, £4.63; Hautes Côtes de Beaune 1985, Ch Mandelot, £4.90; Penfolds Dalwood Cabernet/Shiraz 1983, £3.51; Alsace wines; Settesoli Bianco and Rosso, £1.89; Chianti Ruffino 1985, £2.86; Rubesco Torgiano 1980, Lungarotti, £4.73

Hopton Wines

Hopton Court, Cleobury Mortimer, Kidderminster,   TEL (0299) 270482
Hereford & Worcester DY14 0HH

OPEN Mon–Fri 9–1, 2–5.30   CLOSED Sat, Sun, public holidays
CREDIT CARDS None accepted; personal and business accounts
DISCOUNTS Available   DELIVERY Free within 35-mile radius of Cleobury
Mortimer (min 1 case); elsewhere £7.50 for 1 case, £6.50 for 2 cases, 3+ cases free;
mail order available   GLASS HIRE Free with 1-case order
TASTINGS AND TALKS Approx 10 in-store tastings per year; to groups on
request   CELLARAGE Available (charges negotiable)   ∎

An attractive, well-balanced list in which every wine is there for a purpose rather than as mere padding.

So you don't get a long list of clarets – just a few from recent vintages (the oldest is 1978), which run the gamut from petit château to first growth. Burgundy, too, is short, but with a good balance of domaine and négociant wines.

Rhône wines include the Côtes du Rhône 1982, Domaine des Aussellons (£3.35) and the Châteauneuf 1983, Bosquet des Papes (£7.72). A few good value wines from the Midi are present (Corbières 1982, Domaine du Bosc, £3.17), and sweet Anjou from Moulin Touchais. From much further afield is a good selection of New Zealand wines from Cooks. For something completely different, try a French honey wine, Hydromel du Pays d'Oc (£8).

Best buys

Coteaux du Tricastin 1982, Domaine de Serre Rouge, £3.22; Coteaux du Languedoc, La Clape, Ch de Marmorières 1983 red, £3; Cooks Dry Red and Dry White, £3.14

House of Townend

101 York Street, Hull, Humberside HU2 0QX   TEL (0482) 26891
16 branches (House of Townend, Townend Wine Centre, Willerby Wine Market) in Humberside and Yorkshire

OPEN Mon–Sat 10–10 (retail) Mon–Fri 9–5.30 (cash & carry) Sun 12–2, 7–10 (retail) public holidays 10–10 (retail) CLOSED Sun, public holidays (cash & carry) CREDIT CARDS Access, Visa; personal and business accounts DISCOUNTS 10% on 1 case DELIVERY Free to Humberside, Lincolnshire and part of North Yorkshire; elsewhere £2.88 per case; mail order available GLASS HIRE Available TASTINGS AND TALKS Weekly tastings in retail outlets; large annual tasting; to groups on request CELLARAGE £3 per case per year (inc insurance)

Retail shops stocking a selection from the main list of J Townend & Sons (*qv*).

Ian G Howe

35 Appleton Gate, Newark,   TEL (0636) 704366
Nottinghamshire NG24 1JR

OPEN Mon–Sat 9.30–7 Good Friday 12 noon–2, 7–9 CLOSED Sun, public holidays CREDIT CARDS Access, Visa; personal and business accounts DISCOUNTS 2½% for 1 case (may be mixed), 3½% for 3 cases DELIVERY Free for 1 case locally and for 2+ cases within 20-mile radius; elsewhere by arrangement GLASS HIRE Free with 1-case order TASTINGS AND TALKS Single wine in-store tasting; to groups on request CELLARAGE By arrangement (space limited)

The South of France obviously holds attractions for this wine merchant, quite apart from the sunshine. Expanding a good range of wines from the South-West, the Midi, Provence and the Rhône means that old favourites like the Mas Chichet Vin de Pays Catalan (try the Cuvée Spéciale made from Cabernet Sauvignon at £4.25), have been joined by Minervois from Ch de Pouzols, Collioure Domaine du Mas Blanc 1983, and a Gaillac 1984 from Ch Laroze. In the Rhône, too, we find the good value, fruity Côtes du Rhône 1985, Grand Moulas at £3.35 and wines from Pascal and Jaboulet Aîné, as well as rarities like a white St-Péray 1980 from Bernard Gripa at £5.95.

The Loire has good representation, as well. The range covers the river from the Gamay of Côtes Roannaises to Sancerre, down to the sea with Muscadet, with some good Vouvrays from Brion, and some attractive reds from Bourgueil, Chinon and Saumur Champigny on the way.

From other regions, Alsace wines all come from Hugel (and are therefore quite pricey). There are a good number of German estate wines, and house Champagne is from Canard-Duchêne at £9.99.

Best buys

Mas Chichet Vin de Pays Catalan 1982, £2.99; Coteaux du Tricastin 1983, St-Rémy, £2.95; Côtes du Rhône 1985, Domaine de la Renéjeanne, £3.65; St-Pourçain-sur-Sioule 1985, Ray, £3.45

Victor Hugo Wines

HEAD OFFICE Tregear House, Longueville, St Saviour, Jersey	TEL	(0534) 78173
3 Stopford Road, St Helier, Jersey	TEL	(0534) 23421
8B Quennevais Precinct, St Brelade, Jersey	TEL	(0534) 44519
Bath Street Wine Cellar, 15 Bath Street, St Helier, Jersey	TEL	(0534) 20237

OPEN Mon–Sat 9–5.30   CLOSED Sun, public holidays   CREDIT CARDS None accepted; personal and business accounts   DISCOUNTS 5% for 1 case DELIVERY Free on Jersey (min 1 case)   GLASS HIRE Free with 2-case order TASTINGS AND TALKS New products offered in-store; to groups on request CELLARAGE Free

Apart from splashes of interest in the Loire, in Alsace and in Italy, this list is really for claret and Burgundy drinkers. They'll do very well in this group of shops on Jersey because, when comparing prices with those on the mainland don't forget that there's no VAT and lower duty in the Channel Islands.

The Bordeaux section of the list is comprehensive. Vintages go back to 1961, but the biggest concentration is in the years between 1983 and 1978, with a good sub-stratum of petit château wines to prop up the fine collection of classed and bourgeois growths. There are good half-bottles, too.

Burgundy can't quite compete with that, but once out of the run of négociant wines you stumble across some interesting domaine wines – from Raoul Clerget, for example, and from Jean Durup in Chablis. Reds fare better than whites.

Elsewhere in France there's a good clutch of Muscadets (the Marquis de Goulaine 1985 at £2.73) and Dopff et Irion Alsace wines. In Italy, look for the Veneto wines from Santi (Valpolicella Castello d'Illasi 1984, £2.56) and Bigi's Vino Nobile di Montepulciano 1980 at £3.09, among the short, well-chosen Tuscan range.

Best buys

Alsace wines; Navarra red, Gran Feudo Julián Chivite 1983, £1.45; Estremadura Portuguese red 1981, J Serra, £1.71; Veneto wines from Santi

Hungerford Wine Company 📧 ☞

128 High Street, Hungerford, Berkshire RG17 0DL   TEL (0488) 83238
SHOP 1 The Courtyard, 24 High Street,   (same for both addresses)
Hungerford, Berkshire RG17 0NF

OPEN Mon–Fri 9–1, 2–5.30   Sat 9.30–1, 2–5   CLOSED Sun, public holidays
CREDIT CARDS Access, Amex, Diners, Visa; personal and and business
accounts   DISCOUNTS Approx 5% on whole cases; special rates negotiable for
large quantities   DELIVERY Free within 15-mile radius (min 1 case) and
nationally (min 4 cases); £5 charge for national deliveries; mail order available
GLASS HIRE Free with 1-case order   TASTINGS AND TALKS Wines always
available in-store; annual tasting for mailing list; to groups on request
CELLARAGE £3.45 per case per year (including insurance)

Expansion is in the air at this merchant. A new shop has been opened, with, it is promised, better parking, and a new wine bar (see WINE BARS section). And there continues to be a stream of mailings from the pen of managing director Nicholas Davies, most of which must keep his customers very well informed.

The strengths of the Hungerford list lie in Bordeaux. Wines from other regions of France – notably Burgundy – and even wines from other countries are acknowledged, but Bordeaux provides the greatest interest and variety.

Hungerford offers what it calls a Prior Commitment scheme for buying claret en primeur – you offer to buy wine at an estimated price, so that Hungerford buyers can go to France armed with firm orders and, it is hoped, get en primeur wines at the best possible price. On the whole, the scheme works, and it also means that the buyers are prepared to buy for their own stocks. So now they hold plenty of good 1985 ex-cellars at very good prices, and can also supply a good range of classed growth wines from previous vintages. Occasional special offers produce an Aladdin's Cave of old vintages.

Burgundy is not neglected in all this, with domaine wines from a wide range of the great and the good. Wines from Jaboulet Aîné (and occasional opening offers of young vintages of these wines) speak for the Rhône; Louis Gisselbrecht for Alsace, and Geoff Merrill for Australia. CVNE Riojas and Torres represent Spain. And, for after the meal, Hungerford have assembled some agreeable vintage Ports and Sauternes.

Best buys

En primeur clarets; Côtes de Duras red, white and rosé, Domaine de Laulan, £3.99; House Claret 1985, Gallaire et Fils, £3.45; Hungerford House Champagne, £8.95; Camarate 1980 red, J M da Fonseca, £3.04

G Hush   🐷

235 Morningside Road, Edinburgh EH10 4QT   TEL 031-447 4539

OPEN Mon–Thur 10–1, 2.30–7.30   Fri 10–1, 2.30–9.30   Sat 9 am–9.30 pm
CLOSED Sun, public holidays   CREDIT CARDS None accepted; business accounts   DISCOUNTS 5% for 1 case (unmixed)   DELIVERY Free within 2-mile radius (with reasonable order)   GLASS HIRE Free with reasonable case order
TASTINGS AND TALKS To groups on request   CELLARAGE Not available

---

We've found Texan wine in this country at last – and Mr Macleod at G Hush is one of the first to bring it to us. So if you've been looking for Ivanhoe Red (£4.75) or Sanchez Creek Merlot (£6.89) and Chambourcin (£5.89) or the white Llano Fumé Blanc 1985 (£7.79), they're all here.

There's much, much more besides. This is one of those Edinburgh treasure troves (see also WHO'S WHERE at the beginning of this section). We start with French regional wines, all at very good prices: look for the Vin de Pays des Côtes de Gascogne, Domaine du Tariquet at £2.62; or the Côtes de Buzet Cuvée Napoléon 1983 at £3.49; or the Vin de Pays de l'Aude of Sichel at £1.95.

Classic areas of France do pretty well, too. In Bordeaux, the emphasis is sensibly on petit château wines, while in Champagne they have Palmer at £9.79. The short Burgundy list has some good value generic wines from the co-operative at Buxy (Bourgogne Passe-tout-grain 1985 is £3.99). Chablis is supplied by Michel Remon, and Alsace from the co-operative of Turckheim.

The Rhône fares less well, but Italy is another strong area, showing off Chianti from Rocca delle Macìe (1985 at £3.15), and the excellent single vineyard Soave Monteleone from Boscaini at £2.89. Look also for the Rosso Cònero San Lorenzo 1981 at £3.65 and the Alto Adige Chardonnay di Appiano 1985 at £3.19. In Spain, Torres is the star, jostled by Cousiño Macul wines from Chile and Ch Musar 1979 (£4.59) from Lebanon. Germany is less interesting, but Bulgaria offers good value. New Zealand weighs in with Cooks wines and Australia with Rosemount, Renmano and Berri Estates. Which brings us back to Texas . . .

Best buys

Gran Sangredetoro 1981, Torres, £3.45; Ch Grand Mazerolles 1983, Côtes de Bourg, £3.75; Soave Classico 1985 Monteleone, Boscaini, £2.89; Sauvignon du Haut-Poitou 1986, £3.25; Ch de Brèze 1983, Coteaux de Saumur, £2.79

Ilkley Wine Cellars

52 The Grove, Ilkley, West Yorkshire LS29 9BN   TEL (0943) 607313
OPEN Mon–Fri 10–8 Sat 9.30–7.30 CLOSED Sun, public holidays
CREDIT CARDS All accepted DISCOUNTS 5% for 1 case DELIVERY Free on
UK mainland (min 4+ cases); otherwise at cost GLASS HIRE Free with order
TASTINGS AND TALKS Occasional tastings CELLARAGE Available

While the main emphasis of this list still veers towards France, we can also find much to recommend from Italy, and a growing range from Australia. Starting with France, the clarets cover vintages back to 1970, mainly crus bourgeois and classed growths, although 1983 has more choice at the less expensive end. In Burgundy, Chablis from Remon and Beaujolais from Sylvain Fessy are worth looking out for, plus domaine wines from Tollot-Beaut. The Rhône has good Côtes du Rhône from the co-operative of Rasteau, while the Loire presents the top quality Vouvrays of Gaston Huet and the Chinon of Raffault. Alsace comes from the co-operatives of Turckheim.

Sadly, the one Moroccan wine from last year has disappeared, but wines from the northern Mediterranean shores are to the fore with the increased Italian range – Tedeschi and Boscaini wines from the Veneto, the attractive Asti Spumante from Calamandrana and Barolo from Borgogno. Chiantis are from Pagliarese, and Ilkley Wine Cellars have hit on the only decent Frascati on the market, from Villa Catone.

Their New World section has increased, with wines from Montrose and Peter Lehmann joining those from Rosemount. And, from California, wines from Prestons Vineyard now get a showing.

Best buys

Côtes du Rhône-Villages, Rasteau 1983, £4.10; Alsace Pinot Blanc 1986, Cave Tradition, £3.73; Chianti Classico Pigiatello 1985, Pagliarese, £4.35

Ingletons Wines

Station Road, Maldon, Essex CM9 7LF   TEL (0621) 52431
OPEN (Cash & carry) Mon–Fri 9–5 Sat 9–4.30; (Warehouse) Mon–Fri 8–4;
(Offices) Mon–Fri 8–5 CLOSED Sat (Warehouse and offices), Sun, public
holidays CREDIT CARDS None accepted; personal and business accounts
DISCOUNTS Not available DELIVERY Free within 150-mile radius of Maldon
(min 5 cases); elsewhere charges on request GLASS HIRE Available
TASTINGS AND TALKS To groups on request CELLARAGE Not available

Ingletons have built up one of the most extensive Burgundy lists in this Guide. Wines at good (never cheap with Burgundy) prices from lesser-known communes join top wines from the best places, and with only a few exceptions, all the wines are domaine-bottled.

In whites, there is Chablis from René Defert and Pierre Rétif. White Burgundy proper is from a whole range of producers: look especially for the Meursaults of René Monnier, the Chassagne-Montrachets of Jacques and Marc Colin, and the Puligny-Montrachets of Etienne Sauzet. Lesser-known communes include Ladoix, Rully and St-Romain.

For reds, Gevrey-Chambertin from Louis Trapet, Nuits-St-Georges from a number of producers, Beaune from René Monnier and wines from Daniel Senard in Corton join forces with less expensive wines from Santenay, Savigny-lès-Beaune and the Hautes Côtes.

As second fiddles are Rhône wines (Côtes du Rhône from the co-operative of the Enclave des Papes), Loire wines (Pouilly Fumé from J C Dagueneau) and a small selection of claret. Alsace wines are produced by the co-operative of Hunawihr; the house Champagne brand is Pol d'Ambert. You could hardly miss the big range of half-bottles.

Best buys

Domaine-bottled Burgundy

Irvine Robertson Wines

10/11 North Leith Sands, Leith,	TEL 031-553 3521

Edinburgh EH6 4ER

ASSOCIATED OUTLET

Graham MacHarg Fine Wines, Fowberry Tower,	TEL (06685) 274

Wooler, Northumberland NE71 6ER

OPEN Mon–Fri 9–5 CLOSED Sat, Sun, Chr and New Year holidays
CREDIT CARDS None accepted; personal and business accounts
DISCOUNTS Case allowances (min 5 cases) DELIVERY Free locally (min 1 case);
elsewhere 1–2 cases £4.03 per consignment, 3+ cases free GLASS HIRE Free
with order TASTINGS AND TALKS Annual tasting (Nov/Dec); to groups on
request CELLARAGE Not available ■

There aren't many wine merchants where you can buy a lusciously
sweet Rumanian wine – but this is one. They recommend the
Pietroasele-Tamiioasa (that's the name of the grape) Romanneasca
1979, which comes in half-bottles at £2.35.

That rarity stands out in a list which is otherwise a good all-round
selection with sensible buying (mainly in France) rather than great
excitements. We admire the well-priced range of clarets (Ch la Gravette
1982 at £3.84 – prices do not include VAT on the list, so we've added
them here – or Ch Pitray 1981 Côtes de Castillon at £3.85). A few wines
from older vintages are available.

Irvine Robertson hold a good number of domaine-bottled
Burgundies (Luc Sorin, Michel Voarick, Clerget, Jacques Prieur, Duc
de Magenta); look also for the Chablis of William Fèvre. Things tail off
along the Rhône (apart from the Côtes du Rhône, Domaine Bel-Air
1984 at £3.64). On the Loire, you could have white and red Sancerre
from Thierry Merlin, and in Alsace wines from the merchant house of
Heim. Then come a few French regional wines from the Midi and
Bergerac. Champagne is by Billecart-Salmon.

Although there's little to report about the rest of Europe (apart from
the Rumanian special), things come to life again in Australia, with a big
range of wines from Penfold's, and in California, where we find the
top wines of Stag's Leap Wine Cellars (and their second wine, Hawks
Crest). Ports are from Churchill Graham and Delaforce, Sherries from
Delgado Zuleta.

Best buys

Champagne J Arnaud Brut, £8.61; Cooks New Zealand wines; Vinho
Verde Casalinho, £2.77; Rioja La Rioja Alta 1980, Viña Alberdi, £3.79;
Gamay Vin de Pays de l'Ardèche 1982, £2.79

Which? Wine Guide does not accept payment for inclusion, and there is no
sponsorship or advertising.

Italian Wine Centre

70 Albion Drive, London E8 4LX   TEL 01-429 9744

OPEN Mail order only   CREDIT CARDS None accepted   DISCOUNTS 5% for 4
cases   DELIVERY Free in UK mainland (min 1 case)   GLASS HIRE Free with
4-case order (London only)   TASTINGS AND TALKS Approximately 4 tastings
annually to customers on mailing list   CELLARAGE Not available   ■

This mail order list brings together a big range of many of the top
names in Italian wines from right round the country. Be warned: prices
are much cheaper elsewhere.

From Piedmont, we find – among others – the Barolo 1978 of Le Due
Torri (£6.90) and the Barbera d'Alba 1985 of Conterno (£6.90).
Lombardy provides the Oltrepò Pavese wines of the Fugazza sisters. In
the Alto Adige, Tiefenbrunner wines stand out, while Masi is the one
big name from the Veneto (the Valpolicella Serego Alighieri 1983 is
£5.47) alongside Boscaini and the wines from Venegazzù.

Further south, Chiantis are from Villa di Vetrice (£3.50) and Ruffino,
but Carmignano from Villa di Capezzana, and Brunello from
Castelgiocondo should not be forgotten, nor in whites, the Pomino of
Frescobaldi (£4.77). In the Mezzogiorno, Sicily comes up with Regaleali
and Corvo wines, plus Mastroberardino's impenetrable Taurasi and
his more accessible white Greco di Tufo and Aglianico del Vulture from
d'Angelo Basilicata (1981 Riserva at £7.39).

All the wines are available as single bottles in a mixed tasting case.

Best buys

Chianti Rufina 1983, Villa di Vetrice, £3.50; Galestro 1985, Antinori,
£3.52; Chardonnay Venegazzù, £3.40; Bonarda Oltrepò Pavese 1985,
Castello di Luzzano, £4.30

Jeroboams

24 Bute Street, London SW7 3EX   TEL 01-225 2232

OPEN Mon–Fri 9–7   Sat 9–6   CLOSED Sun, public holidays
CREDIT CARDS Access, Visa; personal and business accounts   DISCOUNTS 5%
for 1 case   DELIVERY Free in South-West London and the City (min 1 case);
elsewhere charges negotiable; mail order available   GLASS HIRE Free with
1-case order   TASTINGS AND TALKS Monthly in-store tastings; to groups on
request   CELLARAGE Negotiable

Jeroboams would feature in a *Which? Cheese Guide* as one of the best
collections in London but the wine list is expanding, too, sticking
pretty firmly to France (apart from a few Ports to go with the blue
cheeses) and principally reds. And, of course, there are a few
Jeroboams (and plenty of half-bottles).

House wines are the red Côtes du Ventoux and the white Côtes du
Luberon from La Vieille Ferme (both £3.45). House Champagne is from

de Horsey at £9.99. Vintages of claret go back to 1945 (Ch Sénéjac at £46.95), but more realistically, there's a good clutch of very drinkable 1980s and some petit château wines from more recent vintages. Elsewhere in France, look for the Châteauneuf of Ch de Beaucastel, and a couple of Sauternes – also good with blue cheeses when they're soft and French.

Best buys

Côtes du Ventoux and Côtes du Luberon 1985, La Vieille Ferme, £3.45; Ch Cana 1982, Côtes de Bourg, £4.95

S H Jones

27 High Street, Banbury, Oxfordshire OX16 8EW   TEL (0295) 51178
WHOLESALE WAREHOUSE/CASH & CARRY
Unit 1, Tramway Road Industrial Estate,   TEL (0295) 51177
Banbury, Oxfordshire OX16 8TD

OPEN (High Street) Mon, Tue 8.30–1, 2–5.30   Wed–Fri 8.30–5.30   Sat 9–1 (Dec all day)   CLOSED Sun, public holidays   CREDIT CARDS Access, Visa; personal and business accounts   DISCOUNTS 5% on 1 mixed case, 7½% on 10+ cases, 10% on 20+ cases   GLASS HIRE Free in Banbury and district and along main wholesale delivery routes (min 2 cases); elsewhere at cost; mail order limited but on request   GLASS HIRE Free with wine order
TASTINGS AND TALKS Continuous in-store tasting; annual tasting in Nov; 2–3 annual wholesale tastings; to groups on request   CELLARAGE £2.90 per case per year

Here we have a good all-round list with plenty in most areas of France, some good estate wines from Germany, and an increased interest in Italy.

Bordeaux seems to be one of the strongest areas in France. Clarets go from 1983 back to 1970, with an especially good selection of half-bottles in both petits châteaux and classed growths. In sweet white Bordeaux, look for the vintages of Ch Rieussec.

The Rhône section is equally strong: northern Rhône wines from Guigal and Ozier in Côte Rôtie and Jaboulet Aîné elsewhere, and a strong showing of Châteauneuf-du-Pape and other southern Rhône wines from Roger Combe (Gigondas L'Oustau Fauquet in various vintages). The Côtes du Rhône's representative is the Ch du Grand Moulas (1986 vintage at £3.55).

Burgundy is dominated happily by growers' wines, with plenty of good names to choose from. There are Beaujolais from Paul Bocuse (a sous-marque of Georges Duboeuf) and a good line in French country wines (the red Domaine de St-Estève, Coteaux Varois is excellent value at £2.16). Also look for the Alsace wines of P Blanck, and the range of Champagnes (including a good few larger bottles).

German estate wines cover the 1981, 1983 and 1985 vintages with some top names prominent. Italy has Barolo from Fontanafredda,

Chianti Rufina from Villa Vetrice, and white Tuscan wines (plus some excellent Vin Santo) from Marchesi de Frescobaldi.

Best buys

Chianti Rufina Villa Vetrice, £3.05; Côtes du Rhône 1986, Ch du Grand Moulas, £3.55; half-bottles of claret; vintages of Châteauneuf-du-Pape, Domaine du Vieux Télégraphe; Coteaux Varois, Domaine de St-Estève, £2.16; Muscat Vin de Liqueur, £2.85

Justerini & Brooks

61 St James's Street, London SW1A 1LZ   TEL 01-493 8721
39 George Street, Edinburgh EH2 2HN   TEL 031-226 4202

OPEN Mon–Fri 9–5.30   CLOSED Sat, Sun, Chr, Easter, public holidays
CREDIT CARDS All accepted; also Grand Metropolitan Shareholders Card and Simpsons (Piccadilly) Signature Card; personal and business accounts
DISCOUNTS 7½% on 24–59 bottles, 10% on 60–95 bottles, 12½% on 96+ bottles   DELIVERY Free in UK mainland (min 5 cases); otherwise 1–6 bottles £3.50 per delivery, 7–59 bottles £2.50 (London postal districts) or £6 (other UK mainland); Northern Ireland and offshore UK £12 per case; details of charges within Scotland may differ; mail order available   GLASS HIRE Free with 1-case order   TASTINGS AND TALKS Tastings for small groups by invitation and to existing customer groups   CELLARAGE £3.50 per case per year (insurance included)

People who think of Justerini & Brooks simply as purveyors of a well-known brand of whisky are missing out on a very good, classic wine list.

Claret and Burgundy are joined by the Rhône as the three great strengths here. There is a good selection of claret from most recent vintages, plus smaller selections back to 1945. For the recent vintages, classed growths and petit château wines offer a useful choice. While fewer Burgundies are in evidence, the range is mainly of domaine bottlings, accompanied by a number of interesting bottles of white Burgundy from the Chassagne-Montrachet holdings of J-N Gagnard and J & F Pillot. In reds, there is perhaps too much reliance on the lesser quality 1984 vintage.

The Rhône – especially the northern Rhône – is very well served. Wines from Guigal in Côte Rôtie and Hermitage are the stars, but Cornas from Guy Barjac should also be considered. In the southern Rhône, Justerini & Brooks have mustered a good number of single vineyard Côtes du Rhône from the Domaine du Vieux Chêne, and Châteauneuf from Ch de Beaucastel.

Alsace wines are by courtesy of Hugel, and there's a good selection of German estate wines. A short list of Italian and Spanish wines, and Californian wines from Wente Brothers, are other bottles worthy of consideration, as are Australian wines from Brown Brothers and the

Rosemount estate. The list ends with an enticing section of vintage Ports (including a few pre-war vintages).

Justerini & Brooks run two Cellar Plan schemes to help you stock your cellar if you find it painful choosing, and they have assembled a number of tasting cases to whet your appetite.

Best buys

Sauvignon Carte Verte 1984, Caves St-Vincent, £3.10; Cabernet Sauvignon Prestige, Chantovent, £3.05; Côtes du Ventoux 1985, Domaine St-Saveur, £3.95; German estate wines

Kershaw's Wine Warehouse

2 Canfield Gardens, London NW6 3BS   TEL 01-328 7317/624 0254

OPEN Mon–Fri 11–9   Sat 10–9 Sun & public holidays 12–2, 7–9
CLOSED 25 & 26 Dec   CREDIT CARDS Access, Visa; personal and business accounts   DISCOUNTS 5% for 1 mixed case, 5+ cases negotiable
DELIVERY Free within 5-mile radius of London NW6 (min 1 case); elsewhere min £5 charge; mail order available   GLASS HIRE Free
TASTINGS AND TALKS In-store tasting every Saturday; to groups on request
CELLARAGE About £3.50 per case per year (via outside warehouses)

Kershaw's don't sport a long list, but their prices continue to be competitive and their wines well chosen.

Bordeaux is the only area to be treated in depth, with a good range of wines in stock from vintages back to a Ch Batailley 1970 (£23.50). 1985 wines are available ex-château, and regular en primeur offers are made. House claret is from Nathaniel Johnston (£3.09).

For everyday drinking, the Listel wines from the South of France are good value, as is the Ch de Fonscolombe Coteaux d'Aix-en-Provence (red and white at £3.25). There's Côtes du Rhône from Guigal and Loron, while Loron and Duboeuf supply the Beaujolais and the co-operative of Eguisheim the Alsace wines. Burgundy remains a dull spot.

A well-balanced selection of wines has been picked from Italy (Alto Adige wines from Lageder, Veneto wines from Masi and Brunello from Villa Banfi). Spain gives us Torres wines, and Rosemount, Jacob's Creek, Hill Smith and de Bortoli make a good showing from Australia. Kershaw's also offer the best Israeli wines from Gamla and Yarden.

Best buys

Jacob's Creek red and white, £3.25; Gran Viña Sol 1985, Torres, £3.25; Listel wines; Pinot d'Alsace 1985, Co-operative of Eguisheim, £3.95

> Cellarage is generally provided at the rates quoted only when the wines have been bought from the merchant concerned.

Kurtz & Chan Wines

1 Duke of York Street, London SW1Y 6JP   TEL 01-930 6981
OPEN Mon–Fri 9.30–8   CLOSED Sat, Sun, public holidays
CREDIT CARDS None accepted; personal and business accounts
DISCOUNTS Not available   DELIVERY Free in London postal area (min 5 cases);
otherwise (Central London) 1–2 cases £6 per delivery, 3–4 cases £3 per case,
(outside London, exc Scotland) 1–4 cases £16 per delivery, 5+ cases £4 per case;
mail order available   GLASS HIRE Free with 5-case order
TASTINGS AND TALKS To groups on request   CELLARAGE £5 per year
(depending on quantity)   ■

Not a new firm, but Brown Brothers Vintners under another name.
They continue, however, to devote themselves to top wines from
Bordeaux, Burgundy, the Rhône, Champagne and vintage Port. Old
vintages – especially of Port and claret – are a speciality, the list
changing constantly as small parcels of wine appear and disappear.

The Burgundy list, while dealing more in recent vintages, has a
plethora of great domaine names, not – sadly – as much as last year,
but still very good. Vintages here currently go back to 1955 in reds,
1969 in whites. Bordeaux vintages – again currently – go back to 1924,
vintage Ports back to 1935. In the Rhône, Kurtz and Chan go mainly for
northern Rhône wines, with Jaboulet Aîné, Chave and Guigal
featuring prominently. Some Châteauneuf-du-Pape comes from Ch de
Beaucastel.

Best buys
Old vintages of Port and claret

Lay & Wheeler

HEAD OFFICE AND WINE SHOP   TEL (0206) 67261
6 Culver Street West, Colchester Essex CO1 1JA
Wine Market, Gosbecks Road, Shrub End,   TEL (0206) 67261
Colchester, Essex CO2 9JT

OPEN (Wine Market) Mon–Sat 8.30–8   (Wine Shop) Mon–Fri 8.30–5.30   Sat
8.30–8   CLOSED Sun, public holidays   CREDIT CARDS Access, Visa; personal
and business accounts   DISCOUNTS Available   DELIVERY Free in Essex and
South Suffolk (min 1 case) and on UK mainland (min 3 cases); elsewhere £3.97
per delivery; mail order available   GLASS HIRE Free with order
TASTINGS AND TALKS Regular in-store tastings and workshops
CELLARAGE £2.90 per case plus insurance; £3 per £1,000 stock

For those who enjoy reading wine lists, this one is a must. Lay &
Wheeler have always prided themselves on the quality of presentation
and information provided in the two mammoths produced each year,
and it shows.

The wines themselves are equally enticing. Few major wine areas of
the world are not covered, and some are covered very well indeed. If

Lay & Wheeler's strengths are in classic areas like Bordeaux, Burgundy and Germany, they also seem to be branching out more and more.

Australia and Italy are two particular new focuses. What is interesting about the Australian section is the way they've searched out small wineries – what the Californians would call boutique wineries – and the majority of the wines from South Australia are not available elsewhere. Brown Brothers are prominent on the Victoria list, while de Bortoli come up with some of their late-harvested botrytised sweet wines.

In Italy, despite the odd bottle from the south (Taurasi and Aglianico del Vulture), the biggest sections are Tuscany (look for Frescobaldi and Antinori wines) and Piedmont, with Barolos from Borgogno and Prunotto.

The German list is one of the best in the country. We can only hope that this spectacular selection is rewarded by sales of the wines. They are mainly estate wines, and top names in all the areas are present and correct. While most wines are from the excellent 1983 and 1981 vintages, one can find occasional older wines – many of which are amazing bargains.

And in France flood more massive listings. Claret vintages go back to 1970, many in magnum for those with a great thirst for these wines. Look also for the special section of Bordeaux second wines (the lesser wines from some of the top châteaux).

Burgundy is approached in the same way: domaine wines in profusion, with occasional négociant wines. For those with smaller budgets, there are separate sections for Mâconnais and Chalonnais white Burgundy. Beaujolais now has some fascinating domaine wines. Lay & Wheeler have newly introduced their own Champagne, proud of its fine bottle age (£9.89).

The list of French country wines criss-crosses the byways very satisfactorily, with concentrations in the South-West (Gaillac, Jurançon, Madiran, Cahors, Bergerac). In the area of fortified wines, you could pick Sherries from the small Sanlúcar bodega of Hidalgo, and a range of vintage Ports back to 1970. And if you can't make up your mind with this plethora of wines, consult the wine buyers' personal selections at the front of the list.

Those who want to avoid the reconstruction of Colchester around Lay & Wheeler's town centre shop should visit the well-laid-out Wine Market on the outskirts, or take advantage of the prompt mail order service.

Best buys

Varietal wines from Haut-Poitou; Ch l'Etoile 1983, Graves red, £5.18; Lay & Wheeler Champagne, £9.89; Cuvée des Jeunes Vignes red vin de table, £4.70; Côtes du Ventoux 1985, Domaine des Anges, £3.30; Spanna del Piemonte 1983, Agostino Brugo, £3.22

Laymont and Shaw

The Old Chapel, Millpool, Truro,   TEL (0872) 70545
Cornwall TR1 1EX

ASSOCIATED OUTLET Real Ale, Wine and   TEL (0872) 72091
Cheese Shop, St Clement Street, Truro, Cornwall TR1 1ER

OPEN Mon–Fri 9–5   Sat (Real Ale Shop only)   CLOSED Sun, public holidays
CREDIT CARDS None accepted; personal and business accounts
DISCOUNTS 3–4 cases £1.50 per case, 5–9 cases £1.75 per case, 10+ cases £2 per
case   DELIVERY Free in UK mainland (min 2 cases); otherwise £3 for 1 case;
mail order available   GLASS HIRE Free   TASTINGS AND TALKS To groups on
request   CELLARAGE £2.30 per case per year   ■

Laymont and Shaw's list continues to be among the very best lists of
Spanish wines in the country, covering areas in greater depth than
other wine merchants and venturing away from the well-trodden
paths of Rioja into some fascinating byways.

This is the firm that brought you the super Valdepeñas Señorio de
los Llanos (the 1978 vintage is £3.36), to which they've added a white
from the same bodega, promising clean, fresh tastes (Armonioso Vino
Joven, £2.75). At the other end of the scale, they are the importers of
the fabled and fabulously expensive Vega Sicilia wines from Ribera del
Duero (Unico 1976 10th year, £22.25).

However, most of their wines reveal the terrific value Spain can still
offer. Wines from La Mancha under the Yuntero brand (red at £2.65)
and from Cariñena (Villalta Tinto Reserva 1980 at £3.47) are not often
found elsewhere. From Navarra come wines from the top firms of
Señorio de Sarria and Julián Chivite (the special red Gran Vino 1981 at
£6.82 is worth snapping up). From Penedès, you can choose from
Torres wines and four different vintages of the Cabernet Sauvignon
from Jean León, plus wines from Masía Bach. There are Cavas here as
well – their house Cava Mestres 1312 (£5.24) is highly praised.

Then to Rioja, with wines from many of the major bodegas: La Rioja
Alta, Lopez Heredia, Muga, Alavesas, CVNE, Murrieta, Beronia, El
Coto, Montecillo and Marqués de Cáceres. A few Gran Reservas are
available at good prices (CVNE Viña Real Gran Reserva 1976 at £5.36).

Sherries and other fortified wines should not be neglected. Look for
Laymont and Shaw's own-label Sherries, plus those of Barbadillo. In
Málaga, Scholtz Hermanos come up with a superb Lagrima 10-year-old
at £5.15.

For those unsure in all this Hispanic wealth, try one of Laymont and
Shaw's tasting cases.

Best buys

Valdepeñas, Armonioso Vino Joven white, £2.75; Señorio de los Llanos
Gran Reserva 1978, £3.36; Laymont and Shaw's Rare Dry Fino, £3.89;
Rioja 1980, Viña Ardanza 6th year, £4.45; La Mancha 1984, Yuntero
Tinto, £2.65

Laytons

20 Midland Road, London NW1 2AD   TEL 01-388 5081
OPEN Mon–Fri 9–6   Sat 9–4   CLOSED Sun, public holidays
CREDIT CARDS None accepted; personal and business accounts
DISCOUNTS Negotiable   DELIVERY Free in UK mainland (min 3 cases);
elsewhere at cost; mail order available   GLASS HIRE Free with 5-case order
TASTINGS AND TALKS Regular informal tastings; monthly organised tastings;
talks and tastings to existing clients   CELLARAGE Sliding scale depending on
quantity: £2.88 per case on 20+ cases   ■

Laytons would be fully justified if they described themselves as
Burgundy specialists. Even the pretty wide range of clarets and the
growing number of Rhônes and Loires pale beside the Burgundies.

Growers' names abound (there's even a full page of photographs of
them), and Marcel Amance and Joseph Drouhin are the two main
négociants represented. The 1983 and 1985 vintages are there in force,
and a few 1986 whites are creeping in as well. Nothing is cheap here,
but that's not the purpose of a list like this.

Claret vintages stretch back to 1975, but occasionally older wines
crop up. The younger wines are from the better vintages: 1985, 1983,
1982, 1981, and in quality terms cross the board from petit château to
first growth.

On the Rhône, there's Châteauneuf from Domaine de Mont-Redon
and from Ch de Beaucastel, plus Côte Rôtie from Guigal and Delas. On
the Loire, Sancerre is from Jean Delaporte, and Pouilly Fumé from Ch
de Tracy. Zind-Humbrecht is behind the Alsace wines, and another
nice pocket on the list is a small selection of vintage Ports back to 1950.
Visitors to the shop in Midland Road will find it has been newly
re-designed. Mail order customers will continue to receive regular
tempting mailings and offers.

Best buys
Domaine-bottled Burgundy; Jolly Good Claret (NV), £2.68; Chardonnay
Vin de Pays du Jardin de la France 1984, Domaine des Hauts Sanziers,
£3.07; Côtes du Rhône Cairanne 1985, Domaine de l'Ameillaud, £3.99

Lockes

5 Jewry Street, Winchester,   TEL (0962) 60006
Hampshire SO23 8RZ

OPEN Mon–Sat 9–5.30   CLOSED Sun, public holidays
CREDIT CARDS Access, Amex, Diners, Visa; personal and business accounts
DISCOUNTS 5% on 1 case; larger discounts negotiable on larger quantities
DELIVERY Free in Winchester and district (min £75 order); elsewhere at cost
GLASS HIRE Free with 1-case order   TASTINGS AND TALKS Regular in-store
tastings (Sat); monthly wine evenings; to groups on request   CELLARAGE Not
available

This is a restaurant, delicatessen and wine merchant rolled into one.
Visitors to the shop in the heart of Winchester will have to tear
themselves away from the tempting delicatessen display to find the
wines. The restaurant – open for morning coffees, teas, lunch and
dinner – is at the back and upstairs.

The main enthusiasm on this comparatively short list is France.
Burgundy gets good treatment, with domaine wines (including the
amazingly expensive Henri Jayer wines of Vosne-Romanée and more
approachable wines from the Hautes Côtes de Beaune and Nuits).
They go in for estate Beaujolais, too. The Bordeaux section is much
shorter, but Lockes have picked out some good wines from the Côtes
du Rhône.

Outside France, wines from João Pires in Portugal (the delicious dry
white Moscato 1986 at £3.55) and the Douro wines of Montez-
Champalimaud look attractive, and in Spain, so do the red Marqués de
Griñon, and Sherry from Lustau. Mondavi and Firestone feature on
the Californian shelves and Rothbury Estate on the Australian.
Taylor's is the featured Port house. Lockes run regular wine evenings
which bring together the restaurant and the wine shop.

Best buys

João Pires Dry Moscato 1986, £3.65; Muscadet sur Lie 1985, Bossard,
£3.95; Bourgogne Passe-tout-grain 1984, Henri Jayer, £4.95; Chianti
Classico 1985, Rocca delle Macie, £3.25

O W Loeb

64 Southwark Bridge Road, London SE1 0AS   TEL 01-928 7750

OPEN Mon–Fri 9–6   CLOSED Sat, Sun, public holidays   CREDIT CARDS None
accepted; personal and business accounts   DISCOUNTS 5% on 1–5 cases, 10%
on 6–10 cases, wholesale prices on 10+ cases   DELIVERY Free in Central
London (min 1 case); elsewhere 1–2 cases £11.50 per consignment, 3–5 cases
£3.45 per case, 6+ cases free; mail order available   GLASS HIRE Not available
TASTINGS AND TALKS To wine-tasting groups on request   CELLARAGE £4 per
case per year or part year (payable in advance)

A top quality range of wines which stays firmly in classic areas:
Bordeaux, Burgundy, Rhône, Alsace and Germany.

The list is packed with famous names, especially in Burgundy:
Armand Rousseau, Dujac, Henri Gouges, Tollot-Beaut, Marquis
d'Angerville, Etienne Sauzet, Bonneau du Martray. Wines are from the
1984 and 1985 vintages for whites, but go back to 1980s for reds. Loeb
are UK agents for Jaboulet Aîné in the Rhône, entitling them to the
biggest selection of their wines in the country (although their prices are
often higher).

The name on the Loire is Foreau at Clos Naudin in Vouvray, but also
look for Pouilly Fumé of Renaud-Bossuat and Chinon from Charles

Joguet. Alsace wines come from the Domaine Weinbach estate of Mme Faller at Kaysersberg, and there's more than a passing interest in the Jura wines of Jean Bourdy at Château-Chalon.

Loeb's origins were as importers of Mosel wines from Germany, and now the firm in Trier is owned by the London office. Needless to say, their range of German estate wines is wide and fascinating, not just from the Mosel, but equally from Nahe (wines from von Plettenberg) and the Palatinate (Bürklin-Wolf). On the Mosel seek out the Friedrich Wilhelm Gymnasium and J J Prüm among many others, and the rare Franconian wines of the Juliusspital.

Best buys

Alsace wines of Théo Faller; Ch le Menaudat 1983, Premières Côtes de Blaye, £4.24; Ch Liot 1983, Barsac, £3.76 (halves); German estate wines

Lorne House Vintners 🐷

Unit 5, Hewitts Industrial Estate, Elmbridge Road,   TEL (0483) 271445
Cranleigh, Surrey GU6 8LW

OPEN Mon, Wed, Fri 9–5   Sat 9–1   CLOSED Tue, Thur, Sun, public holidays
CREDIT CARDS None accepted; personal and business accounts
DISCOUNTS Not available   DELIVERY Free within 25-mile radius and Central London (min 2 cases); elsewhere £5 per consignment; mail order available
GLASS HIRE Free with 1-case order   TASTINGS AND TALKS Monthly in-house tastings; to groups on request   CELLARAGE Not available   ■

This range stays very firmly in the track that Lorne House Vintners do so well: everyday drinking between about £2 and £5, many of the wines imported direct to cut down the price as much as possible.

The list is short but every wine has a reason for being there. So, on the Loire, we find a number of Muscadets of different quality levels, and a reasonably priced Sancerre from Domaine de Marcigoi (1986 vintage at £5.25).

In pursuit of their value for money philosophy, Lorne House list only a few Bordeaux and only two wines from Burgundy, but they have now introduced Alsace wines from Louis Gisselbrecht and Rhône wines from a number of estates (including Mont-Redon in Châteauneuf and Maby in Lirac), plus négociant wines from Pascal. Northern Rhône wines are from de Vallouit.

There's excellent value to be had in both Portugal and Spain: old vintages of Portuguese reds (1966 Casal da Azenha of da Silva from near Colares is a bargain at £6) and really dry Vinho Verde. From Penedès, they've discovered a new supplier, Jaume Serra, and now list his red, white and Cava sparkling.

> Why not club together with friends to enjoy volume discounts and free delivery?

Best buys

Tinto 1982, Jaume Serra, Penedès, £2.50; Garrafeira Particular 1974, A B da Silva, £3.90; Vin de Pays des Côtes de Gascogne Colombard 1986, £2.60; Touraine Sauvignon 1986, Domaine Guénault, £2.85

Luxembourg Wine Company

80 Northend, Batheaston, Bath, Avon BA1 7ES   TEL (0225) 858375

OPEN Mon–Sun, public holidays 7–9   CREDIT CARDS None accepted; personal and business accounts   DISCOUNTS Negotiable   DELIVERY Free in UK (min 3 cases or by negotiation); mail order available   GLASS HIRE Free with 3-case order   TASTINGS AND TALKS In-store tastings if requested; to groups on request; wine-tasting tours organised by sister company   CELLARAGE Not available ∎

This is still the only importer of Luxembourg wines in any quantity – which suggests that in that wealthy country they drink most of the wine they make.

The wines are produced along the Moselle which runs down the eastern border of the country, and are Germanic in style. But some of the grapes are different: the Elbling, for example, which emerges as the basic Luxembourg white at £2.35 a bottle. Other than that, the Riesling and Gewürztraminer grapes provide the most interesting still wines, or you might like to try the sparkling wines, such as Le Comte de Wormeldange at £4.85.

Best buys

Gewürztraminer Premier Cru 1985, £4.55; Elbling 1985, £2.35; Riesling Nussbaum Premier Cru 1985, £4.50

Graham MacHarg Fine Wines

See Irvine Robertson Wines.

Majestic Wine Warehouses

HEAD OFFICE 421 New King's Road, London SW6 4RN   TEL 01-731 3131

21 branches in London, Birmingham, Bournemouth, Bristol, Cambridge, Gloucester, Guildford, Oxford, Salisbury and Swindon

OPEN (Generally) Mon–Sat 10–8   Sun 10–6   public holidays 10–8
CLOSED 2/3 days at Chr; 2 days at New Year   CREDIT CARDS Access, Amex, Visa, Majestic Charge card   DISCOUNTS 5% on large quantities
DELIVERY Free local delivery; elsewhere mail order (TEL 01-736 1515) 1 case £3, 2–5 cases £2.50 per case, 6–9 cases £2.20 per case, 10+ cases free
GLASS HIRE Free; delivery with order (deposit of £6 per dozen)
TASTINGS AND TALKS Regular in-store tastings; to groups on request
CELLARAGE Not available ∎

By the time you read this there are probably many more branches than the 21 we knew of when we went to press. With over 1,000 wines on the list, and new arrivals all the time, for many people in the south of England these wine warehouses must provide all the wines they could ever need.

And, on the whole, what they do buy, they buy well and sell at very good prices. It's an extension of the old pile-it-high-and-sell-it-cheap philosophy of the early wine warehouses, with the important element of quality thrown in. Which is why, again this year, we have given Majestic all the special awards we make.

The range is wide, and the strengths many and varied. In clarets, for instance, they not only buy some good, basic easy-to-drink wines (Ch Léon 1984 at £2.89, or Ch Méaume 1984 at £3.49), but they also carry a range of 1985s from J-P Moueix, the man who put Ch Pétrus on the map. In Burgundy, the highlighted firm is négociant Labouré-Roi, but if you want to pay £29.50 for one bottle, you can have Richebourg 1983. Good quality Alsace has been sought out from the Caves St-Hippolyte, and the Rhône features wines from Jaboulet Aîné. There's a big list of Loire wines, including seven Muscadets and a clutch of Sancerres. House Champagne is from de Telmont at £7.95.

And so it goes on: an extensive selection of French country wines, some Italians moving from basic white Tocai at £1.99 up to Venegazzù della Casa Black Label 1982 at £9.75. If Germany is duller, that only reflects the current German wine market. Even the Bulgarian wines go from the cheap varietals at £1.99 to the reserve wines at the high (for Bulgaria) price of £2.59.

Australia and California make considerable contributions (Penfolds, Rosemount, Brown Brothers and Hardys, and Firestone, Clos du Bois and Robert Mondavi). A few vintage Ports and top quality Sherries from Lustau and Garvey are not neglected.

Best buys

Ch la Jaubertie Cépage Sauvignon 1986, £3.49; Ch de Montdespic 1985, Côtes de Castillon, £3.89; Bourgogne Pinot Noir 1985, Caves de Buxy, £3.99; Pinot d'Alsace 1985, Caves St-Hippolyte, £2.99; wines from Jaboulet Aîné; Crémant de Bourgogne 1983, Caves de Bailly, £5.85; Gaillac Rouge 1985, Domaine de la Gravette, £2.25; Australian wines from Penfolds

---

The Wine & Spirit Education Trust is the body in charge of educating those in and on the fringes of the wine trade. They offer a series of courses right up to Master of Wine level, the more basic of which are open to non-trade members who can convince the Trust of their intention to enter the wine trade. Contact them at: Five Kings House, Kennet Wharf Lane, Upper Thames Street, London EC4V 3AJ; TEL 01-236 3551.

The Market ✿ ⊟

12 Craven Road, London W2 3PX	TEL 01-723 6965
165 Haverstock Hill, London NW3 4QT	TEL 01-722 6521
213/215 Upper Street, London N1 1RL	TEL 01-3595386
700/702 Fulham Road, London SW6 5SA	TEL 01-736 4348
32/34 Highgate High Street, London N6 5JG	TEL 01-348 2422
14/17 Regent Parade, Brighton Road, Sutton, Surrey SM2 5BQ	TEL 01-643 5284
53/55 Balham Hill, Clapham South, London SW12 9DR	TEL 01-675 6901
Le Provençal, 167 Haverstock Hill, London NW3 4QT	TEL 01-586 7987

This group of shops has expanded in the past year, and now the wine drinkers of Sutton and Clapham can benefit from one of the best ranges of wines to be found in any supermarket group.

The wines are from the mammoth list of Winecellars (*qv*), and while not all wines are stocked in the supermarkets, any can be ordered for collection at one of the branches.

Market Vintners ⊟

11/12 West Smithfield, London EC1A 9JR	TEL 01-248 8382

OPEN Mon–Fri 9–6 Sat 10–1 CLOSED Sun, public holidays
CREDIT CARDS Access, Visa; personal and business accounts DISCOUNTS 5%
for 3 cases (min) DELIVERY Free within Greater London (min 1 case);
elsewhere £3 per case; mail order available GLASS HIRE Free
TASTINGS AND TALKS Tasting available daily; to groups on request
CELLARAGE £3 per case per year (including insurance)

'We want to establish Market Vintners as a force to be reckoned with in the City of London.' So, sensibly enough, they went initially for classic areas – Bordeaux, Burgundy, et al. And then something obviously happened, because they got sidetracked to Italy, Spain and the Rhône and then the New World as well. Big Bang is even having an effect on City merchants' wine lists.

Italy has seen the biggest changes. Sensibly chosen wines crop up from a number of regions: Tuscany with Chianti Rufina from Gratti as well as Sassicaia; Piedmont and Barbera from Ronco and Barolo from Oddero; a super Recioto Valpolicella from Allegrini in the Veneto; the Rosso Cònero Vigneti San Lorenzo; Alto Adige wines from Lageder; and Orvieto from Bigi.

One of the best New World bottles would be the superb Sauvignon/Semillon 1985 from Tisdall (£4.95) and the Liqueur Muscat from Morris. Market Vintners have got together a small selection of Riojas and the Cabernet Sauvignon of Jean León, besides almacenista

Sherry, a small selection of vintage Ports, and Ch Carras red from
Greece.

In France, the Champagnes are from Bruno Paillard. Guigal supplies
the top Côte Rôtie wines and Louis Gisselbrecht the Alsace wines.
Which leaves the increasing range of domaine-bottled Burgundy and a
well-balanced claret list.

Best buys

Vin de Pays de l'Aude Merlot, £2.55; Ch la Chapelle 1983, Bordeaux
Supérieur, £3.98; Dolcetto d'Asti 1985, Ronco, £3.79; Vinho Verde Casa
do Laueiro, £3.35; Ch Musar 1979, £5.25

Market Wine Stores

The retail shops of G M Vintners (*qv*).

Marks & Spencer

Michael House, 47–67 Baker Street,   TEL 01-935 4422
London W1A 1DN
257 licensed branches nationwide

OPEN Generally Mon–Fri 9–5.30   Sat 9–6   CLOSED Sun, public holidays
CREDIT CARDS Marks & Spencer Chargecard   DISCOUNTS, DELIVERY,
GLASS HIRE, TASTINGS AND TALKS, CELLARAGE Not available

While this list is not as long as those from many chains, it is very much
in keeping with the policy of M&S's food departments, which rely on
well-selected, high quality lines.

Because Marks & Spencer's wines are obviously chosen with care,
very few don't justify their place on the list. The range is divided into
two – the standard section which is available in all 257 licensed
branches, and a Vintage Selection to be found in the larger stores only.

Inevitably, most interest centres around the latter. We would
recommend their various Chablis (the basic Chablis at £6.50 is a good,
straightforward wine), and their Muscadet sur Lie 1986 is attractively
fresh (£3.25). In reds, look for the good choice of clarets – including an
excellent Médoc 1985 at £3.75, and the Ch Sables Peytraud 1985,
Bordeaux, terrific value at £2.99. Other wines in the Vintage Selection
to look out for include the Savoie Apremont (£3.75), the Rioja Marqués
de Romeral 1981 at £3.99 and the Fleurie 1986 from Jean Bedin at £5.99.

In their standard range, we like the selection of Italian white wines
(Chardonnay 1986 at £2.99), the deliciously sweet Moscatel de Valencia
(£2.75), the equally appealing Italian Moscato Frizzante (£2.50) and –
on a drier note – the Sauvignon de Touraine (£2.75). M&S Champagnes
are good – such as the vintage St-Gall at £10.99 – and they carry a good
value Crémant de Bourgogne at £5.99.

Best buys

Italian Chardonnay, £2.99; Vin de Pays des Bouches du Rhône, £2.15;
Ch Sables Peytraud 1985, £2.99; Jeunes Vignes white, £4.50

The Marlow Wine Shop

See Addison Avenue Wine Shop.

Marske Mill House

London Road, Sunninghill, Ascot,   TEL (0990) 22790
Berkshire SL5 0PN

OPEN Mail order only but telephone enquiries welcome at any time
CREDIT CARDS None accepted   DISCOUNTS Variable   DELIVERY Included in
price to whole of UK mainland (min 1 case)   GLASS HIRE Not available
TASTINGS AND TALKS To groups on request   CELLARAGE Not available   ■

Marske Mill House (otherwise known as Prestige Wines of Italy) has
probably the smallest list in the Guide – with only nine wines currently
– but its place here is justified because the wines are not otherwise
available in the UK. They all come from the Italian region of Umbria.

The basic bottles are a red and white from the man who developed
Lamborghini cars – the red more interesting than the white (£4.04).
There's a Rosso di Montefalco made by Arnaldo Caprai (£4.12) and a
Sagrantino di Montefalco, a wine from a rare local grape which makes
very concentrated red wines (£5.25). Other good choices would be the
top class red Rubino 1981 from Polidori in the Upper Tiber valley
(£4.58) and wines from the Colli del Trasimeno DOC area in the west of
the region.

Best buys

Colli de Trasimeno 1983, Fiammetta, £4.92; Rosso Colli Altotiberini
1983, Carlo Polidori, £3.79

Martinez Fine Wine   ▱ ☞

36 The Grove, Ilkley, West Yorkshire LS29 9EE   TEL (0943) 603241
Corn Exchange Cellars, The Ginnel, Harrogate,   TEL (0423) 501783
North Yorkshire HG3 4JS
60 Street Lane, Leeds, West Yorkshire LS8 2DQ   TEL (0532) 668310

OPEN Mon–Fri 9.30–6.30 Sat 9–6 CLOSED Sun, Chr, Good Friday
CREDIT CARDS Access, Visa; personal and business accounts DISCOUNTS 5%
for 1 case   DELIVERY Free in Yorkshire (min 1 case); elsewhere 1–4 cases £2.50
per case, 5–9 cases £1.75 per case; mail order available GLASS HIRE Free
TASTINGS AND TALKS In-store tastings in spring, summer and autumn;
8 tastings annually through the Wine Club; to groups on request
CELLARAGE £2.75 per case per year

Martinez seem to go from strength to strength. The original shop at Ilkley and the splendidly organised branch at Harrogate have now been joined by a third in Leeds – and the list has also continued to expand. In addition to the regular standard range, Mr Martinez has developed a small collection of fine wines.

Starting in France, the list displays a well-priced range of clarets, mainly from recent vintages, but with some wines back to 1969. Look especially for wines from the 1983 and 1982 vintages. In Burgundy, the wines come principally from Jaffelin, who also supplies the Beaujolais. On the Loire, Sancerre and Pouilly Fumé are covered well – we would recommend the Sancerre Cuvée des Moulins Bales at £5.75. While the Rhône list is short, the Côtes du Rhône 1985, Domaine la Soumade (£4.30) is good, as are the more basic Coteaux du Tricastin and Côtes du Ventoux at £2.80. Alsace wines come from Willy Gisselbrecht.

Elsewhere in France, we see wines from Listel, the Cahors of Ch St-Didier Parnac 1983 (£4.70) and the super Jurançon sweet and dry from Clos Guirouilh. The Italian range is growing, too, with Veneto wines from Santa Sofia, the Venegazzù della Casa 1981 (£5.95) and the Masi vino da tavola Campo Fiorín 1980 at £5.35.

Spain is another great strength, offering plenty of choice from a big range of Reserva and Gran Reserva Riojas (including, on the fine wine list, some vintages back to the 1960s), wines from Torres, the Agramont from Navarra, a good value red and white from La Mancha, Castillo de Alhambra (£2.85), not to mention the excellent range of Sherries. From beyond Europe come wines from Wyndham Estate in Australia and Cooks in New Zealand.

Best buys

Castillo de Alhambra red and white, £2.85; Gran Reserva and Reserva Riojas; wines from Listel; Vin de Pays des Coteaux de Quercy, £2.65; Ch la Clare 1981, Médoc, £5.30

Master Cellar Wine Warehouse

5 Aberdeen Road, Croydon, Surrey CRO 1EQ   TEL 01-686 9989
Associated with Davisons shops

OPEN Mon–Fri 10–8   Sat, Sun 10–6   CLOSED Public holidays
CREDIT CARDS Access, Visa   DISCOUNTS 2½% for (min) 10 cases
DELIVERY Free locally; elsewhere 1 case £6, 2–5 cases £4 per case, 6–9 cases £3 per case, 10+ cases free; mail order available   GLASS HIRE Free with order
TASTINGS AND TALKS Monthly tutored tastings; wines for tasting available daily; to groups on request   CELLARAGE Not available

This is the wine warehouse belonging to the same company as the Davisons chain of off-licences. As with the shops, the biggest strengths of the list are in Bordeaux and Burgundy. Watch out for more branches.

What is so good about the clarets here is that so many are ready to drink, rather than mere infants. J T Davies, the owning company, still manage to afford to mature wine before putting it on sale – so you get vintages of first growths back to 1970 at what are very good prices, and, for lesser clarets, wines from the 1979 and 1978 vintages – as well as plenty from 1981 – which you could drink today with pleasure. In white Bordeaux, consider any vintage of Ch Rieussec Sauternes.

The Burgundy sector is strong on Georges Duboeuf in the Mâconnais, with a good mix of domaine and négociant wine from further north. Duboeuf also supplies the Beaujolais. Alsace and the Loire have a little less to offer, but there's an attractive smattering of Rhônes (Gigondas Domaine de Montmirail 1982 at £4.75) and Midi wines (Minervois Domaine Ste-Eulalie 1986 at £2.65).

Outside France, the German list is dominated by Huesgen, and an expanding Italian section includes Regaleali wines from Sicily, and the single vineyard Jago Valpolicella from Bolla (1983 vintage at £3.95). Also look for the sparkling Prosecco di Valdobbiadene (£4.25). Spain revolves round a number of good Riojas (the house Rioja is El Coto at £2.59), and very good value is to be had in Bulgarian wines (varietal wines at £1.85). Ports are good, Sherries much less interesting. The New World brings in Rosemount, Brown Brothers, McWilliams and Lindemans in Australia; and Cuvaison, Preston and Mondavi in California.

Best buys

Champagne (NV), Ellner, £7.35; El Coto Rioja 1985, £2.59; Bulgarian wines; mature petit château wines; Cuvée Duboeuf Rouge, £2.29

Mayor Sworder

21 Duke Street Hill, London SE1 2SW   TEL 01-407 5111

OPEN Mon–Fri 9–5   CLOSED Sat, Sun, public holidays   CREDIT CARDS None accepted; personal and business accounts   DISCOUNTS Not available DELIVERY Free in Greater London; elsewhere charges dependent on distances; mail order available   GLASS HIRE Free   TASTINGS AND TALKS Private tasting evenings; annual tasting by invitation; to groups on request   CELLARAGE £2.99 per case per year

---

This list survives in the Guide on the strength of its clarets and German wines. Much of the company's trade is with business customers in the City, so list prices do not include VAT. We find that, once the tax has been added (as in this entry), prices are not cheap.

However, they do list a good number of petit château wines from 1981, 1982 and 1983, with an obvious interest in the environs of St-Emilion and in the left bank Côtes de Bourg and Blaye. So these wines are not too expensive (Ch Haut Peyches 1983, Fronsac, is £4.71, for example; Ch Paradis Casseuil 1983, Bordeaux, is £3.83). Above this level are bourgeois growths and some classed growths, with vintages going back to 1966.

Burgundy is well spoken for, but mainly by négociant wines rather than domaine bottlings. However, we would recommend the white St-Aubin 1984 of Brenot (£7.47) or the Irancy Rouge 1985 of André Vannier at £4.71 as attractive propositions. Also look for the Alsace wines of J Becker.

There are a few French regional wines (the Clos Bagatelle, St-Chinian 1981 at £3.33 is a top quality wine). In Germany, the Mosel does best, with wines from Bert Simon, Langguth and the Trier Vereinigte Hospitien, mostly from the 1983 vintage. As well as Australian wines from Idyll Vineyard, fortified wines look good: Madeira from Rutherford and Miles, and Mayor Sworder's own Crusted Port (£7.76).

Best buys

St-Chinian 1981, Clos Bagatelle, £3.33; Idyll Vineyard Gewürztraminer 1984, £4.60; Claret de Mestrezat Bordeaux Rouge, £3.26

Andrew Mead Wines

Shovelstrode, Presteigne, Powys LD8 2NP   TEL (05476) 268

OPEN By appointment only   CREDIT CARDS None accepted   DISCOUNTS Not available   DELIVERY Free within 15-mile radius of Presteigne; elsewhere 3 cases free, £4 for smaller orders   GLASS HIRE Free for regular customers
TASTINGS AND TALKS Very occasional tasting for regular customers
CELLARAGE Only exceptionally   ■

Andrew Mead takes a practical view of his customers. The first section of his list is entitled Daily Drinking, and contains a well-balanced range of wines, all under £4 and many under £3. He has assembled some good Vins de Pays from Gascogne (£2.80) and from the Ardèche (red at £2.34 and Syrah £2.65), with the Burgundian-style Marcilly Extra (£2.88) and the red Domaine Herbe Sainte 1986 from the Midi (£2.95) as other possibilities. We would also recommend – from elsewhere in the list – the wines of Jean Cros in Gaillac.

After that, to more heady Special Occasion Wines. Burgundy is a domaine-bottled delight, with wines from Lafarge, Henri Jayer, Michel Colin, Luc Camus, Jean Chauvenet, Lequin Roussot. The reds are better than the whites – a reflection of the lack of availability of white Burgundy.

Clarets include plenty of good value petit château wines. The strongest vintages are 1983, 1982 and 1981, in company with some top wines from the 1978 vintage. On the Rhône, one finds good bottles from Guigal and Alphonse Desmeure, plus Châteauneuf-du-Pape from Domaine du Vieux Télégraphe. Alsace presents wines from Rolly Gassmann.

There's little outside France, apart from fortified wines: good vintage Ports (Ramos Pinto 1980 is good value at £9.80), and Sherry from Sanchez Romate, with a couple of Madeiras from Cossart Gordon.

WHERE TO BUY

Best buys

Domaine Herbe Sainte red 1986, £2.95; Ch le Bourguette 1983,
Bordeaux, £3.45; Côtes du Rhône 1983, Guigal, £4.70; Mâcon Rouge
Bray 1985, Henri Lafarge, £4.40

J H Measures & Sons

The Crescent, Spalding, Lincolnshire PE11 1AF   TEL (0775) 2676

OPEN Mon–Sat 9–6   CLOSED Sun, public holidays   CREDIT CARDS Access,
Visa; personal and business accounts   DISCOUNTS 5% for 1 case
DELIVERY Free in South Lincolnshire and East Midlands (min 1 case); elsewhere
at cost; mail order available   GLASS HIRE Free   TASTINGS AND TALKS Regular
in-store tasting; major annual tasting in October; to groups on request
CELLARAGE Not available

This shop is part of G E Bromley & Sons (*qv*), and operates the same
list.

Michael Menzel Wines

297–299 Eccleshall Road,   TEL (0742) 683557
Sheffield, South Yorkshire S11 8HX

OPEN Mon–Sat 10–9   Sun 12–2, 7–9   CLOSED Public holidays
CREDIT CARDS All accepted; personal and business accounts
DISCOUNTS 10–15% (min 1 case)   DELIVERY Free in South Yorkshire,
Humberside and north Derbyshire (min 3 cases locally, min 5 cases elsewhere);
mail order available   GLASS HIRE Free with 1-case order
TASTINGS AND TALKS Occasional tastings for regular customers
CELLARAGE Not available

Michael Menzel Wines keep a good, solid selection of wines, sticking
to négociants in France, but being more adventurous elsewhere.
So, in Burgundy, wines come from Louis Jadot and Joseph Drouhin
(who also offers the Beaujolais range). There are, though, a few of the
top wines from Domaine Leroy which, though expensive, are
first-class. A short range of claret from recent vintages offers some
good value in petit château wines. In Alsace, wines are from Hugel,
mainly now the 1985 and 1986 vintages, and on the Loire, Vouvray
from Daniel Jarry and Muscadets from the Marquis de Goulaine
provide excellent quality from their areas. Further south, the Rhône
offers wines from Jaboulet Aîné, and Provence has the rare (and
pricey) Ch Simone from the tiny Palette appellation.
Spanish bottles include wines from Torres and Riojas from CVNE,
Faustino and La Rioja Alta. Italy supplies some wines from top names:
Boscaini in the Veneto, Frescobaldi in Tuscany, Pio Cesare and Gaja in
Piedmont, and Villa Catone Frascati.

Best buys

Torres wines; Beaujolais from Joseph Drouhin

Mi Casa Fine Wines

77 West Road, Buxton, Derbyshire SK17 6HQ   TEL (0298) 3952
OPEN Mon–Fri 3–10   Sat 11–10   Sun, Good Friday, New Year's Day 12–2,
7–10   Chr Day 12 noon–1; other public holidays as if a normal day
CREDIT CARDS None accepted; personal and business accounts
DISCOUNTS 5% for 1 case   DELIVERY Free within 10-mile radius of Buxton
(min 1 case); mail order available   GLASS HIRE Free with ½-case order
TASTINGS AND TALKS To groups on request (Spanish wines only)
CELLARAGE Not available

This is an almost entirely Spanish list, and though short, is a good,
representative range across the country.

Rioja names include Campo Viejo, Muga, Marqués de Cáceres, Viña
Alcorta and the single vineyard Contino (1980 vintage at £4.95). Look
also for their various Reservas and Gran Reservas.

Penedès is similarly well subscribed with wines from Torres, René
Barbier and Cavas Hill. Navarra wines are made by Bodegas Magana (a
Cabernet Sauvignon/Merlot blend at £6.75), as curiosities up pop the
Galician wine Albarino Noso at £3.50 and the Priorato wine from de
Muller – better known for altar wines. Valdoro red and white from
Valdepeñas is good value at £2.55. De Soto and Berisford have
supplied the Sherries, and the sparkling Cavas come from Freixenet,
Conde de Caralt and Monistrol.

Best buys

Valdepeñas Valdoro red and white, £2.55; Rioja Reserva 1981, Campo
Viejo, £3.97; Rioja Blanco 1982, Muga, £3.95 ·

Millevini

3 Middlewood Road, High Lane, Stockport,   TEL (0663) 64366
Cheshire SK6 8AU

OPEN 7 days a week (an answering service operates after 3 on weekdays)
CREDIT CARDS None accepted; business accounts   DISCOUNTS Up to 15%
according to quantity and delivery (min 1 case)   DELIVERY Free within 20-mile
radius of High Lane (min 1 case) or with 6+ case order; otherwise £5 charge per
order; mail order available   GLASS HIRE Free
TASTINGS AND TALKS Occasional tastings organised locally or on request
CELLARAGE Not available

We're not sure if there are actually a thousand wines on this list – we
gave up counting – but it's definitely one of the most comprehensive
collections of Italian wines in the country, and it seems to get longer
every year.

Piedmont is perhaps the very best section, expanded since last year
and now full of treats. Apart from Barolos and Barbarescos in
profusion (from names such as Ronco, Barale, Bartolo Mascarello,

Cavallotto, Conterno and Roberto Voerzio), there are Dolcettos and the Carema 1980 of Ferrando (£7.38), a couple of good Nebbiolo delle Langhe from Voerzio (his 1985 is £4.90) and a Gattinara from Brugo (1980 vintage at £6.23). Don't ignore an outstanding Moscato d'Asti from Voerzio (£5.45) among the sweet sparklers.

Then on to Lombardy, with Franciacorta wines from Longhe-de Carli and white Lugana from Zenato. From the Alto Adige, the wines are all from Tiefenbrunner. Further down the Adige valley, in Verona, the Valpolicellas are those of Tedeschi and Allegrini (La Grola 1985 at £6.67), next door to wines from Loredan, the producer of the famous Venegazzù (and also a good value Chardonnay at £3.72). Collavini supplies wines from Friuli.

Tuscany brings in Chiantis from Brolio, Rocca delle Macie, Fattoria dell'Ugo and Pagliarese, as well as the Brunello of Fattoria dei Barbi and a super vino da Tavola Morellino di Scansano from Le Pupile (1983 vintage is £6.79).

From further south, interest centres on the red Rosso Cònero and white Verdicchio of Bianchi; the Abruzzo wines of Cornacchia and Valentini; the rare red Torre Ercolana (1981 vintage is £10.30); the Taurasi of Mastroberardino (the 1981 at £12.90 is still much too young, but getting there); Aglianico del Vulture from d'Angelo; and the Malbec-based wines of Torre Quarto in Puglia (1979 Riserva at £4.96 is a bargain). Look also for the Vecchio Samperi Marsala (with a difference) of de Bartoli (£12).

Best buys

Barbaresco 1978, Ronco, £4.98; Franciacorta Rosso 1984, Longhe-de Carli, £4.43; Chardonnay 1985, Loredan, £3.72; Rosso Cònero 1982 San Lorenzo, Bianchi, £3.98; Torre Quarto Riserva 1979, £4.96

Mitchell & Son

21 Kildare Street, Dublin 2, Republic of Ireland   TEL (0001) 760766
OPEN Mon–Fri 10.30–5.30   Sat 10.30–1   CLOSED Sun, public holidays
CREDIT CARDS Access, Amex, Diners, Visa; personal and business accounts
DISCOUNTS 5–10% (min 1 case)   DELIVERY Free in Dublin City and County,
Wicklow, Meath (min 2 cases); mail order available   GLASS HIRE Available with
suitable order   TASTINGS AND TALKS Regular in-store tastings; to groups on
request   CELLARAGE Not available

Considering the problems – and high taxes – of getting wine to Ireland and then selling it, Mitchells do a good job. Their list contains few excitements, but it does offer a solid core of wines in most areas.

Clarets are well chosen, with a mix of petit château and cru bourgeois wines from more recent vintages (Ch St-Germain 1982 is I£6.63 – all prices are of course in Irish punts; Ch Canteloup 1983 is I£6.50). Vintages go back to 1979, with a particularly interesting range from Ch Rausan-Ségla.

In Burgundy and Beaujolais most wines come from négociants Mommessin (including wines from Clos de Tart which they wholly own), with a few from Prosper Maufoux; Mommessin also supply the Rhône wines. In Alsace, the wines come from Dopff au Moulin, mainly from the rich 1983 vintage. Laurent Perrier is the featured Champagne house.

In Germany, many Deinhard bottles are to be found among a good selection of estate wines, plus wines from the Königin Victoriaberg vineyard in Hochheim on the Rheingau (Riesling Spätlese 1983, I£12.75). Small sections of Spanish and Italian wines (for instance the Chianti Classico Castello Vicchiomaggio) accompany the New World wines of Christian Brothers and Sequoia Grove from California and Hardys from Australia. Fonseca Ports and La Riva Sherries account for the fortified wines.

Best buys

Corbières 1983, Ch de la Condamine, I£4.99; Ch Canteloup 1983, Bordeaux, I£6.50; German estate wines; Viña Tere red and white Spanish, I£4.95

Moffat Wine Shop

15 Well Street, Moffat, Dumfriesshire DG10 9DP   TEL (0683) 20554
OPEN Mon–Sat and public holidays 9–5.30   CLOSED Sun
CREDIT CARDS Amex, Visa; personal and business accounts   DISCOUNTS 5% for 1 case   DELIVERY Free in Dumfriesshire (min 1 case); elsewhere 2 cases £4.90 per case, 2+ cases £14.38 flat fee; mail order available   GLASS HIRE Free with wine order   TASTINGS AND TALKS To groups on request
CELLARAGE Free

Moffat Wine Shop's list has grown longer in the past year, with Australia, Portugal and Spain all bursting forth, and New Zealand squeezing in for the first time, all rubbing shoulders with the huge range of malt whiskies and imported lagers.

To start with France, one finds small selections of claret and one or two interesting Sauternes (Ch Raymond Lafon 1980 is £11.28). Next come Alsace wines from Hugel, Burgundy from négociants (Bouchard Aîné and Drouhin), and some interesting regional wines (Jurançon from Guirouilh and Ch de Fonscolombe Coteaux d'Aix-en-Provence red and white).

Italy displays Alto Adige wines from Tiefenbrunner and Lageder, Barolo and Dolcetto d'Alba from Pio Cesare and Chianti Machiavelli from Serristori, plus Masi's Campo Fiorín red super vino da tavola. From Spain, there's more: Rioja from Faustino, Berberana, CVNE, plenty of Torres wines from Penedès and Monte Ory from Navarra. Top producer J M da Fonseca supplies the Portuguese wines. Moffat have decided to stock the new reserve wines from Bulgaria.

New World names include Cooks from New Zealand and Hardy and Hill-Smith from Australia.

Best buys

Periquita 1981, J M da Fonseca, £3.39; Hardy's Keppoch Cabernet/Shiraz 1983, £3.85; Bulgarian wines; Chianti Classico 1983, Machiavelli, £2.99; Jurançon Moelleux 1982, Guirouilh, £4.07; Ch Livran 1979, Médoc, £3.96

Moreno Wines ✉

11 Marylands Road, London W9 2DU	TEL 01-286 0678/9029
2 Norfolk Place, London W2 1QN	TEL 01-723 6897
	and 01-724 3813

OPEN Mon–Fri 9–9 Sat 10–9 Sun 12–2 CLOSED Public holidays CREDIT CARDS Access, Visa; personal and business accounts DISCOUNTS 5% on 1 case (collected), 7½% on 10+ cases DELIVERY Free throughout UK (min 3 cases); mail order available GLASS HIRE Free with 1-case order TASTINGS AND TALKS Approx once a month in-store tastings; to groups on request CELLARAGE Not available

---

One of the most comprehensive collections of Spanish wine in the country, this list concentrates not only on Rioja but also brings in other areas of the country.

Rioja, certainly, is important, showing off wines from many of the major bodegas (and some of the smaller ones). Current vintages range from 1978s in Gran Reservas to the 1986s for the modern-style whites, but a supplementary reserve list of older vintages goes back to the 1960s.

That same reserve list covers other areas of Spain. In pride of place are old vintages of Torres wines and of the legendary Vega Sicilia, Spain's most expensive wine. Coming back to more recent times, Torres still features in plenty, as do other Penedès bodegas. You can buy wines from Navarra, Jumilla, León, Priorato, Galicia (where the white wines are similar to the Vinho Verde of neighbouring Portugal), Rueda, Cariñena, Valdepeñas, Ribera del Duero (home of Vega Sicilia, but also less expensive co-operative wines).

Further bottles include sparkling Cavas from Penedès, as well as a range of Sherries from Barbadillo, Bobadilla, Garvey, Don Zoilo, Gonzalez-Byass and Domecq. Málagas and Montillas complete this great all-rounder of a list.

Best buys

Condestable 1983, Jumilla red, £1.99; Rioja Alavesa red and white, £1.99; Reboreda Blanco 1985, Galicia, £2.49; Conde de Caralt Tinto 1983, Penedès, £2.59; Ribera Duero 2 año, 1983, Co-operative of Ribera del Duero, £3.12

Philip Morgan & Sons

126 Wyndham Crescent, Canton,
Cardiff CF1 9EG

TEL (0222) 31570

OPEN Mon–Sat 10–10   Sun, public holidays 12–2, 7–10.30   CLOSED 25 & 26
Dec, 1 Jan   CREDIT CARDS Access, Visa; personal and business accounts
DISCOUNTS 10% on 1 case wine (may be mixed)   DELIVERY Free in Cardiff and
surrounding area (min 1 case), elsewhere 1–5 cases at cost, 6+ cases free
GLASS HIRE Free with 1-case order   TASTINGS AND TALKS Occasional tastings
on bin-ends   CELLARAGE £1.80 per case per year (in bond)

Come here for the prices, not for the wide range of wines. What you
will find are some good value French country wines such as the Vin de
Pays du Tarn white at £2.35 (prices on the list exclude VAT – we've
added it here), or the red, white and rosé from Ch la Coste in Coteaux
d'Aix-en-Provence (£3.11), or the Ch Gourgazaud Minervois red and
white at £2.50.

   The other areas to look at in France are the Loire (a good Sancerre
from Domaine des Garennes at £4.93) and Bordeaux, which offers
some straightforward wines (Ch de Grange 1979 at £4.22 is the oldest
wine). Outside France, only Marqués de Cáceres is worth looking out
for.

Best buys

Fitou, Mme Claude Parmentier 1982, £2.64; Minervois, Ch de
Gourgazaud red and white, £2.50; Coteaux du Tricastin 1984, Domaine
des Rozets, £2.74

Morris & Verdin

28 Churton Street, London SW1V 2LP

TEL 01-630 8888

OPEN Mon–Fri 9.30–5.30   Sat 10–3   CLOSED Sun, public holidays
CREDIT CARDS None accepted; personal and business accounts
DISCOUNTS £1 per case after 5 cases   DELIVERY Free in London and Oxford
(min 1 case); elsewhere £6.90 per consignment; mail order available
GLASS HIRE Free with any case order   TASTINGS AND TALKS In-store tastings
on Saturday mornings; occasional tastings for regular customers
CELLARAGE £2.30 per case per year plus insurance   ∎

In the classic wine trade debate about whether one is a claret man or a
Burgundy man, we think we know where Jasper Morris would side.
He keeps some very high class domaine-bottled Burgundies – but does
allow mere mortals the chance to try some of the treats, because he has
discovered a good number of wines at the cheaper end of the scale as
well.

   For instance, there are three well-made Bourgogne Aligotés
(Domaine Daniel Rion 1986 is £5.90) and a Bourgogne Blanc 1984 from
Domaine Pitoiset-Urena at £8.90 (and, as Mr Morris says, even in 1984,
good producers made good wine). In reds, he has a superb Bourgogne

Passe-tout-grain 1985 from Daniel Rion at £5.10. At a pricier level, one finds domaine wines from Louis Pinson, Comtes Lafon and François Jobard in whites; Daniel Rion, Monthélie Douhairet, Girard Vollot and Girard in reds.

The Loire and Alsace – though shorter – are two other places to peruse. Interesting bottles include the Sancerre from Jean-Max Roger (the 1985 vintage is £6.30; also a red at £6.50), and reds from Chinon and Bourgueil. In Alsace, the wines of André Ostertag are featured. Bordeaux offers a short range, especially of Fronsac wines. Wines we would even more strongly recommend are the Côtes de Provence wine of Domaine St-André de Figuière (1982 red at £4.70), plus wines from Ch de Beaucastel in Châteauneuf and La Vieille Ferme on the southern Rhône, as well as Jaboulet Aîné, Domaine Pierre Barge (for Côte Rôtie) and Jean Pinchon (for Condrieu) further north. A new interest is Australia with wines from Mosswood and Cape Mentelle in Western Australia.

Best buys

Alsace Pinot Blanc 1984, Ostertag, £3.90; Côtes du Ventoux 1985, La Vieille Ferme, £3; Bourgogne Passe-tout-grain 1985, Daniel Rion, £5.10; Ch La Tour St-Bonnet 1982, Haut-Médoc, £6.50

William Morrison

HEAD OFFICE Lifestyle Warehouse   TEL (0274) 497421
Young Street, Thornton Road,
Bradford 8, West Yorkshire BD8 9SB
35 branches in Yorkshire, Lancashire, Co Durham, Lincolnshire, Derbyshire, Merseyside, Northumberland and Cheshire
OPEN Hours may vary from store to store, but generally Mon, Tue, Sat 8.30–5.30 Wed, Thur, Fri 8.30–8 CLOSED Sun, public holidays
CREDIT CARDS None accepted   WHEELCHAIR ACCESS , DELIVERY, GLASS HIRE, TASTINGS AND TALKS, CELLARAGE Not available

---

Morrisons continue to offer terrific value for money across quite a wide range of wines, while regular special promotions bring prices even lower. They've revamped the wine sections of most of their supermarkets to make very attractive separate display areas, and also publish a regular newsletter for customers.

Wine areas new to their list include Australia (Wyndham Estate Bin 44, Cabernet Sauvignon at £2.95), Greece, and Portugal (Periquita 1982, J M da Fonseca at £2.89). Wines we have enjoyed recently include the Pouilly Fumé 1985, Ch de Tracy (5.65), the Rioja Reserva 1980 from Campo Viejo (£3.39), the Beaujolais Villages 1985 of Chanson Père et Fils (terrific value at £3.19), and the Spanna del Piemonte of Berteletti at £2.55. Morrisons specialise in the good value wines from Listel in the south of France, and have built up a good range of vins de pays from the Hérault and the Aude.

While Germany tends to follow supermarket standards, Italy is more adventurous, with wines from Boscaini and Santi in the Veneto, and the Verdicchio of CaSal di Serra and Barolo from Fontanafredda. Spain has wines from Torres, and Marqués de Monistrol and Marqués de Cáceres Riojas.

Best buys

Ch la Cardonne 1982, £4.79; Wyndham Estate Bin 44, Cabernet Sauvignon, £2.95; Periquita 1982, J M da Fonseca, £2.89; Rioja Reserva 1980, Campo Viejo, £3.39; Ockfener Scharzberg Riesling Kabinett 1983, £3.29; Vin de Pays des Côtes de Gascogne 1986, Domaine de Tariquet, £2.29

Morris's Wine Stores

HEAD OFFICE AND WAREHOUSE Stirling Road,   TEL 021-704 3415
Cranmore Industrial Estate, Shirley, Solihull,
West Midlands B90 4XD
26 branches in the West Midlands (4 are known as Astral Wines,
1 as Woodleys Wine Stores and 1 as W R Wines)

OPEN Every day; opening hours vary   CREDIT CARDS Access, Amex, Visa; personal and business accounts   DISCOUNTS Negotiable   DELIVERY Free within 30 miles of Birmingham (min 1 case); elsewhere £2.50 per case; mail order available   GLASS HIRE Not available   TASTINGS AND TALKS Regular in-store tastings   CELLARAGE Free

---

This continues to be a solid, all-rounder of a list which has expanded from the classic regions to bring in wines from most parts of the world. Not all shops stock the full range but will order.

Bordeaux remains the starting point. Wines in a wide price range come from most recent vintages, with occasional older bottles going back to 1967. There are a few interesting Sauternes (such as Ch la Chartreuse 1981 and 1983). The Burgundy list is a mix of négociant and domaine wine – reds are more interesting than whites – and Beaujolais is from the négociant firm of Trenel et Fils.

The northern Rhône section now boasts Guigal, Chapoutier and Jaboulet Aîné; Côtes du Ventoux, Domaine des Anges is a bargain in the south, alongside some more serious bottles from Côtes du Rhône and Châteauneuf-du-Pape. The Loire offers some good Pouilly Fumé, and Alsace wines are mainly from Hugel. House Champagne is by Baron de Beaupré. The rest of France has yet to reach Morris's.

Germany's selection is quite extensive, relying on estate wines from Deinhard. In Italy, most of the major regions are represented – Chianti from Frescobaldi and Ruffino, Valpolicella and Soave from Santi, Barolo from Villa Doria. There's a smaller selection of Spanish table wines, but plenty of Sherry.

Best buys

Côtes du Rhône-Villages Vacqueyras 1985, Troubador, £2.50;
Minervois 1983, Domaine Ste-Eulalie, £2.40; Chiantis from Frescobaldi;
Domecq Sherries

Newman & Gilbey

186 Trinity Road, Wandsworth Common,   TEL 01-416 0054
London SW17 7HR

OPEN Mon–Sat 10–9   CLOSED Sun, public holidays   CREDIT CARDS Access,
Visa; personal and business accounts   DISCOUNTS 5% for 1 case
DELIVERY Free locally (min 6 bottles), elsewhere at cost; mail order available
GLASS HIRE Free   TASTINGS AND TALKS Bottle open every Sat in-store; to
groups on request   CELLARAGE Available

A well-chosen list with interest in most areas brings this firm into the
Guide for the first time. They are particularly good at a range of
affordable clarets – from the 1983, 1982 and 1981 vintages (they also
offer claret en primeur), and at Burgundy, where they have a number
of good domaine wines. Their house Champagne is Petit le Brun
(£8.95) and they also offer the popular sparkling G F Cavalier Brut.

Outside France, Italy provokes some interest (such as the Le Cane
vino da tavola from Boscaini at £5.10 and the Chardonnay di Appiano
from the Alto Adige at £4.15), and Spain has some decently priced
Riojas. Australia provides wines from McWilliams, Hardys and Brown
Brothers among others, New Zealand with wines from Cooks, and
California with wines from Clos du Bois and Clos du Val.

Best buys

Chianti Classico Riserva 1979, Pagliarese, £5.35; Champagne (NV), Petit
le Brun, £8.95; Ch Bel-Air 1983, Bordeaux Supérieur, £4.45; Listel Gris
de Gris Rosé, £2.99

Le Nez Rouge/Berkmann Wine Cellars

12 Brewery Road, London N7 9NH   TEL 01-609 4711

OPEN Mon–Fri 9–5.30   Sat 10–1.30 (except Sat preceding public holidays)
CLOSED Sun, public holidays   CREDIT CARDS Access, Visa; personal and
business accounts by arrangement   DISCOUNTS £1.50 per case collection
allowance (case may be mixed)   DELIVERY Free to London postal addresses
(min 1 case) and mainland UK (min 5 cases); otherwise 1 case £4, 2 cases £2 per
case, 3–4 cases £1.50 per case; mail order available   GLASS HIRE Free with
1-case order   TASTINGS AND TALKS Regular tastings throughout the year;
in-store tastings on Saturday mornings; to groups on request
CELLARAGE £3.45 per case per year

Le Nez Rouge is the retail wine club side of Berkmann Wine Cellars.
You can deal with them either by mail order, or collect wine from their

Cellar Shop at Brewery Road. The club side of the business is expanding (see the WINE CLUBS section), with spectacular dinners in London and a lively magazine, apart from plenty of special offers and an entertaining list.

The list has undergone considerable expansion since last year, with the unveiling of some new stars. Bruno Paillard's Champagne has arrived, along with Côte Rôtie from Vidal-Fleury and Sancerre from Pascal Jolivet.

The heart of the list, though, remains firmly in Burgundy and Beaujolais. Wines from Georges Duboeuf – for whom Berkmann Wine Cellars are principal UK agent – dominate Beaujolais and the southern part of Burgundy. As we went to press, they were still offering some cru Beaujolais from 1985, which should be snapped up if possible. In Burgundy proper, some great domaine names resound, some at very fair prices for Burgundy. Le Nez Rouge made an opening offer of 1985 Burgundy.

In other parts of France, the Loire also features strongly, first with Muscadet from Jean Sauvion at Ch de Cléray and now Sancerre and Pouilly Fumé, again from Jolivet. Bordeaux has acquired a good range of petit château wines from 1982 and 1983, and the Alsace wines of Gaston Beck would also be worth a look.

Best buys

Beaujolais from Georges Duboeuf; Côtes du Rhône 1985, Domaine du Grand Prieur, £3.30; Côtes de Duras Sauvignon 1986, Les Vignerons des Coteaux de Duras, £3.25; Coteaux d'Aix-en-Provence 1983, Domaine les Bastides, £4.50

Nickolls & Perks

37 High Street, Stourbridge — TEL (0384) 394518
West Midlands DY8 1TA
ASSOCIATED COMPANY Greenwood & Co, — TEL (038 482) 2217
178 High Street, Lye, Stourbridge,
West Midlands DY9 8LH

OPEN Mon–Sat 9–10   Sun 12–2, 6–10   CLOSED Public holidays
CREDIT CARDS Access, Amex, Visa; personal and business accounts
DISCOUNTS 10% for 1 case   DELIVERY Free within 12-mile radius (min 1 case); otherwise £3 per case; mail order available   GLASS HIRE Free with wine order
TASTINGS AND TALKS Monthly in-store tastings   CELLARAGE £5 per case per year on sliding scale

This is a long and elaborate fine wine list, concentrating on claret, Burgundy, vintage Port and vintage Champagne.

All areas abound with old and rare vintages of the wines. This is especially true of claret – a recent list went back to 1949, but they often have pre-war wines as well. Many of the wines are available by the bottle as well as the case. The most recent vintage is 1982, although keeping bang up to date, they also make en primeur offers of claret.

While much of the older Burgundy is négociant wine, newer vintages have a good gathering of domaine bottling and négociant bottling. On a current list, vintages of red Burgundy went back to 1953, of white back to 1970. There is a small selection of German estate wines, with occasional old vintages, and a strange, out-of-place range of standard Italian wines. But we're back to finest and rarest with some of the vintage Champagnes (there are non-vintage wines as well) and a big range of vintage Ports.

Best buys

Old vintages of claret

The Nobody Inn

Doddiscombsleigh, nr Exeter, Devon EX6 7PS   TEL (0647) 52394
OPEN Mon–Sat 10.30–3, 6–11   Sun 12–3, 7–10.30   CREDIT CARDS Access, Visa; personal and business accounts   DISCOUNTS 5% for 1 case
DELIVERY Free within 10-mile radius (min 6 bottles); mail order available
GLASS HIRE Free   TASTINGS AND TALKS Monthly tutored tastings; tastings for selected customers; willing to open bottle for tasting   CELLARAGE Free for wines purchased from the premises

While we concentrate on the wines, whisky connoisseurs will have a happy time at this shop attached to a Devon pub just outside Exeter.

On the wine side, not forgetting their proper interest in local Devon vineyards at Whitstone and Yearlstone, their greatest strengths seem to be in the New World – especially Australia – and in a marvellous range of sweet wines, particularly the under-rated dessert wines of the Loire. We have long advocated the Quarts de Chaume from Jean Baumard and Laffourcade and Bonnezeaux, forgotten stars and very good value. Also try wines from the other Loire sweet areas, Vouvray and Montlouis. There are some old vintages – for instance, Bonnezeaux 1935, Ch des Gauliers at £52.

Elsewhere in France, a big range of clarets (back to the 1961 vintage, mainly of classed growths) is offered at some good prices. More recent vintages have petit château wines and crus bourgeois. Beaujolais does well, too, with Duboeuf wines in evidence, and a few domaine wines, too. Burgundy is less interesting, but there's a good selection from Alsace.

Beyond France, consider the German estate wines (Schloss Johannisberg in the Rheingau and Friedrich Wilhelm Gymnasium on the Mosel are among the top names), and Torres wines and La Rioja Alta Riojas from Spain.

Then to the New World. California (with Heitz, Ridge, Beaulieu and Stags Leap among others) is joined by wines from Yamhill Winery in Oregon and by Carnelian wines from Texas. And in Australia, we find a big range – Tyrrells, Lindeman's, Penfold's, Stanley Leasingham, Rothbury, Yalumba, Idyll Vineyard.

Best buys

Coteaux du Layon, Chaume 1985, Ch de la Roulière, Jaudeau, £6.36; Gewürztraminer 1985, Stewart Vineyards, Washington State, £4.84; German estate wines; De Bortoli Chardonnay 1984, £4.73

Rex Norris

50 Queens Road, Haywards Heath,   TEL (0444) 454756
West Sussex RH16 1EE

OPEN Mon–Thur, Sat 9–5.30   Fri 9–7.30   CLOSED Sun, public holidays
CREDIT CARDS Access, Visa; personal and business accounts
DISCOUNTS 10% for whole cases   DELIVERY Free in Sussex
GLASS HIRE Free   TASTINGS AND TALKS Monthly in-store tastings
CELLARAGE Not available

A well-balanced list which is constantly changing as new lines get added. One area in focus at the moment is the New World, with wines from Lindeman's and Brown Brothers being added in Australia, as well as Stag's Leap in California and Cooks in New Zealand – watch out for more to follow in all these parts of the world.

In Europe, a major strength is Spain, with a good range of Riojas (including Gran Reservas back to 1973 – the Marqués de Villamagna is £8.50), Torres wines from Penedès and the Valdepeñas Señorio de los Llanos 1975 Reserva at £3.65. Italy seems less interesting, although the house wines from the Veneto are all good value. There are Chiantis from Ruffino (Riserva Ducale 1979) and Villa Cerna (the 1981 vintage is £3.83), and look also for the Valpolicella Castello d'Illasi from Santi.

In Germany, Rex Norris has assembled an interesting selection of half-bottles of top quality Eisweinen, Trockenbeerenauslesen and Beerenauslesen. Most French areas are covered: the Pouilly Fumé of Ch de Tracy (1985 vintage at £6.75) or Rhône wines from Pascal or the Châteauneuf-du-Pape of Domaine du Vieux Télégraphe can be recommended. We find reasonable ranges of French country wines, Beaujolais from Chauvet (Chénas 1985 at £6.50), and clarets moving from petit château up to the very good value Ch Gruaud-Larose 1976 at £12.50. Vintage Ports go back to 1963.

Best buys

Lirac red and white Domaine Maby, £4.45; Chianti Classico 1981, Villa Cerna, £3.83; Valdepeñas Reserva 1975, Señorio de los Llanos, £3.65; half-bottles of German wines

Send us **your** views on the report forms at the back of the book.

Oddbins

HEAD OFFICE 31–33 Weir Road,   TEL 01-879 1199
Durnsford Industrial Estate, London SW19 8UG
100 branches in London, South-East, West Country, North-West and
Scotland

OPEN Generally Mon–Sat 9–9 Sun 12–2, 7–9.30 CLOSED Chr Day
CREDIT CARDS Access, Visa; personal and business accounts DISCOUNTS 5%
on 1 unmixed case DELIVERY Free to area local to branch (currently no min);
elsewhere no charge (within reason) GLASS HIRE Free with suitable case
order TASTINGS AND TALKS In-store tastings; to groups on request
CELLARAGE Not available

When one of our correspondents noted that his local branch of Gough
Brothers was being turned into an Oddbins, we were concerned that
only the sign outside would change. But we need not have worried:
the interior was transformed, the range of wines increased, a new and
interested manager took over – and another genuine Oddbins had
arrived.

Gough Brothers in southern England and Agnews in Scotland are all
part of the same group as Oddbins. Although they do not carry the
same range of wines, the quality in those shops has improved
dramatically under the influence of the Oddbins buying team.

Those buyers have been busy this year. They seem to have spent
much of their time in Australia, emerging with the most astonishing
range of top quality wines at ludicrously low prices. Penfolds have
supplied many of the bottles, but the real bargains go under the name
of Barossa Valley Estates.

The buyers have also nipped across the Channel, looking at the
French regions, and have come up with some star bargains such as the
red Coteaux de Quercy from Rigal in Cahors (£1.99) and an excellent
Fitou 1985 from Jean Jean (£2.25). There's more serious stuff in France
as well: Rhônes from Jaboulet Aîné, a small range of Burgundy, a good
collection of 1983 and 1985 clarets, and a stunning range of Champagne
(seven bottles for the price of six).

Elsewhere, watch out for a good number of bargain Bulgarians, an
Italian list that continues to take note of the quality that country can
produce, and some old vintages of Portuguese reds.

Best buys

Australian wines; Bulgarian wines; Vin de Pays du Quercy, Coteaux de
Quercy, Rigal et Fils, £1.99; Côtes du Rhône 1983, Guigal, £4.49;
Champagnes; Bonarda Oltrepò Pavese 1985, Fugazza, £3.69

Old Street Wine Company

See Prestige Vintners.

Oriel Wines

133 Upper Authton Road, Birkdale, Southport,   TEL (0704) 62074
Merseyside PR8 5NJ

OPEN Mon–Fri 9–5   CLOSED Sat, Sun, public holidays
CREDIT CARDS Access, Visa; personal and business accounts
DISCOUNTS 2–7% depending on quantity   DELIVERY Free to Southport,
Formby and Ormskirk; otherwise £2 in Merseyside, £3 per case in rest of UK
GLASS HIRE Free with any order   TASTINGS AND TALKS Monthly in-store
tastings and on request; to groups on request (min 10 people)   CELLARAGE Not
available ■

A small company who come into the Guide on the strength of their
German list (although Italian wines have been promised and they stock
already Granier Champagne). The German range covers all the main
regions, including Franconia, with wines from the Prince of Castell and
Johann Ruck in Iphofen. There are estate wines from a number of top
names – the State wine domaine in the Nahe, Louis Guntrum in the
Mosel, Langwerth in the Rheingau, and the good value wines from the
co-operative at Herxheim in the Rheinpfalz. Sparkling Sekt from
Schloss Wachenheim is also available.

Best buys

Schlossböckelheimer Kupfergrübe Riesling Kabinett 1983, Staatlichen
Weinbaudomänen, £4.36; Erbacher Marcobrunn Riesling Spätlese
1982, Freiherr Langwerth, £6.44

Ostlers

63A Clerkenwell Road, London EC1M 5NP   TEL 01-250 1522

OPEN Mon–Fri 9.30–7   Sat 10.30–4   CLOSED Sun, public holidays
CREDIT CARDS None accepted   DISCOUNTS Negotiable   DELIVERY Free
locally (min 1 case); mail order available   GLASS HIRE Free
TASTINGS AND TALKS Weekly in-store tastings (Sat); to groups on request
CELLARAGE Negotiable

Last year, Ostlers sold nothing but Australian wines. Now, while
they've kept their position as one of the best sources of wines from
Down Under, they've expanded and extended – into Europe
(especially Italy) and California.

But we should start with Australia. All the major wine-producing
areas of the country are rounded up: wineries include the big names
(Hill Smith, Rosemount, Lindeman's, Berri/Renmano, Hardys,
McWilliams, Tyrrells, Brown Brothers), but there are also quite a
number of smaller estates – especially in Western Australia (Vasse
Felix, Moss Wood, Leeuwin Estate). Most estates, can offer something
at any price level.

The new California range is becoming almost as extensive, with a
display of wines from Fetzer, Acacia, Pine Ridge, Tjisseling, Ch

Bouchaine, Montevina, plus the Gold Seal wines from Taylors in New York State.

In Italy, Ostlers have gone for top quality producers, so you get Pieropan in Soave (look for his sweet Recioto di Soave 1985, £10), Barale and Gemma in Barolo, Castello di Neive and the Confratelli di San Michele in Barbaresco, Allegrini in Valpolicella.

Old Madeiras and Ports are another satisfying corner of the list. Regular tutored tastings and dinners bring many wine producers to lecture to guests.

Best buys

Australian wines; Soave Classico 1985, La Rocca, Pieropan, £2.99; Fetzer California wines

---

Oxford & Cambridge Fine Wine

106 Walton Street,   TEL (0865) 57734
Oxford, Oxfordshire OX2 6AJ
48 Clifton Estate, Cherry Hinton Road,   TEL (0223) 215274
Cambridge, Cambridgeshire CB1 4FQ

OPEN Mail order only from Cambridge address during normal office hours
CREDIT CARDS Access, Visa   DELIVERY Free in Oxford, Cambridge and
London (min 1 case); elsewhere at cost   GLASS HIRE Available
TASTINGS AND TALKS Not available   CELLARAGE Available   ■

This is the company which took over the two Dolamore shops in Oxford and Cambridge. Although the Oxford shop remains, the Cambridge one has closed and a wine warehouse opened instead.

They've stayed very much in a French tradition – possibly in deference to their principal customers, the universities' colleges. Indeed, their house range is called the College Range and consists of good representative examples of a claret, a hock, a moselle, red and white Burgundy and two sparkling wines, one of them a Champagne, plus Port and Sherry. All are well bought and very reliable.

In the body of the list, it's the classic French areas which fare the best, so there'a a good cross-section of clarets back to 1975, with some decently priced petit château wines in more recent vintages (Ch Beauguérit 1982, Côtes de Bourg at £3.97; Ch de Cardaillan 1981, Graves at £5.51 – prices on the list do not include VAT, but we have added it here). Burgundy comes from a mixture of négociants and domaines (Savigny-lès-Beaune 1979 from Maison Forest de Chamilly looks a good buy at £9.12), while Beaujolais comes from Thorin.

On the Loire, we would enjoy the sweet Vouvray Moelleux of Gaston Huet (1976 vintage at £8.56), while on the Rhône there are wines from La Vieille Ferme and Ch de Beaucastel; Alsace wines come from the Turckheim co-operative.

Other parts of the wine world fare more briefly. There are a few

German estate wines, very little from Italy, some good names from
Spain (CVNE Riojas, Raimat Abadía and Jean León Cabernet
Sauvignon). There are Bulgarian wines offering their usual good value,
a few Australians (Brown Brothers and Hill Smith) and Montana from
New Zealand.

Best buys

Côtes du Roussillon, Domaine du Mas Sibade, £2.24; Ch Beauguérit
1982, Côtes de Bourg, £3.97; College Red Burgundy, £4; Rioja Reserva
1981, Añares, £3.75

Pavilion Wine Company

Finsbury Circus Gardens   TEL 01-628 8224
Finsbury Circus, London EC2M 7AB

OPEN Mon–Fri 9–8   CLOSED Sat, Sun, public holidays   CREDIT CARDS None
accepted; personal and business acounts   DISCOUNTS 2% for 6 cases
DELIVERY Free on UK mainland (min 2 cases); mail order available
GLASS HIRE Free   TASTINGS AND TALKS Occasional tastings
CELLARAGE £4.60 per case per year   ■

The Pavilion Wine Company's is not a long list, sticking mainly to top
producers in the classic regions of France, but there are one or two
pleasant surprises.

Look, for instance, for the Balgownie wines from Australia – if you
can get hold of the Balgownie Chardonnay 1985, this is a must at £7.54
(prices do not include VAT, we have added it here). Or try the fine
Joseph Phelps California wines, or wines from Jean León in Spain, or
the famous Mas de Daumas Gassac wines of the Hérault in southern
France (but wait at least ten years before drinking the 1985 red).

In a more traditional vein, we move to Bordeaux, with a small
selection of crus bourgeois and a few more pricey classed growths,
plus some 1985 wines to lay down. In sweet white Bordeaux, there's
the remarkable Ch Gilette 1955 at £47.44 a bottle which spent 25 years
in a sealed vat before bottling, and, for its age, is astonishingly fresh. In
Burgundy, the Pavilion Wine Company have found a good basic
Bourgogne Rouge from Aubert de Villaine (Clos de la Fortune 1985 at
£6.52), as well as more serious domaine wines. The Loire's stars are
Marc Brédif in Vouvray and the Savennières of Soulez, or you might
prefer the less common Gamay-based Côtes Roannaises from the
foothills of the Auvergne (1985 at £3.31).

On the Rhône, Jaboulet Aîné is the favoured supplier, but there's
also Guigal's Côtes du Rhône. In Alsace, the wines are from
Zind-Humbrecht. House Champagne is from Ailerons et Baie (Cuvée
Le Pavillon at £9.87).

If you want to try any of these wines before buying, visit the
Pavilion's wine bar at its premises in the old cricket pavilion in
Finsbury Circus Gardens (see WINE BARS section).

Best buys

Alsace Marée 1983, Zind-Humbrecht, £3.68; Savennières Ch de Chamboureau, Soulez, £4.85; Vin Blanc Chardonnay, Marcel Vincent, £4.60; Côtes Roannaises 1985, £3.31; Manzanilla La Gitana, £3.26

Peatling & Cawdron

HEAD OFFICE Westgate House, Bury St Edmunds,   TEL (0284) 5948
Suffolk IP33 1QS
33 branches in Suffolk, Norfolk, Essex, Cambridgeshire, Hertfordshire, Lincolnshire and Northamptonshire

Hours vary from branch to branch CREDIT CARDS Access, Visa; personal and business accounts DISCOUNTS 5% on 1 case DELIVERY Free in Eastern Counties (min 1 case); elsewhere at cost; mail order available GLASS HIRE Free with case order TASTINGS AND TALKS Regular in-store tastings; to groups on request CELLARAGE Free for wines purchased from the store

Anybody who lives in East Anglia would be well advised to visit this group of shops whose wine-buying is consistent and sensible. While keeping up their concentration on Bordeaux and Burgundy, Peatling & Cawdron have expanded into many other regions, and have produced an enormous list of over 800 wines.

They maintain the traditional wine merchants' service of buying young claret and then maturing it before putting it on sale. Consequently, you find plenty of wines from vintages back to the mid-1970s, and some bottles of older wines (including 1961). The petits châteaux are especially good, plenty of bargains among them (look especially in 1979 and 1981).

Burgundy goes in for a mix of négociant and domaine wines, and there are still plenty of 1983 wines as well as older vintages. The Rhône selection is shorter but contains good items from Salavert and from Paul Avril in Châteauneuf-du-Pape. On the Loire, we have enjoyed the Ménétou-Salon of Jacky Rat and the sweet Anjou wines of Jean Baumard. Some 1983 Alsace wines can still be had at very good prices.

The German estate wine list is extensive, covering wines from 1985, 1983 and even back to 1976. Peatling's interest in Italy and Torres wines from Spain is growing. A few Sherries, some vintage Ports and the short New World list are well chosen.

Best buys

Petit château claret; Bulgarian varietal wines; Listel wines from the south of France; Cahors Tradition, £3.49; Alsace wines

Pennine Wines

See the Wine Schoppen.

Pennyloaf Wines

96 Station Road, Odsey, Ashwell,   TEL (046 274) 2725
Hertfordshire SG7 5RR

OPEN Most of the time; advisable to telephone before calling
CREDIT CARDS None accepted; personal and business accounts
DISCOUNTS Variable (min 3 cases)   DELIVERY Free within 10-mile radius (min
1 case); elsewhere at cost   GLASS HIRE Free with 1+ case order
TASTINGS AND TALKS Approx 6 tastings (each 3 days' duration) held
throughout the year; to groups on request   CELLARAGE £1.75 per case per
year   ■

Pennyloaf's is a short list which homes in particularly on South-West
France and the Loire. As most interesting from the South-West, we
pick out the Cahors, Bergerac and Côtes de Buzet wines. Look for the
Cahors 1979 of Ch de Cayrou at £5.35 (prices on the list do not include
VAT, but we have added them here), or the rare, sweet white
Saussignac 1980 Moelleux of Pierre Sadoux at £3.89. Bergerac comes
from Ch la Jaubertie, Buzet wines from the main – and good –
co-operative.

On the Loire, there's a good showing of red wines from Chinon,
St-Nicolas de Bourgueil and Saumur-Champigny (Ch de Chaintres
1983 at £5.17), plus Vouvray from Gaston Huet and Pouilly Fumé Les
Bascoins from Domaine Masson-Blondelet. In sweet whites, we would
go for the Coteaux du Layon Rochefort of Domaine de la Motte.

Elsewhere, Duboeuf Beaujolais, small selections of claret and
Burgundy and Clairette de Die sparkling wines complete the
inventory.

Best buys

Côtes de Buzet 1985, Cuvée Napoléon, £4.04; Cépage Sauvignon,
Vignerons de Saumur, £3.16; Touraine Rouge 1985 Cabernet Franc,
Berger Frères, £3.97

Christopher Piper Wines   🗁 ☞

1 Silver Street, Ottery St Mary,   TEL (040 481) 4139/2197
Devon EX11 1DB

OPEN Mon–Fri 9–1, 2.30–6   Sat 9–1, 2.30–5   CLOSED Sun, public holidays
CREDIT CARDS Access, Visa; personal and business accounts   DISCOUNTS 5%
for 1 mixed case; trade prices for 3+ cases   DELIVERY Free in mainland UK;
10-mile radius min 1 case, South-West England min 4 cases, elsewhere min 6
cases; mail order available   GLASS HIRE Free with 1-case order; free if a regular
customer   TASTINGS AND TALKS Once a fortnight in-store tastings (Sat); to
groups on request   CELLARAGE £3.60 per case per annum

While Burgundy and Beaujolais are the stars of this list, other areas have come on apace – the Rhône, for example, and the Loire.

Some fine wines from the southern Côtes du Rhône are very impressive: the Vacqueyras 1985 of J Ricard at Domaine le Sang des Cailloux is one (£4.46), as is the Rasteau 1985 of Domaine la Soumade (£4.49). Also in this section, try the Châteauneuf-du-Pape of Daniel Brunier.

On the Loire, we like the look of wine from Ménétou-Salon (Domaine Georges Chavet) and the surprisingly tasty Muscadet sur Lie of Domaine de la Bodinière (1986 vintage at £3.88). Other areas of interest in France (outside the classic areas) are the wines from Provence and the Champagnes of George Goulet.

Bordeaux is sensibly assembled, but more interest focuses on a solid phalanx of domaine Burgundies, including – for those with slim wallets – whites and reds from the Mâconnais and the Côte Chalonnaise. For Beaujolais, there is a strong showing of Georges Duboeuf wines, and some from Mr Piper's own estate at Ch des Tours in Brouilly.

Beyond France, he offers plenty of German estate wines, and some good value (and quality) in Italy from Masi in Veneto, Lageder in the Alto Adige and Franco Fiorina in Piedmont. A round-up of the rest of the list produces CVNE Riojas, and reds from J M da Fonseca in Portugal, Brown Brothers in Australia, Cooks in New Zealand and Mondavi in California. Sherries are from Barbadillo. A particular feature of Christopher Piper's list is the terrific range of half-bottles.

Best buys

Bourgogne Rouge Pinot Noir 1985, Caves des Vignerons de Buxy, £4.70; Duboeuf Beaujolais; Vacqueyras 1985, Cailloux, £4.46; German estate wines; Mâcon-Lugny 1986, Duboeuf, £4.75

Plumtree Wines

8 Normanton Lane, Keyworth,   TEL (06077) 5615
Nottinghamshire NG12 5HA

OPEN Every day 9–11   CREDIT CARDS None accepted; personal and business accounts   DISCOUNTS 10% for 1 case (selected wines)   DELIVERY Free within 25-mile radius of Nottingham (min 1 case); elsewhere at cost
GLASS HIRE Free   TASTINGS AND TALKS To groups on request
CELLARAGE Not available   ■

This company started trading in 1986 but has already built up an attractive list, with the current emphasis on Spain and short selections from France. Australian wines are promised for the future, and Plumtree are also planning to open a wine warehouse.

While the Spanish range includes Riojas, it also manages to offer interest in other areas. León comes up with some good, basic house wines (Viña Coyanza red and white at £1.99 – prices on the list do not include VAT, but we've added it here – plus the more familiar Palacio de León red at £2.38). Then we find wines from J Ferret in Penedès and the Cava of the Louis de Vernier, and the Cabernet-Sauvignon-based Marqués de Griñon (1983 vintage at £7.42).

France contributes wines from the Midi (a good Côtes du Roussillon 1985 at £2.92 and a Merlot-based vin de pays), a few clarets and Beaujolais from Loron.

Best buys

Cava Louis de Vernier Brut, £4.60; Palacio de León red and white, £2.38; Rioja 1980, Viña Ramona, £3.89

Stephen Porter Wines

Turvey House, 104 Oxstalls Lane,   TEL 0452) 415160
Longlevens, Gloucester, Gloucestershire GL2 9HX

OPEN Mon–Sat 9–6 (by appointment only) Sun, public holidays by appointment   CLOSED Chr, New Year   CREDIT CARDS None accepted; personal and business accounts   DISCOUNTS Negotiable   DELIVERY Free within 50-mile radius from Gloucester and Central London (min 1 case); elsewhere £3 per case; mail order available   GLASS HIRE Free with 1-case order   TASTINGS AND TALKS To groups on request   CELLARAGE £3 per case per year

Mr Porter has been on the move in the past year – twice in six months, in fact. But he has now settled permanently just outside Gloucester, where he runs his business from home.

It's a fine wine list, with a strong emphasis on claret (including an opening offer en primeur for 1986s), and older vintages of top châteaux (Ch Pétrus seems to be strongly featured at the usual amazingly high prices, with even older vintages of Pétrus in the Bin Ends list). Classed growths from the Médoc at more reasonable prices are also available. Recent vintages of Mas de Daumas Gassac from the Hérault, Ch de Beaucastel Châteauneuf-du-Pape from the Rhône, a top-class Brouilly from Domaine Cret des Garanches (1985 vintage at £4.99) are other draws.

From much further afield, it might be interesting to try the Bordeaux-style discovery from New Zealand, called The Antipodean, for which Stephen Porter at the moment is exclusive world wide agent. Prices, says Mr Porter, will not be inexpensive.

Best buys

Ch Paret Beauséjour 1985, Côtes de Castillon, £4.25; Brouilly 1985, Cret des Garanches, £4.99; Côtes du Rhône 1985, Cru du Coudoulet, £4.99

Premier Wines

Building 20, Stevenston Industrial Estate,   TEL (0294) 602409
Stevenston, Ayrshire KA20 3LR

OPEN Mon–Fri 9–5   CLOSED Sat, Sun, public holidays   CREDIT CARDS None
accepted; personal and business accounts   DISCOUNTS Quantity discounts
(min 2 cases)   DELIVERY Free in Scotland (min 5 cases)   GLASS HIRE Free with
2-case order   TASTINGS AND TALKS Monthly tastings in-store; to groups on
request (one month's notice required)   CELLARAGE Negotiable   ■

While this list has a decent claret section, with a good number of wines
back to 1976 and earlier, and some Alsace wines from Léon Beyer, it's
best when it strays from the classic areas.

We suspect there could be an interesting Italian list – if only we knew
who made the big range of wines from Piedmont. But in Portugal,
information is given about the Bairrada wines of Barrocão (some old
vintages here – 1970 and 1974), about the dry Vinho Verde of Cinco
Cidades, the famous red Colares of Chitas – 1970 vintage means it's
just about ready to drink – and the reds from Estremadura.

Other specialities seem to be in Eastern and Central Europe, with a
range of Austrian wines (from Sepp Hold and Franz Mayer) that
probably makes them the biggest stockists of Austrian wine in the
country at the moment. Familiar Bulgarian wines, and a bigger than
usual selection of wines from Hungary, are additional attractions.

The other good section is the fortified wines. Most Ports are from
Niepoort, while Premier Wines obtain their Madeiras (with several
vintage bottles) from Cossart Gordon.

Best buys

Vintage Madeiras; wines from Bairrada, Portugal; Bulgarian wines

Premier Wine Warehouse   🖙

3 Heathmans Road, London SW6 4TJ   TEL 01-736 9073

OPEN Mon–Fri 11–8   Sat 10–7   Sun 11–4   CLOSED Public holidays
CREDIT CARDS Visa; business accounts   DISCOUNTS Negotiable (trade only)
DELIVERY Free within 3-mile radius north of Thames (min 1 case); elsewhere at
cost; mail order available   GLASS HIRE Free with 1-case order
TASTINGS AND TALKS Theme tastings every 6–8 weeks; to groups on request
CELLARAGE Not available   ■

French country wines and Spanish wines are the two areas to note at
this Parsons Green warehouse, as well as the good, everyday drinking
from a range of house wines.

In the house wines, we would recommend the Chardonnay del
Veneto Valdizze at £2.25; or the Vin Rouge de Labastide de Lévis in the
Gaillac region of South-West France (£1.79). Only slightly further up
the scale, price-wise, we'd pick the crisp Sauvignon de St-Bris of Luc

Sorin (1985 vintage at £3.69) and consider a good – if small – selection of rosés. In the reds, some good things from the Rhône and from Beaujolais have been brought together, plus a few pricier offerings from Bordeaux.

Spain gives plenty of choice. The range goes from basic red and white from Cariñena and La Mancha up through standard Riojas from Solar de Samaniego, through Torres, to some reservas from Lopez de Heredia, Muga and CVNE. Torres also supply some Chilean wines.

From Italy, there are whites from Tiefenbrunner in the Alto Adige, and the 'rest of the world' section covers Australia, Lebanon and Portugal (with wines from J M da Fonseca). Good Champagne and a selection of Spanish sparkling cavas round off the list.

Best buys

Monte Ory 1978 Gran Reserva, Navarra, £2.99; Marqués de Murrieta 1982 Blanco, £3.99; Crozes-Hermitage 1982, Michel Bernard, £3.99; Torres Gran Coronas 1982, £4.25; Rioja Tondonia 1979, £4.59

Prestige Vintners

15 Stucley Place, London NW1 6NS   TEL 01-485 5895
The Old Street Wine Company,   TEL 01-729 1768
309 Old Street, London EC1V 9LE (Retail)

OPEN Mon–Fri 11–7   Sat 11–2   CLOSED Sun, public holidays
CREDIT CARDS None accepted; personal and business accounts
DISCOUNTS 5% on orders over 5 cases   DELIVERY Free within area of
North/South Circular (min 1 case); elsewhere 1 case £6.79, 2 cases £3.68 per case,
3–5 cases £2.58 per case, 6–9 cases £2.01 per case, 10–24 cases £1.15 per case,
24+ cases free; mail order available   GLASS HIRE Free with wine order
TASTINGS AND TALKS To groups on request   CELLARAGE Negotiable   ■

This isn't a long list, but treats in the most unexpected places make it very worthwhile.

One of those areas is the South-West of France. There are wines from the top co-operative in Buzet who produce the splendid-sounding red Cuvée Napoléon (the 1985 vintage is £4.28 – beware the price list does not include VAT, although we have added it here). We like the look of the Jurançon from Ch Jolys (both sweet and dry), the Cahors of Reutenauer (Cuvée Royale Prestige at £4.93), red Madiran and white Côtes de Saint-Mont, and red and white Gaillac.

Another good area is the Loire. The sweet wines of Coteaux du Layon, Bonnezeaux and Quarts de Chaume are all present, as is Savennières from Coulée de Serrant. There are Chinon and Bourgueil in reds, and Vouvrays from Gaston Huet.

Other areas worth perusing in this interesting lists are the good range of Champagnes, the Sherries from Valdespino, German wines from Balthasar Ress, and single vineyard Alsace from Clos St-Landelin.

Best buys

Vin de Pays des Côtes de Gascogne Colombard 1985, £2.53; Jurançon Ch Jolys dry, £3.20, and sweet, £3.63; Chinon 1985, Domaine René Couly, £4.57; Martinez Selected Tawny Port, £5.63; Deliciosa Manzanilla Sherry, Valdespino, £3.97

Le Provençal

See The Market and Winecellars.

Pugsons Food and Wine

82 Wandsworth Bridge Road, London SW6 2TF   TEL 01-736 6145

OPEN Mon–Fri 10–8   Sat 10–6   CLOSED Sun, public holidays
CREDIT CARDS Access, Visa; personal and business accounts
DISCOUNTS Available   DELIVERY Free in Central and parts of South-West London (min 1 case); otherwise £2.90 charge; mail order available
GLASS HIRE Free with 1-case order   TASTINGS AND TALKS Annual tasting; occasional in-store tastings; to groups on request   CELLARAGE £3.20 per case per year

A display of well-chosen wines has been carefully chosen to go with the food in this attractive shop. Considerable inspiration from chef Roger Vergé is apparent in the food, and this extends to the range of Provençal wines which are sold as house wines in the Vergé restaurant, Le Moulin de Mougins. Other house wines come from Nathaniel Johnston in Bordeaux.

Pugsons also stock a few clarets from recent vintages, a small range of growers' Burgundies (with the emphasis on wines from Bernard Rossignol) and similarly short selections from Beaujolais, the Rhône, Alsace and the Loire. Prices tend to be on the high side.

Best buys

Rouge de Provence 1985, £4.50; Cuvée Champfleury, Nathaniel Johnston, £3.25

Queens Club Wines

2 Charleville Road, London W14 9JL   TEL 01-385 3582

OPEN Mon–Sat 10.30–10.30   Sun 12–2, 7–9   CLOSED Suns during public holiday weekends   CREDIT CARD None accepted; personal accounts
DISCOUNTS 5% for 1 case   DELIVERY Free in West Kensington (min 1 case)
GLASS HIRE Not available   TASTINGS AND TALKS Occasional tastings held in restaurant; to groups on request   CELLARAGE Not available

We can't give you many details about the wines at this small shop because the list changes so frequently, but we recommend a visit just to meet the people whose claimed ambition is 'to make a million'.

Recent lists included the João Pires Moscato from Portugal (1986 vintage at £3.95); Tyrrell's Long Flat Red from Australia (1982 vintage at £4), a red and white Vin de Pays de l'Aude at £2.55; the Lebanese Ch Musar 1979 at £5.50; and Bulgarian Chardonnay at £2.60.

Best buys

Regular special offers

Arthur Rackhams

CELLARS AND ADMINISTRATION CENTRE   TEL (09323) 51585
Winefare House, 5 High Road, Byfleet,
Weybridge, Surrey KT14 7QF
14 branches in London and Surrey

OPEN Hours vary   CREDIT CARDS All accepted   DISCOUNTS 5% on 1 case;
special prices for Vintner Wine Club members   DELIVERY Free (min 3 cases);
mail order available   GLASS HIRE At managers' discretion
TASTINGS AND TALKS Regular in-store tastings during weekends; to groups on
request   CELLARAGE Not available

Having dropped the 'wine warehouse' part of their name, and gone back to plain 'Arthur Rackhams', this small group of shops now describes itself simply as a 'good wine merchant'.

Certainly their list is looking good, and one to watch. It has an old-fashioned feel to it, with a solid range of clarets: plenty of classed growths back to 1976 and a choice of younger wines to lay down – plus petit château wines to drink now. They buy quite heavily from Cordier estates like Ch Gruaud-Larose and Ch Talbot (including those estates' second wines). Prices start from £2.95 for Ch Bel-Air 1983, Bordeaux Supérieur.

Another strong area is Champagne. Alfred Gratien is the preferred name, with some remarkable old vintages (back to 1964) of this firm's Crémant. Charles de Muret supplies the basic house Champagne (£7.99).

For yet more interest, look to a good selection from the South and South-West of France (Corbières 1984, Domaine Surbezy-Cartier, £3.45). Italy is perking up with Veneto wines from Zenato (Soave and Valpolicella) and some super vini da tavola from Monte Vertine in Chianti.

Other parts of the world also fare well. From Australia, there are wines from Brown Brothers, de Bortoli and Lindemans; Montana wines from New Zealand, and the animal duo from California – Stag's Leap and Hawk Crest.

The Vintner Wine Club offers discounts and tastings (see the WINE CLUBS section).

Best buys

Corbières 1984, Domaine Surbezy-Cartier, £3.45; Soave Classico 1985, Zenato, £3.65; Siglo Saco Tinto Rioja 1984, £3.45; The Vintner Claret (NV), £2.75; Champagne Charles de Muret (NV), £7.99; Australian Chardonnay 1985, de Bortoli, £4.55

Raeburn Fine Wines and Foods

23 Comely Bank Road, Edinburgh EH4 1DS   TEL 031-332 5166

OPEN Mon–Sat 9–8   Sun 9.30–6 (*not* open for sale of alcoholic drinks) public holidays 9–8   CREDIT CARDS None accepted   DISCOUNTS 5% on unmixed cases, 2½% on mixed cases   DELIVERY Free in Edinburgh area (min 1 case); elsewhere charges negotiable; mail order available   GLASS HIRE Free with 1-case order; delivery free with order   TASTINGS AND TALKS For local groups on request   CELLARAGE Not available

This small grocery shop continues to be a revelation. We heard about it when an inspector – three years ago now – discovered a bottle of Krug Champagne between the baked beans and the pickles. Even then we didn't expect to find one of the country's best wine lists. Because of the restricted space in the shop, much of the stock – especially of finer wines – is stored elsewhere, so it is advisable to give Zubair Mohamed time to bring it to the shop for you.

This year, he has completely re-organised his list in order to start importing as many as possible of the wines direct, so that although some familiar wines are still there, much is new, especially in France.

Mr Mohamed's interests remain in certain areas: French regional wines, for example, where he offers a big range of Cahors wines (Clos Triguedina 1982 is £4.95; Domaine de Paillas 1983 is £3.99). He has assembled a good few 1985 Beaujolais, and Chablis is well treated with wines from Jean-Paul Droin and Louis Pinson. Domaine wines cover Burgundy proper as well: Domaine Vincent and Domaine Corsin in Pouilly-Fuissé, Domaine de la Folie in Rully, Leflaive in Puligny-Montrachet, Comtes Lafon in Meursault, Henri Jayer, Tollot-Beaut and Pousse d'Or. Drouhin supplies the négociant wines.

In Bordeaux, the focus is on certain châteaux: Ch Rouet in Fronsac, Ch Sociando-Mallet in Haut-Médoc, Ch Deyrem-Valentin in Margaux, Domaine de Chevalier and Ch Malartic-Lagravière in Graves, Vieux Château Certan in Pomerol. Other clarets and good Sauternes are for sale, too – with vintages back to 1978.

On to a big selection of Rhône wines – from Jaboulet Aîné in the north and Roger Combe in the south, among many others. Loire wines come from Delétang in Montlouis, Huet in Vouvray, Cotat in Sancerre and Leblanc in Coteaux du Layon, while Alsace wines are those of Rolly Gassmann, and Champagne is from the co-operative of Le Mesnil sur Oger.

In Germany, the list continues to bring together a fine collection of estate wines, with the State Domaine on the Nahe featured, von Schubert in the Ruwer and Bassermann-Jordan in the Rheinpfalz.

Passing Spain (Beronia and Murrieta Riojas, Torres wines, old Sherries from Gonzalez Byass) and Italy (Quintarelli in the Veneto, Monsanto in Chianti, the rare Fiorano Cabernet Sauvignon/Merlot wine from the Principe di Venosa in Latium), the list sails across the oceans. Wines are from Moss Wood, Cape Mentelle, Redgate, Leeuwin Estate in Western Australia; Balgownie in Victoria; Selaks supply New Zealand wines; and Californian names include Clos du Bois, Joseph Phelps and Heitz.

Not the least feature of this remarkable list is the number of half-bottles from many areas.

Best buys

Cuvée des Maréchaux red vin de table, Vermorel-Gaudet, £2.95; Côtes du Frontonnais 1985, Domaine de Callory, £3.99; Lirac 1981, Les Queyrades, £2.99; wines from Cahors; German estate wines; Hardy's Australian wines

Rattlers Wine Warehouse

Arch No 2, Viaduct Estate, Carlisle,   TEL (0228) 43033
Cumbria CA2 5BN

OPEN Mon–Fri 10.30–5.30   Sat 10.30–6.30   CLOSED Sun, public holidays
CREDIT CARDS Access, Visa; personal and business accounts
DISCOUNTS Negotiable   DELIVERY Free within 60-mile radius of Carlisle (min 1 case); elsewhere £1.55 per case   GLASS HIRE Free
TASTINGS AND TALKS Regular in-store tastings   CELLARAGE Negotiable   ■

There's a promise that the railway arch in which this merchant has his premises will be refurbished by owners British Rail, which will mean a tasting room and fewer draughts in the winter. But, for the time being, we are happy to make do for warmth with some of the wines on the list.

We would home straight in on some of the sensibly chosen petit château clarets, for instance, especially Ch Mayne-Vieil in Fronsac, or Ch Caronne Ste-Gemme in the Médoc . . . or some of the beefy reds from the southern Rhône – Domaine des Anges in the Côtes du Ventoux or Côtes du Rhône from the Rasteau co-operative. As a pricier choice, look for some of the Châteauneuf-du-Pape of Domaine Chante Cigale (1982 vintage, £6.29).

The rest of France now holds more interest: new wines from the South-West include the Jurançon sweet and dry of Clos Guirouilh, and the wood-aged Domaine de Tariquet Vin de Pays des Côtes de Gascogne (at £4.30). On the Loire, Sancerre is from Gitton Père et Fils; Sauvignon de Touraine – for those who want the taste of Sauvignon slightly cheaper – is from Domaine Guenault (£2.99).

Italy is coming along nicely, with some decent wines from Villadoria in Piedmont, plus Frescobaldi and Castelgiocondo in Tuscany. Spain is doing even better: a good set of Riojas from CVNE, wines from Ribera del Duero and Penedès (from Torres); Navarra and Valdepeñas also getting a look in. Rattlers have also rounded up a few Portuguese reds, more Bulgarians, Australian wines from Brown Brothers and Yalumba, and California wines from Joseph Phelps, Clos du Bois and Firestone. Sherries are from Garvey, Madeira from Blandys.

Best buys

Bulgarian wines; Côtes du Luberon Cuvée Spéciale 1985, Cellier de Marrenon, £2.59; Faugères 1984, Cuvée Jules Gaston, £2.59; wines from Listel; Ribera del Duero 2° año Tinto 1983, £3.39; Señorio de los Llanos Gran Reserva 1975, £3.69

Redpath and Thakray

WAREHOUSE AND OFFICE (mail order enquiries)   TEL (0223) 833495
Common Lane, Sawston, Cambridge,
Cambridgeshire CB2 4HW
RETAIL SHOP Joshua Taylor, Market Passage,   TEL (0223) 316455
Cambridge, Cambridgeshire CB2 3JN

OPEN (Shop) Mon–Sat 9–5.30   CLOSED Sun, some public holidays
CREDIT CARDS Joshua Taylor account cards only; personal and business
accounts   DISCOUNTS Trade list for 5+ cases   DELIVERY Free nationwide
(min 1 case); mail order available   GLASS HIRE Not available
TASTINGS AND TALKS 3–4 tastings annually in-store; specialised tastings for
college and trade customers at Oxford and Cambridge Universities
CELLARAGE Not available

This mail order and wholesale merchant now also operates from Joshua Taylor's department store in Cambridge, from where they sell a selection of their wider range.

The mail order list is larger but still quite selective: Burgundy comes from Jean Grivot and Fromont-Moindrot as well as the Buxy co-operative. On the Loire, the Quincy of Domaine Meunier is a delicious substitute for more expensive Sancerre (1985 vintage at £4.99). The short claret range contains the attractive Ch la Tour-Haut-Caussan 1983 at £5.85, while on the northern Rhône look for the superb Cornas 1983 of Maurice Courbois – but don't drink it for at least ten years.

The Rhône, in fact, is obviously a favourite area, and the Côtes du Rhône selection one of the highlights of the list – and at good prices. Roger Combe's Vacqueyras Domaine de la Fourmone is one of the dearest at £5.22, but there's also the basic Côtes du Rhône-Villages of the beautifully named co-operative of St-Pantaléon-lès-Vignes at £3.97. Look also for the Châteauneuf-du-Pape from Ch de Beaucastel.

Best buys

Côtes du Rhône-Villages 1985, St-Pantaléon-lès-Vignes, £3.97; Coteaux du Tricastin 1985, Co-opérative de St-Pantaléon-lès-Vignes, £3.35; Quincy 1985, Domaine Meunier, £4.99

Reid Wines

The Mill, Marsh Lane, Hallatrow,   TEL (0761) 52645
Nr Bristol BS18 5EB

Reid Wines Warehouse, Vestry Trading Estate,   TEL (0732) 458533
Otford Road, Sevenoaks, Kent TN14 5EL

OPEN Mon–Fri 9.30–6   Sat 9.30–1; (Hallatrow) by appointment on Sun and public holidays   CLOSED Sun, public holidays   CREDIT CARDS All accepted at Sevenoaks; Access, Visa at Hallatrow; personal and business accounts by arrangement   DISCOUNTS 5% on orders over £250 at Sevenoaks only (not available with delivery)   DELIVERY Free in London and within 20-mile radius of Hallatrow and Sevenoaks (min 1 case); elsewhere 1 bottle £2.50, 2 bottles £3.25, 3–6 bottles £5, 7–12 bottles £7, 12–24 bottles pro rata, 3–5 cases £4.50 per case, over 5 cases free; mail order available   GLASS HIRE Free with order; delivery with wine   TASTINGS AND TALKS Wine weekends; constant tastings at Sevenoaks   CELLARAGE £3 per case per year (not available to overseas customers)

This is the place to come for that bottle of Ch Latour 1925 at £85 you've always promised yourself. Or Ch Beychevelle 1934 at £45. Or even two bottles of Beaune Dr Barolet 1929 at £55. What this all means is that Reid Wines have one of the biggest collections of what the auctioneers like to call 'finest and rarest' wines in the country.

Obviously such a list changes rapidly, so you will need to contact them to find out what's available, and ask them in good time to get a wine you might need for a birthday, for instance, whether claret, Sauternes, red Burgundy (and younger vintages of white) or, of course, vintage Port and vintage Champagne.

More up-to-date sections cover the Rhône, the Loire and Alsace (there are also old vintages of sweet Loires and Alsace wines).

Reid Wines are strong across the oceans, too, with California wines in profusion from Clos du Val, plus a few wines from Heitz, Ridge, Mondavi, Phelps, Stag's Leap and others. There are Australian wines from Taltarni, and some old vintage Madeiras and almacenista Sherries.

Best buys

Old and rare wines; Clos du Val California wines; Taltarni Australian wines

Prices were current in summer 1987 to the best of our knowledge but can only be a rough indication of prices throughout 1988.

La Reserva Wines

Unit 6, Spring Grove Mills, Manchester Road,   TEL (0484) 846732
Linthwaite, Huddersfield, West Yorkshire HD7 5QG
ASSOCIATED OUTLET Grapehop,   TEL (0484) 533509
17 Imperial Arcade, Huddersfield,
West Yorkshire HD1 2BR (limited selection of Spanish wines)

OPEN Mon–Fri 9–5.30 Sat 9–5 CLOSED Sun CREDIT CARDS Access, Visa
DISCOUNTS 10% for 1 case DELIVERY Free within 15-mile radius (min order
depends on distance) GLASS HIRE Free with 1-case order
TASTINGS AND TALKS Some bottles open on Saturdays; occasional tastings by
invitation CELLARAGE Not available

While wines from France, Germany and Italy join a good Portuguese
range (especially the wines from J M da Fonseca), it's for Spanish wines
that we should look to this merchant.

Starting with Rioja, most of the major bodegas – and many of the
smaller ones, some of which are not otherwise available in the country
– contribute examples: Martinez Lacuesta, Santa Daria, Campillo, Viña
Salceda, with a number of Reservas and Gran Reservas.

Most areas of Spain are represented: Navarra with wines from
Señorio de Sarria and Julián Chivite; the Marqués de Griñon red from
Rueda; in Penedès, Conde de Caralt, Jean León (Cabernet Sauvignon
1980 at £7.60) and Torres. There are wines from Galicia, Lerida (Raimat
wines from here), Ribera del Duero (with wines from the co-operative
as well as from Vega Sicilia), Valdepeñas (the wines of Señorio de los
Llanos), from La Mancha and León (the Palacio de León wines).

Other big ranges cover Cavas (from six different producers) and
Sherries (from Bobadilla, Sanchez Romate, Jose de Soto, Garvey and
Lustau. Look also for the almacenista Sherries.

Best buys

Valdepeñas 1978, Señorio de los Llanos Reserva, £3.70; Palacio de León
Tinto, £2.43; Parxet Cava, Brut, £5.50; almacenista Sherries from
Lustau; Rioja 1981, Viña Salceda, £3.99

La Réserve

56 Walton Street, London SW3 1RB   TEL 01-589 2020
47 Kendal Street, London W2 2BU   TEL 01-402 6920

OPEN Mon, Tue 10–7 Wed 9.30–8 Thur, Fri 9.30–7 Sat 9.30–5.30
CLOSED Sun, public holidays CREDIT CARDS Access, Visa; personal and
business accounts DISCOUNTS 5% for 1 case, 10% for mixed and unmixed
cases of house wines DELIVERY Free in Central London (min 1 case);
elsewhere at cost; mail order available GLASS HIRE Free with 1-case order
TASTINGS AND TALKS In-store tastings every Saturday; to groups on request
CELLARAGE Not available

This is the regular retail side of the fine wines of College Cellar (*qv*). While wines from Spain, Italy and the New World do appear, the list concentrates on France. A long list of claret kicks off, mixing petit château wines with crus bourgeois and some classed growths. Vintages go back to several from 1970 (Ch du Glana, St-Julien is £11.55). There's also plenty to choose from if you want sweet white Sauternes or Barsac.

In Burgundy, domaine wines dominate – Morot in Beaune is to be highly recommended, but there are plenty more. The Rhône presents a well-balanced list, with, unusually, some old vintages (Ch Rayas, Châteauneuf du Pape 1974 at £22.50). The Loire brings on the Vouvray Clos Naudin of Foreau, while Alsace offers Louis Gisselbrecht.

In Italy, the stars are Borgogno's Barolos, while in California, Clos du Bois and Edna Valley are the chosen wineries; in Australia, Yalumba and Idyll Vineyard (plus the top Grange Hermitage from Penfold's) should be considered. Sherries come from Barbadillo, Madeiras from Cossart Gordon – and La Réserve stocks plenty of Champagne.

Best buys

Côtes du Ventoux, La Vieille Ferme, £3.45; Touraine Sauvignon 1985, Plouzeau, £3.99; Beaujolais-Villages 1985, Domaine des Colombières, £4.95; Montepulciano d'Abruzzo 1982, Illuminati, £6.45; Merlot 1983, Clos du Bois, £5.65

Reynier Wine Libraries

Reynier at Fleet Lane, The Old Bailey, 29 Fleet Lane, London EC4M 4YA	TEL 01-236 0552
Reynier Wine Library, The Hole in the Wall, Little Castle Street, Exeter, Devon EX3 3PX	TEL (0392) 51657

See Eldridge Pope.

Richmond Wine Warehouse

138c Lower Mortlake Road, Richmond, Surrey TW9 2JZ	TEL 01-948 4196

OPEN Mon, Tue, Wed, Thur, Sat 10–7   Fri 10–8   CLOSED Sun, public holidays   CREDIT CARDS None accepted; personal and business accounts   DISCOUNTS Discretional   DELIVERY Free locally (min 1 case); elsewhere £5 per case; mail order available   GLASS HIRE Free with case order   TASTINGS AND TALKS Informal tastings on Saturdays   CELLARAGE Not available ∎

It's still the clarets (and the lovely large bottles of Louis Roederer and Joseph Perrier Champagne) that keep this warehouse in the Guide.

They keep a good choice of petit château and cru bourgeois clarets at attractive prices. For a lovers' tiff we would recommend Ch Jalousie 1983 at £3.48, or, more seriously, Ch Pabeau 1981, cru bourgeois at £4.50; or Ch Fourcas-Hosten 1979 at £7.79 – the same price as last year. There are classed growths as well.

Elsewhere, look for the French regional wines (Ch la Condamine Corbières 1985 is £2.60), the Chianti Classico of San Felice (1983 vintage at £3.45), Torres Spanish wines, or Australian wines from Wyndhams and Geoff Merrill.

Best buys

Petit château and cru bourgeois clarets

Roberts & Cooper

This chain of off-licences was bought by Peter Dominic (*qv*) during 1987, and shops are being converted to the Peter Dominic style and appearance – as well as taking on their range of wines. Some of the smaller branches may close.

Alexander Robertson & Partners

2 Church Street, Warwick,   TEL (0926) 492888
Warwickshire CV34 4AB

OPEN Mon–Fri 9.30–5 CLOSED Sat, Sun, public holidays
CREDIT CARDS Access, Visa; personal and business accounts
DISCOUNTS Only on case price DELIVERY Free within 50-mile radius; elsewhere by mail order GLASS HIRE Free with wine-case order; delivery available TASTINGS AND TALKS Monthly in-store tastings by invitation; on request CELLARAGE Not available

This new entry to the Guide relies mainly on wines from Barwell and Jones (*qv*), so the strong areas are in Italy and the South of France, with occasional forays elsewhere.

Italy is the best: wines from Guerrieri-Rizzardi in the Veneto (Soave and Valpolicella), plus Col d'Orcia Brunello di Montalcino and the lesser (often more approachable) Rosso di Montalcino. Spain produces Riojas from Bodegas Montecillo and a pair of almacenista Sherries.

In France claret vintages go back to 1985 (but in small quantities). Rhône and Burgundy come mainly from Jaboulet-Vercherre, and Alsace from Pierre Sparr. Southern French wines include the Commanderie de la Bargemone in Coteaux d'Aix-en-Provence and the Cabernet Sauvignon Vin de Pays de Mont Caume 1985 (£3.86).

Best buys

Bergerac 1985, Ch Belingard Rouge, £3.27; Côtes du Rhône 1985, Domaine de St-Estève Blanc, £3.41; Rosso di Montalcino 1983, Col d'Orcia, £3.63

C A Rookes

Birds Building, Birmingham Road,   TEL (0789) 297777
Stratford upon Avon, Warwickshire CV37 0AZ

OPEN Mon–Fri 8.30–6   Sat 9–5   CLOSED Sun, public holidays
CREDIT CARDS Access, Visa; personal and business accounts
DISCOUNTS Variable to Wine Club members   DELIVERY Free in Stratford upon
Avon district; elsewhere at cost; mail order available   GLASS HIRE Free with
1-case order   TASTINGS AND TALKS Regular tastings for Wine Club members;
to groups on request   CELLARAGE £3 per case per year

As we noted last year, this list works best when it moves away from
Bordeaux and Burgundy. (Prices do not include VAT, but we've added
it here.)

The French regions are looking good, with wines from Listel, the
excellent Côtes du Luberon, wines of Ch Val-Joanis (red 1984 at £3.36),
and in the South-West, from Fitou, Côtes du Marmandais and Cahors.
On the Loire, there's a fine Pouilly Fumé, Coteau des Girarmes 1985 at
£7.06; on the Rhône, the Châteauneuf is from Clos du Mont Olivet.

C A Rookes must be proud of an extensive selection of Champagnes
from Gosset and Laurent Perrier, including large bottle sizes. German
wines are mainly from Louis Guntrum, and Italian wines have some of
the single vineyard Orvieto of Bigi (Toricella Seco 1986 at £4.27), as well
as the fine Verdicchio Casal di Serra of Bianchi. Riojas are from Lopez
Heredia, Faustino and Torres.

New Zealand bottles are more numerous than Australian here
(Montana and Cooks) and, round the other side of the globe, England
is represented by wines from Wootton Vineyards in Somerset. Sherries
are by Valdespino, Madeiras by Cossart Gordon.

There is a fine wine list of clarets and vintage Ports.

Best buys

Ch Val-Joanis Rouge 1984, £3.36; Listel wines; Valdespino Sherries;
C A Rookes Finest Hunting Port, £5.85

William Rush

Tecklewood, Uplands Close, Gerrards Cross,   TEL (0753) 882659
Buckinghamshire SL9 7JH

OPEN All reasonable hours   CREDIT CARDS Access; trade accounts
DISCOUNTS 5% for 1 unmixed case   DELIVERY Free within 15-mile radius of
Gerrards Cross (min 1 case); elsewhere £1.15 per delivery to West/Central
London, £4.50 per delivery beyond; mail order available   GLASS HIRE Free
TASTINGS AND TALKS Tastings available 'at all times' in-store   ■

This is an unusual list for someone who regards himself as a Burgundy
specialist: no wine costs more than £10 a bottle. It does perhaps mean
that there aren't many Burgundies (but then, the whole list is short)
but it also suggests that you get value for money here.

Although Spain and Australia have arrived, it's still very much a French collection. We would indeed recommend the Burgundy range – all from domaines, and many not available elsewhere (such as the Bourgogne Pinot Noir 1983 from André Sorin, £3.90, and the Bourgogne Chardonnay from the same producer, £4.95). From the Loire, Mr Rush has winkled out an attractive Muscadet Domaine de la Carisière at £3.65, plus a red St-Nicolas de Bourgueil 1984 at £4.20. Other areas of interest are the dry white Muscat Les Quatres Saisons from the Vignerons Catalans in Roussillon, a few Beaujolais and Alsace wines from Muré.

Look, too, for the English Chalkhill Bacchus and Churchills Ports.

Best buys

Bourgogne Pinot Noir 1983, André Sorin, £3.90; Bourgogne Chardonnay 1985, André Sorin, £4.95; Minervois 1986, Domaine Haute Galine, £3.15

Russell & McIver

The Rectory, St Mary at Hill   TEL 01-283 3575
London EC3R 8EE

OPEN Mon–Fri 9–5.30   CLOSED Sun, public holidays   CREDIT CARDS None accepted; personal and business accounts   DISCOUNTS By arrangement DELIVERY Free on UK mainland (min 1 case London, 5 cases country); otherwise £4.60 charge; mail order available   GLASS HIRE Available TASTINGS AND TALKS Regular tastings for customers in London, Home Counties and as far afield as Chester and Swansea; to groups on request CELLARAGE £2.76 per case per annum

All the classics still rule at this City firm of wine merchants. Bordeaux and Burgundy are tops, with nods in the direction of the Loire and Rhône, and, of course, a good range of fortified wines.

However, it's not all big names and big prices. In Bordeaux, for example, we find good, ready-to-drink claret for under £4 (Ch Beaulieu 1984 at £3.45 and Ch Gromel Bel-Air 1983, Bordeaux Supérieur at £3.68). Wines from Côtes de Castillon and Côtes de Bourg get a look in before the more famous appellations.

Plenty of domaine wines hold sway in Burgundy. Look for the simple Mâcon Uchizy Rouge 1985 of Talmard at £4.03 if you want very good value, or the Mâcon-Villages Chanterelles 1985 at £4.72. Further

---

We have tried to make the *1988 Which? Wine Guide* as comprehensive as possible, but we should love to hear from you about any other wine merchants you feel deserve an entry, or your comments on existing entries. Write to us either by letter or using the report forms supplied at the back of the book.

up the scale are the top wines of Jean Germain, Patrick Javillier, Prieur Brunet and of Jean Durup in Chablis.

Outside those areas, country wines like the Vin de Pays des Collines Rhodaniennes from Domaine Vallouit or good Côtes du Rhône-Villages from the Rasteau co-operative (1985 vintage at £3.97) might appeal. On the Loire, there's a delicious Sauvignon de Touraine from Yves Barras (£3.74). Alsace wines come from Louis Gisselbrecht and Hugel.

Some German estate wines (Langguth, Max Ferd Richter, Hans Lang) look attractive, along with California wines from Wente, and Gawler Estate and Rothbury bottles from Australia. Lastly with fortified wines, look for the Lomelino Madeiras, the own-label wood Ports and a small range of Sherries from Diez Hermanos.

Best buys

Bergerac, Ch de Fayolle red and white, £3.17; Ch Bonnet 1986, Bordeaux, £3.45; Mâcon Uchizy Rouge 1985, Paul et Philibert Talmard, £4.03; Sauvignon de Touraine 1986, Domaine de la Chapinière, £3.74

Safeway

HEAD OFFICE Beddow Way, Aylesford,   TEL (0622) 72000
Nr Maidstone, Kent ME20 7AT
140 licensed branches throughout the UK

OPEN Varies from store to store but generally Mon–Thur 8–8   Fri 8–9
Sat 8–7   CLOSED Sun, some public holidays   CREDIT CARDS Access, Visa (in most stores)   GLASS HIRE Free with order (deposit required)   DISCOUNTS, DELIVERY, TASTINGS AND TALKS, CELLARAGE Not available

As with many supermarket wine ranges, Safeway's own-label wines are available at most stores, but their fine wine selection tends to vary from store to store. Unlike some other supermarkets, though, it's the own-label wines which we prefer.

Not that there's much for great excitement, but we have enjoyed the basic Safeway Rioja (£3.99), the Coteaux du Tricastin and Côtes du Ventoux and the wines from the Côtes du Luberon. In Italy, there's the Frascati from Villa Catone and the Verdicchio Casal di Serra of Bianchi. The Hungarian wines are not everybody's cup of tea. Also steer clear of the rather old-fashioned Burgundies and the rather expensive clarets. You won't go too wrong, though, with Cooks New Zealand Chardonnay at £4.25 (even if it's expensive for a supermarket) or Rosemount Australian wines. There are even a few Austrian wines left over from better days.

Best buys

Chianti Luigi Cecchi, £2.29; Vin de Pays de Vaucluse red, £1.89; Cooks Dry Red wine, £2.75; Frascati Villa Catone, £3.59

Sainsbury Bros

On the High Pavement, George Street, Bath,   TEL (0225) 60482
Avon BA1 2EG

OPEN Mon–Fri 10–7   Sat 10–6   CLOSED Sun, public holidays
CREDIT CARDS Visa; personal and business accounts   DISCOUNTS 5% for
1 unmixed case   DELIVERY Free within 50-mile radius of Bath (min 1 case);
otherwise 1 case £4.50, 2 cases £2.70, 3 cases £1.80, 4 cases £1.35; mail order
available   GLASS HIRE Free with wine   TASTINGS AND TALKS Weekly
in-store tastings; 2 annual tastings for retail customers; to groups on request
CELLARAGE £1.15 per case per year

This long-established firm of merchants deals mainly with the trade,
but has a small amount of retail business. Their shop in the centre of
Bath boasts fine vaulted cellars used for tastings.

Only recently has their list begun to move with the times, away from
négociant Burgundy and claret and vintage Port, and some rather
uninspired buying continues. But interesting bottles do crop up, and
there is also a fine wine list which changes frequently.

On Sainsbury Bros' standard list, look for wines from Listel in the
Salins du Midi, Beaujolais from Loron, Alsace from the Co-operative of
Pfaffenheim, Perrier-Jouët Champagnes, Torres wines from Spain and
Penfold's Australian wines. Bulgaria offers good value, as do the
Sherries of Wisdom and Warter.

Best buys

Ménétou-Salon 1985, Domaine de Chatenoy, £4.08; Penfold's Dalwood
Shiraz/Cabernet 1983, £3.35; Alsace wines

J Sainsbury

HEAD OFFICE Stamford House, Stamford Street,   TEL 01-921 6000
London SE1 9LL
270 licensed branches; 6 licensed SavaCentres

OPEN Mon–Sat 8.30–6 (may be local variations; some stores have late-night
closing on various days)   CLOSED Sun, public holidays   CREDIT CARDS None
accepted   DISCOUNTS, DELIVERY, GLASS HIRE, CELLARAGE Not available
TASTINGS AND TALKS Occasional in-store tastings; to groups on request (min 50
people) – details from Public Relations Dept at Head Office address

The country's largest wine retailer continues to expand its list in all
directions, both in the own-label range, available in every licensed
store, and in the Vintage Selection, which has more limited
distribution.

The range is wide, and most areas of the world are covered.
Particular strengths lie in parts of France – petit château Bordeaux, for
example – and in Italy. Sparkling wines, too, get good treatment.

In the higher quality Vintage Selection, Sainsbury's have found
some extremely good wines at excellent prices. In France, we

recommend a classic Quincy 1985, Duc de Berri at £3.95; the Alto Adige Chardonnay 1986 from Italy at £3.25; and Portuguese reds such as Quinta da Bacalhôa or the Romeira Garrafeira 1978 at £2.95. The Bordeaux range includes half-bottles of Ch Filhot 1981, Sauternes at £4.65 as well as the super Ch Barreyres 1985 Haut-Médoc at £4.45.

Recent introductions include such wines as a Jura white, Ch d'Arlay 1983 at £8.75, the Khan Krum Chardonnay from Bulgaria at £2.69, and the Beaujolais Moulin-à-Vent Domaine Labruyère 1985 at £5.45.

The own-label range is more variable. Part of the problem must come in the vast quantities of wine needed to keep all the branches supplied. Sometimes it must mean that they can't buy a particular wine because there just isn't enough of it to go round. Given such constraints, Sainsbury's do remarkably well in some areas, for example, in some of their wines from the South-West of France, and in Alsace (amazingly competitive prices here), but much less well in Germany and Spain. Their claret and Médoc are also excellent value, especially compared with the price of Mouton Cadet which they also stock. Sainsbury's Champagne continues to maintain its quality and good price (£7.95); also look out for their Vintage Champagne (1982 vintage at £9.95) and the rosé at £8.75.

Best buys

Vernaccia di San Gimignano 1986, San Quirico, £3.45; Sainsbury's Chardonnay Alto Adige 1986, £3.25; Romeira Garrafeira 1978, £2.95; Ch du Bousquet 1985, Côtes de Bourg, £3.85; Orlando Cabernet Sauvignon 1984, £3.95; Sainsbury's Vintage Champagne 1982, £9.95

Paul Sanderson Wines

67–69 Main Street, Davidsons Mains,   TEL 031-336 6190
Edinburgh EH4 5AD

OPEN Mon 12.30–7   Tue–Thur 10–7   Fri, Sat 10–8   CLOSED Sun, 25 & 26 Dec, 1st week of New Year   CREDIT CARDS None accepted; personal and business accounts   DISCOUNTS 5% for 1 mixed case   DELIVERY Free in Edinburgh (min 6 bottles); elsewhere at cost; mail order available
GLASS HIRE Free   TASTINGS AND TALKS To groups on request
CELLARAGE Not available

Edinburgh is very lucky in its wine merchants, and we're delighted to welcome another strong newcomer to the Guide. Paul Sanderson's interest lies in Spanish wines and Sherries, but has built up a good showing in other areas, too. Prices are good throughout the list.

Spain first, though. The Rioja range is full and lengthy, with ordinary Riojas alongside Reservas and some Gran Reservas (back to a 1973 Gran Reserva 1973 from La Rioja Alta at £6.99). A large number of bodegas are represented including Faustino, Olarra, Domecq, Beronia, Muga and Marqués de Murrieta. Other areas include Penedès with wines from Torres, Navarra with wines from Chivite and Castillo de

Tiebas, Ribera del Duero with the ultra-serious Vega Sicilia, and
various wines from other areas, including Cavas from Marqués de
Monistrol.

The Sherry list is equally impressive. Producers include Hidalgo,
Barbadillo, De Soto and a considerable number of almacenista Sherries
from Lustau.

Although other wine regions pale by comparison, they are not
neglected. We would recommend looking at the decently priced
mature clarets (Ch Fourcas-Hosten 1979, Listrac at £6.99); the Alsace
from the Turckheim co-operative; some good estate German wines;
and a strong Italian list which contains some top quality Reciotos and
Barolos as well as less usual wines from the south (Castel del Monte
red from Torre Sveva in Puglia at £2.99 and the fabulous Nico 1983
from Illuminati in Abruzzo at £10.79).

Best buys

Rioja 1983 red, Carta de Plata, £3.15; Beronia Reserva 1980, £3.65; Rioja
Gran Reserva 1973, Reserva 904, La Rioja Alta, £6.99; Chardonnay di
Appiano 1985, Viticoltori Alto Adige, £3.49

Sapsford Wines

33 Musley Lane, Ware, Hertfordshire SG12 7EW   TEL (0920) 67040
OPEN 'All hours'   CREDIT CARDS None accepted   DISCOUNTS 2½% for 5
cases, 5% for 10 cases   DELIVERY Free within 12-mile radius of Ware (min 1
case); elsewhere £3.50 per case; mail order available   GLASS HIRE Free with
4-case order   TASTINGS AND TALKS Regular tastings held locally; to groups on
request   CELLARAGE £15 per year   ∎

Although this firm is basically a Loire specialist, they have expanded a
little recently, and now take in some petit château clarets, a few Italian
and Portuguese wines, Ports from Pocas Junior and Sherries from
Palomino y Vergara and De Soto.

The Loire covers the full range of vineyards as far up as Sancerre and
Pouilly-sur-Loire. If we were told a little more about the names of the
producers of the wines on the list, we would be able to recommend
specific bottles rather than just the fact that the list is wide and seems
good value for money.

We suspect, however, that sweet wines from the Coteaux du Layon
would be worth searching out, as would the wines from Montlouis (the
dry sparkling Cuvée Gabrielle d'Estrées at £5.97) and the unusual
Cheverny wines from the Romorantin grape.

Best buys

Sweet wines from the Coteaux du Layon

SavaCentre

See J Sainsbury.

David Scatchard

The Wine Shop, 4 Temple Court, Liverpool L2 6PY   TEL 051-236 6468
OPEN Mon–Fri 9.30–6   Sat 9.30–1   CLOSED Sun, public holidays
CREDIT CARDS Access, Visa; personal and business accounts   DISCOUNTS 5%
for 1 case; quantity discounts on 4+ cases   DELIVERY Free nationwide (min 2
cases locally, min 6 cases elsewhere); £2 per case charge for Isle of Wight and Isle
of Man; mail order through Wines of Spain (UK) at same address
GLASS HIRE Free with case order   TASTINGS AND TALKS Monthly in-store
tastings (lasting 1 week); private evening tastings by invitation; to groups on
request (min 60 people tutored tastings on Spanish wines)

The list tells only half the story at David Scatchard's shop. You must
look for the bin-ends and fine wines – old clarets, old Riojas and
vintage Ports – as well as perusing the standard range, because of the
regularly changing treats.

David Scatchard started his career as a Spanish specialist. Although
he has since become more international, moving as far afield as
Wyndham Estates in Australia, Spain continues to be the most
interesting part of his list. Wines include Riojas from Viña Alcorta,
Marqués de Riscal, and Campo Viejo and its top wines, the fine
reservas of Marqués de Villamagna. From elsewhere in Spain, Mr
Scatchard has brought together Navarra wines from the main
co-operative, the Condestable wines from Jumilla and Torres and
Marqués de Monistrol wines from Penedès.

A curiosity on his list are the Falerno wines from Italy – described as
Roman wine because Falernian was the most highly prized wine for
the ancient Roman wine connoisseur.

Best buys

Condestable Tinto, Jumilla, £1.98; Castillo de Tiebas 1976, Navarra,
£3.55; Fino Soto, £3.19; Falerno Nobile 1982, £5.45

Sebastopol Wines

Sebastopol Barn, London Road, Blewbury,   TEL (0235) 850471
Oxfordshire OX11 9HB

OPEN Tue, Wed, Thur, Sat 10.30–5.30   Fri 10.30–6.30   CLOSED Mon, Sun,
Good Friday   CREDIT CARDS Access, Visa; business accounts
DISCOUNTS 5% on 1 unmixed case; collection discount   DELIVERY Free within
10-mile radius of Blewbury (min 1 case); elsewhere 1 case £5, 2 cases £4.50 per
case, 3 cases £4 per case, 4+ cases free; mail order available   GLASS HIRE Free
with 1-case order   TASTINGS AND TALKS 4–6 tastings annually; theme wines
tasted on specified Saturdays; to groups on request   ■

While France continues to be the cornerstone of this list, expansion in the Spanish and Australian sections has brought in some very drinkable top value wines.

In France, the areas of specialisation are the Loire, the Rhône and Burgundy. On the Loire, look for sweet wines from the Coteaux du Layon and Bonnezeaux, plus the dry Savennières from Yves Soulez; or try the Vouvrays of Marc Brédif and the Chinon of Couly-Dutheil. The Rhône offers wines from Jaboulet Aîné in the north and Ch de Beaucastel and the red La Vieille Ferme, Côtes du Ventoux from the Perrin family. The Chablis of Louis Michel accompany excellent domaine Burgundies, which come in both white and red (Simon Bize, Dujac, Voarick, Abel Garnier).

Sebastopol also have a good selection of French regional wines (the Coteaux des Baux en Provence wine of Domaine de Trévallon, the Côtes de Buzet, Cuvée Napoléon and the Syrah and Cabernet wines of Domaine Richeaume in Côtes de Provence, for example).

In Spain, wines that have recently arrived include Torres in Penedès, Raimat, Marqués de Griñon, the Señorio de los Llanos of Valdepeñas and Riojas from Muga. The Sherries are from Lustau. Besides Hill Smith and Brown Brothers, Australia now has wines from Tisdall and Geoff Merrill.

Best buys

Côtes de Buzet 1984, Les Vignerons Réunis, £3.57; Côtes du Ventoux 1985, La Vieille Ferme, £3.14; Viña Sol 1986, Torres, £3.39

Seckford Wines

2 Betts Avenue, Martlesham Heath, Ipswich,   TEL (0473) 626072
Suffolk IP5 7RH

OPEN Tue–Sat 10–6 Sun 10–1 CLOSED Mon, public holidays
CREDIT CARDS Access, Visa; personal and business accounts
DISCOUNTS Approx 5% for 1 case DELIVERY Free within 25-mile radius (min 2 cases); elsewhere at cost GLASS HIRE Free with 1-case order
TASTINGS AND TALKS 5–6 weekend tastings annually (by invitation); to groups on request CELLARAGE By arrangement ■

The standard list at this wine merchant certainly has plenty to get to grips with, especially if Australia is your interest. It has expanded even more since last year and now takes up six pages of a 16-page list. Brown Brothers feature in particular, but Hill Smith, De Bortoli (look for the botrytised sweet wines), Gawler River Estate, Hardy's, Orlando, McWilliams, Rosemount and Wyndham Estate are also represented, as well as some smaller producers such as Montrose and Peter Lehmann. Also from Down Under, look for the Selaks wines from New Zealand (the Sauvignon 1986 at £6.89 is regarded by many as one of the great Sauvignon wines of the world).

Seckford's other main focus is France and a constantly changing fine claret list – ask them what they have in stock. They entertain a special interest in Ch la Tour de By and Ch Patache d'Aux (also try the underrated Ch St-Gènes 1985, Bordeaux Supérieur at £3.75). The Rhône produces wines from Dervieux Thaize in Côte Rôtie as well as Guigal's Côtes du Rhône. In Burgundy, one finds domaine wines as well as those from Louis Jadot and Chanson.

Germany provides a short list of estate wines – some from as far back as the great vintages of 1971 and 1976.

Best buys

Australian wines; Ch St-Gènes 1985, Bordeaux Supérieur, £3.75; Alsace Riesling 1983, Hauller, £3.75; Vin de Pays des Côtes de Gascogne Colombard, £2.49; Bairrada 1980, J M da Fonseca, £3.65

Selfridges

400 Oxford Street, London W1A 1AB   TEL 01-629 1234

OPEN Mon–Sat 9–6 (7.30 Thur)   CLOSED Sun, some public holidays
CREDIT CARDS All accepted; Sears Credit Card   DISCOUNTS Available
DELIVERY Free in London postal area (min £10 order); elsewhere at cost; mail order available   GLASS HIRE Not available   TASTINGS AND TALKS Weekly in-store tastings Thur–Sat   CELLARAGE Not available

Big developments and improvements have taken place in the wine department of this famous London store over the past year and a very good list indeed is emerging. Even the classic areas are becoming wider and more varied.

Certainly Bordeaux is still a major part of the list, but the range goes from petit château wines such as Ch le Gardéra 1983, Bordeaux Supérieur at £4.50, all the way up to first growths of the 1960s (Ch Lafite 1966 at £140), by way of a big selection of bourgeois and classed growths. The pattern is similar in Burgundy, with a few basic generic white and red Burgundies at fair prices, then plenty of domaine wines from growers including Ch du Meursault, Jacques Prieur, Simon Bize, René Lamy and Luc Sorin.

While the Rhône list is still short, we would recommend some of the Loire wines – the Sancerre of Jean Vacheron, the Bourgueil of Saget or the sweet wines from Lalanne in Quarts de Chaume (1979 at £6.60). The Champagne array is enormous – 29 vintage and de luxe wines followed by non-vintage from a good proportion of the grande marque houses.

Elsewhere in France, the shelves hold some good regional wines (Faugères, Cuvée Jules Gaston at £2.60 and the rosé Coteaux Varois Domaine des Charberts 1983 at £2.50), plus a few Alsace wines from Hugel and Léon Beyer. New Italian purchases have brought in the Barolos of Ceretto, Chianti Rufina from Frescobaldi and the

Montepulciano d'Abruzzo of Illuminati at £3.65. In Italian white, look for Antinori's Galestro, or the top whites of Frescobaldi.

There's a good line in Eastern European wines, with Hungarian Tokay, and the Greek red Calliga Ruby at £4.35. Selfridges have assembled what must be the biggest range of Israeli Kosher wines in the country (including the enjoyable wines from Gamla Vineyards in Galilee). Spain brings in Marqués de Murrieta Riojas, Torres wines and a considerable number of Sherries (recommended are Don Zoilo, Barbadillo and the old Gonzalez Byass wines).

In the New World, we have California wines from familiar and less familiar names like Paso Robles and Mark West Vineyards, while Australia offers good value from all round the country (look for the sweet wines from Brown Brothers and other producers). The Te Mata wines from New Zealand join Babich and Montana.

Best buys

Faugères 1985, Cuvée Jules Gaston, £2.60; Quarts de Chaume 1979, Ch de Belle-Rive, £6.60; non-vintage Champagnes; Montepulciano d'Abruzzo 1984, Illuminati, £3.65; Rioja Reserva 1981, Faustino V, £4.10

Edward Sheldon

New Street, Shipston-on-Stour, Warwickshire CV36 4EN   TEL (0608) 61409/61639/62210

OPEN Mon–Fri 8.30–1, 2–5.30 Sat 8.30–1 CLOSED Sun, public holidays
CREDIT CARDS All accepted; personal and business accounts DISCOUNTS 5% on 1 case, 10% on 6 cases DELIVERY Free to certain areas of Cotswolds, Avon, Oxfordshire, Birmingham, Gloucestershire, Northamptonshire, Warwickshire, Shropshire, Staffordshire and London (min 1 case); elsewhere 1 case £6, 2–5 cases £3, 6–10 £2, 11+ cases free; mail order available GLASS HIRE Free TASTINGS AND TALKS Annual spring and autumn tastings; smaller regular tastings; to groups on request CELLARAGE £3.45 per case per year

This is a serious list, with emphasis on claret, Burgundy and vintage Port. We particularly like the variety of magnums (and even some double-magnums) of claret – and half-bottles from many parts of the list.

Wine in bag-in-box ages and spoils quicker than in bottle. If you buy boxes, buy and drink up one box before you buy the next. Boxes in the store-cupboard will lose their freshness. Used or unopened, a wine box will keep better if you store it tap downwards, keeping wine, not air, in the valve.

Claret spans wines from most recent vintages, and a section of older vintages (on a recent list as far back as 1947). The main emphasis is on classed growth wines rather than petit château wines, although in 1983 and 1982 there are a number that are less expensive (but not cheap).

Burgundy now has a good few domaine-bottled wines to set against the négociant wines, again with some old vintages in reds. Beaujolais comes from Thévenin and Loron. We like the range of Champagnes (some magnums and even a Jeroboam here). Other areas of France are more lightly served.

Vintage Port is a star section: the oldest wine on a recent list was Cockburn 1955, but the range shows some depth from 1970 onwards. Edward Sheldon also sells tawny and crusted Ports to those who can't wait to drink their vintage wines. The other area still worth looking at is Germany, where the estate wines include some from the legendary 1976 vintage.

Best buys

Ch Haut-Sociondo 1982, Premières Côtes de Blaye, £4.44; Finest Manzanilla Sherry, Hidalgo, £4.21; Alsace Pinot Blanc 1985, Kuentz-Bas, £4.79; German estate wines

---

Sherborne Vintners

The Old Vicarage, Leigh, Sherborne, Dorset DT9 6HL

TEL (0935) 873033

OPEN Every day 8–10   CREDIT CARDS None accepted; personal and business accounts   DISCOUNTS £1 off 6 cases, £2 off 11+ cases   DELIVERY Free within 20-mile radius of Sherborne (min 1 case); elsewhere £2.30 for under 2 cases; mail order available   GLASS HIRE Free with 1-case order locally
TASTINGS AND TALKS Tastings arranged; to groups on request
CELLARAGE £3 per case per year ■

Ian Sinnott has made an extremely ambitious start to trading by issuing two mammoth lists, one covering Spain, the other France. He promises more in due course from the rest of Europe and the New World.

We start with Spain: immediately the depth and range is apparent. Almost at random, we could pick out the Málagas of Scholtz Hermanos, Sherries from Valdespino and Gonzalez Byass (including their fine old wines), the good value Condestable from Jumilla, the straightforward Viña Albali from Valdepeñas (Tinto 1981 at £3.01), wines from the co-operative of Ribera del Duero as well as Vega Sicilia, a full page of wines from León, wines from Alella and Ampurdan on the Costa Brava and a huge collection of sparkling Cavas and Torres wines from Penedès – plus Raimat wines, the wines not often seen from the far west of Extremadura, and many others. And, of course, pages of wines from Rioja and Navarra. Drink your way round Spain.

You could do much the same – even if to a lesser degree – from parts of France: the Loire, the Rhône, Alsace and some of the smaller regions. Bordeaux is well served with a serious list of clarets back to the 1975 vintage (and a decent selection of Sauternes and Barsac). Burgundy gets in-depth treatment with domaine wines (and a good number of Chablis for those who can afford them). Mr Sinnott specialises in Domaine de la Romanée-Conti (nothing but the most famous here, it seems).

Descending from those dizzy heights, look to plenty of country wines from Cahors, Bergerac, the varietal wines of the Ardèche, the Cabernet Sauvignon Mas de Daumas Gassac from the Hérault, Madiran, Jurançon and Jura wines. From Alsace, suppliers include Muré, Charles Schléret, Léon Beyer.

Areas well treated in the Rhône include Gigondas and Vacqueyras in the south, St-Joseph, Côte Rôtie and Hermitage in the north. The Loire takes in many good reds from Chinon, Bourgueil and Saumur-Champigny, as well as whites from some fine producers.

Best buys

Viña Bonita La Mancha red and white, £2.28; Palácio de León Tinto, £2.47; Valdespino Sherries; Rioja 1983, Campo Burgo, £3.37; Jurançon Moelleux 1984, Ch Jolys, £3.90; Corbières red 1985, Ch de Belle Isle, £2.59; Côtes du Rhône 1985, Ch du Grand Moulas, £3.80

Sherston Wine Company

HEAD OFFICE 1 Church Street, Sherston, Malmesbury, Wiltshire SN16 0LA	TEL (0666) 840644
15 Broad Street, Banbury, Oxfordshire OX16 8BN	TEL (0295) 66112
14a Chatham Row, Walcot Street, Bath, Avon BA1 5BS	TEL (0225) 62034
The Pitching, Market Place, Castle Cary, Somerset BA7 7AL	TEL (0963) 50124
4 Deneside, Great Yarmouth, Norfolk NR30 2HL	TEL (0493) 853090
35 Fortune Green Road, London NW6 1DU	TEL 01-794 1143
57 Winterslow Road, Porton, Salisbury, Wiltshire SP4 0JU	TEL (0980) 611098
97 Victoria Street, St Albans, Hertfordshire AL1 3TJ	TEL (0727) 58841
10 Stafford Road, Wallington, Surrey SM6 9AA	TEL 01-669 6661

OPEN Mon–Sat 10–1, 2–6 Sun, public holidays 12–2 CLOSED 25 & 26 Dec, Good Friday CREDIT CARDS Access, Visa; personal and business accounts DISCOUNTS 5–15% for 1 case collected (min) DELIVERY Free in England and Wales (min 3 cases); otherwise 1–2 cases £3, delivery to Scotland £3 for 3+ cases, 1–2 cases to Scotland £6; mail order available GLASS HIRE Free with 1-case order TASTINGS AND TALKS Tastings in-store (local conditions vary); Wine Club holds regular tastings and events; to groups on request CELLARAGE Not available

Spain, the original mainstay of Sherston's list, is still the most interesting area. Wines from right round the country crowd the shelves of these franchises, inevitably with a major interest in Rioja (look for the big listing of reservas and gran reservas). Muga 1982 is one such, offering terrific value (£4.55). Other areas well covered are Navarra, Penedès (with Torres wines), a couple of Vega Sicilias from Ribera del Duero, the Señorio de los Llanos from Valdepeñas and Sherries from Pedro Rodriguez, Romate Sanchez and Barbadillo.

The French section is shorter but still manages to cover most areas. We would pick out the Champagne of Bruno Paillard (non-vintage at £11.48), the Côtes du Frontonnais 1985 from Ch Bellevue-la-Forêt at £3.85, and the wines from Jean-Michel Masson in Pouilly-sur-Loire (but including a Sancerre and Quincy as well as an unusual Coteaux de Giennois from just down river).

Italy now offers the top-class Soave and Valpolicella of Guerrieri-Rizzardi as well as the good value Chianti Classico from Torrequercie. Portugal has come on apace, giving us the dry Vinho Verde of the Ponte do Lima co-operative and a good range of red Bairradas, plus wines from J M da Fonseca. And the New World brings in the superb Quelltaler aged Semillon (1982 vintage at £7.95), and the good value Orlando wines.

Best buys

Toro-Zamora Gran Colegiata Red 1982, £4.45; Costières du Gard 1985, Domaine de Mourier, £3.35; Vinho Verde Ponte do Lima, £3.30; Pasmados 1980, J M da Fonseca, £3.65

André Simon

14 Davies Street, London W1Y 1LJ	TEL 01-499 9144
50/52 Elizabeth Street, London SW1W 9PB	TEL 01-730 8108
21 Motcomb Street, London SW1X 8LB	TEL 01-235 3723
66 Fulham Road, London SW3 6HH	TEL 01-589 1238

OPEN Mon–Fri 9.30–7 (Elizabeth Street 9.30–8.30) Sat 9.30–6 (Elizabeth Street 9.30–7.30, Davies Street 9.30–1) Sun (Elizabeth Street 12–2) CLOSED Sun (except Elizabeth Street), public holidays CREDIT CARDS Access, Amex, Visa; personal and business accounts DISCOUNTS 5% on 1 case; further discounts on large quantities DELIVERY Free in Central London (min 1 case preferred); elsewhere at cost GLASS HIRE Free with 1-case order
TASTINGS AND TALKS Occasional in-store promotional tastings
CELLARAGE £3.50 per case per year

Wines for this small group of shops are now purchased in conjunction with Laytons (*qv*). This has meant a greater emphasis on Bordeaux and especially on Burgundy, and a lessening of interest in other parts of the world.

Not that the rest of the world is neglected. Worthwhile French bottles include the Rhône wines from Jaboulet Aîné and the Perrin family in Côtes du Ventoux (Cuvée Cézanne 1984 at £3.70). Then there's plenty of Champagne (house Champagne is £9.95), Alsace from Hugel (at top prices) and the delicious Savennières Clos du Papillon 1983 from Jean Baumard (£5.75).

The Bordeaux list goes back in vintages to 1949, but while there are some petit château wines, it tends to leap to high prices fairly fast. A number of half-bottles of Sauternes may appeal. Burgundy is still dominated by négociant wines, but there is now a fair sprinkling of domaine wines as well. Again prices are not cheap.

Outside France parade some top Italian names (Antinori, Conte Loredan's Venegazzù, Badia a Coltibuono), Australian Hill-Smith wines, and Mondavi, Ch St Jean, Heitz and Acacia in California.

Best buys

Christopher Tatham Monopole (NV), La Chablisienne, £4.95; Côtes du Rhône 1983, Domaine Ste-Anne, £4.65; Valdepeñas 1978, Señorio de los Llanos Reserva, £3.55

The symbol ■ indicates that wine can be sold only by the case. However, most wholesalers are usually happy to sell mixed cases.

Smedley Vintners

Restory Cottage, Lilley, Luton, Beds LU2 8LU   TEL (046 276) 214

OPEN Every day 8–10   CREDIT CARDS None accepted; personal and business
accounts   DISCOUNTS Variable (min 10 cases)   DELIVERY Free within 50-mile
radius of Lilley (min 1 case); otherwise £1.50 per case; mail order available
GLASS HIRE Free   TASTINGS AND TALKS 2 tastings annually; to groups on
request   CELLARAGE Not available   ∎

This recently established company has developed a short list with a
strong Italian accent, but most areas of France are also covered. Here
we find an attractively priced range of country wines, including the
Vin de Pays des Côtes de Gascogne of Pierre Grassa at £2.68, and the
top cuvée white Domaine de Grandchamp from Henry Ryman in
Bergerac (1986 vintage at £3.82). In reds, the Côtes du Marmandais Ch
de la Couronne (£2.96) and Minervois 1985, Ch de Fabas (£2.58) are
both good value.

   A modest number of clarets from recent vintages, several under £4,
has been assembled, along with a few Burgundy domaine wines and
Beaujolais from Georges Duboeuf. Michel Thomas supplies the
Sancerre – both white and red – and Théo Cattin the Alsace wines.

   In Italy, the two stars are Antinori (Santa Cristina, Chianti Classico
1985 is £3.28) and Lungarotti (his Rubesco di Torgiano 1982 is £4.44 – a
good price for this wine). There are Riojas from CVNE and Torres
wines, Ports from Quinta do Noval and Madeira from Cossart Gordon,
plus Garvey Sherries. In the New World, good bottles include
Trefethen Eschcol red (£4.24) and white (£4.40) in California, and one
from Plantagenet Winery in Western Australia.

Best buys

Chardonnay 1986, Rosemount Estates, £4.07; Rubesco di Torgiano
1982, £4.44; Chianti Classico 1985, Santa Cristina, Antinori, £3.44;
Côtes du Marmandais 1985, Ch de la Couronne, £2.96

Snipe Wine Cellars

87 High Street, Needham Market,   TEL (0449) 721943
Suffolk IP6 8DQ
30 North Hill, Colchester, Essex   TEL (0206) 45505
WAREHOUSE A93 Cowdray Centre,   TEL (0206) 67670
Cowdray Avenue, Colchester, Essex CO1 1BG

OPEN Mon, Wed–Sat 10–9   Sun 12–2   CLOSED Tue 10–5
CREDIT CARDS Access, Visa; personal and business accounts   DISCOUNTS 5%
for 6 bottles, 10% for 1 case   DELIVERY Free in Essex and Suffolk (min 2 cases);
elsewhere 1–4 cases £3 per case, 5 cases free; mail order available
GLASS HIRE Free with order   TASTINGS AND TALKS Tastings held on 1st
Friday of each month at Colchester; to groups on request (min 20 people)

An expanding range of wines brings this wine warehouse into the Guide for the first time, helped by keen prices, particularly at the Colchester warehouse.

A few interesting French regional wines include some from Corsica, and the unusual Vin Gris from Henri Maire in the Jura. In Bordeaux, we would recommend some decent petit château wines from the 1981 vintage. Beaujolais from Sarrau is the best value from Burgundy, while the Rhône offers more good value in a Coteaux du Tricastin from Domaine Tour d'Elyssas at £2.89. Alsace brings in Zind-Humbrecht wines.

Italy is still oriented towards party wines (not the Barolo 1980 of Fontanafredda, though), but there are Riojas from Campo Viejo and Portuguese reds from the Cantanhede co-operative in Bairrada (1980 vintage at £3.69). It's nice to see local English New Hall wines. Australian wines come from McWilliams.

Best buys

Ch Pitray 1983, Côtes de Castillon, £4.32; Coteaux du Tricastin, Domaine Tour d'Elyssas £2.89; Bairrada 1980, Vinícola Cantanhede, £3.69; Ch Castellot 1983, Bergerac, £3.25

Sookias and Bertaut   🏳 ☞

The Cottage, Cambalt Road, Putney Hill,   TEL 01-788 4193
London SW15 6EW

OPEN Tue–Fri 10–6   Sat 10–1   CLOSED Mon, Sun, public holidays
CREDIT CARDS Access, Visa; personal and business accounts
DISCOUNTS Small discounts on unmixed cased; collection discount from Putney; 5+ cases by arrangement   DELIVERY Free in London postal districts (min 1 case); elsewhere £6 per case per delivery; mail order available
GLASS HIRE Not available   TASTINGS AND TALKS Monthly in-store tastings; to groups on request   CELLARAGE Not available   ∎

If you want to know anything about wines from the South-West of France, this is where to come, since they have more wines from this mysterious corner of France than any other merchant.

In fact, that's all they have. But when you are landed in such strange spots as Pacherenc du Vic Bilh or L'Entraygues et du Fel or Irouléguy – who needs anything else? Sookias & Bertaut have winkled out wines from Ch Court-les-Mûts in Bergerac, from Clos Triguedina and Domaine de Gaudou (among others) in Cahors, from Domaine de Labarthe in Gaillac, plus wines from Côtes de Buzet, Côtes du Frontonnais, Madiran, Jurançon (including a super sweet white Domaine Cauhape from the 1983 vintage), and a brand new sparkling Blanquette de Limoux.

They buy from small producers rather than from the co-operatives, which means that you get the authentic tastes of the regions. Anything on the list will be of interest.

Best buys

Côtes du Frontonnais 1985, Ch Flotis, £3.50; Cahors 1983, Domaine de Paillas, £3.95; Gaillac Sec 1985, Domaine de Labarthe, £3.80; Côtes de Buzet 1982, Ch des Jonquilles, £4.25

Frank E Stainton

3 Berrys Yard, Finkle Street, Kendal,   TEL (0539) 31886
Cumbria LA9 4AB

OPEN Mon–Sat 8.30–6   CLOSED Sun, public holidays   CREDIT CARDS Access; personal and business accounts   DISCOUNTS 5% for 1 case   DELIVERY Free in South Cumbria (min 1 case); elsewhere at cost; mail order available
GLASS HIRE Free with 1-case order   TASTINGS AND TALKS Wine available for tasting in-store every Saturday; to groups on request   CELLARAGE Free

We are delighted to welcome this Cumbrian firm into the Guide. Rather than go for a mammoth listing, Mr Stainton has developed the sort of list where every wine has a purpose. He's also maintaining competitive prices.

The list starts with fortified wines and a good selection of Garvey Sherries, and then moves to France. In Bordeaux, better value than the house claret from Schröder and Schyler would be wines such as Ch Bel-Air 1985 at £3.50 and Ch Falfas 1982 at £5.30, plus a good number of other wines around these prices, before the classed growths make an entry. Beaujolais features the delicious wines from Duboeuf, while négociant wines from Drouhin and Prosper Maufoux dominate Burgundy. House Champagne is Guy Beauregard (£9.75), with others from Louis Roederer.

The Loire has the deliciously fruity Ménétou-Salon from Henri Pellé at £5.60, and the pricier Pouilly Fumé Ch de Tracy 1985 at £7.15, while Alsace comes up with wines from Hugel and Kuentz-Bas.

There's a surprisingly long list of German wines (some from Deinhard estates), while a well-chosen Italian selection offers the top quality Verdicchio Casal di Serra, the Chianti Classico of Rocca delle Macie and the Venegazzù Black Label (£9.75). Spain's range takes in Riojas from CVNE and Torres wines. In the New World, look for the Hawk's Crest wines from California, Hill-Smith from Australia and the Delegats Chardonnay from New Zealand (1985 vintage at £6.80).

Best buys

Rioja 1980, Contino, £3.95; Corbières 1985, Ch de l'Ille, £3.50; Garvey Sherries; Chianti Classico 1985, Rocca delle Macie, £3.40; Hill-Smith Estate Semillon 1985, £4.80

Stapylton Fletcher   🐷

North View Oast, Forge Lane, East Farleigh,   TEL (0622) 20200
Maidstone, Kent ME15 0JH

OPEN Mon–Fri 8–6   Sat 8.30–12.30   CLOSED Sun, public holidays
CREDIT CARDS None accepted; personal and business accounts
DISCOUNTS 6–11 cases 2%, 12–25 cases 3%, 26–49 cases 5%, 50+ cases 7½%;
cash and carry discount 7½% on 1+ case   DELIVERY Free UK mainland (min 2
cases); £2 surcharge on 1 case outside London, Kent and East Sussex; mail order
available   GLASS HIRE Free with 1-case order   TASTINGS AND TALKS Two
annual tastings; to groups on request   CELLARAGE £2.30 per case per year   ∎

Some very good value is to be encouraged at this wine merchant,
especially in French regional wines. They have the varietal white and
red wines from the co-operative of Haut-Poitou (Chardonnay 1986 at
£3.58, Gamay 1986 at £3.19), as well as the popular Vin de Pays des
Côtes de Gascogne, wines from Côtes du Roussillon, Coteaux du
Languedoc (especially for the St-Chinian red), Gaillac and Fitou.
Another interesting choice would be the Côtes de Thongue – one of the
better vin de pays areas in the wine lake land of Hérault.

Moving on to more exalted bottles (and pricier – though prices
throughout the list are good), look for the wines from Fronsac in an
attractive range of clarets. Stapylton Fletcher also stock several good
Beaujolais and domaine-bottled Burgundies, and some attractive red
Loire wines. There's more interest in Italy than there was last year and,
from Portugal, one of the top bone dry Vinhos Verdes (Solar das
Boucas at £4.46).

Outside Europe, the Mount Helen vineyard wines from Australia
and a range of top Sherries from Gil Luque. Decent value California
wines from Inglenook, Concha y Toro wines from Chile, Cooks from
New Zealand and the local Penshurst wines fill out a satisfying list.

Best buys

Wines from Haut-Poitou; wines from Côtes de Thongue; Quincy 1985,
Domaine de la Maison Blanche, £4.51; Campo Fiorín 1980, Masi, £4.90;
Rioja 1985, Monet Llano, £3.19; Bairrada 1982 Caves do Barrocão, £3.51

Special awards

🐷 means bargain prices (good *value* may be obtained from merchants
without this symbol, of course, if you are prepared to pay for service)

✹ means that the wines stocked are of consistently high quality

▱ means that the merchant stocks an above-average range

☞ means that extra-special service is offered: helpful advice, informative
lists and newsletters, tastings etc.

Stones of Belgravia

6 Pont Street, London SW1R 9EL   TEL 01-235 4133

OPEN Mon–Fri 9.30–8.30   Sat 10–8   CLOSED Sun, public holidays
CREDIT CARDS Access, Amex, Visa; personal and business accounts
DISCOUNTS Variable   DELIVERY Free in Central London (no min) and UK
mainland (min 6 cases); otherwise £5 for 1 case, £15 for 5 cases; mail order
available   GLASS HIRE Free with case order   TASTINGS AND TALKS Occasional
tastings; to groups on request   CELLARAGE Not available

It's expensive to buy wine at Stones, but if you live round here that
probably doesn't matter. In any case, if you want to buy fine claret,
vintage Port or Champagne, this is a very good shop to visit.

Champagne kicks off with a good gallery of big names both in
non-vintage and vintage, plus magnums and double-magnums (there
are also half-bottles, but we doubt if anybody buys those in Belgravia).
House Champagne is £8.95. Then we move to clarets, with more big
names at their equally big prices – a wide range from all the recent
vintages and with a few older wines from the 1960s (including some
1966s) and other vintages back to 1905. We can't quite see anybody
paying £321 for a bottle of Ch Pétrus 1975 . . .

After this, Burgundy is a disappointment. Although the list is long,
it's heavily dominated by dull négociant wines at rather high prices
(although in between are domaine wines from Henri Clerc, Emile
Voarick and Duc de Magenta). The Rhône is a much better bet, taking
in Côte Rôtie from Jasmin and Champet, Hermitage from Grippat (also
his St-Joseph) and Chave, and Cornas from Clape.

While Alsace has wines from Trimbach, Léon Beyer and Dopff au
Moulin, Italy is relatively neglected. Spain offers Riojas from a number
of the major bodegas in Rioja as well as wines from Torres. There's a
brief nod to the New World (Australian wines from De Bortoli and
Brown Brothers, California from Mondavi and Jordan). And then we're
into the superb range of vintage Ports, starting off with 1945 Sandeman
at £130 and ending up with 1982 Churchill at £11.95.

Best buys

Old vintages of claret; Ch Lagarosse 1982, Côtes de Bordeaux, £4;
vintage Ports; St-Joseph 1983, Grippat, £9.75

Supergrape

203 Munster Road, London SW6 6BX   TEL 01-381 6930

OPEN Mon–Fri 10–2, 5–9.30   Sat 10–9.30   Sun, public holidays 12–2, 7–9
CLOSED 25 & 26 Dec   CREDIT CARDS Access, Visa   DISCOUNTS Negotiable;
further discounts through their Wine Club   DELIVERY Free within inner
London (min 1 case); elsewhere at cost   GLASS HIRE Free with appropriate
order   TASTINGS AND TALKS Tasting sample always available in-store; to
groups on request   CELLARAGE Available

This is a small shop which seems to pack in an awful lot of wine, with the sort of jolly service beloved of the Fulham locals.

Inevitably, given the clientele, Champagne flows – house Champagne from Georges Gardet is £9.95, and in large bottles, too. Bordeaux is well covered with wines back to 1961, but concentrating on 1983, 1982 and 1981 at prices up from about £3.50. Again, magnums are in evidence.

Burgundy is its usual expensive self, but outside France Italian Borgogno Barolos and Antinori's Tignanello look good. Spanish wines take in big names right round the country – look for the CVNE, Berberana and Murrieta Riojas, René Barbier and Jean León in Penedès, the Señorio de los Llanos in Valdepeñas and, at the top of the scale, wines from Vega Sicilia (1973 vintage at £25).

Best buys

Raimat Chardonnay, £3.85; Geoffrey Roberts California red and white, £2.95; Cooks Chardonnay 1985, £3.90; Pasmados 1977, J M da Fonseca, £3.80

T & W Wines

51 King Street, Thetford, Norfolk IP24 2AU   TEL (0842) 65646
OPEN Mon–Fri 9.30–5.30   Sat 9.30–5   Sun, public holidays on request
CREDIT CARDS Access, Amex, Diners, Visa; personal and business accounts
DISCOUNTS Not available   DELIVERY Free within 15-mile radius of Thetford (min 1 case or 4 cases for rest of UK); otherwise £9.77 for 1–3 cases, £6.32 for 3–4 cases; mail order available   GLASS HIRE Free with order
TASTINGS AND TALKS On request in-store; to groups on request
CELLARAGE £3.16 per case per year or part-year; insurance £8.50 per £1,000.

At heart this is one of the finest fine wine lists in the country. Nothing here is ordinaire, even their new venture into California wines, where they've unearthed wineries which have not exported to the UK before: Costello Vineyards, Dunn Vineyards, Duckhorn Vineyards, Grace Family Vineyards, Far Niente, Flora Springs, St Clement and Silver Oak Cellars. The only large winery they're buying from is Louis Martini.

The huge list of clarets brandishes vintages back to 1900; red Burgundies go back to 1962 and feature Domaine de la Romanée-Conti; and white Burgundy, Rhône wines from Jaboulet Aîné, and German estate wines are no less exalted. Many wines are available in half-bottles, many in magnums. There are smaller selections of Alsace wines (with Vendange Tardive wines from Hugel in the 1960s) and, from Spain, Marqués de Murrieta Riojas. And moving up from T & W's house Champagne of André Clouet (£9.75), the selection of

Send us **your** views on the report forms at the back of the book.

Champagnes (including many vintages of the fabulous Krug Collection – 1947 at £150) is enormous. Oh, and don't overlook the vintage Ports.

Best buys
Old and rare wines

Tanners Wines   ✼ ▱ ☞

26 Wyle Cop, Shrewsbury, Shropshire SY1 1XD	TEL (0742) 232400
72 Mardol, Shrewsbury, Shropshire SY1 1PZ	TEL (0742) 66389
39 Mytton Oak Road, Shrewsbury, Shropshire SY3 8UG	TEL (0742) 66387
36 High Street, Bridgnorth, Shropshire WV6 4DB	TEL (07462) 3148
4 St Peter's Square, Hereford, Hereford & Worcester HR1 2PG	TEL (0432) 272044
The Old Brewery, Brook Street, Welshpool, Powys SY21 7LF	TEL (0938) 2542

OPEN (Wyle Cop) Mon–Sat 9–6; (Mardol) Mon–Sat 9–5.30; (Mytton Oak Road) Mon–Wed 9–6   Thur–Fri 9–7   Sat 9–5.30; (Bridgnorth and Hereford) Mon–Sat 9–5.30; (Welshpool) Mon–Fri 9–5.30, Sat 9–12 noon   CLOSED Sun, public holidays   CREDIT CARDS Access, Visa; personal and business accounts   DISCOUNTS £1.20 for 6+ unmixed cases, £1.80 for 12+ unmixed cases; on Champagne £2 per case on 6 cases and £3 per case on 12 cases; £1 case collection discount   DELIVERY Free in Shropshire, Hereford & Worcester and mid-Wales (min 1 case); elsewhere orders under £50 value £4.50, over £50 free; mail order available   GLASS HIRE Free with wine order   TASTINGS AND TALKS Series of in-store tastings and for customers by invitation; group tastings   CELLARAGE Not available

Tanners are one of that select band of traditional wine merchants who have adapted to the new world of wine retailing while managing to retain their old world courtesy. It's a difficult balancing act, and one in which few succeed.

This year, Tanners have developed an enterprising Wine Market at the main shop in Shrewsbury (Wyle Cop) and greatly expanded the number of wines on display there. Similar plans are afoot for Bridgnorth.

The list covers France comprehensively but also moves widely within Europe, so that the Italian section, for instance, sparkles with wines from top producers in most of the major regions: Tiefenbrunner in the Alto Adige, the top Barolos of Ratti, a clutch of big names in Tuscany, Aglianico from Basilicata, Regaleali from Sicily.

Spain, too, is well served. Apart from Torres wines in Penedès, and Riojas from Lopez de Heredia, Murrieta, CVNE and Marqués de Cáceres, there is a splendid group of Sherries from Hidalgo, a family-owned bodega in Sanlúcar, matched in Portugal by an equally interesting range of Ports.

In France, while Bordeaux and Burgundy form a strong backbone to the list, other areas are not neglected. Plenty of good value wines from the south and the Midi include Ch de Fonscolombe Coteaux d'Aix-en-Provence; the Faugères wines of Benezech; and the Minervois of Domaine Ste-Eulalie (1985 vintage at £3.15). Alsace produces wines from Hugel and Blanck, and the Loire has Savennières from Jean Baumard and Ch de la Roche aux Moines, as well as Pouilly Fumé from Didier Dagueneau (1986 vintage at £6.75).

The claret list starts well and gets even better. Tanners Claret, chosen by Peter Sichel, one of the owners of Ch Palmer, is excellent value at £3.25, fitting the requirements for house claret extremely well. There are good petit château wines, and an enticing range of bourgeois growths. Vintages of these and the classed growths go back to 1966.

Burgundy is full of top domaine names: Jean Durup in Chablis, Etienne Sauzet, Henri Germain, Hubert Lamy, Pousse d'Or, Dujac. There are some magnums of Champagne for those with a big thirst, and Rhône wines from Jaboulet Aîné and some of the top Châteauneuf estates for those who want something beefier.

Best buys

Coteaux d'Aix-en-Provence 1986 red, Ch de Fonscolombe, £3.12; Minervois 1986, Domaine Ste-Eulalie, £3.15; Tanners Claret, £3.25; Ribera del Duero 1983 red, Penalba Lopez, £3.19; Chianti Colli Fiorentini 1985, Fattoria dell'Ugo, £3.57; Tanners Sherries; half-bottles of claret

---

Taste Shops

HEAD OFFICE 9 Ashmere Terrace, Loverock Road, TEL (0734) 393277 Reading, Berkshire RG3 1DZ
11 branches in and around the Home Counties

OPEN Mon–Fri 12–7 (9 on Thur) Sat 9–6 CLOSED Sun, public holidays
CREDIT CARDS All accepted; personal and business accounts
DISCOUNTS Negotiable DELIVERY Free on UK mainland (min £50 order); otherwise £3.50 carriage charge; mail order available GLASS HIRE Free
TASTINGS AND TALKS Regular in-store tastings; July festival; to groups on request CELLARAGE Not available

---

The shops that used to trade under the name of Bordeaux Direct (*qv*) are now being run independently, although under the same overall management and buying control. This means that although some of the wines on the lists of Bordeaux Direct and these Taste Shops will be the same, some differences will develop. (See also The Wine Club in the WINE CLUBS section.)

The Taste Shops' list is a well-organised one, divided by style and price rather than by country of origin. So, for example, under the heading Everyday Whites, you will find – rubbing shoulders – Bulgarian Chardonnay, a Bergerac Blanc de Blancs, a Vin de Pays des

Pyrénées Orientales, a dry Jurançon, some Saumur, a trio of German wines and a classy Grave del Friuli Tocai from Italy.

Other sections of this list are equally eclectic. Bordeaux Direct's buying team has long been known for searching out the unusual and the good value, often combining the two very satisfactorily. But at the other price extreme, they've come up with wines like the Condrieu of Georges Vernay (at £16.65) or the finest Soave Classico from Pieropan (£4.99 – who would think of paying this price for Soave until they tasted the wine?). Curiosity corner includes a big range of Madeiras from Leacocks, the Chilean Los Vascos Cabernet Sauvignon (1983 vintage at £3.99) and wines from Château de Pech-Redon in Coteaux du Languedoc.

Best buys

Ramitello Riserva 1982, Montepulciano del Molise, £3.25; Sakar Estate Merlot 1981, Bulgaria, £3.95; Coteaux du Languedoc La Clape 1985, Ch de Pech-Redon, £3.65; Vin de Pays d'Urfe, Cépage Gamay, Vignerons Foréziens, £3.15

Joshua Taylor

See Redpath and Thakray.

Tempest, Slinger & Co

See Chesterford Vintners.

Tesco 🐖

HEAD OFFICE New Tesco House, PO Box 18,   TEL (0992) 32222
Delamare Road, Cheshunt, Hertfordshire EN8 9SL
331 licensed branches nationwide

OPEN Generally Mon–Sat (every day in Scotland) 8–9 (but may vary from branch to branch)   CREDIT CARDS Access, Visa, Tesco Checkout Card
DISCOUNTS, DELIVERY, GLASS HIRE, TASTINGS AND TALKS, CELLARAGE Not available

More than some of the other supermarket groups, Tesco seem unable to offer their full range of wines outside the few mega-branches, according to complaints to us when we recommend their wines in our sister publication, *Which? Wine Monthly*. Perhaps as more out-of-town shops open, things will improve: we hope so, because the wine list is wide and many of the better wines are good value.

The own-label selections *are* found in most of the licensed stores; but the fine wine range appears only in the larger branches. Although the former covers most of the familiar generic territory, it's the less usual wines which score best – French vins de pays and wines from the Midi, the own-label Rioja Lan Viejo Gran Reserva 1978 at £3.65, or, from

Italy, the Nebbiolo del Piemonte at £2.69, or the Tiefenbrunner Pinot Grigio at £3.25.

In the fine wines, France produces some good value clarets (Ch St-Nicolas, Fronsac at £5.29), but again, it's wines like the Chianti Classico of Villa Cerna at £3.29 or some of the German estate wines, or the Pouilly Fumé les Griottes at £5.29 which stimulate more interest. We would also recommend their premium range of Sherries and the Israeli wines.

Best buys

Chianti Classico Villa Cerna, £3.29; Cooks New Zealand Chardonnay, £3.49; Tesco Bairrada, £2.25; Tesco Vin de Pays des Bouches du Rhône, £1.99; Tesco Cahors, £2.39

Thresher

HEAD OFFICE Sefton House, 42 Church Road,   TEL (0707) 328244
Welwyn Garden City, Hertfordshire AL8 6PJ
Over 850 branches nationwide

OPEN Hours vary from branch to branch but generally Mon–Sat 10–10   Sun 12–2, 7–9   CLOSED 25 Dec   CREDIT CARDS Access, Visa; personal and business accounts   DISCOUNTS 5% for orders £25–£90, 7½% for £91–£149, 10% for £150+   DELIVERY Free nationwide through selected branches (min order at discretion of branch manager)   GLASS HIRE Free
TASTINGS AND TALKS Occasional in-store tastings (varies from branch to branch)   CELLARAGE Not available

Despite the facelift most Threshers branches have received, we suspect that the focus is rather more on cigarettes, crisps and spirits than on wines. There are far too many branded wines, for a start.

However, some nuggets are nevertheless worth calling in for. From recent tastings we would certainly recommend the Antinori wines from Italy, the Ferreira Ports, some of the German wines (Riesling 1983, Adolph Huesgen at £3.99) and a few wines from Bordeaux and the South-West of France (look for the Cahors 1985, Domaine de la Croze-de-Pys at £2.99 or the Médoc (NV), Delaunay Frères at £3.99, or, from the Rhône valley, the Coteaux du Tricastin 1986 at £2.19.

Best buys

Ferreira Ports; Galestro Capsula Vila 1985, Antinori, £3.99; Riesling 1983, Huesgen, £3.99; Côtes de Bourg 1982, Ch Monichot, £3.99

Philip Tite Fine Wines

73 Whitehall Park Road, London W4 3NB   TEL 01-995 0989

OPEN Open all hours but by appointment only   CREDIT CARDS All accepted; personal and business accounts   DISCOUNTS Not available   DELIVERY Free in Greater London and surrounding counties; otherwise 3 cases £5.75, 3–5 cases

£3.45, 5+ cases free; mail order available   GLASS HIRE Not available
TASTINGS AND TALKS 2 annual tastings for customers on mailing list; periodic
tastings of fine wines   CELLARAGE Free for wines purchased from premises
(insurance at customer's expense)   ∎

We continue to admire the attractive presentation of this fine and rare
list, which looks more like a book of Victorian verse than a brochure for
wine.

It's somehow inevitable that the main emphasis at Philip Tite should
be on Bordeaux: on the standard list there are vintages back as far as
1953, and on the fine wine list, they come much older – a recent list
showed Vieux Ch Certan, Pomerol, 1926 at £218 for a magnum (prices
on the list do not include VAT, but we have included it here). Strong
vintages in the current list included 1970, 1975, 1978, 1982 and 1983.
There are crus bourgeois as well as classed growths to widen the price
range.

Burgundy is less exciting, but interest revives with plenty of old
vintages from Jaboulet Aîné in the northern Rhône and a good
selection of Châteauneuf-du-Pape in the southern Rhône (Domaine du
Mont-Redon 1971 at £27). More recent vintages (1983, for example) are
there as well.

In other parts of the world, Philip Tite offers Borgogno Barolos from
Italy, as well as Chianti from Badia a Coltibuono and Brunello from
Biondi-Santi (the 1970 is £34 a bottle). And in California we have the
rare chance to taste some older wines such as a Cabernet Sauvignon
varietal back to 1968 (Beaulieu Vineyards, Georges de Latour at £109 a
bottle). Look also for the slightly more recent wines from 1974.

Best buys
Old vintages of claret; old Rhône wines

J Townend & Sons

HEAD OFFICE Red Duster House, York Street,   TEL (0482) 26891
Hull, Humberside HU2 0QX
(Cash & Carry) The Wine Cellars, Oxford Street,
Hull, Humberside HU2 0QX

OPEN Mon–Fri 9–5.30   Sat (only in Dec) 9–12   CLOSED Sat (except Dec), Sun,
public holidays   CREDIT CARDS None accepted; personal and business
accounts   DISCOUNTS Quantity discounts available on unmixed cases
DELIVERY Free within 50-mile radius, otherwise £2.50 per case
GLASS HIRE Nominal charge   TASTINGS AND TALKS 1 annual major tasting;
monthly tastings through Wine Club; to groups on request   CELLARAGE £2.76
per case per year (plus insurance)   ∎

This is the wholesale side of the Hull-based chain of retail shops of
House of Townend (qv). The cash and carry warehouse in York Street
carries the full range, and has been joined by a Wine Market at

Willerby. The other branches of House of Townend carry a large selection.

It's a traditional list, dominated by claret, but with occasional inspiration from elsewhere. For instance, Beaujolais comes from Paul Bocuse (a sous-marque of Georges Duboeuf), and there's some good Châteauneuf from Ch de Beaucastel and Côtes du Rhône from Ch du Grand Moulas. Sancerre from Guy Saget, and the Ch de Fonscolombe, Coteaux d'Aix-en-Provence are two more possible choices. Some German estate wines are rather anonymous (with only a few producers' names), but the rather feeble Italian range is redeemed by Frescobaldi wines in Tuscany and Tiefenbrunner in the Alto Adige. Sherries are from Wisdom and Warter. The odd New World wine puts in an appearance.

And so back to Bordeaux. There's plenty here of interest in claret (though a distinct lack in Sauternes), and some very good prices for petit château wines as well. Classed growths go back to 1970.

Best buys

Paul Bocuse Beaujolais; Ch Tour du Mirail 1983, Haut-Médoc, £4.35; Vin de Pays des Côtes de Gascogne 1985, Colombard, £2.40; Garrafeira Tinto 1974, Solar, £3.98

Henry Townsend

OFFICE (not shop) York House, Oxford Road,   TEL (049 46) 78291 Beaconsfield, Buckinghamshire HP9 1UJ

OPEN Mon–Fri 9–5.30   1st Sat in month 9–12.30 (other Sats by arrangement) CLOSED Sun, public holidays   CREDIT CARDS None accepted DISCOUNTS 5% on unmixed cases   DELIVERY Free to South Buckinghamshire, Ascot and Windsor area, Berkhamsted, Chinnor and Bicester, Central London, City of London, Hampstead, Highgate, Fulham and Chelsea (min 1 case); elsewhere 1 case £4.50, 2–5 cases £3.15 per case, 6–10 cases £2.55 per case, 11+ cases £2.15 per case; mail order available   GLASS HIRE Free with 1-case order, delivery available   TASTINGS AND TALKS Series of tastings in London and Coleshill and on request   CELLARAGE £3.50 per case for the 1st year, £3 for subsequent years (includes insurance)   ■

A heavyweight range of wines in the main list is supplemented by enticing special offers, particularly of wines for laying down: during 1987 Alsace, Germany, Burgundy and the Rhône joined claret.

The emphasis on fine wines is reflected in the main list, which only briefly looks at French country wines and sets its sights firmly on top wines from other parts of the world. The heart of the list is certainly in classic French areas: claret has vintages going back to 1966 – with a few wines from 1961 – but there is a happy blend of petit château and classed growths wines in younger vintages. Look also at the big range of Sauternes. For Burgundy, domaine wines – from Rousseau,

Tollot-Beaut, Dujac, Bernard Morey – are joined by a few négociant wines from Louis Latour.

Other French areas to be well covered are the Rhône, with wines from Jaboulet Aîné and Guigal; a delightful selection of Alsace mainly from Trimbach and Rolly Gassmann; and some fine Sancerres and Pouilly Fumés.

The German estate list is like a sonorous roll-call. Prices are good for these wines – even for the 1976s which are still listed. The Mosel–Saar–Ruwer is best served, but there are wines from all areas – even from Franconia. The rest of Europe is much less interesting, except for the almacenista Sherries and vintage Madeiras.

In the New World, a small selection from California is overshadowed by a much more impressive one from Australia, with an attractive smattering of small estates (Hollick, Leconfield, Adams & Wray) alongside larger firms. Chilean wines have been supplied by Concha y Toro and a lone New Zealand Chardonnay by Cooks.

Best buys

German estate wines; domaine-bottled Burgundy; Ch Thieuley 1983, Bordeaux, £4.20; Ch des Gondats 1981, Bordeaux Supérieur, £4.83; Chilean wines

---

Ian & Madeleine Trehearne Wines   ☞

20 New End Square, London NW3 1LN   TEL 01-435 6310

OPEN 24 hours, 7 days a week   CREDIT CARDS None accepted; personal and business accounts   DISCOUNTS 5% for 6 cases or over   DELIVERY Free locally; mail order available   GLASS HIRE Free with 1-case order; free local delivery TASTINGS AND TALKS 4 in-store tastings annually for mailing list; to groups on request   CELLARAGE £3 per case   ∎

From an elegant house in Hampstead, this two-person band operates one of the shortest lists in the Guide, but for anybody interested in finding wines from small estates, this is a very good place to come . . .

. . . Especially if that interest centres on the Loire. The Trehearnes have pinpointed an attractive Montlouis Sec from Berger Frères (who also provide a sparkling wine), and Ménétou-Salon in all three colours from Bernard Clément. There's also a superb Quarts de Chaume from Ch de Belle-Rive. Staying with northern growing areas of France, Champagne is from Jean-Jacques Cattier, and Alsace from Edouard and Catherine Leiber.

Elsewhere, look for a few domaine-bottled Burgundies and Italian Piedmont wines from the small firm of Ascheri in Bra (Barbera d'Alba 1980 at £4.30 a bottle).

Best buys

Saumur 1985, Cave Co-opérative des Vignerons de Saumur, £3.75;

Bourgogne Passe-tout-grain 1985, Bernard du Breuil, £5.35; Dolcetto d'Alba 1984, Ascheri, £4.30

Turl Wine Vaults

16 Turl Street, Oxford, Oxfordshire OX1 3DH   TEL (0865) 247966
OPEN Mon–Sat 9.30–5.30   CLOSED Sun, public holidays
CREDIT CARDS Access, Visa; personal and business accounts   DISCOUNTS 5%
mixed case, 10% unopened case   DELIVERY Free within 30-mile radius (min 4
cases); elsewhere £4 per case; mail order available   GLASS HIRE Free with
1-case order; delivery available   TASTINGS AND TALKS On request
CELLARAGE £26 per case per year or 5p per case per week

Turl Wine Vaults keeps a select range of wines with stars particularly in Italy but some interesting bottles in most areas of France, too. It's a pity that everything is so expensive.

In the Italian range, we would recommend the Friuli wines of dal Moro (Tocai di Lisón Classico 1983 at £4.83) and the house Chianti from Fattoria dell'Ugo (1985 vintage at £3.36). From within France, the Côtes de Provence rosé 1986 from Domaine des Aspras and the Coteaux de l'Ardèche reds from Gérard Sauzon are high quality, if pricey. There's a small number of clarets (again rather expensive) and a few wines from the Loire. Also look for the Bergerac wines of Ch le Fage. Portugal offers Ports from Ramos-Pinto, and a good, dry Vinho Verde from the co-operative of Ponte de Lima. Sherry is from Barbadillo, and Madeira from Rutherford, Osborne and Perkin.

Best buys
Chianti Putto 1985, Fattoria dell'Ugo, £3.36; Bairrada 1980, São Domingos Garrafeira, £4.35

Ubiquitous Chip Wine Shop   🐷

8 Ashton Lane, Glasgow G12 8SJ   TEL 041-334 7109
OPEN Mon–Fri 12 noon–10   Sat 10–10   CLOSED Sun, 25 Dec, 1 & 2 Jan
CREDIT CARDS Amex, Diners, Visa; personal and business accounts
DISCOUNTS 5% on 1 case   DELIVERY Free within 10-mile radius of Glasgow
(min 3 cases); otherwise £1.50 for the first case, £1 for the second case; mail order
available   GLASS HIRE Free with wine purchase
TASTINGS AND TALKS Tutored tastings held throughout the year; weekly
tasting group in restaurant   CELLARAGE Free if wine purchased from the
premises

This list comes from what *The Good Food Guide* has described as the 'benchmark against which all other Glasgow restaurants should be judged'. As far as the wines are concerned, this means that it is particularly strong on France and, to a lesser extent, on Germany. Other areas are looking up, though, compared to last year. (And there are always the malt whiskies . . .)

Above the level of basic claret, prices are good in Bordeaux – some Pomerols in particular are very good value. Most of the communes in Bordeaux are accounted for, with vintages going back to 1975. There may be some half-bottles, but it's a pity – since this list supports a restaurant – that there aren't more.

Burgundy offers less interest than Bordeaux, but we would recommend the Beaujolais of Loron. We would also pick out the Côtes du Rhône from Les Dames Chartreusines, made on vineyards owned by nuns, and the Châteauneuf from Domaine du Mont-Redon. Attractions on the Loire include the red Sancerre of Paul Millerioux (1985 vintage at £5.65) and the Savennières of Jean Baumard (1985 vintage at £5.35). Alsace comes mainly from Dopff et Irion. A small selection of country wines feature the Chardonnay and Sauvignon from Haut-Poitou.

Since last year, Italy has expanded, taking in Barbera from Pio Cesare, Recioto Amarone della Valpolicella from Sartori, Soave from Santa Sofia and Chianti Classico from Santa Caterina (1983 vintage in magnums at £8.50). In Spain, we like the look of the Riojas from Faustino and CVNE, and there's Quinta do Cotto Douro red from Montez Champalimaud (1982 vintage at £3.70). There are good estate wines from Germany – including the occasional 1976 wine.

On to the New World, and here things have expanded, with Australia featuring Orlando, Hardys, Brown Brothers, Seppelt and McWilliams; and California with Mondavi and Firestone.

Best buys

Valdepeñas 1975, Señorio de los Llanos Gran Reserva, £3.35; Alsace Auxerrois 1984, Rolly Gassmann, £4.15; Côtes du Roussillon 1983, Ch de Cap de Fouste, £3.45; Gutturnio dei Colli Piacentini 1985, Fugazza, £3.45; Ch Malartic-Lagravière 1980, Graves red, £5.95

Unwins

HEAD OFFICE Birchwood House, Victoria Road, TEL (0322) 72711
Dartford, Kent DA1 5AJ
Approx 300 branches in South-East England

OPEN Mon–Sat 10–2, 4–10 Sun 12–2, 7–9.30 public holidays open during licensing hours (shops open 7 days a week, most of them all day)
CREDIT CARDS All accepted; personal and business accounts
DISCOUNTS 10% for table wine (min 1 mixed case), 5% for sparkling wine (min 1 mixed case) DELIVERY Free in South-East England; elsewhere at cost; mail order available GLASS HIRE Free with order; delivery free with order
TASTINGS AND TALKS Regular in-store tastings; to groups on request
CELLARAGE Negotiable

Prices are still remarkably high here when compared with those of other High Street off-licences. Unwins counter this by pointing to the 'knowledgeable and friendly service'. Perhaps if they improved the environment of their shops at the same time, and concentrated less on cigarette sales, we would be more convinced.

Despite that, some good things are to be found. There's a good range of claret, including petit château wines, mainly from the 1983 vintage. Burgundy produces less of interest, apart from the occasional wine from the top 1978 vintage – but on the Rhône there's some good Châteauneuf from Fines Roches. Unwins have built up a top-rate Champagne list (including plenty of vintage wines).

Outside France, Italy comes off well with Ruffino Chiantis and Spain has Faustino Riojas and Torres wines. And there are a number of estate wines from Germany.

Best buys

Rioja 1982, Faustino V, £4.65; Ruffino Chiantis; Renmano Chairman's Selection, Cabernet Sauvignon 1981, £4.69

The Upper Crust

3/4 Bishopsmead Parade, East Horsley,   TEL (04865) 3280
Surrey KT24 6RT

OPEN Mon–Sat 9–9   Sun 12–2, 7–9   public holidays 10–1, 6–8   CLOSED Chr Day   CREDIT CARDS Access, Visa   DISCOUNTS 5% for 1 mixed case, 2½% for case of Champagne   DELIVERY Free to London (min 3 cases) and Surrey (min 1 case); otherwise at cost   GLASS HIRE Free with corresponding order TASTINGS AND TALKS Weekly summer in-store tastings   CELLARAGE £2 per case per year

A good all-round list – and a number of recommendations – bring this shop into the Guide for the first time. The Upper Crust inventory of wines – to judge from recent additions – continues to expand at a breathtaking rate. The shop has recently been re-organised to make the layout more accessible.

Areas which look good include some solid clarets (Nathaniel Johnston's House Médoc and St-Emilion are top quality house wines) with vintages going back to the early 1960s. Burgundy has some domaine wines, and Beaujolais comes from Loron. The Loire chips in with Muscadet from Marcel Guilbaud and Sancerre from Vacheron, but not much in between. More French attractions are Provençal wines from Ch la Coste (red at £2.99) and Alsace from Trimbach. There's a big range of Champagne, with an emphasis on Pol Roger.

Outside France, Germany produces some decent estate wines, but the Italian selection could be livened up. Spain flaunts Torres, and CVNE and Beronia Riojas, plus Sherry from José Pemartin (Rare Old Fino at £3.89) and a good choice of vintage Ports.

The New World range has increased with Rosemount from Australia and a few wines from Almadén in California. Lamberhurst supplies our home-grown bottles.

Best buys

Côtes de Provence, Ch la Coste red, white and rosé, £2.99; Coteaux du Tricastin 1984, Pascal, £2.89; Montepulciano d'Abruzzo 1983, Bianchi, £2.79; Concha y Toro Chilean wines; Rioja 1983, Beronia, £3.59

Valvona & Crolla

19 Elm Row, Edinburgh EH7 4AA   TEL 031-556 6066

OPEN Mon–Thur, Sat 9–5.30 Fri 9–6 CLOSED Sun, public holidays, 1–7 Jan
CREDIT CARDS None accepted; business accounts DISCOUNTS 5% for 1 mixed
case, 8% for 5+ cases DELIVERY Free locally (min £40); elsewhere at cost; mail
order available GLASS HIRE Free with 1-case order
TASTINGS AND TALKS Wine Tasting Club to start in Oct 1987 CELLARAGE Not
available

To a long-established Italian delicatessen has been added a wine list to match the quality of the food. So, now, alongside the salamis and pasta, we find a splendid range from right round the country. In Piedmont, there is a pride of Borgogno Barolos (including old vintages back to 1947 at £36.47 a bottle), plus Barolos from other producers and Barberas, a Carema and Barbarescos and a Chardonnay from Angelo Gaja. Then in the Veneto, wines from Santi and Masi have been assembled, plus a good selection of Amarone Reciotos and wines from Venegazzù. A few Friuli wines and more from Lombardy (Franciacorta and Inferno) are no less significant.

Down in Tuscany, the super vini da tavola appear like I Sodi di San Niccolo from Serrestori, Sassicaia and Tignanello. Chiantis represent a whole clutch of producers, but home in on Ruffino. When you get as far as Rubesco di Torgiano and Orvietos from Bigi, look for the single vineyard wines, and away on the east coast, seek out the super vino da tavola Nico of Illuminati (£10.88) in the Abruzzo, and Bianchi's Rosso Cònero San Lorenzo.

In the deep South, we find d'Angelo's Aglianico del Vulture, the super, smooth, rich Torre Ercolana (three vintages of this rare wine). Corvo and Regaleali wines come from Sicily, as does the Vecchio Samperi Marsala of de Bartoli. And don't forget the Sardinian wines from Sella e Mosca . . .

Best buys

Settesoli red and white, £1.98; Montepulciano d'Abruzzo 1984, Tollo, £2.49; Barolo 1981, Le Due Torri, £3.89; Ruffino Chiantis; old vintages of Barolo; Gutturnio dei Colli Piacentini 1984, Cantine Romagnoli, £3.59

Please write to tell us about any ideas for features you would like to see in next year's edition or in *Which? Wine Monthly*.

Helen Verdcourt Wines

Spring Cottage, Kimbers Lane, Maidenhead,   TEL (0628) 25577
Berkshire SL6 2QP

OPEN All hours (24-hour answering machine)   CREDIT CARDS None accepted;
personal and business accounts   DISCOUNTS On case prices   DELIVERY Free
in Central London and most of South-East England (min 1 case); mail order
available   GLASS HIRE Free with 2+ case order
TASTINGS AND TALKS Regular tutored tastings to 2 local wine clubs every
month; to groups on request   CELLARAGE Free (limited space)   ■

If new lists keep on appearing from this one-woman business, it's not
because the very reasonable prices are going up, but because Helen
Verdcourt keeps on finding new wines and wants to let her customers
know about them. Not only does she go on buying trips to find these
wines, but she also organises tastings and tours and runs a wine club
(see the WINE CLUBS and TOURS section at the end of the Guide).

The most recent list we have seen covers most of the world, but with
an extra concentration in the Rhône and Australia. From the Rhône, for
instance, Helen Verdcourt has marshalled a considerable collection of
wines from Jaboulet Aîné, and some Côte Rôties from Guigal, while in
the South the range goes from the familiar Côtes du Ventoux, La Vieille
Ferme (1985 vintage at £2.95 – one of the cheapest prices for this wine
around), up to Châteauneuf-du-Pape from Ch du Beaucastel, as well as
Ch Rayas and Domaine du Vieux Télégraphe.

The Australian list has lengthened since last year: now we see wines
from Rosemount, Wynns, Brown Brothers, Taltarni and Moss Wood.
The sweet Muscats from Brown Brothers and Stanton & Killeen
provide an extra thrill.

If those are currently the strongest areas, other regions also do well.
The Loire produces Vouvray Clos Naudin and a luscious Bonnezeaux
from J Boivin (£7.50); Bordeaux's small selection contains a good range
of wines, and other sound areas are domaine wines from Burgundy,
the Beaujolais of Duboeuf, Alsace from the co-operative of Turckheim
and the Vin de Pays de l'Hérault of Mas de Daumas Gassac.

Other European countries fare more briefly: Murrieta Riojas, wines
from J M da Fonseca in Portugal, the Carmignano Tenuta di Capezzana
and Venegazzù white label from Italy.

Best buys

Champagne Granier (NV), £8.90; Les Sables Vin de Pays Rhodaniennes
1986, pure Syrah, £2.85; Côtes du Rhône 1981 Cuvée Supérieure,
Vignerons à Rasteau, £3.30; Barco Reale 1982, Tenuta di Capezzana,
£3.55; Wynns Ovens Valley Shiraz 1983, £4.40

Prices are only a rough indication, and were current in summer 1987.

Victoria Wine Company

HEAD OFFICE Brook House, Chertsey Road,   TEL (04862) 5066
Woking, Surrey GU21 5BE
864 branches nationwide

OPEN Hours vary from branch to branch CREDIT CARDS All accepted
DISCOUNTS For light and sparkling wines 3% on 6 bottles (mixed), 5% on 12
bottles (mixed) DELIVERY Not available; mail order available
GLASS HIRE Free with any order TASTINGS AND TALKS Promotional tastings
in selected stores; to groups on request CELLARAGE Not available

We are getting worried about the Victoria Wine Company. Recent
tastings of additions to their list have been invariably disappointing.
There appears to be an unhappy tendency to go for the safest, lowest
common denominator when deciding what goes on the shelves in the
864 branches of this nationwide chain.

A typical example was the recent introduction of the Grants of St
James's Selection, a range of varietal and generic wines designed, to
quote the publicity blurb to 'capitalise on Grants' image of experience,
expertise and trustworthiness'. Rarely has a new range of wines
received such a bad – and unanimously bad – press. They were
expensive and they were dull.

So we feel Victoria Wine must decide in which direction it wishes to
go, as High Street off-licences look around for a new role in wine
retailing. At the moment, there are certainly areas worth looking at –
but they are covered better by some other High Street groups, certainly
by supermarkets and wine warehouses.

Sections of the list, however, which are worth considering include
Bordeaux (with some decent petit château wines), Alsace (with wines
from Preiss-Zimmer), a reasonable range of German estate wines (von
Buhl and Bürklin-Wolf in the Rheinpfalz and some of the Mosels),
Antinori wines from Italy, Wynns wines from Australia and Montana
from New Zealand. Look also for a good range of vintage Ports and
Harvey's range of 1796 Sherries.

Best buys

Vin de Pays de l'Uzège, £1.99; Pinot Oltrepò Pavese 1983,
Fontanafredda, £4.19; Faugères 1984, Cuvée Jules Gaston, £2.69;
Raimat Sparkling Chardonnay, £4.99

La Vigneronne

105 Old Brompton Road, London SW7 3LE   TEL 01-589 6113
L'Alsacien (address as above)   TEL 01-589 3320

OPEN Mon–Fri 9.30–10 Sat 10–10 Public holidays (advisable to telephone
first) CREDIT CARDS All accepted DISCOUNTS 5% for 1 case
DELIVERY Free in Central London (min 1 case); otherwise Outer London £3.50
per case, UK mainland £7.50 per case; mail order available GLASS HIRE Free

with 2-case order   TASTINGS AND TALKS Wines available Sat pm; tutored
tastings every Mon and Thur at local hotel; occasionally to groups on request
CELLARAGE £5 per case per year

105 Brompton Road now houses two businesses. Since last year,
Elizabeth and Mike Berry have launched a new mail order venture,
L'Alsacien (note: this is masculine – it was Mike's turn to have a
business, we are told), which is devoted wholly to Alsace wines. And
what a splendid job they've made of it, with wines from small estates
that have never appeared before in this country. Many of the wines are
from some of the new grand cru vineyards, and cover the full extent of
the Alsace region from the north down to the far south.

A random dip into this list at any point will reveal treats most of us
didn't know Alsace ever possessed, and, after exhausting the grands
crus, we can still find plenty of wines from other small growers and
more familiar merchants, grouped under grape varieties. One
particular producer they specialise in is Marc Kreydenweiss.

And then, of course, there's always La Vigneronne's standard list.
We say 'standard', but that's the last thing it is, being made up of 1,000
wines. Although it covers the world, there are definite specialisations.
One is old vintages of fine wines: so you get old claret, Madeira, vintage
Port, Sauternes, some old Burgundy, even old Rioja and Rhône wines.

Certain areas come out most strongly, apart from Alsace. The New
World is a particular attraction with huge ranges from Australia (Moss
Wood, Cape Mentelle, Penfold's, Brown Brothers, Lakes Folly,
Balgownie). There is an extraordinary panoply of producers, large and
small (and even some old wines here: Grange Hermitage in vintages
back to 1962). More unusually, La Vigneronne stocks relatively old
vintages of California wines (Heitz's Martha's Vineyard 1977 at £37.50)
to join the wide selection of younger wines from the region: producers
include most of the familiar names and some less well known (Smith
and Hook, Carmenet, Calera, Jensen, Chalone). Pudding lovers will
detect a special interest in dessert wines from here.

But if we've picked those areas out, nobody else is really neglected.
Spain displays a big range (including, almost inevitably, some old
vintages of Vega Sicilia), Italy comes up with a big selection of Antinori
wines, and wines flood in from all the major estates in Coteaux des
Baux en Provence. La Vigneronne is one of the few sources of supply
for Ch Simone from the tiny Provençal appellation of Palette. Top
domaine names from Burgundy occur in profusion, and surprisingly
good value Chablis from Domaine de Varoux is on offer. There are
even old vintages of Bourgueil – just to prove that this wine can age.

Best buys

Sauternes and Barsac; Australian wines; Rioja Gran Reservas; Côtes du
Roussillon 1982, Ch de Jau, £4.95; Syrah, Vin de Pays de Drôme, Vidal
Fleury, £3.50; almacenista Sherries

Vinceremos

Beechwood Centre, Elmete Lane, Leeds, TEL (0532) 734056
West Yorkshire LS8 2LQ

OPEN Mon–Fri 9–5 CLOSED Sat, Sun, public holidays, 25 Dec–2 Jan
CREDIT CARDS Access; personal and business accounts DISCOUNTS 10–19
cases 70p per case, 20+ cases £1.20 per case DELIVERY Free to UK mainland
(min 6 cases), any order within 25-mile radius of Leeds; other orders £3.20 per
case; mail order available GLASS HIRE Free; charge for delivery
TASTINGS AND TALKS Twice-yearly tastings by invitation CELLARAGE Not
available ∎

A short list which comes into the Guide for the first time for two
reasons: its collection of organically produced wines; and the unusual
countries of origin of some of the bottles.

For instance, those who hanker after wines from Zimbabwe need
look no further. The Flame Lily range of two whites and a red arrived
on their list in summer 1987, and are an inexpensive experiment at
£2.75 each. The same could be said for the Crimean red table wine, also
at £2.75, which, we are told, is a blend of Cabernet, Metrasse and
Seperavi grapes. Also listed are the good quality Omar Khayyam
méthode champenoise sparkler from India, and three decent reds from
Algeria.

The organic wines are mainly French, including a number of clarets
and a couple of Côtes du Rhône in the reds and a Muscadet and a
sweet Monbazillac in the whites. The English Avalon Seyval 1984
(£3.75) is also part of this group, and a Spanish Valdepeñas.

Other names include Montrose and Peter Lehmann wines from two
small wineries in Australia; and some attractive wines from Touraine
on the Loire.

Best buys

Vin de Pays de l'Aude 1986, Domaine de l'Isle, £2.99; Valdepeñas 1986,
£2.75; Peter Lehmann Cabernet/Shiraz 1983 and Dry Semillon 1984
£3.45; Algerian wines

Vintage Roots

88 Radstock Road, Reading, TEL (0734) 662569
Berkshire RG1 3PR

OPEN Mon–Sat 9–5.30 CLOSED Sun CREDIT CARDS None accepted;
personal and business accounts DISCOUNTS 5–10% (min 2 cases) (charities
12%) DELIVERY Free within 30-mile radius of Reading and West London (min
1 case); elsewhere £2.95 charge; mail order available GLASS HIRE Not
available TASTINGS AND TALKS 2 annual tastings; to groups on request
CELLARAGE Not available ∎

Vintage Roots is a new firm specialising, like the previous entry, in organically produced wines. Although the list is still short, they've come up with some interesting wines, not just from France, which seems to dominate the organic wine world, but from Germany and Italy as well.

From Germany, for example, they have unearthed wines from the Rheinhessen vineyards of Walter Hauck (Bermersheimer Hildegardisberg Müller-Thurgau Kabinett 1985 at £4.15). From Italy, wines come from Guerrieri-Rizzardi, one of the top producers of Soave, Bardolino and Valpolicella, who also produce a white vino da tavola called Bianco San Pietro (£3.15).

The bulk of the wines, though, do come from France. In whites, they include the Muscadet Domaine des Dorices (1985 vintage at £3.95) and the sweet Coteaux du Layon of Yves Freulon (£3.65). In reds, look for a wider range which includes Bordeaux and Bergerac, and a good value Vin de Pays du Gard at £2.45. There are sparkling wines from Bergerac and Saumur.

Best buys

Vin de Pays du Gard, Albaric, £2.45; Bianco San Pietro, Guerrieri-Rizzardi, £3.15; Cabernet d'Anjou 1985, Domaine de Dreuille, £3.42

The Vintner

7 Le Feugeral, Mont de la Pulente,   TEL (0534) 42186/44143
La Moye Station, St Brelade, Jersey

OPEN Mon–Sat & public holidays 8 am–9 pm   CLOSED Sun, 25 Dec, Good Friday   CREDIT CARDS None accepted; personal and business accounts DISCOUNTS 5% 1–4 cases, 10% 5+ cases   DELIVERY Free; not available outside Jersey; mail order available   GLASS HIRE Not available TASTINGS AND TALKS On request   CELLARAGE £1 per case per year

This merchant now offers wines from the Eldridge Pope list (qv), and is recommended on that basis.

A L Vose & Co

(OFFICE) 92 Kentsford Road,   TEL (044 84) 3328
Grange-over-Sands, Cumbria LA11 7BB
(SHOP) The Wine Store, Hampsfell Road, Grange-over-Sands, Cumbria LA11 6BE

OPEN Mon–Fri by appointment   Sat, public holidays 9–4   CLOSED Sun CREDIT CARDS None accepted; personal and business accounts DISCOUNTS 10% for 1 case   DELIVERY Free in Cumbria and North Lancashire; elsewhere at cost; mail order available   GLASS HIRE Free with case order TASTINGS AND TALKS In-store tastings most weekends; to groups on request CELLARAGE Not available

Much of this list – especially the German and Portuguese wines – is based upon wines offered at the Wine Schoppen (*qv*), but there are some areas where each shop operates independently. (Note that if you want to visit the shop on a weekday you need to make an appointment.)

One such area is Austria, where A L Vose import wines from the co-operative of Krems and offer a well-priced selection (Kremser Schmidt 1983, a dry white wine made from the Grüner Veltliner, £3.07; or the red Kremser Kaisersteige 1983 at £5.05). Another is Brazil, which supplies three whites and two reds, all varietal wines (Pinot Noir at £3.76; Chardonnay at £3.76) from the huge Palomas winery in the south of the country. While in South America, look also for wines from Cousiño Macul in Chile. Back in Europe, there is a wide range of Swiss wines at gnomic prices (the white Aigle les Festons at £8.63; the red Pinot Noir Dôle de St-Léonard at £7.15).

Best buys

Palomas Brazilian wines; German estate wines; Casaleiro Garrafeira 1975, £3.49

Waitrose

HEAD OFFICE Doncastle Road, TEL (0344) 424680
Southern Industrial Area, Bracknell, Berkshire RG12 4YA
81 licensed branches in London, Midlands and the Home Counties
OPEN Mon 12–6 Tue, Wed 9–6 Thur, Fri 8.30–8 Sat 8.30–5.30
CLOSED Sun, public holidays CREDIT CARDS None accepted
DISCOUNTS 5% for £100 of fortified, table or sparkling wines DELIVERY Not available GLASS HIRE Free (deposit required)
TASTINGS AND TALKS Occasionally to groups CELLARAGE Not available

The 81 licensed Waitrose stores – sadly (for Northerners) all in the south of England – continue to offer the best supermarket range in the country, both for variety and for quality. Having fewer branches than some of the other supermarket groups does mean that it's easier to buy smaller quantities of wines, which gives the buying team more scope.

Waitrose go in for very few own-label wines. Those that they do tend to be very basic – for a few pence more plenty of exciting wines can be found. For example, we have recently enjoyed some of their Italian selection – the Montepulciano d'Abruzzo of Illuminati (£3.35), the excellent Venegazzù of Gasparini-Loredan (£4.75) and the Campo ai Sassi 1985, Rosso di Montalcino (£3.35) which is the second wine of Brunello Castelgiocondo. In whites, the Soave from Zenato (£2.99) is good quality, or look for the Lugana from Villa Flora (£3.59).

In France, the Cinsault-Syrah from Cante-Cigale in the Hérault is good value at £2.25, and the Cahors Domaine de Léret-Monpezat 1983 is full of ripe fruit (£3.25). Of the more serious clarets, the priciest is Ch

Langoa-Barton 1977 at £9.75. Head to the South and South-West of France for plenty of good value. Waitrose Champagne (£7.95) always comes out well in supermarket Champagne tastings.

The list ranges much further than these two countries. Other wines to look out for are the Gran Condal Rioja Reserva 1978 (£3.49), the Marqués de Murrieta white Rioja (1982 vintage at £4.45), or the Periquita and Tinto da Anfora from Portugal (there are a number of good Portuguese reds on the list), or wines from Berri Estates in Australia or Cooks in New Zealand.

Best buys

Ch le Gardéra 1983, Bordeaux Supérieur, £3.95; Vin de Pays de l'Hérault Cinsault-Syrah 1985, Cante-Cigale, £2.25; Bairrada 1982, Mealhade co-operative, £2.25; Soave Classico 1985, Zenato, £2.99; Crémant de Bourgogne Rosé 1985, Bailly, £4.95

Wapping Wine Warehouse

The Old Pumping Station, St Katharine's Way, London E1 9UP

TEL 01-265 0448

OPEN Mon–Fri 9–7   Sat 10–6   Sun 10–4   CLOSED Public holidays
CREDIT CARDS Access, Visa; personal and business accounts   DISCOUNTS 5% (min 1 case)   DELIVERY Free locally (min 1 case), inner London (min 2 cases), outer London (min 5 cases); elsewhere at cost; mail order available
GLASS HIRE Free with 1-case order   TASTINGS AND TALKS Occasional in-store tastings; to groups on request   CELLARAGE £3 per case per year

---

The prices are good at this wine warehouse near St Katharine's Dock in East London, and while the selection is not big, there are plenty of well-chosen wines here.

From France, they have amassed some good value regional wines (look for the Minervois 1984 Ch Canet at £2.37 or the Fitou 1983 of Paul Herpé at £2.73 or the unusual Irouléguy 1985 at £3.68). In more classical mode, there are some well-chosen petit château clarets from the 1982 and 1983 vintage, and Beaujolais from Georges Duboeuf. The Rhône range is good, but short, the Loire slightly longer but less interesting. The house Champagne is by Pannier Brut at £8.54.

Good bargains from other countries are not hard to find either. There's a decent group of Riojas and the bargain Valdepeñas Señorio de los Llanos Reserva 1978 at £3.12, plus, for much more, Vega Sicilia's second wine, Valbuena 1982 (£11.10). From plenty of Italian wines, look for Le Cane, the red vino da tavola from Boscaini in the Veneto, at £4.70; or Chiantis from Antinori and Villa Banfi, or the Cirò Classico Riserva 1977 from Calabria at £4.31; or the Frascati Colli di Catone at £3.79.

There are short selections of Port and Sherries from de Terry. Finer wines – especially from France – are available through a separate list.

Best buys

Bulgarian Sakar Mountain Cabernet Sauvignon 1978, £2.87; Syrah and
Cabernet Sauvignon Vins de Pays d'Oc, Chantovent, £2.55; Corbières
1983, Paul Herpé, £2.72; Valpolicella Classico 1983, Zenato, £3.61;
Jacob's Creek red and white, £2.95

Peter Watts Wines

Wisdom's Barn, Colne Road, Coggeshall,   TEL (0376) 61130
Colchester, Essex CO6 1TD

OPEN Mon–Fri 9–1, 2–5.30   Sat 9–1   CLOSED Sun, public holidays
CREDIT CARDS Access, Visa; personal and business accounts
DISCOUNTS 2½% + free delivery for 10+ cases, 5–9 cases free delivery
DELIVERY Free locally and nationwide (min 5 cases); otherwise £6 per order;
mail order available   GLASS HIRE Free   TASTINGS AND TALKS Various
CELLARAGE £2 per case per year

Here we have a short list with French wines mainly from individual
domaines and selections from Germany, Italy, Spain and Australia.
   Area of interest include the domaine wines from Burgundy
(Domaine Jeanin-Naltet, Mazilly Père et Fils, Domaine des Varoilles)
and wines from Aujoux in Beaujolais. A few clarets are available, but
more rewarding would be to look at the Alsace wines of Louis Siffert,
or the red Vin de Pays de l'Hérault of Domaine de Luch (£2.60), or
indeed the Champagne from Joly or the Châteauneuf-du-Pape of
Domaine des Chanssaud.
   Italian wines include Soave and Valpolicella from Masi and Chianti
Classico from Villa Banfi, while Spain has Marqués de Cáceres Riojas.
Peter Watts has decided on wines from Orlando and Jacob's Creek as
his Australian section. Look also for the Souza Ports and Valdespino
Sherries.

Best buys

Vin de Pays de l'Hérault 1985, Domaine de Luch red, £2.60; Bourgogne
Passe-tout-grain 1985, Mazilly Père et Fils, £4.30; Côtes du Rhône
Rouge 1985, Domaine des Chanssaud, £3.69

Welbeck Wine

3 Montrose Road, Dukes Park, Springfield,   TEL (0245) 461210
Chelmsford, Essex CM2 6TE

OPEN Mon 9–5   Tue, Wed, Thur 9–6   Fri 9–7   Sat 9.30–6   Sun 10–5
CLOSED 25 & 26 Dec; 1 Jan   CREDIT CARDS Access, Visa; business accounts
DISCOUNTS Negotiable   DELIVERY Free in Essex area (min 2 cases); elsewhere
£3 per case; mail order available   GLASS HIRE Free with suitable order
TASTINGS AND TALKS Occasional tastings; 2–3 wines available at weekends; to
groups on request   CELLARAGE (Claret and vintage Port only) £4.50 per case ■

This well-balanced list, obviously at its best in France, also branches briefly into Italy and Australia, and has a good range of vintage Ports tucked away.

House wines seem to centre around Bergerac; then comes a useful range of clarets starting at the house claret for £2.79 and moving on to more serious stuff via the strangely Scottish-sounding Ch la Claymore in Lussac St-Emilion (1985 vintage at £3.84) and other wines from the satellite villages of St-Emilion and Pomerol. In Burgundy, reasonable value is to be had in the Sauvignon de St-Bris and Bourgogne Aligoté (£4.39) of J-M Brocard, while on the Rhône we find the Châteauneuf of Domaine de Mont-Redon. On the Loire, Guy Saget's Pouilly Fumé is first-rate (1986 vintage at £5.99).

Beyond France, there are a few German estate wines (Dr Bürklin-Wolf among them) and, in Italy, we find Borgogno Barolos and the Chianti of Fattoria dell'Ugo (the 1983 vintage excellent value at £2.94), plus the Chardonnay di Appiano from Alto Adige. Bulgaria offers more superb value and Australia comes up with Rosemount wines.

Best buys

Ch Musar 1979, £4.99; Bulgarian wines; Chianti Putto 1983, Fattoria dell'Ugo, £2.94; Ch du Breuil 1981, Cissac, £4.49; Vin de Pays des Côtes de Gascogne, Colombard 1985, £2.49

Wessex Wines

197 St Andrews Road, Bridport, Dorset DT6 3BT   TEL (0308) 23400
OPEN Mon–Sat 8.30–9   Sun, public holidays on demand
CREDIT CARDS None accepted; personal and business accounts
DISCOUNTS 5% for 6 bottles (min 1 case)   DELIVERY Free within 20-mile radius of Bridport (min 1 case); otherwise 1–2 cases £5 per case, 3–5 cases £3 per case, 5–9 cases £1.50 per case, 10+ cases free; mail order available
GLASS HIRE Free   TASTINGS AND TALKS Regular annual tastings for customers; informal tastings; to groups on request   CELLARAGE Not available■

Wessex Wines' is not a long list, but much pleasure can be found in the wines of this Dorset merchant.

In France, they have put together a good selection of petit château Bordeaux (Ch la Valade 1982, Côtes de Fronsac at £4.20, or Ch La Rose du Pin 1985 Bordeaux at £3.86), as well as wines from Côtes de Bourg and Côtes de Blaye, plus crus bourgeois. From the South-West of France come a few wines from Bergerac and the excellent value Vin de Pays des Coteaux du Quercy (from vineyards just outside Cahors) at £3.10. Labouré-Roi, Jules Belin, Charles Quillardet in Fixin and the Cave Co-opérative of Buxy have been nominated to represent Burgundy.

Côtes du Rhône offers a well-priced selection, while Alsace brings in wines from Laugel in the north and Muré further south. Champagne is from Maurice Delabaye and Pol Roger.

There's an increasing selection of Italian wines (look for the Venegazzù wines from Conte Loredan-Gasparini or the Chianti of Rocca delle Macie) and a decent range of Riojas from Spain taking in CVNE and Bodegas Riojanas. Bulgaria offers probably the best value on the list. And the New World comes in much more strongly than last year with co-operative wines from California (yes, they have them there), Cooks wines from New Zealand and Berri and Rosemount wines from Australia.

Best buys

Bulgarian wines; Bairrada Garrafeira 1975, Caves Aliança, £5.22; Ch la Valade 1982, Fronsac, £4.20; Vin de Pays des Coteaux du Quercy 1985, C Laur, £3.10

White Hart Vaults

See Wines Galore.

The Wholefood Shop (Bridge of Allan)

See J E Hogg.

Whynot Wine Warehouses

HEAD OFFICE The Ladybrook Hotel, Fir Road, Bramhall, Stockport, Cheshire SK7 2NP   TEL 061-439 8969

Unit 2A, Deanway Trading Estate, Wilmslow Road, Handforth, Wilmslow, Cheshire SK9 3HW   TEL (0625) 527471

222 Buxton Road, Davenport, Stockport, Cheshire SK2 7AE   TEL 061-483 0414

Unit 2, Baildon Bridge Estate, Otley Road, Shipley, West Yorkshire BD17 7EX   TEL (0274) 596391

County Hotel, Church Road, Lytham St Annes, Lancashire FY8 5LZ   TEL (0253) 739646

Yarwood Street, off Tipping Street, Altrincham, Gtr Manchester WA14 2HB   TEL 061-941 2002

OPEN Mon–Fri 9–7 Sat 9.30–6 Sun 10–4 CREDIT CARDS Access, Amex, Visa, Whynot Wine Credit Card; personal and business accounts DISCOUNTS 2½% for 1 unmixed case DELIVERY Free within 5-mile radius of each warehouse (min 1 case); elsewhere £4.75 for 1 case, £3.75 for 2 cases, £3.20 for 3 cases, £2.25 for 4–7 cases, £1.50 for 8–9 cases, 10+ cases free; mail order available GLASS HIRE Free with wine order TASTINGS AND TALKS Wines available daily; various other tastings throughout the year CELLARAGE £3.50 per case per year ∎

The list continues to flourish at this group of Manchester based wine warehouses. The atmosphere is relaxed and friendly, and you can taste before you buy – especially useful when so many of the wines are at bargain basement prices.

Good prices are prevalent, for example, in the French country wine range which includes a Vin de Pays des Bouches-du-Rhône at £1.89 and the red Ch Vieil-Orme 1985 from Bergerac at £2.55. Rock bottom prices are also asked for the selection of Bulgarian wines and many of the Portuguese bottles (which include the Tinto da Anfora of João Pires (£3.75) or the Bairrada 1985 of Borges & Irmão (£2.69).

Whynot Wines don't ignore the more classic areas: clarets range from Ch Faurie Pascaud 1985, Bordeaux at £2.85, up to Ch d'Issan 1982, Margaux at £16.50, with plenty of wines in between. Burgundy seems to be dominated by Louis Latour wines, but Alsace has plenty of promise in wines from Louis Gisselbrecht, and Duboeuf supplies the Beaujolais.

Other parts of France that are well served include the Rhône (Côtes du Rhône 1985 Rasteau, £3.29) and Champagne (starting with the house variety at £7.89). Outside France, Spain is dominated by Torres wines and Domecq Domain Riojas (Gran Reserva 1976 at £5.25), while Verdicchio Casal di Serra 1985 (£3.85) is one of the occasional treats in Italy. There's much more interest overseas, with a big range covering Rosemount, de Bortoli, Tisdall and Orlando from Australia, Cooks from New Zealand and Clos du Bois and Mondavi from California.

Best buys

Vin de Pays des Coteaux de l'Ardèche, £1.99; Bulgarian wines; Ch Fonsèche 1982, Haut-Médoc, £4.99; Monte Ory Navarra Gran Reserva 1978, £3.09; Orlando RF Cabernet Sauvignon 1982, £4.49

Willoughbys

53 Cross Street, Manchester M2 4JP	TEL 061-834 0641
100 Broadway, Chadderton, Oldham,	TEL 061-620 1374
Greater Manchester OL9 0AA	
1 Springfield House, Water Lane, Wilmslow,	TEL (0625) 533068
Cheshire SK9 5AE	

OPEN Mon–Fri 9–5 Sat 9–5 CLOSED Sun, public holidays (Chadderton also closed afternoons on Wed & Sat) CREDIT CARDS Access, Visa; Wilmslow and Chester cards; personal and business accounts DISCOUNTS 5% on 1 case, others negotiable DELIVERY Free within 25-mile radius (min 1 case); otherwise at cost GLASS HIRE Free with order TASTINGS AND TALKS Weekly in-store tastings; regular customer tastings for trade & retail; to groups on request CELLARAGE Available

---

Willoughbys also own George Dutton in Chester and Thomas Baty in Liverpool, as well as their own three shops in Greater Manchester.

They have built up a big range of clarets, Champagnes and Burgundies on their firmly traditional list. But other parts of the world are not entirely neglected: for example, there are Brown Brothers wines from Australia and Hamilton and Tuttle examples from California (as well as some of the Firestone wines). Back in Europe, Willoughbys have picked Italian Alto Adige wines from Tiefenbrunner, the Brunello di Montalcino of Villa Banfi and Sassicaia 1982 vintage. In Spain, we find Muga Riojas, as well as Torres wines from the Penedès. A small selection of German wines includes some good quality from Louis Guntrum.

In France, we move straight to Champagne, with a wide range from De Venoge and representatives from many of the grande marque houses. In Bordeaux, clarets go back to 1975, with a strong showing from the 1983 and 1982 vintages. In Burgundy, although négociant wines from Chandesais and Labouré-Roi dominate, wines from Domaine Chantal Lescure (Beaune Premier Cru 1985 at £10.71) and Antonin Rodet are also in evidence.

Whisky aficionados will salivate over a huge range of malts.

Best buys

Willoughbys Sunday Claret 1985, £3.61; Willoughbys White Burgundy 1985, Rodet, £5.32; Blanquette de Limoux, Domaine de Martinolles, £4.80; Brown Brothers Chenin Blanc 1985, £4.17; Ch Guirauton 1984, Graves, £4.35

Windrush Wines

The Barracks, Cecily Hill, Cirencester,   TEL (0285) 67121
Gloucestershire GL7 2EF

OPEN Mon–Fri 9–6   Sat 9.30–1   CLOSED Sun, public holidays
CREDIT CARDS None accepted; personal and business accounts
DISCOUNTS Negotiable for 10+ cases   DELIVERY Free local delivery (min 5 cases) and UK mainland (min 5+ cases); elsewhere at cost; mail order available
GLASS HIRE Available   TASTINGS AND TALKS Available by arrangement to all customers; to groups on request   CELLARAGE £3.45 per case per year (min charge £30)   ∎

Mark Savage held a London tasting at the beginning of 1987 in which, he said, he had decided to show no wines from an area with which he is closely associated – the Pacific North-West of the USA. In one way he was wise, because the rest of his list is just as interesting. It's just that he is one of the pioneers to import wines from such vineyards as Eyrie, Alpine, Elk Cove, Tualatin (all in Oregon), Columbia in Washington State and Covey House and Ste Chapelle in Idaho. He also keeps a good range of California wines – Stag's Leap, Hawk Crest, Cuvaison, St Clement, Round Hill, Philip Togni, Diamond Creek, Mantanzas Creek and others.

But he wanted to point out his European wines, and to introduce his expansion into Italian wines. He has been in Tuscany and Piedmont searching out super vini da tavola (those wines that break the constricting DOC rules) from top producers. Look for the Grosso Sanese 1985 of Il Palazzino in Chianti, or the Opera Prima of Roagna in Piedmont as examples. He also carries the DOCG wines of these top producers, and wines like the Avignonesi Vino Nobile di Montepulciano (£7.86), and the Barolo 1983 of Luciano Sandrone (£9.87).

Continuing interest occurs in the German estate wines of Balthasar Ress, and the Champagne of Billecart-Salmon. Once in France, clarets from featured châteaux include Ch Le Tertre Rôteboeuf in St-Emilion, Ch Cabannieux in Graves and Ch du Palanquey in Côtes de Castillon. Burgundy likewise has featured producers and plenty of domaine wines. Other bottles worth homing in on are the Beaujolais of Sylvain Fessy, and Rhône wines from Jaboulet Aîné in the north and Domaine de la Fourmone in the south (Vacqueyras Maître des Chais 1984 at £4.89), as well as Bandol wines from Domaine Tempier, and Côtes du Lubéron from Ch Val-Joanis.

Best buys

Beaujolais-Villages, Sylvain Fessy, £3.96; Côtes du Rhône, Cuvée des Muses 1984, Domaine de la Fourmone, £3.95; Wines from Ch Val-Joanis, Côtes du Luberon, £3.45; Chianti Classico 1985, San Giusto a Rentennano, £4.68; Manzanilla La Guita Perez Marin, £3.95

Wine Case Place 🗩

56 Bedford Street, Leamington Spa,   TEL (0926) 881421
Warwickshire CV32 5DT

OPEN Tue–Fri 10–6   Sat 9–5   CLOSED Mon, Sun, public holidays
CREDIT CARDS Access, Visa   DISCOUNTS 5% for 1 mixed case, 10% for 1 unmixed case   DELIVERY Free on UK mainland (min 1 case locally, 5 cases nationwide); mail order available   GLASS HIRE Free with 1-case order
TASTINGS AND TALKS Regular in-store tastings (Sat, sometimes at other times); to groups on request   CELLARAGE Not available

Prices are still very competitive at this shop (in fact many haven't changed since last year). Don't take any notice of the name – they will sell by the single bottles as well as the case, although good discounts are offered if you do buy by the case.

Bordeaux is one of the good value areas, with mainly petit château wines (Ch Chantegrive 1983, Graves at £4.25 or Ch Ramonet 1979, Bordeaux at £5.25), with a few classed growths at the top. While Burgundy is not so interesting, the Rhône (with wines from Jaboulet Aîné and Pascal) and the Loire (look for the fresh Touraine Blanc from the Oisly-et-Thésée co-operative at £4.40) are much better. So is the South of France, featuring the red and white Coteaux d'Aix-en-

Provence of the Marquis de Saporta (£2.95 for the red, £2.97 for the white), wines from Listel and the Vin de Pays d'Oc 1985, cépage Syrah (£2.65), plus, at the top end, the wines of Mas de Daumas Gassac.

Germany and Italy are still weak spots, but we like the look of the Spanish wines – Riojas from CVNE and Penedès wines from Torres and Jean León. California beckons with Mondavi and Jekel wines, and Australia with Brown Brothers and Taltarni wines.

Champagne from de Venoge (Cordon Bleu Brut at £9.95) is joined by grande marque wines. Ports include Fonseca aged tawnies, Sherries almacenista wines from Lustau. English wines are supplied by Three Choirs and Lamberhurst vineyards.

Best buys

Bergerac red and white, Ch la Jaubertie, £3.88; Listel wines; Côtes du Ventoux 1985, La Vieille Ferme, £3.35; Colombard, Vin de Pays de Gascogne, £2.79; Alsace Pinot Blanc 1985, Louis Sipp, £3.98; Rioja Reserva 1976, CVNE Imperial, £4.99

Winecellars

153–155 Wandsworth High Street, London SW18 4JB   TEL 01-871 3979

HEAD OFFICE Bretzel Foods Ltd, 213/215 Upper Street, London N1 1RL   TEL 01-359 6238

OPEN Mon–Sun 10–8.   CLOSED 25 & 26 Dec   CREDIT CARDS Access, Visa; personal and business accounts   DISCOUNTS 7½% for 1 case   DELIVERY Free in Wandsworth (min 1 case) and Central London for larger orders; elsewhere at cost; mail order available   GLASS HIRE Free with 1 case order
TASTINGS AND TALKS Wine always available to taste in Winecellars; tutored tastings in spring and autumn; to groups on request
CELLARAGE Not available   ∎

Winecellars are the wholesale side of The Market/Le Provençal supermarkets (*qv*). The full, splendid list is here, and good reading it makes.

It helps – certainly with the Italian range – that the wine buyer (Nick Belfrage) is an acknowledged expert on this tortuous subject which defeats so many wine trade buyers. His Italian selection is enormous and full of quality.

With such a wealth, we are hard put to pick out particular treats, but we would certainly suggest looking at the super vini da tavola listed here. In Tuscany, for example, Winecellars have Palazzo Altesi (£7.45) and Alte d'Altesi (£10.35) from Altesino in Montalcino. They stock Cepparello from Isole e Olena in Chianti Classico and Il Sodaccio from Monte Vertine, as well as the more familiar Tignanello from Antinori and Sassicaia from Incisa della Rocchetta (the 1982 vintage is £18.79).

More down to earth, equal quality is to be found in Soaves from Zenato and Tedeschi, as well as top Veneto reds such as the Amarone of Masi, and the vino da tavola Le Cane of Boscaini (£4.49). In Piedmont, we find plenty of Barolos and the good value Barbera of Ronco. Alto Adige wines come from Tiefenbrunner and Lageder. Southern Italy also has a showcase of wines – look especially for the Abruzzo wines of Valentini and the Merlot-based Torre Quarto from Puglia (1981 vintage at £3.99). And don't forget the marvellous Vecchio Samperi Marsalas of de Bartoli.

Although Italy is the star, the rest of the world is not forgotten. Nick Belfrage has picked good value clarets (Ch Haut-Peyraguey 1985 is £2.99), and chosen an inevitably shorter list of Burgundies and some decent Loire wines (Quincy 1986 Domaine de la Maison Blanche, £3.69). Look, too, for the range of wines from the Midi and the South-West, and Alsace wines from the co-operative of Turckheim.

The range of Spanish wines is representative, while Portuguese wines come from J M da Fonseca. The New World list is enlarging too, and Sherries, especially, are well covered in the fortified wine section.

Best buys

Barbera d'Asti 1982, Ronco, £3.29; Chianti Rufina 1985, Grati, £2.89; Chianti Classico 1985, Isole e Olena, £4.25; Lugana 1986, Dal Cero, £4.19; Corbières 1984, Ch de Belle Isle, £2.49; Sauvignon du Haut-Poitou, £3.09

The Wine Centre

3 Lowesmoor Wharf, Worcester,   TEL (0905) 21231
Hereford & Worcester WR1 2RS

OPEN Tue–Fri 9.30–6.30   Sat 9.30–5.30 (other times by appointment only)
CREDIT CARDS None accepted; personal and business accounts
DISCOUNTS 5% for orders over £75   DELIVERY Free within 20-mile radius (min
1 bottle) and for orders over £50; otherwise £5 per consignment; mail order
available   GLASS HIRE Free   TASTINGS AND TALKS Monthly tutored and
informal tastings; to groups on request   CELLARAGE Quotations on request

Spain is the best part of this short list. Riojas from many of the major bodegas are impressive (including Gran Reservas back to 1973 – look for the Tondonia Gran Reserva 1973 at £9.50, and the CVNE Imperial Gran Reserva 1976 at £6.25). The Wine Centre has also gathered in wines from the Penedès (Masía Bach and Torres), Navarra (Señorio de Sarria and Julián Chivite) and from regions like Valdepeñas (with the Señorio de los Llanos Reserva 1975 at £3.75) and the Marqués de Griñon Cabernet Sauvignon 1982 at £6.25.

A few other specialisations are the German estate wines and a decent range of California wines. In France, good buys would be the Sancerres (white and red) from Paul Millerioux, Rhône wines (look for the Côtes du Rhône 1983, Ch de Ruth at £3.90), Alsace bottles from Lucien Albrecht and the varietal wines from the co-operative of Haut-Poitou.

Best buys

Sauvignon du Haut-Poitou 1985, £3.35; Gran Reserva Riojas;
Valdepeñas Señorio de los Llanos Reserva 1975, £3.75; Chilean
Chardonnay 1985, Concha y Toro, £3.75

The Wine Gallery

See Brinkley's Wines.

Wine Growers Association

MAIL ORDER ONLY 430 High Road, Willesden,   TEL 01-451 0981/1135
London NW10 2HA *or*
Freepost, London NW10 1YA

CREDIT CARDS Access, Amex, Diners, Visa, THF Gold Card; business
accounts   DISCOUNTS Available   DELIVERY Free for 6 cases   GLASS HIRE,
TASTINGS AND TALKS Not available   CELLARAGE £2.40 per case per year for
straight cases of wine purchased from premises

This mail order merchant should not be confused with the two Wine
Growers Association shops in Norwich and Brighton which are run
independently from a different list (not in this Guide).

The Association operates in conjunction with wine shippers GB
Vintagers and their Italian division, Italian Wine Agencies. Last year
we recommended them entirely for those Italian wines, but can now
include more French wines. The good range of clarets is on the
expensive side but work has been done to widen the selection of
Burgundy, also bringing in the Alsace wines of Jules Müller and
regional wines from the South of France (for instance, the Ch de
Beaulieu in Coteaux d'Aix-en-Provence). Champagne is from Ayala.
Look also for Rioja from Don Jacobo.

Most wine merchants will hire out glasses free of charge, provided they are
collected and returned clean, and that you are buying enough wine to fill
them! In most cases, it's first come, first served, so get your order in early to
ensure supply.

Special awards

🐷 means bargain prices (good *value* may be obtained from merchants
without this symbol, of course, if you are prepared to pay for service)

🏵 means that the wines stocked are of consistently high quality

🗔 means that the merchant stocks an above-average range

☞ means that extra-special service is offered: helpful advice, informative
lists and newsletters, tastings etc.

And then we turn to the big Italian section. While many of these wines are available elsewhere (often cheaper), here the full Italian Wine Agencies list is available under one roof, so to speak – and very good reading it makes. Wines include Barolos from Borgogno, Barbaresco from La Brenta d'Oro, the Veneto wines of Boscaini and Tedeschi (including their super vini da tavola Le Cane and Capitel San Rocco). In the Alto Adige wines are from the main co-operative, and in Lombardy the Oltrepò Pavese wines of the Fugazza sisters.

Tuscany brings in Chianti from Pagliarese and Brunello from Tenuta Caparzo, while Latium has the superb vino da tavola Torre Ercolana (so little is made, it's normally sold by the bottle). There's also the unusually good Frascati Villa Catone (look for the single vineyard Vigneto Colle Gaio). Further south, we come across wines from d'Angelo in Aglianico del Vulture and Mastroberardino's Taurasi, and in Sardinia bottles from Sella & Mosca, many offering very good value.

Best buys

Cabernet del Veneto, £2.60; Coteaux d'Aix-en-Provence 1986, Ch de Beaulieu red, £3.60; Spanna del Piemonte 1984, Brugo, £3.25; Chardonnay di Appiano 1986, Viticoltori Alto-Adige, £4.10; Sardinian wines from Sella & Mosca

Wine Market

See Lay & Wheeler.

The Wine Schoppen

1 Abbeydale Road South, Sheffield, South Yorkshire S7 2QL	TEL (0742) 365684/368617
ASSOCIATED OUTLETS Wine Warehouse, Holme Leigh, East Lane, Stainforth, Nr Doncaster, South Yorkshire DN7 5DT	TEL (0302) 841254
A L Vose & Co, Barnton, Kentsford Road, Grange-over-Sands, Cumbria LA11 7BB	TEL (044 84) 3328
Pennine Wines, 5/7 Station Street, Huddersfield, South Yorkshire HD1 1LS	TEL (0484) 25747
C C Enterprises, 157 Woodlands Avenue, Eastcote, Ruislip, Middlesex HA4 9QX (mail order only)	TEL 01-866 9745

OPEN Mon–Fri 9.30–6 Sat 9–5 CLOSED Sun, public holidays
CREDIT CARDS Access; personal and business accounts DISCOUNTS 2½% for 3–5 cases, 5% for 6–9 cases, 7½% for 10–15 cases, 10% for 16–25 cases; 4% for Leicester Card holders DELIVERY Free within 15-mile radius of any branch (min 1 case); otherwise at cost; mail order available GLASS HIRE Free with 1-case order; delivery not available TASTINGS AND TALKS Regular in-store tastings and on request CELLARAGE £1.95 per case per year

The range of German wines is still the most important aspect of this list, but other areas have expanded (Australia) and others moved out (inevitably, Austria) – generally fuelling our interest in this merchant.

But to Germany first. The range is not from the top estates, but comes from good, middle of the road producers at attractive prices. What is especially interesting is the number of wines from areas not normally seen in this country – the Ahr, Franconia and Baden – as well as the number of Spätlese and Auslese wines from the better-known regions.

French wines take in examples from most areas, including a decent number of vins de pays and Rhône wines, a few clarets and Burgundies and a single vineyard Beaujolais (Beaujolais-Villages Lantignie 1984, Gilles Ducroux, £4.40). The Portuguese range from Caves Dom Teodosio has a number of old-style Dãos and some more approachable Garrafeiras as well as branded Teobar wines. There are also Calem Ports.

New to the list are wines from Tisdall's Mount Helen winery and the Mildara winery in Australia, the latter being especially good value.

See also the entry for AL Vose & Co.

Best buys

German estate wines; wines from Caves Dom Teodosio in Portugal; Mildara Cabernet Sauvignon/Merlot 1984, £3.77

The Wine Shop

7 Sinclair Street, Thurso, Caithness KW14 9AJ   TEL (0847) 65657

OPEN Tue–Sat 9.30–5.30   CLOSED Mon, Sun, public holidays
CREDIT CARDS Access, Visa; business accounts   DISCOUNTS Approx 15% for 6 bottles   DELIVERY Free within 10-mile radius of Thurso (min 6 bottles); otherwise £1.50 for 1 case in Caithness and Orkneys   GLASS HIRE Free with 6 bottles   TASTINGS AND TALKS Occasionally by invitation   CELLARAGE Free

Antony Collett's shop is still the most northerly in the Guide, but distance doesn't seem to stop him putting together a very interesting range of wines. Plenty of good things from France, Italy, Portugal are now joined by some from the New World.

While the clarets and Burgundies remain good, other parts of France have been boosted – notably in the regional wines like those from Cahors, Côtes de Buzet, the Jurançon wines of Clos Guirouilh and the Bandol Mas de la Rouvière. The Rhône offers the good value Côtes du Ventoux, Domaine des Anges (£3.80) and Liracs from Domaine Maby; Alsace has wines from Heim.

The Italian range has expanded, too: alluring are more wines from Chianti, Barolos from Borgogno and Vietti, the Fugazza Oltrepò Pavese wines and, from much further south, the Aglianico del Vulture of d'Angelo and the Cirò Classico Reserva 1977 (£4.59) from Calabria.

Mr Collett has shipped more Riojas, too. Portugal continues to offer the well-made J M da Fonseca wines.

And – distance definitely no object – Australia is out in force with Rosemount, Penfold's and Hill-Smith wines joining those from Brown Brothers.

Best buys

Vin de Corse Porto-Vecchio, Domaine de Torraccia 1982, £3.20; Chianti 1985, Fattoria dell'Ugo, £3.59; Corbières 1984, Ch des Ollieux, £2.90; Jurançon Sec 1985, Clos Guirouilh, £4.60

The Wine Society

Gunnels Wood Road, Stevenage, Hertfordshire SG1 2BG TEL (0438) 314161

53 Bolsover Street, London W1P 7HL TEL 01-387 4681

OPEN Mon–Fri 9–5   Sats leading up to Chr 9–1   CLOSED Sat, Sun, public holidays   CREDIT CARDS Access, Visa   DISCOUNTS £1.20 per unmixed case; £2.40 per collected case   DELIVERY Free in UK (inc Northern Ireland) (min 1 case); elsewhere at cost; mail order available   GLASS HIRE Free
TASTINGS AND TALKS 12 tutored tastings annually; tastings all over the country for members; to members on request   CELLARAGE £3 per case per year

You need to be a member to use the services or buy wines from the International Exhibition Co-operative Wine Society, but it's certainly worth joining for the wide and continually expanding range of wines at an equally wide range of prices (see WINE CLUBS section).

The Society have moved a long way since the days of being known only for their clarets, but still have a strong interest in Bordeaux (including sweet white wines). They have just introduced a Society's Médoc (£3.95) to complement the top-selling Society's Claret at £3.10. They buy claret for laying down, but also have wines which are ready for drinking. The same policy is followed in Burgundy (from where they buy a good range of domaine wines as well as a few from négociants such as Remoissenet). They have been specialising in lesser communes of Burgundy, especially for whites (such as the St-Aubin La Pucelle 1984 of Roux Père et Fils at £7.35).

An area into which the Society have greatly expanded is the Rhône, and new to the list are a number of Côtes du Rhône bottles (look for the Côtes du Rhône-Villages Valréas of Bouchard at £4.40 and the Rasteau 1985, Domaine de la Soumade at £4.70). More expansion has been going on in Italy, with some of the new breed of super vini da tavola as well as wines from DOC and DOCG zones: Piedmont and Tuscany are particularly well served.

Back in France, Alsace is obviously a popular area, to judge by the range of wines from top producers, while across the Rhine are some good estate wines to top up some of the more attractive house German wines around. The Society's Champagne is good – with plenty of bottle age – but quite pricey at £11.40; it has recently been joined by a Blanc de Blancs from Le Mesnil at £12. Vintage Ports go back to 1963, and some almacenista Sherries have come on to the standard range.

And, of course, the Society offers a big range of 'Everyday Wines', which takes in all its own wines, and an attractive collection of reasonably priced wines from round the world – from the Cabernet Vin de Pays de l'Hérault at £2.95 to the dry Vinho Verde Casalinho at £3.25 to the Chilean Cabernet Sauvignon of Concha y Toro (£3.40).

Best buys

The Society's Médoc, £3.95; Minervois 1985, Domaine du Moulin Rigaud, £3.10; Sauvignon de Touraine, £3.10; almacenista Sherries; clarets under £4

The Wine Spot

200 Stretford Road, Urmston, Manchester M31 1NA	TEL 061-748 2568
Wine Spot 2, 408A Manchester Road, Heaton Chapel, Stockport, Greater Manchester SK4 5BY	TEL 061-432 1646

OPEN Mon–Thur 10 am–10.30 pm   Fri–Sat 10 am–11 pm (Stockport 10.45 pm) Sun, Chr Day, Good Friday 12–2 and 7–10.30   CREDIT CARDS None accepted; personal and business accounts   DISCOUNTS 5% on unmixed cases
DELIVERY Free locally, min quantity negotiable; elsewhere at cost
GLASS HIRE Free with appropriate order; free local delivery
TASTINGS AND TALKS Sample bottles regularly opened for customers
CELLARAGE Not available

This is becoming a very interesting range of wines. Australia and Italy have been particularly boosted over the past year, but other areas have been strengthened as well. Prices remain sensible.

Bordeaux has some good petit château wines from Fronsac, Côtes de Castillon and Blaye, as well as some bourgeois wines from the Médoc. Burgundy is less interesting, and the Rhône section is short, but instead they've concentrated on a good range of French country wines, especially from the Midi (Fitou, Faugères), plus Terres Blanches from the Coteaux des Baux en Provence and wines from Listel.

Germany was one main area we noted last year. It still offers a good range of estate wines, now mainly from the 1985 vintage, and especially good in the Rheingau. Spain provides a big range of Riojas, including plenty of mature Reservas and Gran Reservas – increasingly unusual.

Then we move to Italy. Here the list has grown very satisfactorily: Piedmont wines from Pio Cesare, Cavalotto and Conterno have arrived; wines from Conte Loredan's Venegazzù range come from the Veneto, as does Pieropan's top quality Soave La Rocca 1985 (£5.25); and Tuscan Chiantis from Frescobaldi and Sicilian Regaleali and Corvo wines rub shoulders. And there's plenty more . . .

The Australian list now takes in some big names from small wineries – Wolf Blass, Rouge Homme, Evans & Tate, Peel Estate, Vasse Felix, Montrose. It's a solid but exciting range at good prices.

Elsewhere in this list we find a surprisingly large number of Yugoslav wines (with specialities from Dalmatia and Montenegro), some decent Bairradas from Portugal and a good range of Champagnes and sparkling Cavas from Spain.

Best buys

Minervois 1985, Ch de Pouzols, £2.79; Listel wines; German estate wines; Chianti Rufina Riserva 1980, Castello di Nipozzano, £4.59; Cabernet Franc di Aquileia 1985, Ca' Bolani, £3.59; Regaleali Bianco 1984, £3.35; Berri Estates Cabernet/Shiraz 1982, £3.99; Raimat Abadía Reserva 1981, £3.99

Wine Warehouse (Stainforth)

See the Wine Schoppen.

Wines Galore

169 Greenwich High Road, London SE10 8JA   TEL 01-858 6014
The White Hart Vaults, 64 South Street,   TEL (0392) 73894
Exeter, Devon EX1 1EE

OPEN Mon–Fri 10–7   Sat 10–5 (White Hart Vaults Mon 5–8   Tue–Thur 10–8 Fri–Sat 10–9)   CLOSED Sun, public holidays   CREDIT CARDS All accepted; Davys of London account card   DISCOUNTS Negotiable   DELIVERY At cost GLASS HIRE Available with order; delivery not available
TASTINGS AND TALKS Monthly tastings in wine bar; possible to sample wines before buying   CELLARAGE Not available

---

Wines Galore and the White Hart Vaults are two retail outlets operated by Davys, whose associated company, Davys of London, run the highly successful chain of wine bars (see WINE BARS section). The list is small and gets into the Guide more on the quality of the buying than the range offered. Nor are prices particularly competitive.

But there are good things to be found. That's true of the basic house claret which *is* good value at £3.15. It's also true of Loron's Beaujolais, and the Côtes du Rhône, Cru du Condoulet 1984 at £5.95. Alsace wines from Louis Gisselbrecht, and a small range of country wines at fair prices also fall into this category.

Italy produces a few good wines, too: look for the Südtiroler (Alto Adige) Chardonnay of Lageder (1985 vintage at £4.80) and Bianchi's Verdicchio dei Castelli di Jesi. Spain offers Riojas from Lopez de Heredia and Marqués de Murrieta. The generous number of Ports and Sherries are very fresh because turnover is so fast (naturally enough for a company with City wine bars). Bulgarian wines are ridiculously expensive but there's better value in Brown Brothers Australian wines.

Best buys

Claret (NV), £3.15; Old Tawny Port No 8, £5.80; Davy's Rioja 1983, £3.70; Chianti Classico Riserva 1973, Lilliano, £7.60

Wines of Interest

46 Burlington Road, Ipswich, Suffolk IP1 2HS   TEL (0473) 215752
Bulls Head, 80 Leadenhall Street,   TEL 01-283 2830
London EC3A 2BH

OPEN Mon–Fri 9–5.45 Sat 9–1 CLOSED Sun, public holidays
CREDIT CARDS None accepted DISCOUNTS Trade only DELIVERY Free
locally; elsewhere £1 per case in London postal area, £1.84 per case for most of
England and Wales; mail order available GLASS HIRE Free
TASTINGS AND TALKS Wines always available for tasting at Ipswich; to groups
on request CELLARAGE £1.50 per case per year

City people may easily have eaten at the Bulls Head in Leadenhall Street without realising that wines from the interesting restaurant and wine bar list could also be bought to drink at home. In addition to the short, standard list is a regularly changing fine wine list, and Wines of Interest have recently acquired a retail licence to sell by the bottle.

Plenty of clarets figure among the fine wines but more notable and better value are wines from other regions, such as those from the Loire (Quincy 1985, Duc de Berri at £4.25), some reasonable white Burgundy (St-Véran 1984, Vincent, £6.90) and Rhône wines from Pascal.

After a few German wines comes a short burst into Rioja (Campo Viejo Gran Reserva 1975 at £5.35); then on into Portugal for wines from J M da Fonseca. Further afield, interesting pockets include the red from Ch Carras in Greece, the Israeli Gamla Cabernet Sauvignon (£4.60), Ch Musar from the Lebanon and Rosemount from Australia. Ports include a few vintages (Gould Campbell 1977 at £12.95).

Best buys

Berri Estates Cabernet/Shiraz 1982, £3.95; Rioja Gran Reserva 1978, Monte Real, £4.65; Ch Segonzac 1978, Côtes de Blaye, £3.10; Quincy 1985, Duc de Berri, £4.25

Wines from Paris

The Vaults, 4 Giles Street, Leith,   TEL 031-554 2652
Edinburgh EH6 6DJ

OPEN Tue–Sat 10–8 Sun 11–6 CLOSED Mon (probably)
CREDIT CARDS Access, Visa; personal and business accounts
DISCOUNTS Quantity discounts; £1 off per collected case DELIVERY Free on
mainland Scotland (min 1 case); elsewhere £2.50 for 1–2 cases, £2 for 3–5 cases,
£1.50 for 5–10 cases, 10+ cases free; mail order available
GLASS HIRE Available TASTINGS AND TALKS Wines always available for
tasting; also one special tasting a month CELLARAGE Not available   ∎

No, they haven't discovered the vineyards of Montmartre, but are just using the name of owner Judith Paris to attract attention to their 800-year-old wine vaults in Leith.

And France is not the only country on this list, although there are plenty of French wines: plenty from the South-West regions – Côtes de Duras, Bergerac (Ch la Jaubertie), Cahors (les Côtes d'Olt), Pécharmant (Ch de Tiregand). They've also gone to the south of France for the varietal Vin de Pays de l'Ardèche, and to the Rhône for some good value Côtes du Rhône and the Côtes du Ventoux, La Vieille Ferme.

The Loire brings in the top quality Pouilly Fumé of J C Dagueneau (1986 vintage at £6.76). Alsace has wines from Rolly Gassmann and the Eguisheim co-operative, and there's domaine Burgundy from Pierre Mazilly.

Italy is a strong area, with some top wines from top producers. Look particularly for the Franciacorta Rossa of Magi (£3.78 for the 1985 vintage) which is still much too young, being Cabernet Sauvignon, but it will be very good, or the Soave Classico of the top producer in the region, Pieropan, or the good value Barbera d'Asti of Ronco (1978 vintage at £3.95). We like the look of the Chianti from Isole e Olena (and their super vino da tavola Cepparello) and recommend the wines from Sardinia for their terrific value.

Australia is another good section – wines from small estates like Evans and Tate, Vasse Felix, Peel Estate (all in Western Australia). New Zealand choices come from Morton Estates and Babich.

Best buys

Côtes du Ventoux 1985, La Vieille Ferme, £2.99; Coteaux du Lyonnais 1986, Guyot, £3.55; Franciacorta Rossa 1985, Contessa Maggi, £3.78; Fitou 1978, Cave Pilote Villeneuve les Corbières, £3.99

Wines of Westhorpe

OFFICE 54 Boyn Hill Road, Maidenhead, Berkshire SL6 4HJ   TEL (0628) 21385

OPEN Mon–Fri & most Sat and public holidays 8–6   CLOSED Sun
CREDIT CARDS None accepted; personal and business accounts (cash with order)   DISCOUNTS 10–24 cases £1.10 per case, 25–49 cases £1.30, 50+ cases £1.70 per case (collection from Luton further 60p on 10+ cases)   DELIVERY Free on UK mainland, Isle of Wight (min 5 cases), Northern Ireland (min 6 cases) and Isle of Man (min 10 cases); under 5 cases on mainland additional £3; mail order available   GLASS HIRE, TASTINGS AND TALKS, CELLARAGE Not available ∎

This is where you come if you want Bulgarian or Hungarian wines. Prices for the standard Bulgarian varietals are noticeably cheaper than anywhere else (Merlot 1983, £1.82; Chardonnay and Cabernet Sauvignon, £1.84). Westhorpe also stock the new Reserve wines, plus the Controliran wines from specified regions. The most expensive wine listed is the award-winning Novi Pazar Chardonnay 1984 at £2.92.

Hungarian wines are here in equal measure. Whether you think they offer such good value depends on whether you appreciate their style – prices are certainly good. We could recommend the sweet white Tramini 1976 at £2.59, or the Merlot 1979, with a touch of peppery flavour that once seemed characteristic of Hungarian wines before they went 'commercial'.

Best buys

Bulgarian wines

Wizard Wine Warehouses

Unit 2, 226 Purley Way, Croydon,   TEL 01-686 5703
Surrey CR0 4XG
95/97 Hawk's Road,   TEL 01-546 9764
Kingston-upon-Thames, Surrey KT1 3JY

OPEN Mon–Fri 10–8   Sat 9–7   Sun, public holidays   CLOSED 25 & 26 Dec,
1 Jan   CREDIT CARDS Access, Amex, Visa   DISCOUNTS 5% for 10 cases
DELIVERY Free on UK mainland (min £100 order); otherwise at cost; mail order
available   GLASS HIRE Free with 1-case order
TASTINGS AND TALKS Thematic tastings every weekend; selected wines always
available; to groups on request   CELLARAGE Not available   ■

The bustling list from these wine warehouses in two London suburbs covers large portions of the world, with competitive prices and a list awash with illegible tasting notes.

Wizard are strong on good value areas like the French regions, the lesser areas of the Côtes du Rhône (such as the Coteaux du Tricastin 1983 of Paul Trufaut at £2.99), and Loire wines from Ménétou-Salon and Quincy. In Bordeaux, they make a sound start with some very good value clarets (Ch le Gardéra 1981 at £3.95; Ch la Barde 1981, Côtes de Bourg at £3.95) and move up to top classed growths.

In Italy, the best value is also to be found at the £3 to £4 mark, with wines like the Chianti Rocca delle Macie 1985 at £2.99 – a very good price, this – and then the range moves up in quality, but not much in price, to the Vino Nobile di Montepulciano of Bigi (1982 vintage Reserva at £3.99). In Spain, the span is from Navarra wines at £2.09 to the Gran Reserva 1973 from Bilbainas at £5.99. There's the usual good value from Bulgaria and a small range of Portuguese wines which includes the smooth red Tinto da Anfora 1982 at £3.49.

Antipodean wines take in Rosemount, Wynns and Stanley Leasingham in Australia, and Selaks in New Zealand. And the Californian section has wines from Bel Arbres, Fetzer (premium red and white at £2.99), Clos du Val and Tjisseling (Ranch Chardonnay 1984 at £8.75).

Best buys

Fetzer premium red and white, £2.99; Bulgarian wines; Valpolicella 1985, Castello d'Illasi, £2.99; Chianti Classico Riserva 1980, Rocca delle Macie, £3.29; Gaillac Rouge les Carmes, £2.59; Côtes du Rhône 1985, Cuvée des Compagnons, Rasteau, £2.99

Woodleys

See Morris's Wine Stores.

W R Wines

See Morris's Wine Stores.

Peter Wylie Fine Wines

Plymtree Manor, Plymtree, Cullompton,   TEL (088 47) 555
Devon EX15 2LE

OPEN Mon–Fri 9–6 (Sat answering machine service only)   CLOSED Sat, Sun,
public holidays   CREDIT CARDS Not accepted; business accounts
DISCOUNTS On unmixed cases only   DELIVERY Free in Central London (min 3
cases) and UK mainland (min 5 cases); elsewhere (London) 1–2 cases £5.75; (UK
mainland) 1 case £6, 2–4 cases £4.60 per case; mail order available; collections
may be made from London cellars by arrangement   GLASS HIRE Not
available   TASTINGS AND TALKS Tastings for customers only
CELLARAGE £3.45 per case per year with insurance at 1%

Peter Wylie's is one of the best fine wine lists in the country, specialising in claret, Burgundy, vintage Port and vintage Champagne.

Not many merchants can offer pre-1860 claret on a printed list, but in the most recent of his constantly changing lists, Peter Wylie comes up with an 1860 Ch Bel-Air Marquis d'Aligré at £201 (prices on the list do not include VAT, but we have added it here). Not content with that, the claret list contains most of the good vintages from the turn of the century in some depth, including plenty from great vintages like 1929, 1945, 1955 and, bang up-to-date, 1961 and 1966. In fact, the most recent claret vintage is 1985.

Sweet white Bordeaux are another major sector, with vintages of Ch d'Yquem prominent, and Mr Wylie carries plenty of red and white Burgundies – here Domaine de la Romanée-Conti appears in most years, but there is a mix of négociant and growers' wines. The oldest vintage Champagne on the current list is a 1921 Moët et Chandon at £138. And so to vintage Port, which is similarly full of treats with many pre-war vintages.

As a bonus to all this are arrayed plenty of half-bottles, magnums and a special list of double magnums, jeroboams, imperials and methuselahs.

Best buys
Rare and old wines

Yapp Brothers

The Old Brewery, Mere, Wiltshire BA12 6DY   TEL (0747) 860423
OPEN Mon–Fri 9–5   Sat 9–1   CLOSED Sun, public holidays
CREDIT CARDS Access, Visa; personal and business accounts   DISCOUNTS For
orders over 5 cases   DELIVERY Free on UK mainland (min 2 cases); mail order
available   GLASS HIRE Free with 2-case order (delivery not available)
TASTINGS AND TALKS Wines of the month available for tasting to customers
(min 3 wines)   CELLARAGE £2.50 per case per year (or part-year)

There can't be many byways left in France for Robin and Judith Yapp to
explore. Each year, they come up with appellations that probably even
the locals didn't know existed, bringing back some splendid wines to
support their discoveries. A recent such appellation was Brezème,
midway between the northern and southern Rhône vineyards in a part
of the world where vines are not supposed to thrive. The Yapps, of
course, found the largest producer in the area (all 1.5 hectares) and
now import a red made from Syrah grapes at £5.75.

Further south, they offer wines from Bellet, just north of Nice, and of
Ch Simone, virtually the only producer in the tiny appellation of
Palette. On the Loire, there are wines from Jasnières (Caves aux
Tuffières 1983 white at £5.50), the Orléanais and Thouarsais, a VDQS
area in Anjou where they buy from Michel Gigon, virtually the only
producer left in the area.

We should, of course, emphasise that Yapp Brothers don't just get
their wines from obscure and out of the way spots. But they do
specialise in the Rhône, Provence and the Loire, and have certainly
covered all the major appellations in those areas as well.

In the northern Rhône, for instance, rewarding bottles would be
Côte Rôtie from Jasmin, Hermitage from Chave and Grippat, Cornas
from Clape and Robert Michel. In whites, you could decide on
Condrieu and Ch Grillet (from the only producer in this single
vineyard appellation). Down in Provence, there's good value Côtes du
Lubéron from Claude Dieudonné in the shape of white and red Mas du
Peyroulet at £3.65; also Bandol Mas de la Rouvière and Coteaux des
Baux en Provence from Domaine de Trévallon, apart from a bigger
range from Coteaux d'Aix-en-Provence and Côtes de Provence.

Back in the chillier north, look for Champagne from Jacquesson and
Alsace wines from Charles Schléret. On the Loire, the principal areas
are covered with Sancerre from André Vatan and Pouilly Fumé from
Guyot, Vouvray from Daniel Jarry and Montlouis from Berger. Further
enticements would be wines from Savennières Coulée de Serrant and
La Roche aux Moines and sweet wines from Bonnezeaux and Quarts
de Chaume as well as Coteaux du Layon Chaume.

271

Best buys

Lirac La Fermade red, rosé and white, £4.40; Côtes du Rhône 1984
St-Gayan, £3.95; Gamay de l'Ardèche 1985, Co-opérative de
St-Désirat-Champagne, £3.55; Côtes du Luberon red 1985, Mas de
Peyroulet, £3.65; St-Pourçain-sur-Sioule 1986 white, Union des
Vignerons, £3.75; Quarts de Chaume 1985, Ch de l'Echarderie, £7

Yorkshire Fine Wine Company   ☞

The Priory, Nun Monkton, York,   TEL (0901) 30131
North Yorkshire YO5 8ES

OPEN Mon–Fri (including public holidays) 8.30–5.30 CLOSED Sat, Sun
CREDIT CARDS All accepted; personal and business accounts DISCOUNTS 4%
for 7-day settlement of invoice DELIVERY Free within Scottish Borders (North)
and Nottinghamshire (South) (min 1 case); elsewhere 1 case £7.50, 2 cases £4 per
case, 3 cases £3.50 per case, 4+ cases free; mail order available
GLASS HIRE Free TASTINGS AND TALKS Tastings from time to time as
requested CELLARAGE £3 per case per annum ■

This firmly traditional list, bristling with clarets and Burgundies,
suddenly gets a delightfully skittish idea and introduces a couple of
Algerian wines or a range of old vintages of Torres Gran Coronas Black
Label (back to 1975) or an expanding range of Italian reds or Cooks
New Zealand wines.

But classic areas are certainly the strength here. The Champagne list
is long and full of famous names in non-vintage and vintage form.
Yorkshire Fine Wines are sitting on a nebuchadnezzar (20 bottles) of
Piper Heidsieck (£252), waiting for someone to throw a very good
party. In Burgundy, domaine wines get a good showing, with names
like Dujac, Raoul Clerget, Jayer Gilles and Marcel Vincent. Bordeaux
contains vintages back to 1961, with a heavy predominance of classed
growths (although not necessarily the most expensive). On the Rhône,
many wines come from Burgundy négocians, but there are also wines
from Ch de Beaucastel in Châteauneuf-du-Pape.

Elsewhere in France appear some of the old vintages of sweet Anjou
from Touchais, Hugel and Trimbach wines from Alsace, Domaines Ott
in the South of France, and Domaine de Trévallon in Coteaux des Baux
en Provence – and further west Cahors from Georges Vigouroux.
There's a good range of vintage Ports (back to Taylor 1945) and a small
showing from Australia and California.

Best buys

Côtes du Luberon red and white, Fleur du Printemps, £3.29; large
bottles of Champagne; vintages of Torres Gran Coronas Black Label;
Alsace Riesling 1985, D'Orschwiller Kintzheim, £4.40; Touraine
Sauvignon 1985, Domaine Octavie, £4.17

Wine at auction

World record-breaking prices are the only time wine auctions make the news. There was the bottle of 1784 Ch d'Yquem which was sold for £36,000 in December 1986. Two years ago, an American paid £105,000 for a bottle of 1787 Ch Lafite which was promptly ruined when the bottle went on display under hot lights, the cork shrank and fell into the bottle – making the contents undrinkable.

But those are rare examples. Most of the time, the lots sold in wine auctions cover a wide spectrum of styles and prices. The auction houses form a useful alternative way of buying fine wine to going to a specialist wine merchant. They are often the only places where mature wines will regularly appear for sale. And since any wine merchant who lists older wines will probably have bought them at auction, you are likely to pay less at auction for a particular wine than you would at a merchant.

Britain is one of the world's principal centres for wine auctions. The two major houses – Christie's and Sotheby's – hold sales regularly in their main rooms in central London, which concentrate on the finest wines, with a strong emphasis on claret and Port. They also have separate auction rooms – Christie's at South Kensington in West London and now in the City, and Sotheby's at Billingshurst in Sussex, where a wider range of less expensive wines are auctioned.

One other London-based firm, International Wine Auctions, holds quarterly sales, again mainly of top clarets. Auctions are also held by country auctioneers on a less regular basis.

Details of all these auction houses are given at the end of this section.

Sticking up your hand

Most people have been to a country auction – or even one in the West End of London – and have bid for something that took their fancy, even if it was only a brass bedhead or a small kitchen table. Bidding for wine is basically no different, except in one thing: you can't always inspect the lots beforehand. There are exceptions even to this: there may be a pre-sale tasting of many of the wines to be auctioned, but not every lot will be available for tasting. However, a knowledge of vintages, and some memory for names, is really all that's necessary to get by, which is where our WHAT TO BUY section can help.

What to buy in 1988

We go to press at the end of the 1986/87 auction season. While prices through the season have remained steady, there are still many bargains around. It's generally agreed that it is the 'off' vintages of claret that are the best value – that is, vintages which are not highly praised and are therefore not bought by the Americans or Swiss, the world's biggest claret buyers. Typical are the 1981, 1980 and 1979 vintages. The 1982 vintage – so heavily over-subscribed when it first came out – is now much better value, since its price has hardly gone up at all this year. Of older vintages, the popular favourites are 1978, 1970, 1966 and 1961. To buy wines from other vintages, you need to be more careful – but it is still possible to find some very good bargains.

Invariably the best value are the second tier of Bordeaux reds – the crus bourgeois. The crus classés, the top-ranking clarets, are always in much great demand, but even then lesser-known names can yield some relatively good bargains. From older vintages (pre-1971), the increasingly rare English bottlings of claret always fetch much lower prices than château bottlings but not many would question that they taste just as good.

Again, if you know what to buy, red Burgundy is generally underpriced, relative to retail prices – though of course Burgundy is always high compared to other wines. The greatest recent vintages – 1978 and 1985 – are rare in the auction houses, the 1978 because there aren't many bottles around, the 1985 because it hasn't reached the auction houses yet – something which may change during 1988. Other wines are less common at the major London auctions, but do crop up at country auctions: for instance, Gran Reserva Rioja and Rhône wines and the occasional Italian or California wine.

There are few bargains to be had with vintages of Ch d'Yquem among the sweet white wines. But lesser châteaux of Sauternes and Barsac offer good value – as do the sweet wines of the Loire. With drier white wines, you need to be careful about the age of the wine, but old vintages of white Burgundy, and better quality white Graves are worth looking out for. Vintage Champagne from most of the major houses matures surprisingly well – and if you stray outside the magic circle of Dom Pérignon, Roederer Cristal and Krug, you will probably find some bargains.

One area where you can almost always find a bargain is fine, mature, German estate-bottled wine: in particular, great sweet wines from the 1975 and 1976 vintages can be bought for ludicrously low sums of money.

Port prices are still rising. The younger vintages – 1977, 1980 and 1982 – are the best buys, with the smaller, less famous, producers offering better bargains than the top names. Often vintage Port from Portuguese-named houses is under half the price of those with English names.

Preparing for the sale

Sale dates *Decanter* magazine gives dates and times of forthcoming sales, and both Christie's and Sotheby's advertise their sales in the national press. You can also put yourself on an auction house's mailing list, which, for a fee, will provide you with pre-sale catalogues, and possibly perks, such as access to the pre-sale tastings. Catalogues are normally sent out three weeks before a sale. If you are not a subscriber, you can buy catalogues individually, by post, or call in to collect one.

Bidding by post Postal bidding forms will arrive with the catalogue: most auction houses provide a free postal bidding service. You merely need to indicate the maximum you are prepared to pay for a particular lot. The auctioneer will secure the lot for you at a lower price if possible. The estimates in the catalogue will be based on prices fetched for the same or a similar wine at recent auctions, and on the reserve price the vendor has placed on his wine. So it's rare to find a successful bid going below the minimum of the estimate.

Pre-sale tastings These are normally held the day before the auction (the catalogue will tell you when and where). Don't expect to taste 1905 Ch Mouton-Rothschild if it happens to be in the sale, but most wines tend to be available for tasting. If you have a particular wine in mind, telephone in advance to see if the wine will be available for tasting, or ask advice. Arrive early and remember that catalogue subscribers are allowed in first.

What's in the catalogue

The estimated price against a wine is only the beginning of what you will have to pay at auction. It pays to read the small print at the front of the catalogue carefully, but here are some pointers.

Duty paid Wines marked 'duty paid' (normally in the second section of the auction) will have been cleared by Customs and Excise, so the estimated price will include duty. Foreign buyers prefer to buy wines 'in bond' (see below) so you will more likely be bidding against British buyers in this section of the sale.

In bond No excise duty has yet been paid. When you have secured the lot, the auctioneers will sort out the Customs paperwork for a small fee. Whatever the price of the wine, you pay a flat rate per bottle.

Duty paid available in bond For British buyers, duty is already paid. For foreign buyers, duty will be subtracted after the auction.

VAT The estimates do not include VAT. VAT is charged only if the wine is being sold by a merchant registered for VAT. Wines being sold by private individuals do not attract VAT. Remember, VAT is payable as a percentage of the final price – and not, as with duty, as a flat rate: so higher-priced bottles attract more VAT than cheaper ones.

FOB Free on Board is the term used to describe wine that is being sold while still overseas. You will have to pay a proportion of the shipping costs, plus duty, VAT and customs clearance charges, which can be arranged by the auction house.

Ex cellar This means that the wine is still in the cellar of the estate where it was made. It's a guarantee that the wine will have been kept in the best possible conditions.

How to bid

You are bidding for a numbered lot. The lot can either consist of one wine (generally in one case or multiples of cases) or what is called a mixed lot – a ragbag of wines which have been lumped together because they are odd bottles. If you only want one particular wine in a mixed lot you will have to buy everything else as well. Occasionally special bottles will be auctioned separately.

Bid steps The catalogue sets out in the front the steps in which bidding is conducted. These vary according to the price reached – lower prices in the bidding will rise by small steps, higher prices by larger steps, for example, by single pounds up to £30, say, then by £2 a time up to £100, £5 a time up to £200 and so on.

Bidding Back to the country auction and the kitchen table. Just raise your hand when you want to make a bid, and preferably wave your catalogue. The auctioneers have eagle eyes, and once your first bid is noted, they'll keep an eye on you until that lot is sold. Once the hammer has fallen, the wine is legally yours. If you make a mistake – such as bidding for the wrong lot, tell the staff at once, before the end of the sale, and it will normally be re-auctioned.

Options The buyer of the first lot may be offered the option to buy the remaining lots of the same wine at the same price. This practice will be announced at the beginning of the sale, and is designed to help trade customers who need to buy large quantities of one particular wine. So if you really want a wine, make sure you bid for the first lot.

Paying for the wine

Once the hammer has fallen, the auction house staff will take your name and address. Invoices are posted after the sale, and you will then be told where the wine can be collected from. If it is actually on the sale room premises, you can pay for it and take it away – but that's less common because it is normal practice not to move the wine too much. Delivery can usually be arranged.

You may have to pay the buyer's premium (see the details for each auction house), normally 10 per cent of the sale price. You will also have to pay VAT on the premium. Vendors have to pay a commission to the auction house, at a percentage depending on the wine and the volume involved.

If the wine is faulty, you should tell the auction house. They are not responsible since they are acting as middlemen between you and the vendor, but they will normally help in negotiations.

London auction houses

Christie's
8 King Street, London SW1Y 6QT   TEL 01-839 9060
85 Old Brompton Road, London SW7 3LD TEL 01-581 2231
50–60 Gresham Street, London EC2V 7BB

They run the largest number of auctions – 46 during 1987 at the King Street auction rooms, once a month at Old Brompton Road, and three in the City. The King Street auctions are of finer wines; Old Brompton Road sells everyday wine as well as finer wines and bin-ends; and the City branch tends to deal in Port, Burgundy and claret. Catalogue subscriptions cost £24 per year (King Street) or £12 (the other two rooms). Pre-sale tastings take place between 11 am and noon the day before the sale at King Street and on the day of the sale at Old Brompton Road and in the City. Advice on the market in general and on whether to sell in particular is available. Delivery from the South Kensington branch to elsewhere in the UK is charged at £4 plus VAT per case or part case, and insurance is the responsibility of the purchaser. Insurance is included in the price and delivery is free from the other two addresses if the wine is paid for within 21 days. There is a 10 per cent buyer's premium.

Sotheby's

34–35 New Bond Street, London W1A 2AA TEL 01-493 8080
Summers Place, Billinghurst, West Sussex RH14 9AD
TEL (040 381) 3933

Sotheby's hold fewer auctions than Christie's – eight during the 1987 season in London and four in Sussex. The auctions in London correspond to the auctions at Christie's King Street rooms, with fine wines dominating. A wider range is sold in Sussex. Sotheby's have set up a computer-linked bidding service. Subscription to the catalogues is £34 (London) and £15 (Sussex). Delivery is free, including insurance, within the UK. There is a 10 per cent buyer's premium. (Wines are also very occasionally sold at the Glasgow and Chester auction rooms.)

International Wine Auctions

PO Box 760, London SE1 9BD TEL 01-403 1140

This auction house attracts the top end of the wine market, and is aimed very much at the international wine-buying connoisseur. They hold six auctions a year. Catalogues are £5, and there is no buyer's premium. Delivery is free during working hours. Insurance is the responsibility of the purchaser after 5.30 pm on the day of the sale.

Country auctioneers

While all the country auctioneers deal principally in goods other than wine, those below do hold a few wine auctions a year. Since international buyers tend not to come to these auctions, you can often find amazing bargains, but prices can also go sky-high for no apparent reason.

Colliers, Bigwood and Bewlay

The Old School, Tiddington, Stratford-upon-Avon, Warwickshire CV37 7AW TEL (0789) 69415

Sales take place on Thursday evening, quarterly. There is a pre-sale tasting that afternoon. Subscription to the mailing list is £8. There is a buyer's premium of five per cent (plus VAT), and the vendor's commission varies. Wines must generally be collected, although delivery can be arranged.

Lacy Scott

10 Risbygate Street, Bury St Edmunds, Suffolk IP33 3AA
TEL (0284) 67121

One sale a year. Subscription to the catalogue is free; wines must be collected. There is no buyer's premium, but vendors pay a 12½ per cent commission. Insurance is the responsibility of the buyer.

Lithgow, Sons & Partners

The Auction House, Station Road, Stokesley, Middlesbrough,
Cleveland TEL (0642) 710158

Two sales a year in December and June. Sales are advertised locally
and sometimes in *Decanter* and the *Daily Telegraph*, but you can be put
on their list to be sent catalogues (30p each). Wines must be collected.
Vendors pay a commission, but there is no buyer's premium.

Phillips, Son & Neil

39 Park End Street, Oxford OX1 1JD TEL (0865) 723524

The largest of the country auctioneers. There are four sales a year, held
on Tuesdays, with a pre-sale tasting on the day of the sale. You can
subscribe to the mailing list for £7 per year. There is a 10 per cent
buyer's premium, and a vendor's commission. Wines must be
collected from the saleroom within two weeks of the sale. Insurance is
the responsibility of the buyer.

Buying wine en primeur

Imagine buying fine wine before it's even in bottle and before anybody can honestly guarantee how it's going to turn out. You might think it seems a risky business – and in a sense you would be right.

But only in a sense – because it all depends on the wine. And the market for buying wine in this way (called buying en primeur) has developed around one of the most reliable of all wine areas – Bordeaux. It has become reliable over the past decade with a series of top-quality harvests. It's also reliable because the market is restricted to the classed growth clarets and to the next category down – the bourgeois growths.

The system works like this. Every spring, wine merchants fly to Bordeaux to assess (as well as is possible with wine that may still be going through its second, malolactic, fermentation and which anyway tastes of little more than tannin) the quality of the wine from the previous harvest. At the same time, the major châteaux announce the selling price on the first amount (or *tranche*) of wine they intend to release. Negotiations between the merchants (merchants from other countries besides Britain are there doing the same thing, of course), the châteaux and the middlemen (the Bordeaux négociants) follow to agree on how much wine the overseas merchant can have – and at what price.

Back in Britain, the wine merchants prepare reports on the quality of the wine they have tasted and send out to their customers brochures offering wines from the château they have selected. The offer is normally based on a first-come-first-served basis, because the amount

280

of wine is limited. The price will not include VAT or duty: this will be payable when the wine arrives in the country two – or even more – years later. One – the Hungerford Wine Company – offer a Prior Commitment Scheme which means that they can go to France armed with orders, which gives them, they claim, an upper hand in price negotiations.

What's the advantage?

There is one major advantage in buying wine en primeur: price. In past years, the minute a classed growth claret reached the open market, its price shot up. It could double in a matter of weeks. Buying en primeur ensured you got in at the ground floor.

That was true especially of good years like 1982, 1983 and 1985. However, in poor years, like 1984, when prices didn't rise, you could wait to buy the wine until you wanted to drink it.

With the 1986 vintage, another factor intervened to make some merchants advise against buying en primeur. Although the en primeur price of many Bordeaux châteaux was lower than for the 1985 vintage, merchants felt that the fall – possibly around 20 per cent – was not sufficient to compensate for the rise in the French franc. They argued that since the Americans – the dominant force in earlier vintages of the 1980s – were not buying, the wines should be cheaper still.

In his report on the 1986 vintage, Simon Loftus, wine buyer for Adnams – one of our top award-winning wine merchants – commented: 'Bordeaux prices have risen too far, too fast, and the market is glutted with wine . . . The idea that you must buy your wine at opening prices every year only makes sense in times of shortage and a rising market, conditions that no longer apply.'

On the whole, this was a minority – if a significant minority – view. Others might have preferred to follow the advice of Nick Davies of the Hungerford Wine Company (another of our award-winning merchants): 'The (Bordeaux) proprietors and négociants have been more reasonable with their prices than I dared hope . . . Because of this I can confidently recommend the 1986s we have selected without hesitation.'

Buying wine en primeur is a risk. In the past few years, it has been a risk amply rewarded. The same could still be true of those who bought in 1986: as we went to press it was too early to say. It could all depend on the 1987 vintage – but by that time it will be too late.

Beyond Bordeaux

In the past two years, the practise of special offers of wine for laying down has been extended to other areas: the Rhône, Burgundy, even California. They are not necessarily wines of the most recent vintage (in 1987, the offer of Rhône wines was for 1985), but they are still wines bought while in cask, rather than from a wine merchant's actual stock.

Here is a list of merchants who made en primeur offers in 1987, and those who might make offers in 1988.

Adnams (*not for 1986*)
Les Amis du Vin
Averys
Ballantynes of Cowbridge (*including Rhône*)
Barnes Wine Shop
Berry Bros & Rudd
Bibendum
Curzon Wine Co (*including Burgundy*)
Domaine Direct (*Burgundy only*)
Eldridge Pope (*not for 1986*)
Ellis Son & Vidler
Friarwood
Andrew Gordon Wines
John Harvey & Sons (*including Burgundy*)
Haynes Hanson & Clark
Hicks & Don
Hungerford Wine Company
Justerini & Brooks (*Burgundy only*)

Kershaw's Wine Warehouse
Lay & Wheeler
Laytons (*including Burgundy*)
Newman & Gilbey
Le Nez Rouge/Berkmann Wine Cellars (*Burgundy only*)
Nickolls & Perks
Stephen Porter Wines
Arthur Rackhams
Raeburn Fine Wines and Foods (*including Burgundy*)
Russell & McIver (*including Sauternes, Burgundy and Rhône*)
T & W Wines
Tanners Wines
Henry Townsend (*including Burgundy, Rhône, Alsace and Germany*)
Welbeck Wine Warehouse
Windrush Wines
The Wine Society

Part II

What to buy

Argentina

Five years or more after the Falklands war, it's still very difficult to find any wines from the fifth largest producer of wine in the world. A pity, really. Apart from regaining a source of good, everyday drinking wine – especially reds – it would be good to give Argentine producers encouragement to improve quality as well.

But the most important British wine trade fair – held in London each spring – went by without any Argentine corks being pulled. So it looks as though another year will pass with little improvement in the situation. Mind you, the Argentines' thirst for their own wines does restrict the scope for exports.

However, the largest wine producer in the country *has* started sending his wines here (see below). They're for good honest-to-goodness quaffing at prices which are still hard to beat.

The Italian influence is strong, with Nebbiolo, Barbera and Sangiovese all adding sophistication to wines made generally from Malbec and Criolla (for reds) and Palomino and Torrontes (for whites). But noble French varieties – Chardonnay, Sylvaner (called Riesling), Chenin Blanc (called Pinot Blanc) and lesser varieties like Ugni Blanc, have started to be added to the whites, and Cabernet Sauvignon, Merlot, Syrah and Pinot Noir have also put in an appearance.

Who's who in Argentina

Peñaflor The largest producer in Argentina. Wines are sold under the Andean brand name.
Continental Warehouse; Grape Ideas Wine Warehouse; Queens Club Wines

Specialist stockist
Grape Ideas Wine Warehouse

The Wine & Spirit Education Trust is the body in charge of educating those in and on the fringes of the wine trade. They offer a series of courses right up to Master of Wine level, the more basic of which are open to non-trade members who can convince the Trust of their intention to enter the wine trade. Contact them at: Five Kings House, Kennet Wharf Lane, Upper Thames Street, London EC4V 3AJ; TEL 01-236 3551.

Australia

One country has been continually on the lips of the wine trade and in the words of wine writers this year: Australia. Last year, we said 1986 was Australia's year. Well, we were right, and 1987 has been the same – with knobs on.

The state of the Australian dollar has helped, of course. Australian wines – even some of the best – are amazingly cheap since the slide of the Australian dollar against the pound. With European currencies going the other way, Australia's chances have been boosted no end.

But in the face of sordid financial calculations, we musn't forget the quality. And here, Australia is scoring time and again. The quality is apparent right across the ever-increasing range of wines we're now seeing in our shops as wine buyers return from the Qantas trail Down Under.

It seems that the Australians have realised that in the UK there's a wine market eager to snap up what's on offer, give it a try and – more often than not – come back for more. Figures are proving just this: 130,000 cases of Australian wine were imported in 1986 – an increase of 98 per cent over 1985. By the end of the first three months of 1987 already nearly 60,000 cases had arrived on these shores.

Moreover, the Australians have got round to promoting their wines seriously in the UK. The Australian High Commission runs one of the wine trade's major diary dates: the Australia Day Tasting on 26 January (in 1987 it was at Lord's Cricket Ground, just to show there were no hard feelings after the 1986/87 MCC tour of Australia). And the whole wine trade turns up, clamouring at the doors. The 1987 tasting, as with the 1986 one, brought forth new producers and new wines that should fill the order books with no problem.

The consumer's turn

Now it's over to us, the consumers. The wines are here, waiting to be drunk. And yet, the other day, we were dismayed to be offered an excellent Australian Semillon by a dinner guest with great excuses and apologies that it wasn't a French wine and that it was 'all we could find' in a hurry. Be thankful those guests were in a hurry, was all we could say as we sipped the first mouthfuls of a luscious, honeyed yet dry, full, fat Semillon unlike anything that could ever come from Bordeaux.

So, we are still just beginning to learn. And it seems appropriate that in 1988, Australia's bicentennial year (when the first expedition arrived with vines as well as convicts), we should try and take advantage of the excellent bargains.

From winery back to vineyard

Much of Australia's success has come from the huge investment in new technology in some wineries, coupled with the skills of an emerging generation of master winemakers. Considerably less attention has been paid, it seems, to the quality of the vineyards.

This has been demonstrated in the way many of even the top wines have been blended from different areas of the states and between, say, South Australia and Victoria. The bigger firms, especially, have been happier creating blends and brands rather than wines with a specific geographical origin.

Once Australian wine pretended it was a copy of European styles. The names Chablis, Burgundy, claret, hock were applied almost at random. It was the same in California. The lax laws only encouraged this: if a wine is described as coming from a particular area, it still need contain only 80 per cent of that area's grapes – the other 20 per cent can come from anywhere.

But as Australian producers have gained in confidence, so they've dropped these misleading names, and developed varietal styles. Now we get straightforward names like Chardonnay or Cabernet Sauvignon. And there are also blends, like Cabernet Sauvignon with Shiraz or Merlot with Shiraz which produce a uniquely Australian style.

So things are changing in the Australian vineyards. The growth of small wineries – 380 now press their own grapes – has led to an awareness of and interest in the qualities of different areas and their success and failure with different styles of wines. Single vineyard wines from smaller wineries have been emulated by the bigger boys who have homed in on their best sites, vinified the grapes separately and sold them under the vineyard name.

Although two states – Victoria and Tasmania – have begun to introduce a form of appellation system, regulating the vineyard territories and the quality of wine produced in them, it's very early days to talk about a full-blown system of denominations of origin on the French model. The argument is still at the stage of whether the rules should be more concerned with quality (as in Germany) or with geographical origin (as in France).

Bladder packs and coolers

While small wineries produce a few cases of fine bottled wines, the few big firms (the top eight producers control 50 per cent of turnover) continue to churn out the packs that every Australian is happiest with: to namby-pamby Poms they're boxed wines, but to your full-blooded Australian they're bladder packs – 65 per cent of the wine they drink comes this way. They didn't quite invent the idea, but they've certainly made it work better than anybody else.

They drink a lot of wine, too. While beer consumption has fallen, wine consumption has risen to 25 litres per head (compared with our 9 to 10 litres a head). The problem is that the rise has stopped, but wine production hasn't. Hence, cynically perhaps, the current interest in exports. Hence the heavy discounting that goes on in the Australian domestic market. And hence, also, the creation of coolers – those fruit-flavoured light-alcohol wines that the Californians have also taken up in a big way.

What's what in Australia

Almost without exception, Australian wines are named after the grape variety from which they are made. Sometimes, they may be a blend of two or more, but these, also, will be indicated on the label.

The success of Australian wines in the UK came with the *Chardonnay* wines. They were larger than life, full of fruit and sweet with the taste of new wood, but despite their near vulgarity, they worked. When softened by a year or so in bottle, the balance of ripe fruit and oak was a fine combination. It produced the finest wines in cool years like 1981, 1984, 1985 and 1986. Most vineyard areas produce excellent examples.

But there has been a change in style with the 1985 and 1986 vintages. Some producers are cutting down on the oak, letting the quality of the fruit come through more easily. It's a more sophisticated approach, but we hope it doesn't take over from the older style completely.

Three other grape varieties produce the rest of the best in whites in Australia.

The *Semillon* (the grape of Sauternes in France) makes really fine dry wines, either with or without oak, and with some ageing potential. Australia has realised the possibilities of the Semillon to produce dry wines in a way that France never has, and good examples are well worth seeking out. It is also blended with Chardonnay and occasionally Chenin Blanc. The Hunter River in New South Wales produces some fine examples.

The *Rhine Riesling* makes full, medium dry and sometimes sweet wines, especially in the Barossa Valley and Clare regions of South Australia.

The *Muscat* makes rich, sweet wines, especially in Victoria.

Reds – fast ageing

Cabernet Sauvignon is the top varietal style in red wines. Wood is an important element of the style, as it was with Chardonnay. The wines

Try Which? Wine Monthly FREE
for 3 months, and see for yourself how it gives you the facts.

The publishers of Which? Wine Guide 1988 present a highly informative companion newsletter, designed to give you the most up-to-date advice on buying wine — including news of special bargains, prices and availability — the results of blind tastings and the latest news and views from the wine world.

Accept this remarkable offer and you'll receive the next 3 issues ABSOLUTELY FREE and WITHOUT COMMITMENT.

See overleaf for further details.

HOW TO CLAIM YOUR **FREE** ISSUES

To receive Which? Wine Monthly FREE for 3 months, just complete and return the direct debiting mandate on the coupon below. We will send you the next three issues of Which? Wine Monthly as they appear. If you do not wish to continue receiving Which? Wine Monthly, you can cancel your subscription by writing to us — and your direct debiting mandate by writing to your bank — before payment is due on 1st March 1988. You can keep everything you have received, and it won't have cost you a penny.

If you want to go on receiving Which? Wine Monthly, you don't need to do anything more. Your subscription will bring you Which? Wine Monthly each month for £3.75 a quarter, until you cancel your mandate or we advise you of a change in the price of your subscription. If there should be any change in the price of your subscription at any time we would advise you at least six weeks in advance. This gives you time to tell us if you do not wish to continue your subscription, and to cancel your direct debiting mandate. You are, of course, free to do this at anytime. To accept this offer, just complete the coupon and post it — you don't even need a stamp. So why not post it off now?

Consumers' Association,
Castlemead, Gascoyne Way,
Hertford SG14 1LH.

DETACH ALONG PERFORATION

WHICH? WINE MONTHLY

I would like to accept this free offer. Please send me the next 3 months' issues of Which? Wine Monthly as they appear. I understand that I am under no obligation — if I do not wish to continue with Which? Wine Monthly after the free trial, I can cancel my order before payment is due on 1st March 1988. But if I decide to continue, I need do nothing — my subscription will bring me Which? Wine Monthly each month for the current price of £3.75 a quarter, payable by Direct Debit.

FREE TRIAL ACCEPTANCE

Direct Debiting Mandate.

I/We authorise you until further notice in writing to charge to my/our account with you on or immediately after 1st March 1988 and quarterly thereafter unspecified amounts which may be debited thereto at the instance of Consumers' Association by Direct Debit.

Date of first payment: on or within one calendar month from 1st March 1988.   WX88A

Signed	Date

Bank Account in the name of	Bank Account Number (if known)

Name and address of your bank in BLOCK LETTERS, PLEASE.
TO_____

Your name and address in BLOCK LETTERS, PLEASE.
Mr/Mrs/Miss_____

Banks may decline to accept instructions to charge direct debits to certain types of account other than current accounts.

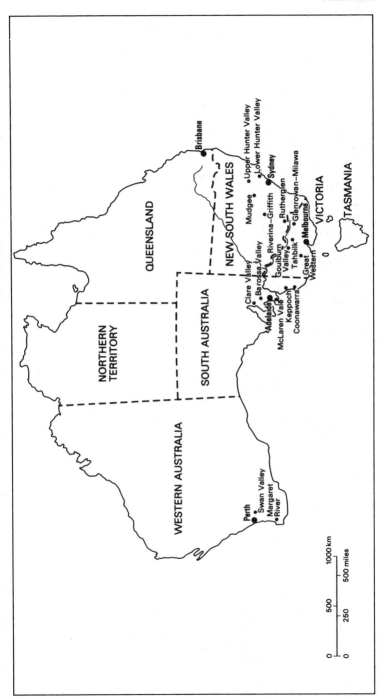

Australia

Brisbane

QUEENSLAND

NEW SOUTH WALES

Upper Hunter Valley
Lower Hunter Valley
Sydney

Mudgee

Riverina–Griffith

Rutherglen

Glenrowan–Milawa

TASMANIA

VICTORIA

Melbourne

Clare Valley
Barossa Valley
Goulburn Valley
Tahbilk
Great Western

SOUTH AUSTRALIA

Adelaide
McLaren Vale
Keppoch
Coonawarra

NORTHERN TERRITORY

WESTERN AUSTRALIA

Perth
Swan Valley
Margaret River

1000 km
500 miles

0   500
0   250

tend to develop fast – faster than they ever do in France, so that three- and four-year-old Australian Cabernets are very drinkable. The best areas for Cabernet Sauvignon wines are Coonawarra in South Australia, Margaret River in Western Australia, and Geelong in Victoria and Tasmania.

Shiraz is the most widely produced red grape. This is supposed to have some relationship with the Syrah of the northern Rhône, but in Australia it makes much more of a hot country wine than it does in France – rich, soft, rounded, peppery, often more approachable than the more tannic Cabernet Sauvignons, with which it is often blended. The Hunter River in New South Wales, the Barossa Valley in South Australia and Victoria are prime areas for this grape variety. Just to confuse us, the EEC is now insisting that the grape is described as Syrah on labels.

Merlot and *Malbec* are also planted in many areas, but are only occasionally seen unblended.

Australian wine regions

SOUTH AUSTRALIA

The state producing 60 per cent of all Australian wine, including most of the boxed wine. Much of it comes from the high-yielding **Riverlands** area, where South Australia, New South Wales and Victoria meet.

Higher quality areas are:

Barossa Valley Best known originally for its Rhine Riesling wines, but increasingly for its Chardonnay and Cabernet Sauvignon. Australia's most expensive wine, Penfold's Grange Hermitage, is made here.

Clare Smaller area, generally considered to be making very high quality wines. Good for Rhine Riesling, but also Cabernet Sauvignon, Malbec and Shiraz, with smaller amounts of Semillon.

Coonawarra Widely agreed to be the area producing the best quality in Australia. Its finest wines are red: Shiraz and Cabernet Sauvignon, but increasingly whites – Sauvignon Blanc, Chardonnay and Gewürztraminer – are being planted.

Southern Vales Small wineries abound in this area just outside Adelaide. McLaren Vale and Reynella are part of this area, and the Adelaide Hills, a new vineyard, is close by. Cabernet Sauvignon, Chardonnay, Shiraz all do well.

NEW SOUTH WALES

The original home of vines in Australia. The vineyards now consist of two areas in the Hunter River Valley.

Hunter Valley First planted as early as 1828, this is now a small area, the furthest north (and therefore one of the hottest) of the quality wine-producing areas. The classic grapes are Shiraz (or Hermitage) and Semillon, but Chardonnay is also planted.

Upper Hunter Valley A new area, on higher land and therefore cooler than the Hunter Valley proper. Chardonnay is the success story here.

VICTORIA

The area under vine in this state was once much larger. But the phylloxera louse reached Victoria while it never even discovered South Australia, and the vineyards have never fully recovered in size. The areas are scattered, and growers seem to have planted where it suits them.

Goulburn Dominated by two estates, Ch Tahbilk and Mitchelton. Cabernet Sauvignon and Rhine Riesling are the specialities.

Rutherglen Best known for its Liqueur Muscats, sweet dessert wines that Hugh Johnson suggests may be the descendants of the Cape Constantia wines of the beginning of the 19th century.

Yarra Virtually every grape variety – including the notoriously difficult Pinot Noir – seems to work in this small area just outside Melbourne.

WESTERN AUSTRALIA

The newest wine state, but one of the most interesting. The best vineyards are clustered in the cool south-western corner of the state, where the Southern Ocean meets the Indian.

Margaret River Cool-climate area producing wines full of flavour. Estates include the Leeuwin Estates, backed by Californian Robert Mondavi. Most grapes seem to work here.

Mount Barker/Frankland River Whites seem to work best here, especially Rieslings.

Swan River The original vineyard area of Western Australia, just outside Perth. Its hot summers make it more suitable for fortified and dessert wines than table wines.

TASMANIA

The southernmost Australian state reproduces northern European growing conditions. White wines and cool climate reds, like Pinot Noir, work best here, although in good years, Cabernet Sauvignon can be very fine too.

Australian vintages – they do matter

Despite its seemingly permanent sunny climate, there are differences in Australian weather from year to year.

1987 A mixed bag vintage, with lower yields and poor weather affecting South Australia and Victoria. Western Australia was better off.

1986 Average crop but exceptional quality. Whites have benefited from cooler weather.

1985 Another cool year, giving flavoursome wines with high natural acidity.

1984 A cloudy period during the harvest has made high-class whites and elegant reds.

1983 A much warmer year producing some great red wines and rather fuller whites.

1982 Some of the best red wines for many years, with quality good to very good.

1981 Variable harvest. South Australia was the best, New South Wales the least successful.

Who's who in Australia

Balgownie (Bendigo, Victoria). Well-balanced wines from one of the coolest areas of Victoria. Wines: Chardonnay, Cabernet Sauvignon, Pinot Noir.
Bow Wine Vaults; Alex Findlater; Raeburn Fine Wines and Foods; La Vigneronne

De Bortoli (Bilbul, New South Wales). Specialising in sweet, dessert whites from botrytised grapes. Wines: Traminer, Riesling, Fumé Blanc, Chardonnay, Cabernet Sauvignon, Botrytised Semillon, Merlot.
Barnes Wine Shop; Alex Findlater; Peter Green; Ostlers

Berri Estates/Renmano (Riverland, South Australia). Major co-operative selling wine in boxes and finer wines in bottle, some very good. Wines: Chardonnay, Fumé Blanc, Rhine Riesling, Traminer Riesling, Cabernet Sauvignon, Merlot, Cabernet/Shiraz.
Widely available, including from Peter Dominic; J Sainsbury; Tesco; Unwins; Waitrose

Brand's Laira (Coonawarra, South Australia). Small, premium winery. Wines: Cabernet Sauvignon, Shiraz, Cabernet Sauvignon/Malbec, Malbec.
Alex Findlater; Ostlers

Brown Brothers (Milawa, Victoria). High-quality family winery, with a full range of whites and reds and excellent late-harvest Liqueur Muscat. Wines: Dry Muscat, Late Picked Muscat, Estate Chardonnay, Estate Shiraz, Cabernet Sauvignon (from cool vineyards at Koombahla).
Bottoms Up; Peter Dominic; Majestic Wine Warehouses; Willoughbys

Conti – Forest Hill (Mount Barker, Western Australia). First vineyard in this cool climate area. Best known for Rhine Riesling and Cabernet Sauvignon. Wines: Rhine Riesling, Cabernet Sauvignon, Traminer, Chardonnay.
Barnes Wine Shop; Alex Findlater; Ostlers

Delatite (Mansfield, Victoria). Small family winery, producing some of the best Australian Pinot Noirs. Wines: Rhine Riesling, Gewürztraminer, Pinot Noir, Cabernet Sauvignon/Merlot.
Anthony Byrne Fine Wines

Evans and Tate (Swan Valley, Western Australia). High reputation for good, flavoured reds, well made. Wines: Semillon, Gnangara Shiraz, Redbrook Cabernet Sauvignon, Redbrook Hermitage.
Alex Findlater

Gawler River Estate (South Australia). Estate wines, best in whites. Wines: Colombard, Rhine Riesling, Sauvignon Blanc, Muscat, Cabernet Sauvignon.
Berry Bros & Rudd; Alex Findlater; Peter Green; Ostlers

Hardy's (based in Adelaide, South Australia). Large company making big wines and a range of lighter, more European-style wines. Wines: Cabernet Sauvignon, Chenin Blanc, Fumé Blanc, Chardonnay, Rhine Riesling, Keppoch Cabernet Sauvignon, Keppoch Cabernet/Shiraz, McLaren Vale Shiraz, Ch Reynella Cabernet Sauvignon and Chardonnay. (See also Houghton.)
H Allen Smith; Majestic Wine Warehouses

Hill Smith Estate (Barossa Valley, South Australia). Family firm making premium varietal wines largely from their own vineyards. Wines: Old Triangle Vineyard Rhine Riesling, Estate Semillon, Estate Chardonnay, Old Triangle Shiraz/Malbec, Estate Shiraz, Estate Cabernet Sauvignon, Botrytised Semillon, own Barossa Valley Estates brand.
Peter Dominic; Waitrose; Whynot Wine Warehouses

Houghton (Swan River, Western Australia). One of the first commercial vineyards of Western Australia, now part of Hardy's. Wines: Chardonnay, Cabernet Sauvignon, Blue Stripe Supreme (blend of Chenin Blanc and Verdelho), Rhine Riesling, Frankland River Cabernet Sauvignon.
Alex Findlater; Waitrose

Idyll Vineyard (Geelong, Victoria). Cool climate vineyards making elegant wines. Wines: Gewürztraminer, Shiraz Rosé, Cabernet/Shiraz.
Alex Findlater; Mayor Sworder; Ostlers

Lake's Folly (Hunter Valley, New South Wales). Only two wines are made here, but they are some of the best. Wines: Chardonnay, Cabernet Sauvignon.
D Byrne; Ostlers

Lindeman's (Hunter Valley, New South Wales). A large firm, one of the top three in Australia, with vineyards in most regions and a number of estate wines. Wines: Padthaway Chardonnay, Rouge Homme Chardonnay, Rouge Homme Cabernet Sauvignon, St George Cabernet Sauvignon, Rouge Homme Pinot Noir, Rhine Riesling.
Cumbrian Cellar; Alex Findlater

McWilliams (Hunter Valley, New South Wales). Estate wines are a welcome addition to a rather dull range of old-style wines. Wines: Hanwood Estate Chardonnay, Fumé Blanc, Rhine Riesling, Cabernet Sauvignon, Shiraz, Beelbangera Semillon, Traminer Riesling, Yenda Cabernet Sauvignon, Hermitage, Pinot Noir, Mount Pleasant Estate.
Peter Dominic; Alex Findlater; Ostlers

Geoff Merrill (McLaren Vale, South Australia). The winemaker at Hardy's also makes two very fine wines from his own vineyards. Wines: Cabernet Sauvignon, Semillon.
H Allen Smith; Bibendum

Mildara (Coonawarra, South Australia and Mildura, Victoria). The best wines, improving all the time, come from Coonawarra vineyards rather than the firm's original Mildura vineyards. Wines: Coonawarra Chardonnay, Sauvignon, Cabernet Sauvignon, Fumé Blanc, Traminer Riesling, Shiraz, Cabernet/Merlot, Church Hill Chardonnay, sparkling wines.
Lay & Wheeler; Ostlers

Mitchelton (Goulburn, Victoria). Commercial vineyard making straightforward wines. Wines: Mitchelton Rhine Riesling, Marsanne (white), Cabernet Sauvignon.
Alex Findlater; Ostlers

Montrose (Mudgee, New South Wales). Award-winning wines, including a remarkably good Pinot Noir. Wines: Chardonnay, Show Reserve Chardonnay, Fumé Blanc, Pinot Noir, Cabernet Sauvignon, Special Reserve Shiraz.
D Byrne; Ostlers

Moorilla Estate (Tasmania). Fine claret-style wines from cool climate vineyards. Wines: Cabernet Sauvignon.
Les Amis du Vin

Morris (Victoria). Morris of Rutherglen makes some of the top Liqueur Muscats in an area renowned for that style. Wines: Liqueur Muscat, Liqueur Tokay, Chardonnay.
Oddbins

Moss Wood Estate (Margaret River, Western Australia). Its high-quality Cabernet Sauvignon gave the winery its reputation. Wines: Semillon, Chardonnay, Pinot Noir, Cabernet Sauvignon.
Adnams; Bibendum; Raeburn Fine Wines and Foods; La Vigneronne

Orlando (Barossa Valley, South Australia). Commercial wines, made on a large scale, but with good quality. Wines: Jacob's Creek brand, RF brand, Rhine Riesling, Chardonnay, Shiraz/Cabernet, St Hilary Chardonnay, St Hugo Cabernet Sauvignon.
Bibendum; Davisons; Gough Bros; Oddbins; Ubiquitous Chip

Peel Estate (Mandurah, Western Australia). Single estate wines from south of Perth. Wines: Shiraz, Chenin Blanc, Cabernet Sauvignon.
Alex Findlater

Penfold's (Barossa, Coonawarra, Clare, Morgan in South Australia). Largest wine producer in Australia, with very high quality in both whites and reds. Wines: Traminer Riesling, Grange Hermitage, St Henri Cabernet/Shiraz, Kalimna Bin, selected Bin wines, Koonunga Hill, Magill Estate, Seaview.
Adnams; Chaplin & Son; Oddbins; Sainsbury Bros; David Scatchard; Yorkshire Fine Wines

Petaluma (Adelaide Hills, South Australia). Some of Australia's finest wines. Wines: Rhine Riesling, Chardonnay, Coonawarra Cabernet Sauvignon.
Adnams; Les Amis du Vin; Majestic Wine Warehouses; Yorkshire Fine Wines

Quelltaler (Clare Valley, South Australia). Best known for its white wines. Wines: Rhine Riesling, Semillon.
David Baillie Vintners; Berry Bros & Rudd; Fortnum & Mason

Rosemount Estate (Hunter Valley, New South Wales). The firm that was in on the beginning of the current enthusiasm for Australian wines. Recent vintages have shown some signs of a falling off in quality, though. Look for the Show Reserve range. Wines: Traminer, Sauvignon Blanc, Fumé Blanc, Chardonnay, Shiraz, Cabernet/Malbec, Cabernet Sauvignon, Show Reserve Chardonnay, Cabernet Sauvignon, sparkling wine.
Widely available

Rothbury Estate (Hunter Valley, New South Wales). Top quality wines made by Len Evans, one of the gurus of Australian winemaking. Wines: Chardonnay, Shiraz, Semillon.
Les Amis du Vin; Majestic Wine Warehouses; Oddbins

Seppelt (Barossa Valley, South Australia). Large-scale commercial producer. Wines: Rhine Riesling, Chardonnay, Shiraz, Cabernet Sauvignon.
Alex Findlater; Reynier Wine Library

Stanley (Clare, South Australia). The Leasingham range is the best of this firm's wines. Wines: Leasingham Rhine Riesling, Bin 56 Cabernet/Malbec, Cabernet Sauvignon, Coonawarra Shiraz/Cabernet.
Alex Findlater; Richard Granger; Grape Ideas

Taltarni (Moonambel, Victoria). Cool climate vineyard, mainly planted with Cabernet Sauvignon. Wines: Cabernet Sauvignon, Shiraz.
Alston Wines; D Byrne; Ostlers; Reid Wines; Wizard Wine Warehouse

Tisdall (Goulburn Valley, Victoria). Pricey but good Chardonnay is the star from this winery. Wines: Traminer Riesling, Mount Helen Chardonnay, Pinot Noir, Cabernet/Merlot.
Alex Findlater; Peter Green; Ostlers; Whynot Wine Warehouses; The Wine Schoppen

Tollana (Barossa Valley, South Australia). Sound commercial wines, but nothing exciting. Wines: Langhorne Creek Chenin Blanc, Barossa Valley Shiraz.
Peter Dominic

Tyrrells (Hunter Valley, New South Wales). Strange names hide some interesting blends. Reds are better than whites. Wines: Long Flat White, Vat 1 Semillon, Vat 47 Chardonnay, Long Flat Red, Pinot Noir, Shiraz.
Averys of Bristol; Christopher & Co; Alex Findlater; Ostlers; Queens Club Wines

Vasse Felix (Margaret River, Western Australia). Small winery producing very fine complex wines. Wines: Riesling, Cabernet Sauvignon, Hermitage.
Alex Findlater

Wolf Blass (Langhorne Creek, South Australia). One of the showmen of Australian wine, Wolf Blass specialises in top quality blended wines. Wines: Classic Dry White, Cabernet/Shiraz.
Averys of Bristol; Nobody Inn

Wyndham Estate (Hunter Valley, New South Wales). The oldest continuously operating winery in Australia, started in 1828. Wines: Chardonnay, Gewürztraminer Riesling, Cabernet Sauvignon, Shiraz, sparkling wine.
Alex Findlater; Ostlers

Wynns (Coonawarra, South Australia). Large firm making sound reds and excellent whites. Wines: Coonawarra Chardonnay, Rhine Riesling, Shiraz, Cabernet Sauvignon, Ovens Valley Shiraz.
D Byrne; Arthur Rackhams; Victoria Wine Co

Yalumba (Barossa Valley, South Australia). Owned by the Hill-Smith family, this winery makes sound commercial wines. Wines: Carte d'Or Riesling, Cabernet Sauvignon, Cabernet Shiraz.
Les Amis du Vin; D Byrne; Cullens; J E Hogg; Ostlers; La Vigneronne

Yarra Yering (Yarra Valley, Victoria). Leading winery in a small, exciting area. Wines: St Huberts Cabernet/Merlot, Leo Buring Chardonnay, Elderton Cabernet/Merlot, Sutherland Chardonnay, Yerinberg Marsanne.
Adnams; Barnes Wine Shop; Wizard Wine Warehouse

Best buys from Australia

WHITE WINES

Hardys Captain's Selection white (*H Allen Smith*)
Orlando RF Chardonnay (*widely available*)
Rhine Riesling 1987, Old Triangle Vineyard (*Cairns and Hickey; Waitrose*)
Chardonnay 1985, de Bortoli (*Arthur Rackhams*)
Seaview Chardonnay 1986 (*GM Vintners; Oddbins*)
Penfold's Hunter Valley Semillon 1982 (*GM Vintners*)

RED WINES

Orlando RF Cabernet Sauvignon (*Alston Wines; Whynot Wine Warehouses*)
Penfold's Koonunga Hill Shiraz/Cabernet 1984 (*Oddbins*)
Rosemount Hunter Valley Shiraz 1984 (*Peter Dominic; Ilkley Wine Cellars; Smedley Vintners*)
Penfold's Dalwood Cabernet/Shiraz 1983 (*J E Hogg; Sainsbury Brothers*)
Wynns Ovens Valley Shiraz 1983 (*Helen Verdcourt Wines; Victoria Wine Co*)
Berri Estates Cabernet/Shiraz 1982 (*Wines of Interest; and many others*)

Specialist stockists

Adnams: H Allen Smith; Averys; Barnes Wine Shop; Bibendum; D Byrne; Alex Findlater; Great Northern Wine Co; Lay & Wheeler; Nobody Inn; Oddbins; Ostlers; Raeburn Fine Wines and Foods; Seckford Wines; La Vigneronne; The Wine Spot

Austria

Austrian wine sales in Britain have still to recover from the effects of the diethylene glycol scandal of 1985. Occasionally, new wines are introduced, new companies put in an appearance – and then they disappear. Why should we be so uninterested in the often high quality wines that do make their way on to shop shelves, when we seem willing to try wines from pretty well everywhere else?

Part of the answer is that the Austrians are uninterested in us. Many growers cannot be bothered to export because, under the strict new wine laws (designed to prevent a further wine scandal), the paperwork involved in exporting is just too complex. Besides, there are enough Austrians and visitors to Austria to drink the wine at home.

Add to that the average or below average quantities of the 1985 and 1986 vintages, and there doesn't seem to be much incentive for the Austrians to tell the world about their wines.

Price is another reason why retailers are unlikely to be stocking many Austrian wines. The Austrian Schilling goes higher and higher against the poor old pound, and the small harvests have forced up the basic price of grapes anyway.

Austrian branded wines are still around but in fewer outlets than before, and their prices are too high to compete in the branded wine market. What interest there is in Austrian wine must now centre around single estate bottles, especially those made in regions such as the Wachau, relatively untouched by the diethylene glycol scandal and specialising anyway in dry wines from the Grüner Veltliner grape. If you do want the special, spicy, peppery taste of white wines from the Grüner Veltliner – which to our mind is the true taste of Austrian wine – then be prepared to pay more.

Government controls

All Austrian wine is now made under sufficiently strict controls for the problems of diethylene glycol to seem far away. The new Austrian wine law is strict, perhaps not strict enough and perhaps watered down by the lobbying of grape growers – but it is better than it was, and it does contain various guarantees.

Firstly, the government has finally managed to include controls on yields: these will come into force with the 1987 vintage, despite intense pressure from the growers of the Burgenland, whose yields have traditionally been enormous.

The government has also made moves to ensure the genuineness of a wine: from now on all the wine in a bottle should contain the grape variety and vintage specified on the label (before, the amount was only 66 per cent). And if the label specifies a particular Grosslage (or collection of villages), then all the grapes should have come from that Grosslage. This means that grapes going to make wines like Falkensteiner and Gumpoldskirchener will no longer be from wide areas but from restricted village vineyards only.

Moreover, every bottle will now have a strip of paper over the cork indicating that the wine has been tested and that it is part of a permitted consignment.

Buy sweet and dry

Despite price rises, any of the sweet dessert wines from the Burgenland (see below) are still bargains compared to their German equivalents, while 1986 vintages of the dry whites are worth buying for their freshness and easy-drinking nature (don't buy dry whites older than the 1985 vintage – they will generally be tired).

Some of the reds, soft and not quite dry, with a vanilla touch, are light and easy to drink, fuller than Germany's pale efforts, but in the same style. Blauer Portugieser and Blaufränkisch (similar to Gamay) are the popular grape varieties here. Reds up to two or three years old are good now, but tend to dry out beyond that.

What's what in Austria

Apetlon Village on the eastern shore of the Neusiedlersee, near the Austrian border. Famous for sweet wines.

Blauer Portugieser Popular red grape variety making wines for early drinking.

Blaufränkisch Red grape similar to the Gamay but not related.

Burgenland Austria's easternmost wine district which includes the shallow Neusiedlersee. Sandy soils and a warm, humid climate encourage a regular production of sweet wines made from botrytis-affected grapes.

Donnerskirchen Town in Burgenland famous for its Trockenbeerenauslese wines.

Dürnstein Town on the Wachau (see below), home of the Wachau co-operative and the castle in which Richard Lionheart was imprisoned.

Falkenstein Village of Lower Austria, north-west of Vienna, producing easy-drinking wines from the Grüner Veltliner grape. Available in the UK.

Grüner Veltliner Austria's own white grape variety, producing slightly spicy, dry wines, with a hint of steeliness. Best drunk young, except for some better Prädikat wines.

Gumpoldskirchen Village south of Vienna, source of modern-style fresh white wines (especially those made at the local co-operative).

Heurigen Jug wines drawn from the barrel, associated especially with the suburbs of Vienna, where they are sold in bars also called Heurigen.

Klosterneuberg Government testing station, viticultural school and wine producer all share this green-domed Abbey complex just outside Vienna. The wines are straightforward, the red very acceptable.

Krems/Langenlois Quality districts just east of the Wachau.

Muskat Ottonel An aromatic grape variety, producing slightly honeyed wines.

Niederösterreich This province of Lower Austria is the largest wine region and is divided into sub-districts (eg Wachau).

Ried Single vineyard (similar to German 'Lage').

Rust Lakeside village in Burgenland famous for its sweet white wines. The surrounding area is called Rust-Neusiedlersee.

St Laurent Red grape variety, producing deep, plum-coloured wines with distinctive flavour.

Spätrot-Rotgipfler Blend of two grape varieties from which much Gumpoldskirchner wine is made.

Vöslau Red wine district just south of Gumpoldskirchen.

Wachau Top quality dry and medium dry white wine area based on vineyards lining the Danube gorge west of Vienna. Some wines are made from the Rhine Riesling and some have keeping qualities rare for Austrian wines.

Weissburgunder The Pinot Blanc of Alsace and the Pinot Bianco of Italy. Makes fresh, dry white wines.

Welschriesling Also the Italian or Laski or Olasz Riesling (depending on which part of central or eastern Europe you're in). Its acidity in Austria makes it a good base for sparkling wines. Also used for some sweet wines in Burgenland.

The Austrian wine law

The basis for the Austrian wine law is similar to Germany's and is based upon the degree of ripeness of the grapes as much as the geographical origin. All the categories are the same as in Germany but are based on different (usually higher) levels of natural sugar in the grape (because Austria is further south, the grapes have a chance to get riper than in Germany).

There is only one extra category of which examples are rarely seen in this country. This is Ausbruch, midway in sweetness between Beerenauslese and Trockenbeerenauslese.

Austria's vintages

1986 A good quality harvest but as with 1985 quantities are down on average. Few top sweet wines were made because it was such a dry summer. The whites from the Wachau have good acidity.
1985 A very small harvest, with wines – especially the sweet Burgenland wines – of high quality.
1984 Wines were fairly acid due to poor weather, but the whites are still fresh. Wait a while for the sweeter wines.
1983 A very hot vintage gave fat wines lacking in acidity. The dry autumn meant that there are few botrytised wines. Most dry wines should have been drunk by now.
Older vintages 1981, 1979 for sweet wines only.

Who's who in Austria

H Augustin Good quality wines, many based on the Grüner Veltliner grape.
Stockist details from H Augustin, 271/273 King Street, London W9

Sepp Hold Burgenland producer of sweet wines.
Premier Wines (Ayr)

Klosterneuberg A range of sound wines, including the branded Klosterdawn and Klostergarten.
Safeway

Franz Mayer Viennese producer of Heurigen wines, who also makes Chardonnay and Riesling.
Premier Wines (Ayr)

Alois Morandell Family firm making a wide range of wine, including dessert wines from Rust.
Stockist details from Whitwham & Co, Old Market Place, Altrincham, Cheshire

Lenz Moser The top quality producer of Austria, now over the financial problems caused by the wine scandal. Produces branded Blue Danube and Schluck, as well as some fine estate wines.
Gerard Harris; Tanners Wines; Victoria Wine Co

Fritz Saloman Small firm near Krems producing some of the best and most long-lasting dry whites.
Alston Wines; E H Booth; Selfridges

Schlosskellerei Uhlheim Producer in Styria in southern Austria. In addition, makes red from Vöslau and white from Krems.
Alston Wines; Ubiquitous Chip

Winzergenossenschaften The best of these co-operatives are at Wachau (*Principality Wines, Llanelli*), Krems (*Alston Wines; A L Vose*), Dürnstein (*Principality Wines, Llanelli*) and Gumpoldskirchen (*Alston Wines; Tanners Wines*).

Specialist stockists
Alston Wines; Premier Wines (Ayr); A L Vose

Brazil

Yes, there's more than coffee in Brazil: there's wine, too. Most of it comes from the south of the country, around São Paulo, where it's not so hot as in Rio de Janeiro. It has become a serious industry, because the American (now British-owned) firm of Heublein set up shop there a few years ago. The Sherry firm of Domecq followed, as well as Cinzano and Moët et Chandon, so there must be something to these vineyards.

Now we have the chance to find out, thanks to one enterprising shipper who is importing wines produced in the 1200-hectare estate of Palomas Wines in the Rio Grande do Sul. They are making varietal wines – Pinot Noir, Cabernet Sauvignon, Chardonnay, Merlot and Chenin Blanc – which are probably not going to set the wine world on fire, but should make an interesting talking point.

Best buys from Brazil
Palomas Cabernet Sauvignon
Palomas Chardonnay
A L Vose

Bulgaria

Going up-market

Sales of Bulgarian wine have continued to rise steadily. We consume more, it seems, than the Bulgarians themselves (probably because most of the wine is sent for export anyway to get much-needed hard currency). And they are still excellent value.

But there has been a change in the style of Bulgarian wine, and the Bulgarians themselves are, with their central control, carefully orchestrating that change. What they have done is to push the quality level of their wine up-market. Notice that we don't say the quality level has gone up – because for their price the standard quality of Bulgarian wines has always been amazingly high. But the Bulgarians, having established a very firm hold on British wine drinkers, want us to take their wines more seriously. They want us to see that Bulgaria can produce top quality wines as well as the everyday stuff with which we are now familiar.

They took the first steps towards this goal some years ago when they introduced a wine called Sakar Mountain Cabernet – the 1976 wine was a superb, classic Cabernet Sauvignon, with a touch of wood and a taste of violets. After an initial hiccough, the 1978 has proved equally good.

Then they decided to go further on the up-market road. They created what they called Controliran regions (listed below), which are specially designated regions like super appellation contrôlée areas. A few wines made under Controliran rules reached the shops in 1986 – the Svichtov Cabernet Sauvignon (*Oddbins*) was an exciting wine.

This year, the plan was moved one stage further with the introduction of Reserve wines. These come from larger areas than Controliran wines, but are made with strict controls yields, are aged in oak barrels smaller than are used for standard Bulgarian wines, are bottled earlier but allowed to rest for some time. The Bulgarians reckon that all this attention to detail will add a layer of complexity to the simple varietal character of their ordinary wines.

And still they're cheap. The Reserve wines made from Cabernet Sauvignon and Chardonnay sell for less than £3 a bottle.

What about the wines we know?

Where does this leave the familiar Bulgarian wines that we've grown to know and drink? At the basic level the Mehana wines are blended from local grape varieties – Pamid, Gamza, Misket and the more stylish

Mavrud. At the next level are the simple varietal wines, made from
Chardonnay and Rhine Riesling (for whites), Cabernet Sauvignon and
Merlot (for reds). We're pleased to report that the quality of the reds,
about which we were worried with all this chasing after more
expensive wines, has gone back to its old level, even though the style
has become more complex.

What's what in Bulgaria

The simplicity of the Bulgarian labelling system is a deliberate added
attraction – most wines are simply sold under their varietal name.
There is also a basic range of wines which are blends of local grapes,
sold either under the Mehana brand name or under a shop's own label.

The middle range consists of the varietal wines which first made
Bulgaria famous. The ones most usually seen here are Riesling and
Chardonnay in whites, Cabernet Sauvignon and Merlot in reds.

Above this come the new Reserve wines – currently available are
Khan Krum Chardonnay (white), Oryahovica Cabernet Sauvignon and
Damianitza Melnik (reds).

Bulgarian at £20 a bottle?

At the top end of the range are the bottles from the delimited wine
production regions whose names appear on the label. These areas have
been defined as best at producing a particular varietal style of wine,
and giving it a distinctive regional character.

The new Controliran wine areas under this arrangement are:
Asenovgrad: makes Cabernet Sauvignon, Merlot and Mavrud
Harsovo (Melnik): makes wine from local grapes
Juzhnyabryag: makes rosé styles
Kralevo and Preslav: make Riesling
Lozica: makes Cabernet Sauvignon
Novo Selo: makes Gamza
Oryahovica: makes Cabernet Sauvignon and Merlot
Preslav: makes Chardonnay
Rozova Dolina: makes Misket – mainly white
Sakak: makes Merlot
Sakar: makes Cabernet Sauvignon
Stambolovo: makes Merlot
Svichtov: makes Cabernet Sauvignon
Varna: makes Chardonnay

More regions are expected to follow.

Ultimately Reserve Controliran wines will appear – but, with tiny
quantities of production, they could sell for as much as £20 a bottle –
a change indeed from £1.99.

Best buys from Bulgaria

WHITE WINES

Bulgarian Chardonnay (*widely available*)
Bulgarian Riesling (*widely available*)
Reserve Khan Krum Chardonnay 1983 (*Majestic Wine Warehouses, Oddbins, Victoria Wine Co, Whynot Wine Warehouses*)

RED WINES

Sakar Mountain Cabernet 1978 (*widely available*)
Bulgarian Cabernet Sauvignon (*widely available*)
Reserve Oryahovica Cabernet Sauvignon 1978 (*Majestic Wine Warehouses, Oddbins, Victoria Wine Co, Whynot Wine Warehouses*)

Specialist stockists

Bordeaux Direct; Direct Wine Shipments; Majestic Wine Warehouses; Oddbins; Taste Shops; Wines of Westhorpe

Canada

Life after hybrids

Canada's wine industry is based mainly on the hybrid *Vitis labrusca* wines (banned in Europe in favour of the better quality *Vitis vinifera*) and Baby Duck, Canada's answer to alcoholic Coca-Cola. Most are well avoided and few are available in Britain.

However, there is a small pocket of *Vitis vinifera* wine production in Ontario where some decent if rather expensive wines are made. The best-known producer is Inniskillin (if only because theirs are the only Canadian wines available here). They make a Chardonnay and a Riesling, both of which have varietal character, and also some of the better wines from the hybrids – a sweet white Vidal and a red Maréchal Foch, as well as a Gamay Noir.

Best buys from Canada

Inniskillin Chardonnay 1983 – white (*Averys*)
Inniskillin Maréchal Foch 1982 – red (*Averys*)

Chile

Chile's wines have still to make the impact on the British market that their quality deserves. But when they do, it will be because of one man – Miguel Torres Jr.

In the late '70s this energetic Spaniard bought estates in some of the cooler wine-growing areas of Chile and already his first achievements have burst upon the wine world, provoking a mixture of suspicion ('Is this really Chilean white? – it's much too clean and fresh') and reluctant admiration ('That man's done it again').

He has applied the techniques he already uses in the Penedès region of Spain. Stainless steel, cold fermentation, only a short ageing time in wood for reds – all these contribute to some very exciting wines. His vineyard is in the Maule valley, well to the south of the existing vineyard area around the capital of Chile, Santiago. That means that the climate is cooler and the ripening period of the grapes is longer – both aids to making good wine.

The Chilean vineyards are just across the Andes from the main Argentine vineyard areas. But the climb up to 17,000 feet and down again does wonders for the climate. Where Argentine vineyards are in almost desert land, in Chile the rainfall is twice as high and the cool, moist winds from the Pacific Ocean give a climate not unlike that of Bordeaux.

There's another link with Bordeaux in the well-drained soil sitting on a high water table which keeps the vines well watered but not sodden.

Add to that the fact that Chile's vineyards are the only major area in the world without phylloxera (so the vines don't have to be grafted on to American root stock as they do everywhere else), plus a low incidence of all the dreadful diseases that can strike vines – and it's not surprising that Chile has the potential to be one of the most exciting vineyard areas in the world.

Mind you, some of the old-style Chilean wines were not much to get excited about: local taste demanded flabby whites and over-oaked reds. Much wine is still made that way, but not all. Top quality producers have been making wine using Cabernet Sauvignon for some time, and, apart from the Torres wines, it's for this grape variety that they've achieved their reputation beyond the Andes and the Pacific.

Drink the whites, keep the reds

Drink the youngest possible vintage of Chilean whites – 1986 or 1987. A few Chardonnay whites are capable of some ageing – Cousiño Macul is one – but the good, modern-style whites, often made from the crisp, grassy-tasting Sauvignon, are delicious when drunk young. Semillon is old-fashioned and heavy. Chardonnay is unexciting but fresh and clean, and the next few years should see great improvements in quality. Of the reds, Pinot Noir tends to be sweet and alcoholic, but Cabernet Sauvignon is the greatest success, making both simple, everyday wines for drinking as soon as they appear on the shelves and wines with considerable ageing potential (ten years or more) and great varietal character.

The 1987 vintage in Chile was a small harvest, especially of whites, because of a poor flowering early in the season. The wine will be expensive.

What's what in Chile

Nearly all exported wines are straight or blended varietals. If a grape is specified on the label, the wine should contain 85 per cent of that grape variety. Areas of production do not have to appear on the label, but some producers print back labels which tell you more about the wine.

The Maipo valley is the traditional wine-growing area, but wines from the Maule and Lontué valleys are gaining in importance.

Chilean wines are categorised like this: the standard quality will have no qualification, but a wine called **Special** will have been bottled after two years in tank or wood; **Reserva** after four years; **Gran Vino** after six years (avoid this category unless you enjoy very dry, tannic red wines).

Who's who in Chile

There are five producers whose wines are available in Britain:

Concha y Toro Chile's largest wine producer who turns out reliable wines but with no great excitement. Wines: Cabernet Casillero del Diablo, Cabernet/Merlot blends, Cabernet Marqués de Casa Concha (worth keeping for six or seven years), white Sauvignon/Semillon blend (drink young).
Kershaw's Wine Warehouse; Yorkshire Fine Wines

Cousiño Macul Make the best red wines coming out of Chile. Some of the Cabernet Sauvignons last for years. Also make Chardonnay wines. Wines: Cousiño Macul Antiguas Reserve (will last ten or fifteen years), Chardonnay (drink at two years).
Barnes Wine Shop; Morris & Verdin; Paul Sanderson Wines; Tanners Wines

Linderos Top quality Cabernet Sauvignon with good ageing potential. The 1982 is good and the 1983 is worth laying down for three or four years. Wines: Viña Linderos Cabernet Sauvignon.
Peter Dominic; Richard Granger; Grape Ideas Wine Warehouse; Wizard Wine Warehouse

Los Vascos Make superb Cabernet Sauvignon wines, full of fruit. Wines: Cabernet Sauvignon (drink now or keep for a couple of years).
Taste Shops; The Wine Club

Torres The great innovator in Chile, as in Spain. Whites and reds are in the modern style but have considerable character. Wines appear under the Santa Digna and Bellaterra names; also Cabernet Sauvignon, Sauvignon Blanc, Rosé (made from Cabernet Sauvignon), Don Miguel (Riesling and Gewürztraminer).
Peter Green; Moreno Wines; David Scatchard; Stones of Belgravia

Best buys from Chile

WHITE WINE

Sauvignon Blanc 1986, Torres (*Peter Green; Premier Wine Warehouse*)

RED WINES

Cabernet Sauvignon 1983, Viña Linderos (*Grape Ideas Wine Warehouse*)
Cabernet Sauvignon 1983, Los Vascos (*Taste Shops*)
Caberbet Sauvignon 1984, Torres (*Barnes Wine Shop; Whynot Wine Warehouses; Wines from Paris*)

Specialist stockists

Peter Green; Henry Townsend

Cyprus

While Hinge and Bracket continue to promote the biggest brand of Cyprus Sherry on British television, no one seems to be acknowledging that this is a market doomed to dwindle. The price advantage these Cyprus Sherries used to enjoy over the Real Thing from Spain is now less important than the fact that they just don't taste as good. As a more discerning Sherry market grows up, Cyprus Sherry will come to seem more and more irrelevant.

Which is sad. What we should be discovering more about are Cyprus table wines, where the future for the island's vineyards really lies. And to judge by wines tasted at the island's wine research institute, there is the potential to produce some good, crisp, modern-style whites and some deep, rich reds.

This research institute has been experimenting for some years with French grape varieties and has come up with some very satisfactory results. As it is a Mediterranean country, the translation of these experimental results into commercial reality is frustratingly slow.

But the most go-ahead of the four firms that dominate the Cyprus wine industry has launched a new modern-style white wine (see Best buys below), showing that modern technology is being used to drag Cyprus into a new era.

But still probably the biggest-selling Cyprus table wine is the sweet style in the Hirondelle range, and the best-selling red is the one that's on every Greek and Cypriot restaurant wine list – Otello.

The one Cyprus wine we think is worth looking out for is the overpoweringly sweet Commandaria of St John. It's made from grapes laid out in the sun to dry and gets its name from the Middle Ages when the island was governed by the Knights Templar, although its origins are much older.

Although much Commandaria is simply straightforward dessert wine used widely as altar wine in churches, some of the better quality wine is available as well – dark and sweet but without losing the taste of grapes.

Best buys from Cyprus

d'Ahera A light style of smooth red wine made from Carignan grapes.
Victoria Wine Co

Bellapais Medium sweet, slightly fizzy white wine, a good example of a modern-style white.
Victoria Wine Co

Commandaria of St John (See above.) The best that is widely available is made by Keo
Victoria Wine Co

Thisbe The new medium dry white wine launched to compete with German-style wines.
Victoria Wine Co

England and Wales

Coping with the climate

Anybody who suffered through the British summers of 1985 and 1986 will be amazed that the English – and Welsh – vineyards managed to produce any ripe grapes to make wine at all. And yet the dedicated band of wine producers grows, wine is made despite the lack of sunshine, and the style that sets these wines apart continues to develop.

Most vineyards produce two styles of white wine: a dry style and a less dry style. In good years (1983, for example) the dry style is superb – making a crisp, clean-tasting wine that some have likened to the smell of an English country garden and which has piercing fruit and acidity. In poor years, the producers need a touch of concentrated must or sugared wine just to keep the acidity from overwhelming the unripe fruit. So – with exceptions – 1985 and 1986 wines are slightly better in a medium dry or off-dry style. Even then, though they may be made with German grapes, they don't taste the same – their acidity is keener and they have a steely quality that still sets them apart.

A few intrepid souls also make red wines, and some achieve surprisingly good results, considering the way nature's cards are stacked against them. But they should be approached with caution, and shouldn't be bought untasted, simply because with their lightness and considerable acidity they are unlike the red wines we are used to.

The problem, though, is to find any of these wines. Many of the vineyard owners only sell at the vineyard gate (on page 569 we give a list of vineyards and their opening hours) simply because they cannot afford distribution costs on the small amount of wine they make. The vineyards that are more widely distributed (because of larger production) are often available only in specialist shops. Only a few are really widely stocked.

The reason is that the British wine trade still cannot bring itself to take English and Welsh wine seriously. This means that consumers are not given the chance to buy bottles of home-produced wines: it is the same attitude that assumed until a few years ago that only the French knew how to cook, so how could we accept the idea of British cooking? Well, that attitude has changed as more and more restaurants have taken up the theme of British food. We reckon it's about time our wines got a similar chance, too.

A word of warning

There are many wines around that describe themselves as British. For those who have never tasted them, we would point out that 'British wines' are not the same as English and Welsh wines which are the subject of this section. 'British wines' are made from concentrated grape must imported into this country, to which is added British water. The resulting combination is best left undescribed.

There is also another category of wine made in this country, which derives from a long and honourable tradition. Called Country Wines, these are the commercial equivalent of home-made wines – damson, elderflower and the like. Some achieve high quality and shouldn't be dismissed as the source of instant headaches. Again, though, they should not be confused with wines made in this country from grapes grown here.

English and Welsh vintages

1986 After a wet, cold summer, sunshine in September and October did much to improve the final quality of wines, although quantity is down on 1985. The wines are attractive to drink now, but should last into the autumn of 1988.

1985 Could almost have been a disaster with a cold, wet summer. But the harvest was again saved by a dry September and October. Although the quantity was down by a third on 1984, the wines from the good vineyards are excellent, crisp and full of summery acidity, as English wine should be. They should be drunk now.

1984 A very good harvest of 1.5 million bottles with every vineyard making some of the best wines they've ever made. Some bottles may still be very attractive in a mature way but should certainly be drunk soon.

Not all English and Welsh wines carry a vintage indication, and may be a blend of two years – rarely more. They will probably be dominated by the most recent vintage, so should be drunk accordingly.

What's what in England and Wales

The Seal of Quality system is run by the English Vineyards Association. Wines which bear the Seal are those which have been submitted for testing in the early part of the summer following the vintage. It's a voluntary system and lack of Seal doesn't necessarily reflect on the quality of the wine.

The grapes

Nearly all English and Welsh vineyards are planted with strains of vine developed in Germany for northerly vineyards. Many actually produce better wine in Britain because the ripening season is long and slow and this brings out their flavours without a loss of acidity.

Many English and Welsh wines are blends of one or more of the following grapes and simply go under a brand name and a description of 'dry' or 'medium'.

White grapes

Bacchus Can be very flowery and fragrant, but also rather sharp.

Gutenborner Neutral-tasting grape giving comparatively fat wines.

Huxelrebe Can be honeyed and muscat-like in good years with firm acidity.

Madeleine Angevine A table grape which has adapted to producing slightly honeyed wines.

Müller-Thurgau The German workhorse grape has been galloping round England as well. It's the most widely planted vine and makes medium-bodied wines of good acidity with a taste reminiscent of blackcurrants.

Ortega An early-ripening variety with a very perfumed flavour, often quite full.

Reichensteiner A neutral grape variety, widely planted, with a hint of honey and ripe fruit.

Schönburger One of the most successful grapes produced in England. Gives a spicy, fruity wine with good balancing acidity. Hints of Muscat and Gewürztraminer in the taste.

Seyval Blanc A hybrid vine (which can be grown in England but not in Europe where hybrids are banned – Britain is still regarded as an experimental vineyard by the EEC). Neutral, light, slightly spicy wines. Will probably disappear when English vineyards are classified under their own appellation contrôlée system.

Red grapes

Triomphe d'Alsace A variety which originates – as its name suggests – in Alsace, but is now little seen there.

Wrotham Pinot A variation of Pinot Noir which was developed in England.

Who's who in England and Wales

Here we give a selection of vineyards with a reliable record and whose wines are distributed beyond the vineyard gate.

The English Vineyards Association publishes a list of vineyards open to the public (38 West Park, London SE9; tel: 01-857 0452; a stamped, addressed envelope must be sent).

Adgestone Wines on the dry side from Müller-Thurgau, Reichensteiner and Seyval Blanc grapes.
English Wine Centre; Gerard Harris; Tanners Wines; Victoria Wine Co (to order)

Barton Manor Medium dry and dry wines, usually blended.
D Byrne; John Harvey & Sons

Biddenden Müller-Thurgau, Reichensteiner and Ortega, plus a rosé from Pinot Noir grapes.
English Wine Centre; English Wine Shop; Fine English Wines (Ashfield Grange, 2 Station Road, Copmanthorpe, York); J Sainsbury; Victoria Wine Co (to order)

Bruisyard St Peter Medium dry wines from Müller-Thurgau. Also a good dry wine. Widely distributed.
Barwell & Jones; English Wine Centre; Majestic Wine Warehouses; Victoria Wine Co; Willoughbys

Carr-Taylor The vineyard that's sold in Fauchon in Paris. Gutenborner, Huxelrebe, Kerner and Reichensteiner grapes all go to make a blended wine.
Peter Dominic; English Wine Shop; English Wine Centre; Fine English Wines (see Biddenden for address); Waitrose

Cavendish Manor Dry wines from Müller-Thurgau grapes.
Bentalls of Kingston, Surrey

Chalkhill Dry wine from Bacchus grapes.
Lockes; C A Rookes; William Rush

Chilford Hundred Müller-Thurgau, Huxelrebe, Schönburger, Ortega, making a dry wine.
Peter Dominic

Chilsdown Müller-Thurgau, Reichensteiner, Seyval Blanc. Full wines in a dry style.
Chaplin & Son; English Wine Centre

Hambledon The first modern vineyard to be planted. Chardonnay, Pinot Noir and Seyval Blanc.
Fortnum & Mason; Harrods

Highwaymans Make a blended medium dry from Huxelrebe and Müller-Thurgau under the brand name St Edmund.
Tesco

Ightham Müller-Thurgau, Reichensteiner, Huxelrebe, Schönburger. Good Müller-Thurgau wine.
Partridges (133 Sloane Street, London SW1)

Lamberhurst The biggest vineyard with the most widely distributed wines. Always high quality.
Peter Dominic; English Wine Centre; Gerard Harris; Victoria Wine Co (to order)

Pilton Manor Müller-Thurgau and Seyval Blanc and a Champagne method sparkling wine.
English Wine Centre

St George's Wine sold in Japan and the House of Commons. Müller-Thurgau and Gewürztraminer.
Ellis Son & Vidler; English Wine Centre; Findlater Mackie Todd

Staplecombe Madeleine Angevine.
A & A Wines (Smithbrook Kilns, nr Cranleigh, Surrey)

Tenterden Müller-Thurgau, Gutenborner. Use the name Spots Farm.
English Wine Centre; Arthur Rackhams; Selfridges

Three Choirs Large vineyard with Müller-Thurgau and Reichensteiner.
H Allen Smith; English Wine Centre; English Wine Shop; Majestic Wine Warehouses; Tanners Wines; Whynot Wine Warehouses

Wootton Schönburger, Müller-Thurgau and Seyval Blanc. Good quality and long established (by English standards).
David Baillie Vintners; Bow Wine Vaults; Gerard Harris; Victoria Wine Co (to order)

Best buys from England and Wales

Bruisyard St Peter 1986, Seyval/Müller-Thurgau (*Willoughbys*)
Chalkhill Bacchus (*Lockes; C A Rookes; William Rush*)
Ightham 1984, Müller-Thurgau (*from the vineyard only – see address on page 571*)
Pulham Magdalen 1985, Rivaner (*Adnams; G E Bromley; Martinez Fine Wines*)
Michaelmas House Dry 1984 (*English Wine Shop*)
St Edmund Medium Dry (*Tesco*)

Specialist stockists

Curzon Wine Co; Ellis Son & Vidler; English Wine Centre; English Wine Shop; Fortnum and Mason; Hicks & Don; Nobody Inn; Tanners Wines

France

CHAMPAGNE

ALSACE

CHABLIS

LOIRE

BURGUNDY

Touraine

Pouilly–
sur–Loire

Côte de Nuits

Sancerre

Quincy

Côte de
Beaune

JURA

Muscadet

Reuilly

Mâconnais

Anjou et
Saumur

Haut
Poitou

BEAUJOLAIS

St Pourçain

Roannaises

Bugey

SAVOIE

BORDEAUX

NORTHERN
RHÔNE

Monbazillac

Clairette
de Die

Bergerac

Duras

Lot

Tricastin

SOUTHERN
RHÔNE

SOUTH
WEST
FRANCE

Cahors

Marcillac

Beaumes
de Venise

Buzet

Gaillac

Costières du Gard

Ventoux

Madiran

Languedoc

THE MIDI

Lubéron

Provence

Irouléguy

Garonne

Minervois

Jurançon

Corbières

Cassis

Bandol

Fitou

Roussillon

Seine

Merne

Loire

Saône

Rhône

0   100   200 km

0   50   100 miles

France

ALSACE

Luck with the harvests

Alsace has been very lucky in the last four years. There have been two
'vintages of the century' in 1983 and 1985 (well, the French do like to
exaggerate these things, but they were both very fine years), and one
good large vintage of decent quality (1986). Even the odd man out
(1984) has filled the gap before the 1985 wines are ready, with
attractive, if slightly more acid, wines.

A couple of years ago, we would have had to write: well, what are
you waiting for – get out to the shops and buy some of these delicious
wines. But we don't need to do that any more: sales of Alsace wines
went up by 45 per cent in 1985.

Much of this increase was due to the fact that we were buying the
1983 wines – and happily coming back for more. Much of what we
bought was the simple, clean fruit of the Pinot Blanc wines, which
have become staple wine bar and aperitif fare. But we are also buying
more of the top estate wines, from small growers who wouldn't have
thought about sending their wines to Britain a few years ago, because
there was no demand.

Now there is, and we can discover in Alsace that there is a
fascinating range of quality, not only from village to village, but also
from producer to producer. Style – some make drier, lighter wines,
others make richer wines – is as relevant to Alsace as it is to, say, the
vineyards of Sancerre on the Loire. But, like Sancerre, there is also an
overall style in Alsace that makes its wines some of the most easily
recognisable (and none the worse for that).

That is because Alsace uses Germanic grapes (on the whole – Pinot
Blanc is an exception), but vinifies them dry so that you get a French
approach and philosophy applied to German raw materials. In true
European spirit (after all Strasbourg, the capital of Alsace, is home to
the European Parliament), the combination works.

Good value – but not cheap

Alsace wines will never be cheap and cheerful. For one thing, the
French themselves drink nearly half of what is made, the Germans take
an awful lot more, so the Alsace growers don't need to discount their
prices to get regular sales.

But what they offer at the moment is value for money. And that covers the full range of quality. That range has extended widely in the last few years. At the cheaper end, the supermarkets have come up with some jolly good wines at around £3 a bottle. At the top end, the Vendange Tardive and Grand Cru wines (see below for both) are showing that Alsace doesn't just produce middle of the road wines, but some great wines as well.

Maturity and reliability

It's these greater wines that reveal a hitherto unrealised aspect of Alsace wines: they age. That's true especially of wines made from the Riesling, the Gewürztraminer and the Tokay Pinot Gris (see below for grape varieties). Wines made from the Riesling, for example, in the superb 1976 vintage, are now perfectly mature, smelling and tasting petrolly (that's a good characteristic in Alsace), still retaining much of their fresh fruit but in a mature way.

One of the attractions about Alsace is that you will almost never find a bad bottle. Controls are probably some of the tightest in France: all the bottling has to be done in Alsace itself where the local officials can keep an eye on what's going on, so the reliability is good.

The language of Alsace

Alsace is the only region of France where the wine is labelled varietally – that is, it will be called after the name of the grape from which it is made. Until very recently, there was only one appellation for the whole region. But then the Alsatians got ideas and thought they would sell wines from some of their top vineyards as Alsace Grand Cru, on the Burgundian model. There's no denying that some of these Grand Cru wines (first made with the 1983 vintage) are top quality wines, but where does it leave the other wines? Now – when we're just discovering Alsace properly – is not the time to confuse us.

Wine politics has entered the argument about Grand Cru. The merchants, who have made their name by buying grapes from different parts of Alsace and doing their own blending, are against the idea. The growers, those who own land in Grand Cru vineyards, that is, are all for it. For consumers, it does add, at one and the same time – a possibility of confusion and an extra element of quality.

At the moment there are 23 approved Grand Cru vineyards and 17 which are using the name but haven't received official approval. Only the top four grape varieties – Gewürztraminer, Tokay Pinot Gris, Muscat and Riesling – are permitted for Grand Cru wines. It is possible to make Grand Cru wines from a number of different Grand Cru vineyards, in which case the name of the vineyards will not be specified on the label. But if the wine is all from one vineyard, the label will carry the name of that site.

Crémant d'Alsace This is the name for all sparkling wine in Alsace. It is made by the Champagne method and much of it is very good. Look for Cuvée Dopff (*Hungerford Wine Company*) or Louis Gisselbrecht (*Christopher Piper Wines*).

Edelzwicker A relatively cheap blend of two or more of the permitted grape varieties (see below). More widely seen in Alsace than outside.

Réserve spéciale, Sélection spéciale, Cuvée spéciale Fancy names which may mean a top cuvée from a producer – or just fancy prices.

Sélection de grains nobles An official category since 1983 describing wine made using grapes infected with noble rot.

Vendange Tardive Late-picked grapes with a higher, more concentrated sugar content. The resultant wines can be sweet or dry. Quality is good – and the price high.

The grapes of Alsace

Gewürztraminer Heavily spicy, perfumed grape variety that made its name in Alsace before spreading elsewhere in the world. Can be a little cloying and unsubtle, but is the easiest wine to spot with your eyes shut.

Muscat Muscat à Petits Grains makes full-bodied, honey-smelling wines. Muscat Ottonel makes lighter wines, and both will be dry. A blend of the two grape varieties is often the best.

Pinot blanc Simple, fruity wines, with just a hint of Chardonnay; to be drunk young. The vineyard area has increased, owing to greater demand.

Pinot noir Some rosé or pale red wines are made in Alsace. They don't leave the region and most shouldn't, although a couple of producers (Hugel among them) are trying some wood-ageing with success.

Riesling The finest wines in Alsace are made from this grape – full but elegant, often steely dry but always giving off perfumed fruit. Quality varies from not bad to very good indeed – prices indicate the range.

Sylvaner Rather dull wines, but in cool years have pleasant, straightforward acidity. Often attractive with a slight prickle.

Tokay Pinot Gris Used to be called Tokay d'Alsace (and still is unofficially) until the EEC thought everyone would confuse the name with the Tokay of Hungary and banned its use. It produces rich, dry, peppery wines, sometimes lacking in acidity, but making up for it in the full body. An underrated grape variety.

The Alsace vintages

1986 A lighter vintage than either 1983 or 1985, producing easy-to-drink wines which should be ready to drink in some cases before 1985 wines. Good quantity, too.

1985 Widely acclaimed as an exceptional vintage. The wines are fine, excellently balanced, with richness but also elegance. The most successful varieties have been Gewürztraminer and Pinot Gris. Large quantities of Vendange Tardive and Sélection de Grains Nobles were made. Apart from high quality, the crop was down by 20 per cent of a normal year.

1984 Not a success, with wines lacking body and high in acidity, that should be drunk up now as stop-gap wines.

1983 Another great vintage, with very full wines, possibly lacking acidity but certainly not alcohol. Rieslings are delicious but will keep for many years. The Gewürztraminer is highly spiced and Pinot Gris is also rich and delicious, but drink them both straight away.

1982 Rieslings and Vendange Tardive wines are the only ones worth drinking now. Others will be tired.

1978 Top Rieslings are still good, as are some Gewürztraminers. Other wines should mostly have been consumed, although some exceptional bottles will last a few years yet.

1976 Still a few miraculous Vendange Tardive Rieslings, which will still keep. A few good Rieslings, Tokay Pinot Gris and Gewürztraminers to be drunk now.

Who's who in Alsace

The Alsace wine trade is divided into growers, some of whom also bottle and export – but only using wines from their own vineyards; and merchants who, as in Burgundy, may own vineyards but also buy in wines. Much of the production also goes through co-operatives, some of a good standard, such as those at Eguisheim and Turckheim, who are supplying much of the wine bought for supermarket brands.

Caves J Becker, Zellenberg Long-established firm, now run by a young brother and sister. One-third of production comes from their own land. Wines: Pinot Blanc, Riesling Hagenschlaff, Tokay Pinot Gris Sonnenglanz.
Mayor Sworder; Le Nez Rouge/Berkmann Wine Cellars

Léon Beyer, Eguisheim Merchant selling full-bodied, very dry wines which can last for years. Also owns vineyards. Wines: Riesling Cuvée des Ecaillers, Gewürztraminer Cuvée des Comtes.
Curzon Wine Company; T & W Wines

Blanck, Kientzheim High quality grower making wines with good ageing potential.
Lay & Wheeler

E Boeckel, Mittelbergheim Long-established grower and merchant making wines in a traditional style. Wines: Zotzenberg Sylvaner, Riesling and Gewürztraminer, Brandluft and Wibelsberg Rieslings, Ch d'Issembourg Gewürztraminer.
Tanners Wines

Dopff au Moulin, Riquewihr Merchant who also has a large vineyard holding in the best wine-growing area, central Alsace. Wines from Schoenenburg (Riesling) and Turckheim (Gewürztraminer) vineyards, Fruits de Mer blend, Crémant d'Alsace sparkling.
Fortnum & Mason

Dopff et Irion, Riquewihr Growers and merchants who have been around for three centuries. Wines: Riesling les Murailles, Gewürztraminer les Sorcières, Muscat les Amandiers, Pinot Gris les Maquisards, branded Crustaces and Crystal, Crémant d'Alsace.
Eldridge Pope; Reynier Wine Libraries

Théo Faller, Kaysersberg One of the top growers, making superb wines from the Clos des Capucins vineyard. Small production, high prices. Wines: Cuvée Théo (Riesling and Gewürztraminer), Vendanges Tardives, Domaine Weinbach.
Fine Vintage Wines; O W Loeb; Raeburn Fine Wines & Foods; La Réserve

Louis Gisselbrecht, Dambach-la-Ville Small vineyard holding and négociant business making some reliable wines. Best are the Rieslings. Wines: Riesling, Gewürztraminer, Pinot Blanc.
Hicks & Don; Hungerford Wine Company; Christopher Piper Wines

Willy Gisselbrecht, Dambach-la-Ville Négociant and grower with a large vineyard holding in Dambach-la-Ville.
Martinez Fine Wines

Hugel et Fils, Riquewihr Most famous – because best at publicity – house in Alsace. Growers and négociants. Their wines tend to be rounder, less dry than others in Alsace. They developed the idea of Vendange Tardive wines. Wines: those from the Schoenenburg and Sporen vineyards; Cuvée Personnelle and Vendange Tardive are top wines; brands are Flambeau d'Alsace, Fleur d'Alsace.
Berry Bros & Rudd; Peter Dominic

Kientzler, Ribeauvillé Grower with land in Grand Cru vineyards around Ribeauvillé. Wines: Grand Cru Geisberg, Grand Cru Kirchberg de Ribeauvillé.
L'Alsacien

Marc Kreydenweiss, Andlau High quality grower and négociant (married to Catherine Lacoste – see below) in the northern Alsace vineyards, including the Domaine Fernand Gresser. Wines: Riesling, Grand Cru Moenchberg, Gewürztraminer, Muscat, Pinot Noir.
L'Alsacien

Kuehn, Ammerschwihr Grower and merchant now owned by, but separate from, a co-operative. Traditional style. Wines: Charme d'Alsace.
Julian Flook (Felix Road, Easton, Bristol)

Kuentz-Bas, Husseren-les-Châteaux Small family house making excellent wines. Wines: Riesling, Gewürztraminer, Muscat, Pinot Blanc, Pinot Gris.
Berry Bros & Rudd; Oddbins

Catherine Lacoste, Andlau Grower (married to Marc Kreydenweiss – see above) in northern Alsace vineyards who produces very good Tokay Pinot Gris. Wines: Pinot Gris, Grand Cru Kastelberg.
L'Alsacien

Michel Laugel, Marlenheim Négociant and grower in the most northerly of Alsace wine villages. Wines: Riesling de Wolxheim, Pinot Rosé de Marlenheim, Gewürztraminer de Wangen.
Bottoms Up; Peter Dominic

Gustave Lorentz, Bergheim Large firm of growers and négociants. Very good Gewürztraminer. Wines: Altenberg, Kanzlerberg vineyards are top crus.
Harrods; Thresher

Jos Meyer, Wintzenheim Grower and négociant making Grand Cru and good Gewürztraminer and Riesling wines from local vineyards. Wines: Gewürztraminer Les Archenets, Riesling, Pinot Blanc, Vendange Tardive wines.
Augustus Barnett (Head Office: North Woolwich Road, Silvertown, London E16 – 700 branches nationwide)

A & O Muré, Rouffach Three-centuries-old firm making intense, smooth wines from a single vineyard. Wines to keep. Wines: Clos St-Landelin.
Alex Findlater

Preiss-Henny, Mittelwihr Grower and négociant with land around Colmar and Riquewihr. Wines: Cuvée Marcel Preiss, Cuvée Camille Preiss.
L'Alsacien

Jean Preiss-Zimmer, Riquewihr Top Rieslings and Gewürztraminers.
Victoria Wine Co

Domaine Ostertag, Epfig Grower making a fine Riesling and Gewürztraminer. Wines: Tokay Pinot Gris, Riesling, Gewürztraminer.
L'Alsacien; Morris & Verdin

Schlumberger, Guebwiller The biggest domaine in Alsace, based in the southern end of Alsace. Firm, concentrated wines of high quality. Wines: Kitterlé vineyard, Gewürztraminer Cuvée Christine Schlumberger.
Alex Findlater; Partridges (132–134 Sloane Street, London SW1); David Scatchard; La Vigneronne; Winecellars

Sick-Dreyer, Ammerschwihr Clean, straightforward domaine wines for early drinking. Wines: Riesling and Gewürztraminer from Kaefferkopf vineyard.
L'Alsacien; Alston Wines

F E Trimbach, Ribeauvillé Family domaine and négociant founded in the 17th century. Fine, lighter style of wine which nevertheless lasts. Wines: Riesling Clos-Ste-Hune, Réserve and Réserve Personnelle wines, Riesling and Gewürztraminer.
Barnes Wine Shop; Berry Bros & Rudd; D Byrne; Green's; Harrods; Oddbins; Yorkshire Fine Wines

Alsace Willm, Barr Best known for Gewürztraminer, but also make good Riesling and Sylvaner. Wines: Grand Cru Gaensbroennel, Riesling Kirchberg de Barr.
L'Alsacien; Christopher & Co

Zind-Humbrecht, Wintzenheim Single vineyard wines made with care from Turckheim, Wintzenheim, Thann. Wines: Thann Clos St-Urbain (Riesling), Turckheim Brand (Riesling), Turckheim Herrenweg (Gewürztraminer).
L'Alsacien; Laytons

Best buys from Alsace

Tokay d'Alsace 1985, Cave Vinicole de Turckheim (*Barnes Wine Shop; The Market/Winecellars*)
Tokay Pinot Gris 1985, Adam (*The Wine Spot*)
Muscat d'Alsace 1983, Cuvée Réserve, Cave Vinicole de Turckheim (*Eaton Elliot Winebrokers*)
Pinot Blanc, Cave Vinicole de Turckheim (*Broad Street Wine Co; Cadwgan Fine Wines*)
Alsace Riesling 1985, Wiederhirn (*High Breck Vintners*)
Pinot d'Alsace 1985, Caves St-Hippolyte (*Majestic Wine Warehouses*)
Alsace Pinot Blanc 1984, Ostertag (*Morris & Verdin*)
Riesling 1985, Catherine Lacoste (*La Vigneronne/L'Alsacien*)

Specialist stockists

*Bibendum; Broad Street Wine Company; D Bryne; Eldridge Pope;
Farthinghoe Fine Wine & Food; Alex Findlater; Peter Green; J E Hogg;
Lay & Wheeler; O W Loeb; Raeburn Fine Wines and Foods;
Henry Townsend; La Vigneronne/L'Alsacien; The Wine Society*

BEAUJOLAIS

Old Nouveau

The date is mid-June 1987, the place London. And as we sit down to
dinner one evening, our chosen wine is two quarter-bottles of
Beaujolais Nouveau 1986, courtesy Air France, from one of the most
respected négociant houses in the Beaujolais.

Why on earth ruin a good meal with wine bottled eight months
earlier for immediate consumption which, by now, must be tasting
distinctly old and tired? Because we wanted to prove the contrary.

And we did. Those two screw-cap bottles contained some super,
simple, still fresh and lively, cherry-like Gamay fruit, tasting better in
many ways than other bottles of the same wine had tasted when drunk
on the flight from France back in December 1986.

Which all goes to prove that Beaujolais Nouveau doesn't have to be
drunk by Christmas but that it will go on well into the next year. And it
shows that in years like 1986, when the Nouveau tasted in November
was distinctly hard and not the easy drink we have come to expect, a
certain amount of time in bottle is probably a good thing.

Not that we want to take the fun out of Beaujolais Nouveau. The
arrival of the marvellous 1985 Nouveau gave us some of the most
enjoyable drinking that year, simply because the wine was so full of
fruit. But it doesn't always happen: in some years even the skills of the
producers back in the hills of the Beaujolais can't quite get the Gamay
to give of its best within six weeks of harvesting.

The best value for money in Beaujolais is certainly Nouveau,
whether drunk in November or the following year. Bottles at £1.99 are
still seen, despite the fall in the pound against the French franc, and
come the following summer any stock left will certainly be on special
offer and worth a try.

Further up the scale of Beaujolais (see below for classifications),
though, things aren't much different. For more serious but still
easy-drinking wine, there's little to beat Beaujolais-Villages. And some
of the wines from the top crus are amazing value (see below for those
which are and those which aren't).

These top wines do age well, and need the respect of some time in
bottle before drinking. Villages wines are normally best left until the
summer after the vintage, while cru wines really don't start giving

everything they've got until at least a year after the harvest. Then those cru wines will last a good four or five years, depending on the vintage. As they mature, they become closer and closer in taste to the Pinot Noir of Burgundy just to the north – meaty, gamey and slightly smoky. It may be a long way from the taste of Nouveau, but it does show the versatility of the Gamay grape in the one place in the world where it really comes into its own.

Where's where in the Beaujolais

Beaujolais classification is divided into three groupings. The basic wine is simply called **Beaujolais** and comes from the southern half of the region. This wine is the basis of most Beaujolais Nouveau and as such is drunk fairly fast. But try it slightly chilled in the summer of the following year for a deliciously fruity drink.

Beaujolais-Villages There are 40 villages in the northern half of the region which are entitled to this appellation. The wine is stronger, has greater depths than ordinary Beaujolais and keeps better. Some is sold as Beaujolais Nouveau, which is a bit of a waste.

Beaujolais crus Nine villages are entitled to their own individual appellations. Their styles vary from quite light to serious wines with some ageing potential. All the villages regard themselves as having individual character.
Brouilly – the lightest and fruitiest style among the crus. Needs to be drunk fairly young.
Chénas – less often seen than some of the crus, but full of flavour and worth keeping.
Chiroubles – another light style, which should be drunk within the year of the harvest. Full of fruit.
Côtes de Brouilly – smallest of the crus making strong wines with some keeping power. They tend to age gracefully.
Fleurie – the most expensive of the cru wines (probably because the name is so attractive). They need to be drunk young. Not worth the money at the moment.
Juliénas – long-lasting wines (for Beaujolais), with a more serious style than other crus.
Morgon – another long-lasting cru. These are the wines which as they age really take on some of the characteristics of Burgundian Pinot Noir.
Moulin-à-Vent – the finest of the crus, the wine of this village will last well and is worth laying down.
St-Amour – soft, easy-drinking wines – as the name might suggest.
(**Régnié** – a cru aspiring to join the ranks of the other nine.)

White Beaujolais
Made from the Chardonnay grape, this normally appears under the Burgundy appellation of St-Véran.

The vintages of Beaujolais

1986 A lean year at first, with some hard, tannic acidity, so the Nouveau was less successful than the 1985. However, the wines have improved and are becoming more attractive. Cru wine should be drunk from early 1988 and will last, Villages wines need consuming before autumn 1988.

1985 A very fine year, compared to 1976, with wines of considerable fruit. The best crus are Fleurie, Juliénas and Côtes de Brouilly. Morgon is disappointing.

1984 Wines with high acidity, most of which should have been drunk by now. Some crus – Morgon, Moulin-à-Vent – are worth keeping.

1983 Longer-lasting cru wines will still be worth keeping. Other crus and Beaujolais-Villages should be drunk by now.

Older vintages 1981, 1978 and 1976 Moulin-à-Vent, Morgon and Côtes de Brouilly are still interesting.

Who's who in Beaujolais

THE GROWERS

Merchants tend to be more important than growers in Beaujolais. Some of the names below are from individual growers, some from merchants.

Brouilly Ch de la Chaize, Ch de Pierreux, Ch de Fouilloux, Domaine de la Combillaty (Duboeuf), Jean Ruet.

Chénas Louis Champagnon, Ch de Chénas, Domaine de la Combe Remont (Georges Duboeuf), Pierre Perrachon, Ch Bonnet, Domaine des Brureaux.

Chiroubles Ch Javernand, Georges Passot, Ch de Raousset, René Brouillard, Dessalle.

Côtes de Brouilly Ch Thivin, Georges Duboeuf, Jean Sanvers.

Fleurie La Madone (Georges Duboeuf), Domaine de la Presle (André Barraud), Ch de Fleurie (Loron), Bernard Paul, Domaine de la Grand' Cour (Jean Dutraive), Chauvet, Caveau de Fleurie, Fernand Verpoix.

Juliénas Duboeuf, Louis Tête, Clos des Poulettes (Loron), Ch des Capitans, Domaine de la Dîme, Domaine de la Vieille Eglise, Ernest Aujas.

Morgon Jacky Janodet, Duboeuf, Ch de Pizay, Domaine de la Chanaise (Piron), Domaine de Ruyère (Paul Collonge), Louis Tête, Jean Descombes, Georges Vincent, Charmes, Aucoeur Noël.

Moulin-à-Vent Ch des Jacques (Duboeuf), Ch du Moulin-à-Vent, Raymond Siffert, Hospices de Romanèche-Thorins, Domaine de la Tour du Bief, Louis Champagnon, Le Vieux Domaine.

St-Amour Loron (Domaine des Billards), Duboeuf, Janin, Ch de St-Amour, Domaine Duc, Elie Mogénie.

Many growers' wines are available from *Roger Harris Wines* (see WHERE TO BUY section).

THE MERCHANTS

Chanut Frères Good quality Beaujolais and Beaujolais-Villages.
Gilbey Wine & Food Company (82–83 High Street, Eton, Berks); Gerard Harris

Joseph Drouhin The only Beaune merchant who takes Beaujolais seriously.
Michael Menzel Wines; Yorkshire Fine Wines

Georges Duboeuf Top quality range, often from individual growers. One of the most reliable names. Also use the Paul Bocuse label.
Widely available

Pierre Ferraud High quality reputation, making good Nouveau and Villages.
Caves de la Madeleine

Sylvain Fessy Good wines at most levels.
Haynes Hanson & Clark; Ian G Howe; Michael Menzel Wines

Loron Sound, fruity wines at all quality levels.
Haynes Hanson & Clark; Hungerford Wine Company; Lay & Wheeler; Tanners Wines

Mommessin Another Burgundy merchant with an interest in Beaujolais, especially of the basic type.
Tanners Wines; Yorkshire Fine Wines

Pasquier-Desvignes Light style of wines, but of good reliable quality. St-Amour is good.
Peter Dominic

Piat Their best claim to fame is the attractive bottle. The wine inside doesn't normally come top in tastings. They also make the branded Piat d'Or which everybody thinks is a Beaujolais but is in fact an ordinary vin de table.
Peter Dominic

Les Producteurs Réunis Excellent co-operative with good basic Beaujolais as well as the crus.
Oddbins

Sarrau Good Nouveau and quality crus and Villages.
Tanners Wines

Louis Tête Serious basic Beaujolais.
Peter Green

Thorin Good wine from Moulin-à-Vent, Ch des Jacques and also Beaujolais Blanc.
Berry Bros & Rudd

Trenel Small firm making good Morgon.
Barwell and Jones

Best buys from Beaujolais

Beaujolais 1986, Ch de Tanay (*Roger Harris*)
Duboeuf Beaujolais (*widely available*)
Moulin-à-Vent 1985, Domaine Labruyère (*J Sainsbury*)
Beaujolais Villages 1985, Domaine des Colombières (*La Réserve*)

Specialist stockists

Anthony Byrne Fine Wines; Roger Harris Wines; Ingletons Wines; Le Nez Rouge/Berkmann Wine Cellars; Nobody Inn; Christopher Piper Wines

BORDEAUX

The firm Number One

Claret – red Bordeaux – is our favourite red wine. It always has been, and it looks like retaining its foremost place in our affections for some considerable time.

Why? There's something about the taste of the wines, certainly, that we find so attractive: the delicate balance between the ripe, blackcurranty fruit of the Cabernet Sauvignon grape or the softer flavour of the Merlot, combined with the firm tannin that softens with age, and the taste of wood. The whole combination is tempered by the cool Atlantic breezes which blow into Bordeaux even in the hottest summers, allowing long ripening seasons to increase the intensity and complexity of flavours.

Just a minute, we hear you cry. How can we poor Brits, with our pound in free fall against the French franc, ever afford to buy claret? We hear prices like £100 a bottle or more quoted for some of the famous châteaux. That's not real, not for any sensible wine drinking.

The tip of the iceberg

What we often forget, in all the hype about top clarets and how much they cost, is that the classed growths – the famous names – represent no more than two or three per cent of Bordeaux's wine production. The other 97 to 98 per cent ranges from crus bourgeois at the level just below the classed growths, down to the simplest Bordeaux made out in the sticks as far from St-Emilion or the Médoc as basic Sauternes is from Ch d'Yquem.

A lot of this wine is inferior stuff: Bordeaux can come up with some pretty dire offerings, but, as far as we in this country are concerned, much of this wine is very attractive, full of fruit, well made, not too awesome – and very good value for money.

The wines continue to be good value for money, despite the pantomime that goes on above their heads in the world of classed growths. While the classed growths – and, we must admit, some of the better-known bourgeois growths – can put up their prices by as much as 50 per cent a year (which is what they did in 1984 and 1985), the ordinary producer of AC Bordeaux is lucky if he can increase his prices at all, especially in a world swimming in wine and continuing to demand much more white than red.

This is good news for us, even if it doesn't help the producer of what is called, sometimes pejoratively, petit château wine. On the other hand, of course, with the teeming numbers of small estates and unknown labels coming out of Bordeaux, how can one tell which are good and which are bad?

Well, this is precisely the role a good wine merchant is there to perform. At the end of this section, we list a number of merchants who specialise in Bordeaux (more information about them will be found in the WHERE TO BUY section). But almost any wine merchant in this Guide will have found some reasonably cheap, and reasonably drinkable, red Bordeaux to add to his list. We also suggest some names of our own – these will be found towards the end of this section. But with over 4,000 properties in the Bordeaux wine area – which, incidentally, is the largest concentration of vineyards in the world – we're bound to miss more than a few.

To give some more guidance, we've included a glossary of Bordeaux names, and an explanation of the way the vineyards are organised.

Glitzy, pricey claret

But first, a word about prices at the top end of the claret market. Bordeaux has been blessed in the past decade with a run of very fine vintages. In this succession of successes, only 1977 stood out as really inferior, while 1980 and 1984 – generally dismissed – have come up with some good early-drinking wines with which to keep our thirst quenched while we wait for the great wines of the other years.

At the same time, the Bordelais have learnt to make more wine. They've improved the clones of the vines in the vineyard, they've bought new sprays to keep down rot, they've taken advice from top

Bordeaux

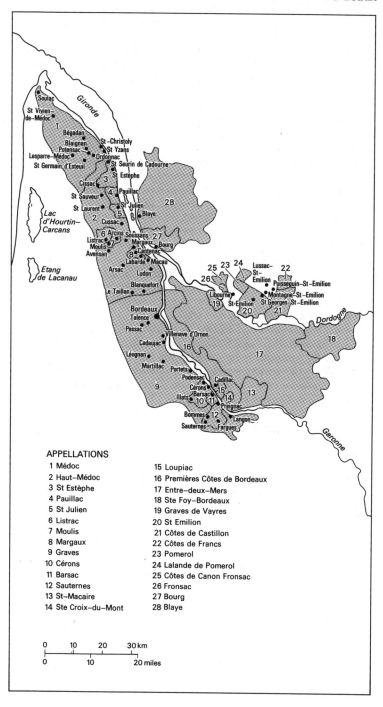

APPELLATIONS

1 Médoc
2 Haut–Médoc
3 St Estèphe
4 Pauillac
5 St Julien
6 Listrac
7 Moulis
8 Margaux
9 Graves
10 Cérons
11 Barsac
12 Sauternes
13 St–Macaire
14 Ste Croix–du–Mont

15 Loupiac
16 Premières Côtes de Bordeaux
17 Entre–deux–Mers
18 Ste Foy–Bordeaux
19 Graves de Vayres
20 St Emilion
21 Côtes de Castillon
22 Côtes de Francs
23 Pomerol
24 Lalande de Pomerol
25 Côtes de Canon Fronsac
26 Fronsac
27 Bourg
28 Blaye

0   10   20   30 km

0   10   20 miles

Bordeaux oenology professors, and they've installed new equipment in their *chais* (cellars).

So we have the spectacle of a series of good vintages, producing more and more wine. By any law of supply and demand, and during a time of increasing interest in white wine at the expense of red, prices of red Bordeaux should be falling. Not a bit of it – not at the top end, anyway, and by the spring of 1986 it looked as though British wine merchants had realised that enough was enough. Some were refusing to buy 1986 wine until they had watched the market carefully over a number of months, others were buying only a few wines – not the most famous names – which tasted good and weren't too expensive.

The Americans, too, have pulled in their horns. After causing the massive price rises in the first place, they seem to have left the field in a shambles, taking their business elsewhere, as the dollar, like the pound, loses value against the French franc.

In the French domestic market – which takes 40 per cent of red Bordeaux – resistance was building up while merchants struggled to sell unwanted 1984 and 1985 wines.

Some château owners realised their dilemma, and by the time 1986 prices were announced – in May and June 1986 – prices were falling by up to 20 per cent. The top châteaux's prices were still ridiculously high, of course, but at least they had reached a plateau.

What Bordeaux would like, now, is a lousy 1987 vintage with a small crop. That way, they hope, demand might again outstrip supply. But even with a small crop in 1987, the stock in Bordeaux will be the equivalent of 26 months' supply. It would take more than one bad vintage to set the balance right – and that, with new methods, just doesn't happen any more.

The taste of Bordeaux

The reds

Claret (red Bordeaux) is a blended wine, containing varying proportions of Cabernet Sauvignon, Cabernet Franc and Merlot. Two lesser varieties (in importance) that are planted increasingly rarely are Petit Verdot and Malbec.

Cabernet Sauvignon Small, thick-skinned berries yielding a deeply coloured, tannic wine, not high in alcohol, but with a dense, complex aroma which evokes the words 'blackcurrant' when young, 'cedar' when older. Subtle, spicy, without doubt the most versatile and important red grape variety in the world.

Cabernet Franc Lower tannin than the Cabernet Sauvignon; gives a fresh, faster-maturing wine which when blended takes the hard edges off the Cabernet Sauvignon.

Merlot Soft, less woody than Cabernet Sauvignon, it makes wines which are fuller, richer, riper. Less complex wines are normally the result, although in St-Emilion and Pomerol it can attain great heights.

The character of red Bordeaux will reflect the proportions of the different grapes in the blend. The choice of the proportions will depend on the soil (so that St-Emilion suits Merlot, the Médoc suits Cabernet Sauvignon) and on the style the château owner wants to create.

The whites

Sémillon Used for sweet wines, this grape produces the luscious, honeyed style of Sauternes and Barsac, with great ageing ability derived from the noble rot (see under The sweet whites of Bordeaux below). In dry whites, it tends to fatness and flabbiness unless treated with care.

Sauvignon The great white grape of the Loire. In Bordeaux, it makes wines which have a crispness and a freshness when young, but which do not age well. A little Sauvignon in some of the sweet whites adds firmness.

The Bordeaux vineyard

The vineyards of Bordeaux spread in all directions from the city of Bordeaux. The most basic wine of the whole region (white as well as red) has an appellation of either Bordeaux or, marginally better (for reds only), Bordeaux Supérieur. But each part of the region also has its own series of separate appellations for the better wines.

These better wines don't just include the top few names. Many small châteaux can claim the same appellation as a first growth: although there will be massive differences in quality, it will mean that both wines share the same basic characteristics, have achieved at least the same maximum yield of grapes per hectare and have passed a tasting test.

The reds of Bordeaux

THE LEFT BANK

To the north of Bordeaux is the Médoc, on a strip of gravelly soil which hugs the left bank of the River Gironde. Wines from this area can have the following appellations:

Médoc This normally refers to wines from the northernmost end of the region, where instead of top quality gravelly soil the land is mainly clay. Formerly almost completely ignored by wine buyers in this country, this is now the home of many up and coming petits châteaux – an area to watch.

Haut-Médoc The term geographically refers to the rest of the Médoc as far as the northern edge of the city of Bordeaux. In wine terms, châteaux using this appellation will generally be further away from the river than the principal Médoc vineyards. In practice, most of this area is covered by one of the village appellations. Villages without their own appellations include: St-Seurin-de Cadourne, Cissac, St-Saveur, St-Laurent, Ludon.

St-Estèphe The northernmost of the great Médoc villages. The wines tend to be sturdier, darker in colour, more tannic than other Haut-Médoc wines.

Pauillac The most famous village appellation because it contains three of the five first growths (Lafite, Latour, Mouton-Rothschild). The wines are intense, full, firm and tannic with the greatest ageing potential. Words like 'blackcurrant' are used to describe the young wines; mature, they can offer some of the greatest wine experiences anywhere – if you can afford them.

St-Julien Elegant, softer, rounder and a little earlier-maturing than Pauillac. The (predominantly male) wine trade sometimes describes them as 'feminine'.

Margaux The perfumed bouquet of a good Margaux is one of its main characteristics. Less concentrated than, for example, a Pauillac, the wines have immense charm, finesse and breeding.

Moulis and Listrac Two smaller appellations in the hinterland of the Haut-Médoc. Less well known and therefore less expensive, making more austere wines but also some wines with class.

To the south of Bordeaux, white wines take over (see the next page). However, the **Graves** vineyards also produce some excellent reds, including one of the first growths, Ch Haut-Brion, and a clutch of almost equally fine châteaux in the southern suburbs of the city. This is a good source of cheaper claret, much of it old-fashioned and tannic in style, some more modern and bursting with fruit.

THE RIGHT BANK

St-Emilion While in the Médoc the Cabernet Sauvignon is king, in St-Emilion on the north bank of the Dordogne it's the Merlot. Soft, plummy, lush wines, these mature more quickly than Médoc wines, taste riper and slightly sweeter, and demand less absolutely serious attention.

Pomerol Next door to St-Emilion, but making wines with much greater intensity and strength. A tiny production from a small vineyard area ensures that even the humblest wines from this appellation are expensive, while Ch Pétrus, at the top, is the most expensive wine in the world.

Côtes de Castillon and Côtes de Francs Two small areas to the east of St-Emilion which make some delicious, easy-drinking wines, mainly from Merlot and Cabernet Franc. Try them if you come across them.

Fronsac A couple of miles west of Pomerol, this area is producing some really exciting wines, still at lowish prices. They have the smoothness of St-Emilion with the intensity of Pomerol. There is also a smaller, slightly superior appellation of Canon-Fronsac. Both are worth looking for.

Côtes de Bourg This is the area facing the Médoc on the north bank of the Gironde. It's a large area with vineyards stretching well back from the river. The best are on the river front itself, but there are smaller châteaux in the hinterland which make good bargains.

Premières Côtes de Blaye A smaller area attached to Côtes de Bourg. Somewhat more refined than the average Bourg wine, they are also more expensive, but still acceptable value.

BETWEEN THE TWO RIVERS

Much of the vineyard area between the Garonne and Dordogne rivers is the source of white wine and some basic Bordeaux and Bordeaux Supérieur reds. But along the north bank of the Garonne is the long slope of the Premières Côtes de Bordeaux which makes some decent, simple reds that don't break the bank.

The sweet whites of Bordeaux

Sauternes and Barsac The two great dessert wine areas, carved out of the forests of the Landes, relying on the noble rot – 'pourriture noble' which grows on the grapes in the humid autumn weather – to make intense, luscious, honeyed sweet wines. Under-valued for many years, their prices are beginning to rise, but the experience of drinking them makes it worth paying the prices (especially if you can find half-bottles).

Cadillac, Côtes de Bordeaux, St-Macaire and Cérons Lesser sweet wines for drinking young and well chilled as aperitifs.

Loupiac and St-Croix-du-Mont Somewhere between the two groups in intensity and with some noble rot in good years. Generally best drunk young, but will keep in better years.

The dry whites of Bordeaux

The range in dry whites is as great as in the reds. Some of the top châteaux in the Graves produce a white wine that matures well to deep, rich flavours (Haut-Brion Blanc, Laville-Haut-Brion, Domaine de Chevalier, Malartic-Lagravière, Rahoul, Carbonnieux).

At the bottom end of the scale, dry white can be downright dull, relieved only by flashes of the grassy acidity of Sauvignon. If the name of one of these wines includes 'Cépage Sauvignon' or an equivalent phrase, the latest vintage will be fresh, crisp and fruity – but the wines fade fast.

There are also six dry white appellations:

Bourg and Blaye A whole range of small appellations using the names of Bourg and Blaye make reasonably fragrant, if unexciting, wines.

Entre-Deux-Mers This used to be the home of over-sulphured sweet wines. Now that modern winemaking techniques have done away with some of the sulphur, they've become dry and can be pleasantly fruity, light and crisp. Drink young.

Graves de Vayres Small area of Entre-Deux-Mers producing wines of a similar style.

Graves Broader and fuller than other Bordeaux dry whites. Will often have a higher proportion of Sémillon, giving fatter, oilier wines. Keep no more than a year or two, except the best (see above).

Graves Supérieur A stronger version of a Graves. Sometimes medium dry, so beware if you want a dry wine.

What's on the Bordeaux label

Château Like a brand name, it signifies a commercial entity which also happens to be a vineyard. There doesn't have to be a castle or even much of a house – a cottage would do – and the vineyard can be broken up into separate parcels provided they are all within the same appellation.

Grand Vin Can be used for any wine from Bordeaux Supérieur upwards. No legal significance, but it helps sales.

Négociant Bordeaux merchant who buys wine to blend, as well as holding stocks of fine wines (see below under Names to watch).

Mis/mise en bouteille au château/à la propriété Loose terms: propriété can mean a huge warehouse in Bordeaux owned by the owner of the vineyard or it can mean a cellar on the estate. Bottled at the château may mean bottled on a bottling line hired for the occasion.

Crus bourgeois A local classification of wines which are just under the formal crus classés. Often good-value wines at this level.

Crus classés Médoc wines are classified into the growths – descending from first to fifth. The main classification set down in 1855 still stands. In St-Emilion, the classification runs from Premier Grand Cru Classé, through Grand Cru Classé and Grand Cru to ordinary St-Emilion. The Graves has 13 classified reds and nine whites. Sauternes has 22 classed growths. Pomerol hasn't seen the need to apply the system to itself.

Second wines Many of the top châteaux do not put all their wine from a vintage into the blend for their best wine. Some wine – good, but not the absolute best (often from more youthful vines) – is put aside and sold separately as a second wine. By any other standards, this is still very good. It's not cheap, but it's cheaper than the first wine and gives some idea of what all the fuss is about.

Good second wines to look for are (with the first wine in brackets): Marbuzet (Cos d'Estournel), La Parde de Haut-Bailly (Ch Haut-Bailly), Les Forts de Latour (Ch Latour), Clos du Marquis (Ch Léoville-Las-Cases), Haut-Bages-Averous (Ch Lynch-Bages), Connétable de Talbot (Ch Talbot), Sarget de Gruaud-Larose (Ch Gruaud-Larose), Prieur de Meyney (Ch Meyney), de l'Amiral (Ch Labégorce-Zédé), de Clairefont (Ch Prieuré-Lichine), la Dame de Montrose (Ch Montrose), Moulin-Riche (Ch Léoville-Poyferré).

Many other classified growth and cru bourgeois châteaux sell a second wine; it would be worth asking your merchant what he or she has in stock.

Bordeaux vintages

THE REDS

Despite the recent run of good years, vintages do matter in Bordeaux to the extent that the climate is not reliable. Being near the Atlantic, it can suffer from the continual low fronts that we in Britain enjoy most summers. At the same time, improvements in vineyard hygiene (more spraying against rot when it rains) and better selection of healthy grapes in the cellar, mean that it's rare now to get really bad years, with bad wines as the result. The last time that happened to any great extent was 1977. Now even poor years produce sound wines.

1986 A year which saw yet another fine vintage in many parts of Bordeaux. Large quantities were the order of the year – especially for the right bank Merlot areas like St-Emilion and Pomerol. There, the best wines will come from châteaux which cut the yield ruthlessly – those who didn't will have made watery wines. In the left bank vineyards – the Médoc and the Graves – some wines will be very fine indeed, often initially very tannic, but with intense underlying fruit. A vintage that looks like taking a long time to mature.

1985 The largest red Bordeaux vintage ever. Generally regarded as a very good year, although not hitting the heights of 1982. Those who picked their grapes late made some very fine wines; those who picked earlier after a scorching summer had problems with fermentation in a heat wave. With high quantities some of the wines lack concentration. The finest wines have immense richness, depth of colour and concentration which presage a long, slow maturation. Lesser wines are developing fast.

1984 Generally lack fruit and also the roundness given by the Merlot, which failed to flower in the cold, damp spring. The wines will have a short life (three to ten years) but when made by a reputable château should give some austere pleasure. Prices were initially too high for the quality, but look likely to fall.

1983 One of the two current bargain vintages, overshadowed by the enormous 1982s. Elegant and stylish, with lighter St-Emilion and not too much tannin anywhere. A beautifully balanced year at all levels, with many of the classic claret qualities.

1982 The big ones – in price as well as quality. At the petit château level, some very fine wines were made, and there are some bargains to be had. At the higher levels, prices are high. The wines may not really mature until the turn of the century.

1981 The other bargain vintage (see also 1983). Lean, austere wines, often well structured. Some of the wines are already mature, but it is generally agreed that the best need another eight years to mature, the petit châteaux another three.

1980 Wines to drink now. Soft, without staying power, they have been tasting very good during 1987. Very few will last, though.

1979 Suddenly, everybody expects these wines to go on developing. The petits châteaux and St-Emilions are tasting good now, but will last. The best Médoc wines will go on for another ten years before reaching their peak.

1978 Slow-maturing wines. Most petit château wines are for drinking now and over the next few years, but the top wines will go on and on.

1977 Some good wines in a generally poor year. Only the very best are worth keeping – and then only those chosen with discrimination. Don't buy from this vintage unless the price is good and you've tasted.

1976 Ripe wines that can be slightly watery as well, but good ones are packed with slightly sweet fruit which tastes good now. Keep top Médocs, drink the rest.

1975 A problem year. After great initial enthusiasm, because the power and tannin suggested a long life, nothing has happened. They're still very dry, tannic wines and don't have much underlying fruit. Only the best will open out, the rest will probably just get drier.

1973 Soft wines that need drinking now.

The duty-free allowance for wine obtained in the EEC is 5 litres of still table wine per person *plus* 3 litres of still table wine *or* 3 litres of fortified/ sparkling wine *or* 1½ litres of spirits or liqueurs. (See also page 584.)

1972 A vintage that was generally dismissed. The wines, though, have aged slowly and some are really attractive now, to everyone's surprise.

1971 Going past their best, these wines confounded the pundits who expected great things of them. Stylish, balanced and rather delicate, they won't keep.

1970 This is a year with a great future still ahead of it. Although petits châteaux should be drunk (if they haven't been already), top wines will go on well into the next century.

THE SWEET WHITES

Recent vintages of good sweet white wines are 1986, 1983, 1979 and 1978.

Drink now – or keep?

As a general rule, the higher up the classification scale, the longer a red Bordeaux will keep. So ordinary Bordeaux appellation wine needs drinking first, basic St-Emilion next – and so on up the scale: the top classed growths of the Médoc seem to last decades. The same rule goes for sweet white Sauternes.

Bordeaux names to watch

It is not possible to indicate stockists against Bordeaux châteaux since British merchants do not buy every vintage. In the WHERE TO BUY section we indicate those merchants who have large stocks of Bordeaux and specialise in buying direct from the area. Get their lists and ask their advice as well as looking for some of the names we give below.

Châteaux listed here are enjoying a high reputation at the moment. Additionally, their wines are good value for money.

THE REDS

Bordeaux and Bordeaux Supérieur Ch Méaume, Ch Timberlay, Ch de Belcier, Ch Tour de Mirabeau, Ch la Combe des Dames, Ch le Peuy-Saincrit, Ch Sables-Peytraud, Ch le Gardéra, Ch la Pierrière, Sandeman Claret.

Médoc Ch du Castéra, Ch la Cardonne, Ch Haut-Canteloup, Ch Livran, Ch Loudenne, Ch Patache d'Aux, Ch Potensac, Ch la Tour de By, Ch la Tour St-Bonnet, Ch Greysac, Ch Hanteillan.

Haut-Médoc Ch de Camensac, Ch Cantemerle, Ch la Lagune, Ch Bel-Orme-Tronquoy-de-Lalande, Ch Caronne Ste-Gemme, Ch Cissac, Ch Citran, Ch Coufran, Ch Lamarque, Ch Malescasse, Ch Reysson, Ch La Rose-Trintaudon, Ch Sociando-Mallet, Ch Villegeorge, Cave Co-opérative Fort Médoc, Ch Fonpiqueyre, Ch Barreyres, Ch Lanessan, Ch la Tour Carnet.

St-Estèphe Ch Calon-Ségur, Ch Beau-Site, Ch Haut-Marbuzet,
Ch Tronquoy-Lalande, Ch Cos Labory, Ch le Crock, Ch
Commanderie, Ch Capbern.

Pauillac Ch Clerc-Milon, Ch Duhart-Milon-Rothschild,
Ch Grand-Puy-Lacoste, Ch Haut-Bages-Libéral, Ch Haut-Batailley,
Ch Pontet-Canet, Ch Fonbadet, Ch Pédesclaux.

St-Julien Ch Lagrange, Ch Léoville-Barton, Ch Talbot,
Ch Terrey-Gros-Caillou, Ch St-Pierre-Sevaistre.

Margaux Ch d'Angludet, Ch d'Issan, Ch Labégorce-Zédé,
Ch Lascombes, Ch Monbrison, Ch Pouget, Ch du Tertre,
Ch la Gurgue, Ch Siran, Ch Dauzac, Ch la Mouline-de-Labégorce.

Moulis and Listrac Ch Chasse-Spleen, Ch Fourcas-Dupré,
Ch Maucaillou, Ch Moulin-à-Vent, Ch Dutruch-Grand-Poujeaux,
Ch Fonréaud, Ch Fourcas-Hosten.

Graves Ch Roquetillade la Grange, Ch Rahoul, Ch Graveyron,
Ch de Fieuzal, Ch Haut-Bailly, Ch la Louvière, Ch Malartic-Lagravière,
Ch la Tour-du-Haut-Moulin, Graves Rouge (Pierre Coste),
Ch les Lauriers, Ch Pouyanne, Ch Coucheroy.

St-Emilion Ch Bellevue-Mondotte, Ch Fombrauge, Ch Fonroque,
Ch la Fleur, Ch Monbousquet, Ch Vieux-Sarpe, Ch Puy-Planquet,
Ch Larmande.
   In the sub-appellations (Puisseguin-St-Emilion, Lussac-St-Emilion,
Montagne-St-Emilion, St-Georges-St-Emilion, Parsac-St-Emilion) look
for Ch Belair-Montaiguillon (St-Georges), Ch des Laurets (Puisseguin),
Ch Maison-Blanche (Montagne), Ch Roudier (Montagne),
Ch St-Georges (St-Georges), Ch Vieux-Bonneau (Montagne).

Pomerol Ch Bel-Air, Clos du Clocher, Ch le Gay, Clos René,
Ch Petit-Village, Ch des Annereaux (Lalande de Pomerol), Ch le Bon
Pasteur.

Fronsac and Canon-Fronsac Ch Coustolle, Ch Dalem, Ch Mausse,
Ch Pichelèbre, Ch de la Rivière.

Côtes de Bourg Ch La Croix de Millorit, Ch Lalibarde,
Ch Mille-Secousses.

Côtes de Blaye Ch Bourdieu, Ch Charron, Ch l'Escadre, Ch Segonzac,
Ch Peyraud, Ch les Moines.

Premières Côtes de Bordeaux Ch le Gardéra, Ch Reynon.

Côtes de Castillon, Côtes de Francs Ch de Clotte, Ch Moulin-Rouge,
Ch Pitray, Ch Laclaverie, Ch Puygueraud, Ch de Belcier.

THE SWEET WHITES

Sauternes and Barsac Ch Sigalas-Rabaud, Ch Broustet,
Ch Doisy-Dubroca, Ch Doisy-Védrines, Ch Bastor-Lamontagne,
Ch du Mayne, Ch Roumieu-Lacoste, Ch Coutet, Ch Cantegril
(second wine of Ch Doisy-Daëne), La Chartreuse (second wine of
Ch St-Amand).

OTHER SWEET WHITES

Ch Loubens, Ch de Tastes (both St-Croix-du-Mont), Ch Fayau
(Premières Côtes de Bordeaux).

DRY WHITES

Ch Malartic-Lagravière, Ch Montalivet, Ch Rahoul (all Graves),
Ch Charron (Premières Côtes de Blaye), Le Bordeaux Prestige de Peter
Allan Sichel (Bordeaux), Maître d'Estournel (Bordeaux).

Best buys from Bordeaux

DRY WHITES

Ch Cabannieux 1984, Graves (*Windrush Wines*)
Ch Respide-Medéville 1984, Graves (*Anthony Byrne Fine Wines; Master Cellar Wine Warehouse*)
Grand Vin Sec du Ch Doisy-Daëne 1986 (*Adnams; Tanners Wines*)
Domaine Benoît Blanc 1986, Graves (*Hungerford Wine Co*)

SWEET WINES

Ch Bastor-Lamontagne, Sauternes (*Richard Harvey Wines; Waitrose*)
Ch Cantegrill, Barsac 1983 (*Tanners Wines*)
Ch la Chartreuse 1933, Sauternes (*Morris's Wine Stores*)
Ch Filhot 1981, Sauternes (*J Sainsbury – half bottles*)

REDS

Ch la Cardonne 1983, Bordeaux (*Asda*)
Claret 1984, Réunis Union (*Whynot Wine Warehouses*)
Ch Tourteau Chollet 1983 (*J Sainsbury*)
Ch la Combe des Dames, Bordeaux (*The Wine Society*)
Ch le Peuy-Saincrit 1982, Bordeaux Supérieur (*Hungerford Wine Co*)
Sandeman Claret (*Gough Brothers; Oddbins*)
Ch Sables Peytraud 1985, Bordeaux (*Marks & Spencer*)
Ch Barreyres 1983, Haut-Médoc (*J Sainsbury*)
Ch Roquetaillade la Grange 1978, Graves (*Davisons*)
Tanners Claret (*Tanners Wines*)
Ch de Belcier 1982, Côtes de Castillon (*Market Vintners*)
Ch Perenne 1982, Premières Côtes de Blaye (*Victoria Wine Co*)

Specialist stockists

Adnams; H Allen Smith; Barts Cellars; Nigel Baring; Barnes Wine Shop; Thomas Baty & Son; Bedford Fine Wines; Berry Bros & Rudd; Bibendum;

E H Booth; Buckinghams; Caves de la Madeleine; Classic Wines; Corney &
Barrow; Curzon Wine Co; George Dutton & Son; Eldridge Pope; Ben Ellis &
Associates; Ellis Son & Vidler; Farr Vintners; Alex Findlater; Fine Vintage
Wines; Friarwood; Andrew Gordon Wines; Greens; Haynes Hanson & Clark;
Hungerford Wine Company; S H Jones; Justerini & Brooks; Kurtz and Chan;
Lay & Wheeler; Laytons; Master Cellar Wine Warehouse; Andrew Mead
Wines; Nickolls & Perks; Peatling & Cawdron; Raeburn Fine Wines and
Foods; Reid Wines; La Réserve/College Cellar; Selfridges; Edward Sheldon;
Sherborne Vintners; Stones of Belgravia; T & W Wines; Tanners Wines; Philip
Tite Fine Wines; Henry Townsend; Willoughbys; The Wine Society; Peter
Wylie Fine Wines; Yorkshire Fine Wines

BURGUNDY

At last it's happened. After several years of price rises that shot up
between 50 and 80 per cent each time, the party is over. The customers
have rebelled, and the producers are having to see some sense.

Prices at the annual Hospices de Beaune auction in November 1986
(when traditionally the trends in Burgundy prices are set) underwent
quite dramatic falls – even if not quite as dramatic as the rises in 1985.
But fall they did – the reds by an average of 40 per cent, the whites by
27 per cent. That brought them back to the prices in 1984. But before
you rush out to your wine merchant, remember that Burgundy – red
and white – is still very expensive, and that's the way it will remain.

The reason is simple: not much Burgundy is made. The whole of the
Burgundy region (including Chablis but not Beaujolais) produces an
average of 14 million cases of wine a year. That may sound a lot, but in
Bordeaux Ch Margaux alone makes 21,000 cases a year and the main
co-operative in St-Emilion 500,000 cases. Back in Burgundy, one of the
major négociant firms, Faiveley, can muster only 50,000 cases.

Yet the taste of Burgundy – good and bad alike – has been the taste of
the '80s. The Americans, who buy a third of the export market, have
been shipping home white Burgundy like there was no Chardonnay in
California. The Swiss and the Germans always buy considerable
amounts of red Burgundy. In the UK, we buy 18 per cent of the total
exports, and in France sales have gone up. There just isn't enough
Burgundy to go round.

Moreover, what Burgundy there is has been getting better since 1982
(on the whole, that is, and with the exceptions and omissions
inevitable in Burgundy – see below). The huge production of that year,
which turned out thin, watery, rot-infested wines, made producers
pause and think: in future, they must control the quality of the grapes
and the amount picked.

Yields had been going up and up as producers thought that this was
the way to keep supply going to an ever more demanding market. But,
as even the Germans have now discovered, high yields have an

immediate downside in loss of quality, of concentration and an increase in thinness and wateriness.

Now, while yields have at least held steady, the new generation of winemakers has rediscovered the art of bleeding the wine during fermentation, taking off some of the pale colour of the juice to give greater colour to the reds, and generally increasing the concentration of the whites.

The tastes of Burgundy

At its best, Burgundy can be a great vinous experience. At that level, price is almost irrelevant. You are talking about some of the most exciting wines made anywhere in the world. The whites, with their rich, luscious, peachy, honeyed fruit, have set the standards against which all other Chardonnay-based wines have been measured. The reds, whose smell is sometimes described as like the richness of rotting leaves, but whose soft, perfumed fruit and complex, often mushroomy flavours are instantly recognisable, are still the only truly successful Pinot Noir wines.

Even at a lower level Burgundy need no longer consist of thick, headache-making red wines, or oxidised and heavy whites. Gone are the days when wines from places further south were added to Burgundy wines to beef them up. Now we are getting the delicate, clean tastes of wines from a northerly wine-producing zone.

But although wine writers enthuse about the taste of Burgundy, that is an almost non-existent idea. It is much more accurate and informative to talk about the taste of Aloxe-Corton or Mâcon or Gevrey-Chambertin. It is the same in Bordeaux – the taste of Bordeaux ranges over such a wide gamut of styles that generalisations become almost meaningless: much better to talk about the taste of the Médoc or of St-Emilion.

Even so, wines from different producers vary enormously: Monsieur X's Chambolle-Musigny will not be a patch on Monsieur Y's, even though the vines from which the two wines come may be only yards apart. If you stop to enquire how this can be, you may find out that Monsieur X over-cropped his vines, which produced watery grapes and watery wine, while Monsieur Y tended his plants with care and rigorously pruned to give a low yield and high quality. This makes the buying and recommending of Burgundy such a minefield of good intentions and misplaced enthusiasm.

Growers and négociants

The solution is to buy from somebody who visits Burgundy regularly and has regular contact with what's going on there. Those visits will be reflected in their list and will concentrate on growers' wines as much as those of the merchants (the négociants), because that is where the excitement of Burgundy is to be found. The growth of domaine bottling by growers is one of the most encouraging signs to emerge from Burgundy in recent years, because it's a sign that some producers really care what happens to their wine: they don't want it to end up in the négociant's blending vats in Dijon or Beaune. This has meant that while there's still an awful lot of indifferent wine flowing out of Burgundy attached to some famous names, there's also a steady and growing trickle of the Real Thing.

Négociant wines shouldn't be dismissed because of this trend towards domaine bottling. Many of the négociants themselves have large vineyard holdings, or buy regularly from the same growers so they can control the quality of the grapes they buy. They've also realised that they have to improve their standards to compete with domaine-bottled wines, so that many firms which were producing soupy reds and oxidised whites have suddenly shown an upturn in quality.

The négociants have also come up with some wines with varietal labels – Chardonnays and Pinot Noirs – which they can blend better than any single grower because they operate in the entire Burgundy vineyard. In many cases, these wines currently represent some of the best value in Burgundy.

But we should also consider some of the lesser-known villages. Burgundy buying often seems to be by name rather than quality, so certain villages have entered the lists of the stratospheric prices as much because their names are memorable and pronounceable as because their wines are good. Why otherwise should Pouilly-Fuissé be twice the price of Pouilly-Vinzelles? Why should Volnay be so much more expensive than Monthélie?

What's what in Burgundy

To add further to the difficulties of buying Burgundy, the appellation system is the most complex in France, with five different levels, from the region-wide appellation to one that refers to a single vineyard.

General appellations A wine bearing an appellation such as Bourgogne or (even lower in quality) Bourgogne Grand Ordinaire can come from anywhere within the whole Burgundy region. The wine can be white or red: Bourgogne Rouge has to be made from Pinot Noir, while Bourgogne Grand Ordinaire can be made from Gamay. Other general appellations include Bourgogne Passe-tout-grain (a blend of Pinot Noir and Gamay) and Bourgogne Aligoté (a white made from the Aligoté grape).

While these are basic appellations, they shouldn't be immediately dismissed. We've already mentioned wines named after varietals – like Pinot Noir and Chardonnay – which carry a simple Bourgogne appellation. In good years like 1983 and 1985, Bourgogne

Passe-tout-grain will contain mainly Pinot and will be a very good bargain (for Burgundy, that is).

Regional appellations Terms like Côte de Nuits Villages, Côte de Beaune-Villages, Hautes Côtes de Nuits fall into this category. Each covers more than one village and the wine will probably be a négociant's blend.

Village appellations Most Burgundian communes or villages are entitled to their own appellation and the vineyards covered by the appellation will be strictly defined. Any vineyards that fall outside the defined area go under one of the more general categories. Typical village appellations are Vosne-Romanée or Savigny-lès-Beaune, Pommard or Nuits St-Georges (see also below).

While these are supposedly not so good as single vineyard wines, it is often the case that village wines are every bit as good and much cheaper. Like the Burgundy-wide appellation wines, but to a lesser degree, they can rely on judicious buying from a reasonable variety of vineyards. The smaller the area from which grapes can come, the greater the risks (from localised hail storms, for instance), but the greater the rewards as well.

Premier cru appellations Confusingly, this is only the second rank of greatness. Certain single vineyards are designated premier cru and are entitled to their own appellation which is normally put on the label in conjunction with the village name, eg Meursault (the village) -Charmes (the vineyard). A wine that is a blend of wines from different premier cru vineyards in one appellation can be called simply Beaune Premier Cru, for example.

Grand Cru appellations These are the very top vineyards, and can appear on the label as appellations in their own right with no reference to the village. At their best, they are the stars of Burgundy but, inevitably, their prices reflect their star quality.

The Burgundy villages

Burgundy's main vineyards are on the east-facing slope of the Côte d'Or. This in turn this is divided into two: in the north is the Côte de Nuits, in the south the Côte de Beaune. In the hilly country behind the Côte d'Or are the Hautes Côtes de Nuits and the Hautes Côtes de Beaune. To the south of the Côte d'Or, the slope breaks up and the vineyards here are called the Côte Chalonnaise. To the south again is the Mâconnais, which leads into the northern part of Beaujolais (see earlier in the book).

Côte de Nuits From north to south, the main villages are: Marsannay, Fixin, Gevrey-Chambertin, Morey St-Denis, Chambolle-Musigny, Vougeot, Vosne-Romanée, Nuits St-Georges.

The village in the Côte de Nuits to watch as offering better value for money than others is Fixin (red wines).

Côte de Beaune Continuing south, the villages are: Aloxe-Corton, Pernand-Vergelesses, Savigny-lès-Beaune, Beaune, Pommard, Volnay, Monthélie, Auxey-Duresses, Meursault, Puligny-Montrachet, Chassagne-Montrachet, St-Aubin, St-Romain, Santenay.

Villages in the Côte de Beaune to watch as offering better value for money than others are: Pernand-Vergelesses (especially for its Aligoté wines), Savigny-lès-Beaune (for reds), Monthélie (for reds), St-Aubin (for reds and whites), St-Romain (for whites), Santenay (for reds).

The Côte Châlonnaise The villages here are: Bouzeron, Rully, Mercurey, Givry, Montagny. Look for Bouzeron whites and Mercurey reds.

The Mâconnais The region is best for whites – and we don't mean the ridiculously over-priced Pouilly-Fuissé. Look instead for St-Véran, Pouilly-Vinzelles, Mâcon-Prissé, Mâcon-Viré, Mâcon-Clessé, Mâcon-Lugny.

Vintages in Burgundy

Any notes on vintages in Burgundy have to be a hit-and-miss affair. There are too many variables – generally involving the quality of the producers and how greedy they were – for anything more than sweeping generalisations.

1986 A classic hit-and-miss vintage. Reds are better than whites, especially in the Côte de Beaune, but even more than in 1985, only producers can guarantee the quality. Whites are immediately attractive, but tend to lack the acidity which would give a long life.

1985 It has been said that it was impossible to make bad wine with the quality of the grapes at harvest time, provided the grower could control his fermentation in the intense heat prevailing then. The *reds* are quite firm with good, rounded tannin and some decent acidity. They should keep. The *whites* are delicious now, somewhat like the 1983s in character but with lower alcohol, more fruit and more acidity. Again, they will age well.

1984 *Reds*: light in colour and alcohol, many of these wines can be drunk now. Premier Cru and Grand Cru will go on until the 1990s. *Whites*: also should be drunk young. They are light and a touch on the acid side (although that aspect has softened in the last year). Drink now.

1983 *Reds*: a fine year, with many of the wines expected to have a long life, but avoid the wines that taste of rot. The vintage has been compared to 1964. *Whites*: full, rich wines that are not typical of

Burgundy and seem to have something of the New World in them. Somewhere along the line, many have lost the elusive taste of Burgundian Chardonnay.

1982 *Reds*: a difficult year. More than ever it depends on the producer. Much of the wine is thin and watery, although better producers made some delicious wines. Drink before 1990. *Whites*: drink any whites you have now and taste carefully before buying any more.

1981 *Reds*: a few fine wines are around in an otherwise mediocre vintage. *Whites*: very varied. Taste before buying.

1980 *Reds*: this vintage is turning out to be better than originally billed, and although most reds need drinking now, the occasional bottle – especially in the Côte de Nuits – will survive for a year or two. *Whites*: most are either too old or too acid.

1979 *Reds*: while some of these easy-to-drink wines will survive for a while, others should be drunk. Taste what you have in order to assess. *Whites*: drink up now – they're still enjoyable in a soft way.

1978 *Reds*: great wines with plenty of life in them yet. Wines from the Côte de Nuits will last longer than those from the Côte de Beaune – but that is generally the case anyway. *Whites*: lesser village wines should be drunk now. The top crus will last another three or four years.

Who's who in Burgundy

This is the vital section. Our advice in Burgundy is always to buy a producer's wines (or a négociant's in certain circumstances). Where the wine was actually grown is often less important. We look at growers first and then merchants. Stockists are indicated in italic type, but the list is not exhaustive.

BURGUNDY GROWERS

Because of the complex vineyard holdings of most growers (with small plots in more than one village) it is not possible in the space to indicate where the growers have their vines. But we can recommend many of the wines from each of the growers listed below because of the care they take with their vines and in their cellars.

Marquis d'Angerville *O W Loeb, Corney & Barrow*
Domaine Comte Armand *Laytons*
Bernard Bachelet *Alex Findlater*
Jean-Claude Bachelet *Bibendum*
Guy Berthault *Hungerford Wine Company*
Simon Bize *Domaine Direct; Haynes Hanson & Clark; S H Jones; La Vigneronne*
Bonneau de Martray *Butlers Wine Cellars; Corney & Barrow; Domaine Direct; Gerard Harris*

Henri Buisson *S H Jones*
Domaine Bzikot *Christopher Piper Wines; Le Nez Rouge*
Luc Camus-Bruchon *Bibendum*
Jean Chauvenet *Christopher Piper Wines; La Vigneronne*
Daniel Chouet-Clivet *La Vigneronne*
Henri Clerc *Averys; David Baillie Vintners; Barwell and Jones; Eldridge Pope*
Georges Clerget *Anthony Byrne Fine Wines; Green's; Justerini & Brooks*
Raoul Clerget *Green's; Yorkshire Fine Wines*
P Cogny *Adnams; Tanners Wines*
Domaines des Comtes Lafon *Domaine Direct; Alex Findlater; Morris & Verdin; Tanners Wines*
J-J Confuron *Alex Findlater; Laytons*
Marc Dudet *Corney & Barrow*
Guy Dufouleur *Davisons; Master Cellar*
Domaine Dujac *Adnams; Averys; Corney & Barrow; Curzon Wine Company; Lay & Wheeler; O W Loeb; Morris's Wine Stores; Tanners Wines; The Wine Society*
Domaine Gagnard-Delagrange *Anthony Byrne Fine Wines; Ferrers Le Mesurier; Gerard Harris; Haynes Hanson & Clark; The Wine Society*
Abel Garnier Fils Aîné *O W Loeb*
Michel Gaunoux *Domaine Direct*
Jacques Germain *David Baillie Vintners*
Jean Germain *Curzon Wine Company; Davisons; Master Cellar; House of Townend*
Vincent Girardin *Le Nez Rouge*
Domaine Girard-Vollot *Morris & Verdin*
Henri Goyard *S H Jones*
Jean Grivot *Anthony Byrne Fine Wines; Haynes Hanson & Clark; Lay & Wheeler; Christopher Piper Wines*
Domaine Antonin Guyon *Curzon Wine Company; Laytons; Willoughbys*
Patrick Javillier *Anthony Byrne Fine Wines*
Henri Jayer *Peatling & Cawdron; Windrush Wines*
Jacqueline Jayer *Haynes Hanson & Clark*
Domaine François Jobard *Morris & Verdin*
Domaine Michel Juillot *Domaine Direct*
Michel Lafarge *Bibendum; Haynes Hanson & Clark; Morris & Verdin*
Henri Lamarche *Lay & Wheeler; Oxford & Cambridge Fine Wine Co*
Hubert Lamy *S H Jones; Lay & Wheeler*
Paul de Launay *House of Townend*
Domaine Leflaive *Adnams; Ballantynes of Cowbridge; Corney & Barrow; Lay & Wheeler; André Simon Wines; Tanners Wines; Yorkshire Fine Wines*
Lequin-Roussot *Anthony Byrne Fine Wines; Justerini & Brooks; Lay & Wheeler; Andrew Mead Wines*
André Lhéritier *Domaine Direct*
George Lignier *Bibendum*
Domaine Machard de Gramont *Adnams; Ballantynes of Cowbridge;*

Bordeaux Direct; Justerini & Brooks; Tanners Wines; House of Townend
Mazilly Père et Fils *Alston Wines; Matthew Gloag & Son; Grape Ideas Wine Warehouse; Ubiquitous Chip*
Bernard Michel *Domaine Direct*
Alain Michelot *Domaine Direct*
Bernard Michelot *Haynes Hanson & Clark; Lay & Wheeler*
Millot-Battault *Averys; Cachet Wines; Eldridge Pope*
Jean-Claude Monnier *David Baillie Vintners*
Domaine Monthélie-Douhairet *Morris & Verdin*
Domaine de Montille *Adnams; Domaine Direct; O W Loeb*
Albert Morey *Le Nez Rouge; Sebastopol Wines*
Bernard Morey *Green's*
Pierre Morey *Haynes Hanson & Clark*
Georges Mugneret *Anthony Byrne Fine Wines; Peatling & Cawdron*
Domaine Mussy *Haynes Hanson & Clark*
Bernard Naune *Bibendum*
Charles Noëllat *Brown Bros Vintners; Grape Ideas Wine Warehouse; Edward Sheldon*
Domaine Parent *Cachet Wines; Gerard Harris*
Domaine des Perrières *Haynes Hanson & Clark*
Jean-Marie Ponsot *Lay & Wheeler*
Potel *Ferrers Le Mesurier; La Vigneronne*
Pothier-Rieusset *Ferrers Le Mesurier*
Domaine de la Pousse d'Or *Averys; Ballantynes of Cowbridge; Anthony Byrne Fine Wines; Domaine Direct; Lay & Wheeler; Tanners Wines; La Vigneronne; The Wine Society*
Jacques Prieur *Chesterford Vintners; La Vigneronne*
Domaine Daniel Rion *Alex Findlater; Morris & Verdin*
Domaine de la Romanée-Conti *Adnams; Rodney Densem Wines; Domaine Direct; Farr Vintners; La Vigneronne*
Philippe Rossignol *Haynes Hanson & Clark*
Cave Roty *Corney & Barrow*
Domaine Guy Roulot *Brown Bros Vintners; Domaine Direct; Windrush Wines*
Georges Roumier *Anthony Byrne Fine Wines*
Domaine Armand Rousseau *Adnams; Eldridge Pope; Matthew Gloag & Son; O W Loeb; Morris's Wine Stores; Stephen Porter Wines; Sebastopol Wines; The Wine Society*
Roux Père et Fils *Gerard Harris; The Wine Society*
Etienne Sauzet *Adnams; James Aitken; Ballantynes of Cowbridge; Ilkley Wine Cellars; Lay & Wheeler; O W Loeb; Tanners Wines*
Jacques Thévenet *Adnams*
Domaine Tollot-Beaut *James Aitken; David Baillie Vintners; Farthinghoe Fine Wine & Food; Grape Ideas Wine Warehouse; Gerard Harris; Lay & Wheeler; O W Loeb; Le Nez Rouge; Stephen Porter Wines*
Domaine Louis Trapet *David Baillie Vintners; Anthony Byrne Fine Wines; Corney & Barrow*

Aubert de Villaine *Adnams; Corney & Barrow*
Domaine Vincent *Adnams; Bibendum; Gerard Harris; Justerini & Brooks;
Lay & Wheeler; Henry Townsend*
Domaine Virely-Rougeot *Laytons*
Emile Voarick *Alex Findlater*
Michel Voarick *Lay & Wheeler; Peatling & Cawdron*
Girard Vollot *Morris & Verdin*

BURGUNDY CO-OPERATIVES

Despite the growth of domaine-bottling, much of Burgundy in the
lesser-known appellations is still handled through the co-operatives.
The biggest concentration is in the Mâconnais and Côte Chalonnaise,
while there are relatively few in the Côte d'Or.

Les Producteurs de Prissé Wines: St-Véran, Mâcon-Prissé.
Haynes Hanson & Clark; The Market/Winecellars

Cave des Vignerons de Buxy Wines: Montagny, Bourgogne Rouge
and Blanc.
Adnams; Les Amis du Vin; Alex Findlater

Groupement de Producteurs Lugny-St-Genoux-de-Scisse Wines:
Mâcon-Lugny, Mâcon-Villages.
Unwins

Cave Co-opérative de Viré Wines: Mâcon-Viré.
Alex Findlater; The Market/Winecellars

Cave Co-opérative des Hautes-Côtes *Direct Wine Shipments; Grape Ideas
Wine Warehouse; André Simon Wines*

BURGUNDY MERCHANTS

Marcel Amance Wines: A subsidiary of Prosper Maufoux (see below).
Hadleigh Wine Cellars; Justerini & Brooks; Laytons

Bouchard Père et Fils Wines: Beaune, Le Montrachet, Corton, Volnay.
Brinkleys; Peter Dominic

Chanson Père et Fils Wines: Beaune, Pernand-Vergelesses.
*Kershaw's Wine Warehouse; J Sainsbury; Edward Sheldon; Whynot Wine
Warehouses*

Doudet-Naudin Wines: Savigny, Beaune, Aloxe-Corton.
Berry Bros & Rudd

Joseph Drouhin Wines: Beaune, Puligny, Corton-Charlemagne,
Corton-Bressandes, Volnay, Chambertin, Chambolle-Musigny,
Echézeaux.
*Connolly's Wine Merchants; Rodney Densem Wines; Haynes Hanson &
Clark; Laytons; André Simon Wines*

Georges Duboeuf Principally in Beaujolais but also in Mâcon and St-Véran.
Brinkleys; Davisons; Le Nez Rouge

Joseph Faiveley Wines: Mercurey, Rully, Corton, Clos de Bèze, Echézeaux, Gevrey-Chambertin, Chambolle-Musigny.
Bedford Fine Wines; Connolly's Wine; Gerard Harris

Geisweiler The négociant firm which opened up the Hautes Côtes de Nuits. Wines: Hautes Côtes de Nuits, Hautes Côtes de Beaune.
Peter Dominic

Hospices de Beaune The charity whose auction each year sets the price for Burgundy. Wines: Most Beaune appellations.
Eldridge Pope; Majestic Wine Warehouses

Louis Jadot Wines: Corton, Beaune, Pernand-Vergelesses. Now own Domaine Clair-Daü.
Cairns & Hickey; Hadleigh Wine Cellars; André Simon Wines; Victoria Wine Co

Labouré-Roi Wines: Meursault, Auxey-Duresses, Beaune, Pommard, Chassagne Montrachet.
James Aitken; Chaplin & Son; Ben Ellis and Associates; Majestic Wine Warehouses; Willoughbys

Louis Latour Wines: Corton, Romanée St-Vivant, Chambertin, Pommard, Beaune, Montagny.
Davisons; Justerini & Brooks; Arthur Rackhams; Whynot Wine Warehouses

Leroy Wines: Pommard, Meursault, Chambertin, Vougeot.
Brinkleys

Loron et Fils Wines: Wide range.
Ellis Son & Vidler; Justerini & Brooks; Tanners Wines; House of Townend

Prosper Maufoux Wines: Best are the Santenay wines.
Berry Bros & Rudd

Moillard Wines: Large vineyard holdings on Côte de Nuits and Côte de Beaune. Wines of 1983 and on are best.
Bedford Fine Wines; Berry Bros & Rudd; Direct Wine Shipments; John Harvey & Sons; J Sainsbury; André Simon Wines

Mommessin Owners of Clos de Tart. Wines: Chassagne Montrachet, Clos de Tart.
Bow Wine Vaults; Waitrose

Remoissenet Wines: Le Montrachet, Beaune.
Averys; The Wine Society

Best buys from Burgundy

WHITES

Sauvignon de St-Bris 1984, J-P Tabit (*Ferrers le Mesurier*)
St-Pourçain-sur-Sioule 1985, Ray (*Ian G Howe*)
Mâcon-Lugny 1986, Duboeuf (*Le Nez Rouge/Berkmann Wine Cellars;
Christopher Piper Wines*)
Bourgogne Chardonnay 1985, Luc Sorin (*William Rush*)

REDS

Bourgogne Rouge 1985, Labouré-Roi (*Rodney Densem Wines*)
Bourgogne 1984, La Digoine, A de Villaine (*Adnams*)
Bourgogne Rouge 1985, Domaine de la Combe (*Bibendum*)
Marcilly Selection NV (*Borg Castel*)
Bourgogne Pinot Noir 1985, Vallet Frères (*Broad Street Wine Co*)
Bourgogne Passe-tout-grain 1985, Daniel Rion (*Morris & Verdin*)
Mâcon Rouge Bray 1985, Henri Lafarge (*Andrew Mead Wines*)
Bourgogne Pinot Noir 1983, Luc Sorin (*William Rush*)
Mâcon Uchizy Rouge 1985, Talmard (*Russell & McIver*)

Specialist stockists

*Adnams; Averys; David Baillie Vintners; Ballantynes of Cowbridge;
Bibendum; E H Booth; Broad Street Wine Company; Anthony Byrne Fine Wines;
Classic Wines; Corney & Barrow; Curzon Wine Company; Domaine Direct;
Farr Vintners; Alex Findlater; Friarwood; Green's; Haynes Hanson & Clark;
Ingletons; Kurtz and Chan; Lay & Wheeler; Laytons; O W Loeb; Andrew Mead
Wines; Morris & Verdin; Le Nez Rouge/Berkmann Wine Cellars; Nickolls &
Perks; Peatling & Cawdron; Christopher Piper Wines; Raeburn Fine Wines
and Foods; Reid Wines; La Réserve/College Cellar; Edward Sheldon; Sherborne
Vintners; T & W Wines; Tanners Wines; Henry Townsend; La Vigneronne;
The Wine Society; Peter Wylie Fine Wines; Yorkshire Fine Wines*

Burgundy

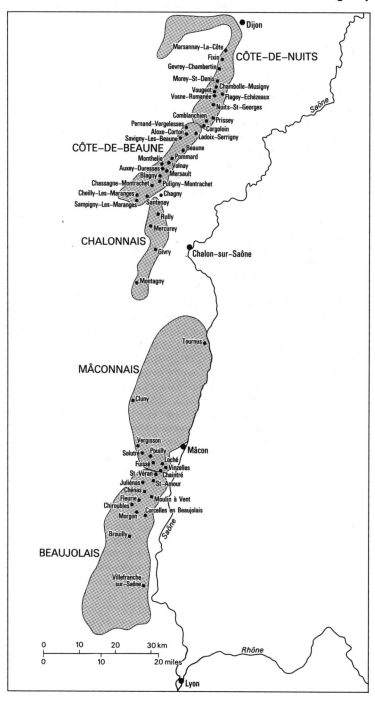

Dijon

CÔTE-DE-NUITS

Marsannay-La-Côte
Fixin
Gevrey-Chambertin
Morey-St-Denis
Chambolle-Musigny
Vougeot
Flagey-Echézeaux
Vosne-Romanée
Nuits-St-Georges
Comblanchien
Prissey
Pernand-Vergelesses
Corgoloin
Aloxe-Corton
Ladoix-Serrigny
Savigny-Les-Beaune
Beaune
Monthelie
Pommard
Auxey-Duresses
Volnay
Blagny
Mersault
Chassagne-Montrachet
Puligny-Montrachet
Cheilly-Les-Maranges
Chagny
Sampigny-Les-Maranges
Santenay

CÔTE-DE-BEAUNE

Saône

Rully
Mercurey

CHALONNAIS

Givry
Chalon-sur-Saône
Montagny

Tournus

MÂCONNAIS

Cluny

Vergisson
Pouilly
Solutré
Mâcon
Fuissé
Loché
St-Véran
Vinzelles
Chaintré
Juliénas
St-Amour
Chénas
Fleurie
Moulin à Vent
Chiroubles
Corcelles en Beaujolais
Morgon
Brouilly

Saône

BEAUJOLAIS

Villefranche-sur-Saône

| 0 | 10 | 20 | 30 km |
| 0 | 10 | | 20 miles |

Rhône

Lyon

CHABLIS

So hands up who bought Chablis this year. You, sir, with the hotel manager's striped trousers? Well, of course, your clients can afford to drink it, can't they? The man from the Swiss bank? Of course, your franc is very strong against the French franc. Anybody else?

No, we thought not. Anybody who bought Chablis in 1987 – or 1986, come to that – either couldn't live without the taste, or he or she had just sold that Van Gogh painting.

We exaggerate? Of course – but not grossly, when the price of Chablis is put into the context of other similar wine styles. By that, we don't mean white Burgundy – although some wines from the Mâconnais were positive bargains by comparison. We mean rather the Chardonnays of Australia, of California, of New Zealand.

Gone are the days, halcyon as they may have seemed, when Chablis was the automatic and essential choice for diners ordering one of a thousand versions of sole in a London fish restaurant. The world is full of Chablis look-alikes, many of them as good or better in quality, and most of them better value for money.

Now, of course, we musn't be too hard on poor old Chablis. Its vineyards do lie relatively north (it's one of the first vineyard areas you meet going south from Paris). So it's going to be cold, and at the beginning of 1985 it was – very cold. The frost killed vines, especially those in the best – Premier and Grand Cru – vineyards (see below for definitions in Chablis). Production of these wines fell dramatically, and prices rose.

However, the frost didn't touch the ordinary Chablis vineyards very much at all, but prices rose just as heavily. Why? Because Chablis suffers much more than other vineyard areas from problems of supply and demand. Because the Americans bought a lot of wine – having just realised that Chablis was a place, not a style of wine that came from California. And because the Chablis growers saw a quick killing.

There came a point when ordinary Chablis cost well over 50 francs a bottle, ex-cellars (which after duty, VAT and profits means around £9 or £10 a bottle). When *Which? Wine Monthly* ran a tasting of 1985 Chablis in June 1987, we could find nothing available under £6.50 a bottle. Our tasters were horrified at the ratio between the quality of the wine (good, but not that good) and the price, and suggested we look elsewhere for our Chablis wines – which takes us back to the New World Chardonnays.

The 1986 vintage of the Premier and Grand Cru wines (see below for vintage notes) has turned out to be not much bigger than the 1985. The vines that were killed at the beginning of 1985 were replaced but are not yielding anything yet, so that's inevitable. But there is the usual amount of ordinary Chablis around – and it's good, better than 1985 – so prices should be falling.

Whether they will fall, of course, remains in the hands of the Chablis growers – and of wine merchants who refuse to buy at silly prices. It has happened before – prices were good between 1979 and 1984 – so there's no reason to suppose it won't happen again.

But wouldn't it be so much better for everybody if the Chablis producers and négociants got together again – as they did in 1984/85 – and ironed out the fluctuations in price that leave the buying field empty apart from the hotel manager and the Swiss banker?

Where's where in Chablis

Chablis' appellation system is much simpler than that of the rest of Burgundy. For a start, only white wine can be Chablis: any red wines made in the area go under the appellation of Bourgogne or of one of the small village names (see below under The other wines of the Chablis region).

The Chablis vineyards are graded on a quality basis. At the bottom, there is the basic Petit Chablis vineyard. Since the name sounds slightly pejorative, nobody wants to make a wine called Petit Chablis, so most producers have managed to get their vineyards upgraded to simple Chablis, the next quality level up, regardless of the soil type or quality of their produce: a classic French sleight of hand.

Above Chablis AC are the Premier Cru vineyards. These are divided into 12 different groupings which consist of more than one vineyard: They are: Beauroy, Côte de Léchet, Fourchaume, Les Fourneaux, Mélinots, Montée de Tonnerre, Montmains, Monts de Milieu, Vaillons, Vaucoupin, Vosgros; plus Vaudevey, new since 1983. If a wine is a blend of more than one Premier Cru, it will simply be called Chablis Premier Cru without a vineyard name.

At the top of the Chablis tree are the seven Grands Crus, making fabulous classic wines, at top prices. These are: Blanchots, Bougros, Les Clos, Grenouilles, Les Preuses, Valmur, Vaudésir.

Vintages in Chablis

The wine-growing society of Chablis is hot in debate about whether their wines are for keeping or drinking young. There are those who make them in stainless steel and expect them to be drunk within a year or two of the harvest. Against them are those who believe a little maturation in oak barrels does wonders to the wines and gives them a potentially longer life. So the keeping qualities of Chablis often depend on the producer as much as the year.

1986 A small crop – not much bigger than 1985. The French say that it is similar to 1985, with the same intensity. Others feel that it has produced wines with greater acidity, hence more typically Chablis.

1985 A small crop of high quality – if quite full – wine, 35 per cent lower than in 1984 because of frost in January and February. The main problems with quantity are in the Grand Cru and Premier Cru vineyards. Quantities of Chablis and Petit Chablis are nearer normal. What top wines there are are maturing well – but should last.

1984 Rot was the problem in the vineyards after a wet September and warm October. The wine has more acidity than vintages immediately preceding and may not last that long. Little has been available in our shops.

1983 Soft, full-bodied wines which lacked the edge that is the hallmark of a good Chablis vintage. If you can still find any, they should be reasonable value (and don't buy if they aren't), but drink up fast.

1982 Even the top wines have suffered from a very soft vintage. Don't keep and don't buy.

1981 Some really good Chablis with intense flavours and a lovely tangy bite were made, but they do need drinking now – except some of the top growths.

Few vintages before 1981 (apart from some Grand Cru 1978) are worth keeping now, and it's unlikely there will be any to buy. If you do see any bottles of 1975 Premier Cru or Grand Cru, these are still worth considering.

Who's who in Chablis

Much standard Chablis AC has lost the steely nervosity and green acidity that made it such a special wine – and that has a lot to do with the way vineyards have been upgraded even though they are not planted in the right soil conditions. It also has to do with the use of stainless steel (see above). But if you want to be sure to taste the Chablis of yore, you will have to go for Premier Cru at the very least (and pay a lot of money) or make sure you are buying wines made by the right producer. This makes names of producers as important in Chablis as they are in Burgundy.

THE GROWERS

J Brocard Makes big, mellow wines, often quite rich. Wines: Domaine Ste-Claire.
Adnams; Berkmann Wine Cellars/Le Nez Rouge; Oddbins; Stapylton Fletcher

René Dauvissat One of the well-established names of Chablis with some complexity to his wines. Wines: Grand Crus – Les Clos and Les Preuses; plus Premier Cru.
Domaine Direct; Tanners Wines

Bernard Defaix Modern winemaking without the use of wood; the wines tend to be fat and Burgundian in taste. Wines: Premiers Crus – Côte de Léchet, Vaillons.
Berry Bros & Rudd; Bibendum

Jean-Paul Droin Very fine Chablis made using judicious amounts of oak-ageing. Wines: Grand Crus – Vaudésir, Les Clos, Grenouilles, Valmur; Premiers Crus – mainly Vaillons.
Domaine Direct; Tanners Wines

Jean Durup Large holding of 140 acres makes him a major force in Chablis. Uses modern stainless steel in his winemaking, and high standards. Wines: Durup, Domaine de l'Eglantière, Ch de Maligny, Domaine de la Paulière, Domaine de Valéry, Les Folles Pensées.
H Allen Smith; Domaine Direct; Gerard Harris; Haynes Hanson & Clark; Tanners Wines

William Fèvre A proponent of the use of new oak barrels for Chablis, making rich, rounded wines. Wines: Grands Crus – Les Clos, Bougros, Les Preuses, Grenouilles, Vaudésir, Valmur; Premier Cru and Chablis.
Berkmann Wine Cellars/Le Nez Rouge; Kershaw's Wine Warehouse

Louis Michel Modern, fruity wines that are ready to drink young. Wines: Grands Crus – Vaudésir, Grenouilles, Les Clos; Premiers Crus – Montmains, Montée de Tonnerre, Domaine de Vaubourg.
Lay & Wheeler; O W Loeb; Oddbins; Wine Society

Louis Pinson Traditional wines, aged in wood, and needing three years before drinking. Wines: Grand Cru – Les Clos; Premiers Crus – Montmains, La Forêt, Montée de Tonnerre.
Bibendum; Morris & Verdin

Jean-Marie Raveneau Often regarded as the finest Chablis producer (formerly shipped under father François' name). Very traditional wines: Grands Crus – Valmur, Les Clos, Blanchots; Premier Cru.
Haynes Hanson & Clark

Robert Vocoret Fermentation as well as ageing in barrels makes his wines good keepers. Wines: Grands Crus – Les Clos, Blanchots, Valmur; Premier Cru, Chablis.
Gerard Harris; Reid Wines

Cave Co-opérative La Chablisienne Controls a quarter of all Chablis production, producing straightforward wines which may lack some of the depths of smaller producers. Wines: about 50 different labels, including La Chablisienne and co-op members' own labels (such as

Domaine Jean Bourcey, Rémy Lefort, Fèvre Frères, Jean-Claude Dauvissat, Michaut Frères).
The most widely available Chablis: look for the co-op's name as bottler on the label

THE MERCHANTS

Bacheroy-Josselin Successful and expanding Chablis merchant with vineyards divided between Domaine Laroche and Domaine de la Jouchère.
Justerini & Brooks

Albert Bichot Burgundy négociant with interests in Chablis including Chablis La Moutonne.
Unwins

Joseph Drouhin Another Burgundy merchant who now owns vineyards in Chablis.
Gerard Harris; Laytons; Michael Menzel Wines

Labouré-Roi Famous Burgundy négociant now taking an interest in Chablis. Wines: Premiers Crus – Montmains, Montée de Tonnerre.
Majestic Wine Warehouses and others

Lamblin et Fils Grower and négociant who owns 26 acres in Grand Cru and Premier Cru vineyards as well as buying in grapes. Serious quality for the top wines. Wines: sells under a number of labels – Jacques Arnois, Jacques de la Ferte, Paul Javry, Bernard Mièle.
Stapylton Fletcher

Moreau The largest landowner and, after the co-operative, the largest producer. Wines are good and reliable if without great excitement, and best drunk young. Moreau Blanc, the firm's branded wine, is not Chablis but Vin de Table. Wines: Domaine de Bieville Chablis; Premier Cru – Les Vaillons; Grand Cru – Les Clos.
Davisons, Wine Society and many others

A Regnard et Fils Firm of négociants owning no vineyards but buying in grapes from a wide range of properties. Now owned by de Ladoucette of Pouilly Fumé. Wines: Albert Pic, Michel Rémon; Premier Cru – Fourchaume; Grands Crus – Valmur, Vaudésir.
Berry Bros & Rudd; Hungerford Wine Company; Lay & Wheeler; André Simon Wines

Simmonet-Febvre Small vineyard holding backed up by large négociant business. Good source of wines from the smaller appellations around Chablis as well as Chablis itself. Wines; Grand Cru – Les Preuses; Premiers Crus – Monts de Milieu, Montée de Tonnerre, Fourchaume, Vaillons.
Christopher & Co

The other wines of the Chablis region

While Chablis itself covers a fairly small vineyard area, in the surrounding country of the Yonne are a handful of tiny appellations which were once mightier. Some have almost disappeared, others are coming back to life. All provide some interest.

Coulanges-la-Vineuse Strictly speaking not an appellation, and the red wine from this village is actually called Bourgogne (but the name of the village will appear as a second thought). The grape is the Pinot Noir, the style light and elegant.
Peter Dominic

Irancy Another red wine village, this time with its own appellation. Pinot Noir is again the grape, with a little César to give body. The wines sometimes have surprising depth.
Domaine Direct; Haynes Hanson & Clark; La Vigneronne

St-Bris-le-Vineux and Chitry-le-Fort The two villages combine to produce Sauvignon de St-Bris, now enjoying something of a cult following. The wines are not dissimilar to some Sancerre – not that far away.
Domaine Direct; Peter Dominic; Hungerford Wine Company; Majestic Wine Warehouses; La Vigneronne; Windrush Wines

Best buys from Chablis and the environs

Folles Pensées 1985, Jean Durup (*Haynes Hanson & Clark*)
Domaine Ste-Claire 1985, J Brocard (*Adnams; Justerini & Brooks*)
Domaine de Valéry 1985, Jean Durup (*Tanners Wines*)
Rémy Lefort 1985 (*Marks & Spencer*)
Christopher Tatham Monopole Vin de Table, La Chablisienne (*André Simon*)

Specialist stockists

Berry Bros & Rudd; Anthony Byrne Fine Wines; Alex Findlater; Lay & Wheeler; Sherborne Vintners; La Vigneronne

CHAMPAGNE

We still drink more Champagne than anybody else in the world – apart, that is, from the French themselves. A couple of years ago, we all thought that was because the country was in decline: we were drowning our sorrows with the most festive drink we could find.

Now we are told that everything is rosy economically so it's the lads in the City who are into Champagne as heavily as they are into futures. With such conflicting reasons, we can only conclude that we drink Champagne because we enjoy the stuff – which, after all, is the best reason.

With all this Champagne gushing down the national throat, it's obvious that the most famous fizz of all has come a long way from the days when it was a drink for the elite or for Very Special Occasions only. It has become a democratic drink, with no class connotations, to be drunk when the mood, rather than the occasion, takes us.

There are a number of reasons for this change in our view of Champagne. One is that it's still surprisingly good value. It was very cheap for one heady period in 1984 and 1985, as huge crops in Champagne and the appearance of supermarket brands in our shops pushed the price of a bottle under £6.

That marvellous time came to an end – pretty abruptly – with the effects of the 1984 and 1985 harvests, made worse by frosts at the beginning of 1985. But even now, with retailers' own-label Champagnes, it is still possible to get a very good bottle for under £8.

Then there has been the growth of the Champagne-by-the-glass trend in all the good wine bars, especially those concentrating on a lunchtime clientèle. So we've been able to enjoy the taste of Champagne regularly, without making too great a dent in our pockets.

Own labels call the tune

When we said that supermarkets – and more recently some wine warehouses – have been supplying good Champagne at modest prices, we were actually understating the case: some of those supermarket Champagnes have actually come out top in blind tastings of Champagnes which have also included some of the most famous names.

Some are such good value that they now work out at less per centilitre than Chablis, despite the extra costs involved in making Champagne.

Supermarkets have also been influential in reviving a style of Champagne that seemed to have disappeared: rosé Champagne. The revival started in the autumn of 1985, when Sainsbury's launched their own-label rosé. We all went out and bought a bottle, just to see what this style of wine that seemed more at home in ladies' dancing slippers than in glasses actually tasted like.

It tasted good, and we came back for more. Then other supermarkets and wine warehouses also cottoned on to selling rosé Champagne. Now everybody is doing it, thank you very much.

Back in the vineyards

In Champagne itself, the annual argument between the growers and the producers over the price of the grapes seems to be permanently swinging in favour of the growers. Champagne is the most closely regulated of all the French vineyard areas, and each year the growers and the producing houses sit round a table, umpired by a French government official to prevent fisticuffs, to thrash out the price that the producing houses will pay for the growers' grapes.

In 1985 the price of grapes represented about 40 per cent of the cost of a bottle of Champagne – and by 1986 it had gone up to 50 per cent. Thirty years ago, grapes represented only 10 per cent of the cost of a bottle.

This means that the growers in Champagne are the wealthiest in France.

Making their own

Traditionally, all the Champagne that we bought came from the major houses (see below under Who's who). They bought grapes from growers and turned them into Champagne. Growers who did not supply grapes to the houses sent them to a co-operative instead.

Then some of the growers got ideas. They liked the idea of seeing their own name on bottles, so they started making, bottling and selling Champagne themselves. The trend took off, and by the early 1980s, around half of the Champagne sold was coming from growers or co-operatives.

The growth of this trend seems to have stopped now, but it has left the major houses with a problem of where to buy grapes. Sometimes they run short, and have to resort to buying wine rather than grapes (which means they lose some control over the way their Champagne is made). It's called buying 'sur lattes' (literally, wine that is in the process of being worked on), and while the houses that buy in this way claim that their Champagne doesn't taste any different, others reckon the taste is affected.

To age or not to age

To most Frenchmen, the British just don't know how to drink Champagne. They regard our predilection for old Champagne as unthinkably perverse. Champagne, they say, is a wine that needs to be drunk young and fresh so that you get the crispness and greenness.

Well, they have a point. But while Champagne is certainly delicious after the statutory two years in bottle, it is the one sparkling wine that matures splendidly. It may lose its freshness, but it acquires enormous depths as it matures, making it a completely different – and revelatory – experience.

To see whether you prefer the French or the British approach to Champagne, when you next buy a bottle, buy two instead. Drink one and put the other aside for a few years – two or three, perhaps – then taste the difference. It doesn't matter whether the wine is vintage or non-vintage, grande marque or supermarket: all Champagne will age gracefully for a few years, although the best will be drinkable for much longer.

White wine from black grapes

Champagne is made from three grape varieties – one white and two black. Because the juice of the black grapes is white (only the skins are black), it is possible with careful pressing of the grapes to extract the white juice completely uncoloured by the skins.

Chardonnay is the white grape, which may appear by itself in Blanc de Blancs.

Pinot Meunier and Pinot Noir are the black grapes. Pinot Noir makes the better quality wine, but Pinot Meunier is an important constituent even of top blends.

What's what in Champagne

Most Champagne is sold under a brand name, whether it's one of the great houses (Bollinger, Veuve Clicquot, Moët et Chandon, etc) or a smaller house or co-operative or under a buyer's own label (Sainsbury's or Tesco's Champagne).

But it is also possible to find out from the label something about the type of producer and his status. At the bottom of the label are two letters followed by a series of numbers. The numbers, if traced back in Champagne, will tell you the name of the maker, the letters what sort of company it is:

NM (négociant manipulant) means that the Champagne was made by a merchant or négociant who buys wine from anywhere in the region and then makes his blend. All the major houses are merchants like this and those two letters are a good guarantee of quality.

RM (récoltant manipulant) indicates that the producer is a grower who is making the wine only from grapes grown in his vineyard. Often this wine can be very good indeed, but because the grower cannot buy in grapes from elsewhere, he is at the whim of weather and general crop failures – always a risk in vineyards so far north as Champagne. Look for growers who describe their wines as grand or premier cru – the terms have a definite quality status in the highly regulated world of Champagne.

MA (manipulant acheteur) indicates that the brand is a buyer's own brand – a merchant or retail chain has put its own name on the label of Champagne which it has bought from a producer. The best guide to the quality of this Champagne is the quality of the merchant or shop.

CM (co-opérative manipulant). This indicates that the wine has been made by a co-operative. The reputation of the brand name is the best guide to quality here.

What else is on the label?

There are many other terms used to describe Champagne on its label. Here are the most familiar:

Blanc de Blancs Champagne made only from the Chardonnay grape. Generally light, flowery, delicate.

Blanc de Noirs Champagne made only from black grapes (Pinot Noir and Pinot Meunier). Full, quite heavy and not often seen.

Bouzy Rouge Still red wine made from Pinot Noir grapes. Expensive and very light in style: an acquired taste.

Brut Very dry, the standard term used to describe most of the Champagne we drink. A few firms make extremely dry Champagne as well as their standard brut: this will be described as something like Ultra Brut (Laurent Perrier) or Brut Sauvage (Piper Heidsieck).

Coteaux Champenois Red, white or rosé still wines made from Champagne grapes grown in Champagne.

Crémant Fermented in the bottle to a lower pressure than Champagne so that the bubbles are creamier and less fizzy.

Crus All the Champagne vineyards are graded on a quality scale. The best are graded at 100 per cent and are called grands crus; the next level – at 90 to 99 per cent – are premiers crus. Deuxièmes crus run from 80 to 90 per cent. Some Champagnes will be made only from grand cru vineyards and can then describe themselves as such. But many of the finest Champagnes use lesser vineyards for their grapes because that's the way they can achieve the consistent blend: it's not necessarily a way of cutting corners.

De luxe or prestige cuvées On the theory that Champagne is like perfume (the more you charge for it, the more people want to buy it), Champagne houses are falling over themselves to launch top-price blends which can be either vintage or non-vintage. They are often distinguished more by the flamboyance of the bottle than the quality of the wine, although some de luxe cuvées are very fine. Better quality and value is to be found in straightforward vintage Champagne or the RD brands (see below).

Demi-sec A medium sweet Champagne, best drunk at the end of a meal.

Doux Sweet Champagne. Not in much demand in the UK, but very popular in South America.

Extra dry Not as dry as brut but drier than sec.

Non-vintage The vast bulk of Champagne is a blended wine using wines from different years to give continuity of style. These Champagnes reflect their house styles, and the master blenders (who may be putting 40 or 50 different wines in the blend) are highly regarded.

RD (Récemment dégorgé) A few houses (Bollinger, Gratien and Joseph Perrier) don't remove the yeasts from the wine as soon as the second fermentation in the bottle has finished, but leave the sediment in the wine for some time afterwards. This gives added richness to the Champagne. It's only done for a small proportion of the production which will be labelled accordingly and for which large sums of money will be charged. But for special occasions, these wines are very memorable – and certainly better value than many de luxe blends.

Riche The sweetest category of Champagne. The term is no longer permitted on its own – it must also say 'doux'.

Rosé Champagne A fuller, richer-tasting Champagne, but still dry. Normally made by adding red wine to white wine to give consistency of colour. The old method was to leave the red grape juice in contact with the skins after pressing to get their colour and then ferment the wine as a rosé. Generally more expensive than white.

Sec Medium dry, less dry than extra brut or brut.

Vintage Champagne A Champagne in which all the wine will be from one year. Vintage Champagne is made only in exceptional years which are 'declared', but not every producer will make a vintage each declared year. This was the way Champagne always used to be made until the Second World War. Vintage Champagne can represent very good value for money for a top-rate wine, but needs some time in bottle before drinking – at least six or seven years. There's no point in drinking vintage too young – you might as well buy the less expensive non-vintage.

Bottle sizes

Apart from the standard 75cl Champagne bottle, Champagne comes in a whole range of other sizes. The larger the bottle size, the more slowly the wine will mature.

Halves and quarters Champagne matures very quickly in these small bottles – especially the quarter-bottles sometimes seen on aeroplanes. Be cautious with quarters – the quality of the wine suffers.

Magnums Two ordinary bottles.

Jeroboam Four ordinary bottles.

Rehoboam Six ordinary bottles.

Methuselah Eight ordinary bottles.

Salmanazar Twelve ordinary bottles.

Balthazar Sixteen ordinary bottles.

Nebuchadnezzar Twenty ordinary bottles.

Champagne vintages

1986 The first big crop since 1983, producing good rather than great quality. It is too early to say if any houses will bottle vintage Champagne, but the general opinion is that Blanc de Blancs style wines will be the best. More importantly, it means that stock levels are high again, and the rise in prices should stop.

1985 Small crop because heavy frosts at the beginning of the year did immense damage to the vineyards. The quality, though, is high after a warm summer and autumn, and some vintage wines are likely. Wine held back from the bumper 1982 and 1983 vintages will be used to augment the quantity.

1984 A pretty awful vintage, small in quantity and with rather thin, acid wines. No vintage wines will be made, and the wines themselves will need considerable additions of older wines to maintain quality for non-vintage blends.

1983 and 1982 Bumper years in Champagne – both for quality and quantity. Most producers have declared vintages which are now available but are too young to drink yet. However, some supermarkets' own vintage Champagne from 1982 is very drinkable at the moment.

1981 The latest crop of vintage Champagne that is ready to drink. The crop was small and the wines tend to be a little acid, so buy vintages with care.

1979 An excellent vintage. Stocks are still around of this year's wines and are showing very well.

1978 A thin vintage, with concentrated acidity. But some vintage wines are developing very well in an austere sort of way, and will last for some time.

1976 Many of the lesser vintage wines from this year are past their best. Some of the top houses' wines, though, are still delicious.

1975 One of the great vintages of the past 20 years. If you see a bottle, buy it, just to see what mature Champagne can really taste like.

Older vintages: 1973, 1971, 1966, 1964, 1961 Generally only the top cuvées from the best producers are worth considering – although there can be surprises.

Who's who in Champagne

Here is a list of producers whose Champagnes are available in our shops. We have not included own-label Champagnes in this list, but since most wine merchants as well as supermarkets and wine warehouses have an own-label brand, we would recommend trying them for value for money.

Ayala Fair, reasonably enjoyable wines with consistent quality and some bottle age. Non-vintage, vintage and rosé are available.
Majestic Wine Warehouses; Wine Growers Association

Besserat de Bellefon Lightish style, better at Crémant than straight Champagne. Non-vintage, vintage, Crémant, Crémant Rosé, de luxe Cuvée B de B.
Peter Green

Billecart-Salmon Serious Champagne in a dry, austere style. Non-vintage, Blanc de Blancs, rosé, de luxe Cuvée Nicolas-François Billecart.
Windrush Wines

Boizel Good value Champagne, without excitement but reliable. Non-vintage, vintage, rosé.
Augustus Barnett

Bollinger Full, rich Champagnes of great quality with a faithful following. Non-vintage, vintage, rosé, RD, Vieilles Vignes Françaises.
Widely available

de Castellane Soft wines with a hint of wood to give them character. Non vintage and vintage.
Hedley Wright

Canard-Duchêne Easy-drinking Champagne of good value. Non-vintage, rosé, de luxe Charles VII.
Waitrose

Charbaut Light, perfumed wine of good quality. Non-vintage, vintage, rosé, de luxe Certificat Blanc de Blancs.
Reid Wines; Seckford Wines; Whynot Wine Warehouses

Deutz Well-aged wines, full and soft. Non-vintage, vintage, rosé, de luxe Cuvée William Deutz.
Laytons

Duval Leroy The suppliers of Sainsbury's and other buyers' own brands, whose wines are also available under their own name. Non-vintage, vintage, rosé, de luxe Cuvée des Roys.
Laytons; Wines from Paris

Roland Fliniaux Small producer with four hectares under vine. Non-vintage, vintage, rosé.
The Champagne House

Gosset Quite rich wines with Pinot predominating. Non-vintage, vintage, rosé, de luxe Grand Millésime, Cuvée Quatrième Centenaire.
The Champagne House; Fortnum & Mason

George Goulet Mature wines on the lighter side. Non-vintage, vintage, Rosé de luxe Cuvée de Centenaire.
Les Amis du Vin; Cullens

Granier Well-matured wines with a high proportion of Pinot. Non-vintage, vintage, rosé, de luxe Cuvée Réserve.
Bowlish House Wines

Heidsieck Light, commercial wines, but good value. Non-vintage, vintage, de luxe H de Heidsieck.
Highgate Wines (9a Swains Lane, London NW6)

Charles Heidsieck Full-bodied wines which sometimes suffer from being too young. From a poor period a few years ago, quality is looking up. Non-vintage, vintage, rosé, de luxe Champagne Charlie.
Widely available

Heidsieck Monopole Attractive, biscuity-yeasty wines, very dry. Non-vintage, vintage, rosé, de luxe Diamant Bleu.
Oddbins

André Jacquart High quality wines from one of the Champagne co-operatives. Good bottle age. Vintage, non-vintage, rosé.
Contact: Champagne Jacquart (7 Rickett Street, London SW6)

Jacquesson Drinkable, soft, high quality. Non-vintage, vintage, rosé, de luxe Signature.
Yapp Brothers

Louis Kremer Full, fruity, quite heavy wines. Non-vintage, vintage, rosé.
Fenwicks (Northumberland Street, Newcastle-upon-Tyne); Winewell (67 Park Parade, London NW10)

Krug Great Champagnes that are (almost) worth the price. Vintages last for years and the rosé is a great experience. Vintage, rosé, de luxe Grande Cuvée.
Adnams; H Allen Smith; Bibendum; Lay & Wheeler; Majestic Wine Warehouses; La Vigneronne; Whynot Wine Warehouses

Lanson Light, fresh wines with a predominance of Chardonnay.
Non-vintage, vintage, rosé, de luxe Noble Cuvée.
Widely available

Abel Lepitre Very high class Champagnes with good bottle age and
maturity in the taste. Non-vintage, vintage, de luxe Prince A de
Bourbon.
O W Loeb

Laurent Perrier Lovely, traditional wines, very clean-tasting.
Non-vintage, vintage, rosé, de luxe Cuvée Grande Siècle.
Widely available

Mercier The second company in the Moët et Chandon group makes
good reliable Champagne which is also generally good value.
Non-vintage, vintage, rosé.
Widely available

Moët et Chandon The biggest seller, often maligned, but actually of
good, reliable quality. Quite full-bodied. Non-vintage, vintage, rosé,
de luxe Dom Pérignon.
Widely available

Mumm Slightly sweeter than most bruts, giving a full, creamy taste.
Non-vintage, vintage, rosé, de luxe René Lalou.
Gough Brothers; Oddbins

Bruno Paillard Delightful Champagne – light, elegant, fruity. Vintage,
non-vintage, rosé.
Le Nez Rouge/Berkmann Wine Cellars; Henry Townsend

Joseph Perrier Ripe, rich, firm Champagne, which matures well.
Non-vintage, vintage, rosé, de luxe Cuvée de Cent-Cinquantenaire.
Bibendum

Perrier-Jouët Light, predominantly Chardonnay wines, with hints of
lemon. Non-vintage, vintage, rosé Belle Epoque, de luxe Belle Epoque,
Blason de France.
Curzon Wine Company

Philipponnat Good value, very approachable Champagne.
Non-vintage, vintage.
Oddbins

Piper Heidsieck Flinty, light wines with good structure. Non-vintage,
vintage, rosé, de luxe Champagne Rare (very dry).
Harrods; Selfridges; André Simon Wines; Stones of Belgravia

Pol Roger Light, elegant, firm wines. Non-vintage, vintage, rosé, de
luxe Cuvée Sir Winston Churchill.
*H Allen Smith; Eldridge Pope; Alex Findlater; Peter Green; Lay & Wheeler;
Whynot Wine Warehouses*

Pommery et Greno Just known as Pommery. Dry, light, balanced wines. Non-vintage, vintage, rosé, de luxe Cuvée Louis Pommery.
Fortnum & Mason; Peter Green; Harrods; Arthur Rackhams

Louis Roederer Fruity, rich, firm wines with a lot of character. Non-vintage, vintage, rosé, de luxe Cristal.
Bibendum; Alex Findlater

Ruinart Another Moët et Chandon company making soft, gentle wine of good quality. Vintage Blanc de Blancs, de luxe Dom Ruinart.
Stapylton Fletcher; La Vigneronne

Salon Tiny production of superb 100 per cent Chardonnay wines only made in the best years. Vintage Salon le Mesnil, de luxe Cuvée S.
Les Amis du Vin

Jacques Selosse Character and depth, wines which age well. Non-vintage, vintage, de luxe Spécial Club.
Oldacre-Field (Hazel Road, Altrincham, Cheshire)

Taittinger Attractive, lively, dry, gentle. Non-vintage, vintage, rosé Comtes de Champagne, de luxe Comtes de Champagne, Taittinger Collection.
Widely available

de Venoge Well balanced with elegance and some finesse. Non-vintage, vintage, rosé, de luxe Champagne des Princes.
Thomas Baty & Sons; Willoughbys

Veuve Clicquot Great quality and consistent style make this one of the most popular Champagnes. Non-vintage, vintage, rosé, de luxe La Grande Dame.
Widely available

Best buys from Champagne

LESS EXPENSIVE NON-VINTAGE

Sainsbury's Non-Vintage
Tesco Non-Vintage
Waitrose Non-Vintage
de Telmont Non-Vintage (*Majestic Wine Warehouses*)
Pierre Vaudon (*Haynes Hanson & Clark*)
Albert Beerens (*Bibendum*)
André Jacquart Carte Blanche (*Morris & Verdin*)
Roland Fliniaux (*The Champagne House*)

MORE EXPENSIVE NON-VINTAGE

Mumm Crémant de Cramant (*Oddbins*)
Pol Roger Non-Vintage (*Whynot Wine Warehouses*)
Bruno Paillard Crémant Brut (*Market Vintners*)

The Chairman's Elegantly Dry (*Eldridge Pope/Reynier Wine Libraries*)
Alfred Gratien Non-Vintage (*The Market/Winecellars; and others*)

VINTAGE

Sainsbury's 1982
Waitrose Extra Dry
de Venoge Brut 1979 (*The Wine Case Place*)
Louis Roederer 1982 (*James Aitken; Highbreck Vintners; Tanners Wines*)
Perrier-Jouët 1979 (*Curzon Wine Company; and others*)
Heidsieck Dry Monopole 1982 (*Oddbins*)

DE LUXE AND SPECIAL CUVÉES

Jacquesson Signature 1979 (*Yapp Brothers*)
Jacques Selosse Grand Cru Brut 1979 Cuvée Club Spécial (*Oldacre-Field, Hazel Road, Altrincham, Cheshire*)
Deutz Cuvée William Deutz (*Laytons*)
Laurent Perrier Cuvée Grande Siècle (*Champagne and Caviar Shop; Morris's Wine Stores*)

ROSÉ CHAMPAGNE

Charbaut Rosé Non-Vintage (*Reid Wines*)
Asda Champagne Rosé Brut
Alfred Gratien Rosé Brut (*Arthur Rackhams*)
Sainsbury's Rosé Champagne Brut
de Telmont Rosé (*Majestic Wine Warehouses*)

Specialist stockists

Thomas Baty; Bibendum; Champagne and Caviar Shop; Champagne de Villages; The Champagne House; Curzon Wine Company; George Dutton; Fortnum & Mason; Gerard Harris; Harrods; Nickolls & Perks; Oddbins; Arthur Rackhams; La Réserve/College Cellar; Selfridges; Stones of Belgravia; T & W Wines; Willoughbys; Peter Wylie Fine Wines

CORSICA

Things are beginning to happen on France's Mediterranean island: some growers are getting modern ideas about producing full-bodied but very fruity reds.

There are a number of appellation contrôlée (AC) areas on the island. Most still produce heavy reds and a few dull whites. Patrimonio is one of the best AC areas, using the Nielluccio grape which is akin to the Sangiovese of Chianti. Another is the AC of Vin de Corse Porto-Vecchio down in the south of the island, source of some good, clean whites.

The main vin de pays for Corsica is the seductively named Vin de Pays de l'Ile de Beauté, and behind such French romance are Cabernet, Chardonnay and Syrah wines of excellent value and reliable quality.

Best buys from Corsica

Domaine de Fontanella (*Harrods; Waitrose*)
Vin de Pays de l'Ile de Beauté (*Harrods; Waitrose*)
Domaine de Torraccia (*Majestic Wine Warehouses*)

HAUT-POITOU

Usually classified as Loire, but actually well to the south of the river on the road to Poitiers, the co-operative of Haut-Poitou produces excellent aromatic Sauvignon similar to that made in the central Loire; light Gamay; and now more and more Chardonnay. Drink the wines young.

Best buys from Haut-Poitou

Sauvignon du Haut-Poitou and Chardonnay du Haut-Poitou (in white), Gamay du Hant-Poitou (in red) (*all widely available*)

JURA

Strange tastes emanate from this mountain fastness in the east of France. While reds, whites and rosés are made (and the rosés are, on the whole, the most successful), it is the vin jaune which is the most familiar name in connection with the Jura.

But it's unlikely to be the most familiar taste. Strong, sherry-like wine which grows a flor and which needs considerable ageing before it's drinkable, this is an acquired taste. But it is one of the more unusual wine tastes of France and worth trying.

The reds are made from the local Trousseau grape and a little Pinot Noir. They're rather heavy and coarse in style and are best appreciated on the spot. The whites also use a local grape variety, the Savagnin, plus a little Chardonnay (which is also used for some sparkling wines).

The rosés, from the Poulsard grape, are also known as vins gris. They're full, dry and quite dark in colour and have a high reputation but little distribution.

The appellations of the Jura are: Arbois, Côtes du Jura, l'Etoile. Village names to look for are Ch Chalon, Poligny and Pupillin.

Who's who in the Jura

By far the biggest shipper of note from the Jura is Henri Maire who makes the full range of styles – try Bonchalaz (*Wizard Wine Warehouse*), or Ch Chalon Vin Jaune (*La Forge Wines, 123 Marksbury, Bath, Avon*). Another name is the single vineyard Vin Jaune Ch d'Arlay (*Eaton Elliot Winebrokers; Harrods*).

Specialist stockists

Eaton Elliot Winebrokers; O W Loeb; Sherborne Vintners

THE LOIRE

The variety of tastes displayed by Loire wines seems to defy categorisation under one heading. There are the crisp, direct, intense tastes of the Sauvignon white wines from Sancerre and Pouilly and points west; the neutral, refreshing qualities of Muscadet at the mouth of the river; the soft, fruity red Gamays; the dull, sweet rosés; the blackcurrant fruit and mellowness of the reds from Chinon and Bourgueil; and the honeyed, apricot-and-cream tastes of the sweet wines of Anjou.

These are northern wines. Champagne, Alsace and Chablis may be further north but the cool, wet winds from the Atlantic blow up the Loire valley, keeping summer temperatures down, dragging out the ripening season dangerously into November, giving poor years even when the wine producers further south are complaining of the heat.

The result for many Loire wines is an intensity of fruit that is unequalled elsewhere. That, coupled with a directness of taste due perhaps to a lack of complexity, makes Loire wines (when they're any good) instantly recognisable and, above all, drinkable. It's no coincidence that the Loire is the second largest producer of sparkling wine in France (after Champagne): good sparkling wine needs a sound, simple tasting base wine to show at its best. It's no coincidence, either, that Muscadet should have become so popular with wine bar habitués – its easy quaffability discourages convoluted tasting notes or too serious discussion.

Sunny days in the vineyards

The quality of many of the wines from the Loire is good – especially good after two fine harvests in 1985 and 1986. In fact, 1985 was too good: it produced white wines that were sometimes too soft, too rounded, without an extra kick of acidity (although reds from 1985 have benefited from the extra sun). 1986 seemed to hit the right note: our tasting records from the cellars of the Loire in the winter of 1986/87 are full of comments on the sharp, green acidity of the young wines – which by the summer of 1987 had turned into deliciously refreshing wines.

If 1985 didn't help the dry white wines, it did wonders for the mostly unsung stars of the Loire: the sweet whites. It never ceases to amaze us that the sweet Anjou wines from Coteaux du Layon, Quarts de Chaume and Bonnezeaux tend to be ignored. Here is a dedicated band of producers, picking the noble-rot-laden grapes as carefully as any château owner in Sauternes, having the advantage over Sauternes that their wines are shot through with acidity to balance the sweetness. And yet the prices their wines command are ludicrous – good for us now, maybe, but not for the long-term future of the wines.

Other prices in the Loire are steadily creeping up – certainly in the fashionable areas. Muscadet (see below) is the villain of the piece at the moment. Last year, we complained about Sancerre and Pouilly Fumé, but their prices have levelled off, and they are beginning to represent better value for money. In between those two extremes of the main Loire vineyards, many of the wines are under-priced. Not just the sweet wines, but the reds of Chinon and Bourgueil, too, are good value, with ageing qualities that are rarely given a chance to prove themselves (we drink the wines too young); the wines of Touraine are excellent buys – especially the Sauvignon and Cabernet; and Vouvray and Montlouis come from another area which deserves more accolades than it receives.

We've divided the section on Loire wines by styles: dry whites, sweet whites, and reds and rosés.

Dry white wines – fashionable freshness

These are the Loire's fashionable wines. From the gooseberry fruit of Sancerre and Pouilly far upstream to the light acidity and slight prickle of a good Muscadet grown at the mouth of the river, these are the wines that have been enjoying huge success in the bistros and smart restaurants of Paris and – increasingly – throughout the world.

In between those two success stories lies a large swath of vineyards making much less exciting wine. Anjou, for instance, is the source of large quantities of often dull whites made from the Chenin Blanc grape, but interspersed with these tracts lie a few highlights – the sweet white areas and a few small dry white appellations.

Touraine, though, manages more interest, with the sparkling wines of Vouvray and Montlouis (see page 527), and attractive still whites from Chardonnay and Sauvignon.

Prices for Sancerre and Pouilly Fumé are now at all-time highs, but at least they seem to have levelled out. Their clean taste has swept a world where only dry wines have a 'healthy' image. The 1986 wines will be very good indeed. There are cheaper alternatives to these wines made from the Sauvignon Blanc grape: Reuilly and Quincy to the south of the Loire valley; Haut-Poitou, where the co-operative makes a good Sauvignon (as well as Chardonnay) – see the separate section; St-Pourçain, made at Vichy to the west of Burgundy; and Sauvignon de St-Bris, a VDQS wine made near Chablis (see under Chablis). But, sadly, none quite achieves the level of completeness and directness that Sancerre and Pouilly do.

Muscadet has seen a rise in price as well. While the quality may be improving, and while individual estate wines and bottling at the vineyard are becoming common (see below), there comes a limit to how much we should be expected to pay for a wine that only 20 years ago was the simple accompaniment for shellfish in the restaurants of Brittany.

Where's where in dry white Loire wines

Sancerre and Pouilly Fumé

These two vineyards face each other across the north-flowing Loire just before it turns west. The whites are the most important wines in terms of quality. Made from the Sauvignon grape they have hints of blackcurrants and gooseberries and a slightly smoky flavour (hence the Fumé in Pouilly Fumé) and at their best are some of the most flavourful wines around. Pouilly Fumé tends to be fuller-bodied than Sancerre.

Other appellation areas producing white wines of similar style, even if not quite up to the same quality, are Reuilly, Quincy and Ménétou-Salon. The appellation of Pouilly-sur-Loire uses the Chasselas grape to make unmemorable whites.

Although it is true that most of these wines don't improve with keeping – so you should be drinking 1985 and 1986 wines now (both very good vintages, with the 1986 wines more acidic and characteristic) – there is a special character to a mature Sancerre or Pouilly Fumé which makes older wines worth seeking out. They certainly don't fade away but develop a mellow acidity that is often less penetrating and more subtle than the taste of the younger wines.

Vouvray and Montlouis

The best vineyards of Touraine in the central Loire are just to the west of the city of Tours. Another pair of towns – Vouvray and Montlouis – face each other across the river. Both Vouvray and Montlouis are made from the Chenin Blanc grape.

We've neglected these wines – unfairly. The trouble is that we've mainly drunk wines bottled by négociants elsewhere on the Loire – and those wines are not very good. Much better to spend a little more and buy wines bottled in Vouvray or Montlouis ('mise en bouteilles au château/domaine' or a Vouvray or Montlouis address will give a clue).

Vouvray wines range from bone dry to sweet and also include sparkling verions (see the section on page 527). It's important to check the style and sweetness or dryness of the Vouvray you're buying. Good, still dry Vouvray can have considerable depth and richness, but the sweeter wines tend to aim higher. Montlouis is softer and more likely to be sweet.

Jasnières

This tiny area of dry white production is away to the north of the Loire on the River Loir (confusingly, the Loire is La Loire, the Loir is Le Loir). The wine made in Jasnières is from the Chenin Blanc which here achieves some quality in a dry, under-ripe sort of way.

Sauvignon de Touraine

A workhorse appellation which covers any wine made in Touraine from the Sauvignon grape. The value for money of these wines is good and the quality reliable, so they make a good cheaper substitute for the Sancerre/Pouilly wines.

Saumur

This small town west of Angers is the first important quality area in Anjou. It's best known in this country for its sparkling wines, made by the Champagne method and using the often under-ripe wines made of the Chenin Blanc (see more under the sparkling wine section on page 527).

Still dry white wines are made here under the Saumur appellation, but few achieve greatness or even leave the area. More important still whites are made in Coteaux de Saumur, but, again, few leave France.

Savennières

A minuscule appellation with a deservedly growing reputation. The wines are some of the best dry wines made in the Loire from the Chenin Blanc grape, with all the overtones of sweetness in the honey and lemon bouquet but crisp, deep fruit on the palate. They need some ageing – around five or six years – to be at their best. Sadly, their reputation has forced up the price of the small amount of wine made. Superior Savennières is made in the single vineyard appellations of Coulée de Serrant and La Roche aux Moines.

Anjou Blanc

Few attractive dry wines appear under this appellation. Even many of the sweet wines (apart from the legendary Moulin Touchais) suffer from too much sulphur and too little attention.

Muscadet

What started life as the base wine made from the Muscadet grape for distillation by the Dutch into brandy has become the drink everybody wants to have by the glass in the wine bar, with fish or shellfish, or any time. It's the second most popular French wine in this country – after red Bordeaux.

But it's also becoming more expensive as the growers have finally told the big merchants that they want more money for their grapes. Top quality Muscadet can fetch more than £4 a bottle, and if you see anything much under £2.50 be very suspicious unless it's on offer. Whether it's worth paying these prices for what is a fairly neutral wine when there are many more attractive dry whites around is another matter.

The new development in Muscadet is the growth of domaine bottling. This has big advantages for the best style of Muscadet – 'sur lie'. It has been known for a while that keeping the wine on its lees until it's bottled (rather than fining and filtering as soon as the fermentation is over) improves the depth and quality of the wine. But then moving the wine for bottling away from the grower's cellar to the merchant's disturbs the lees and spoils the flavours. The less disturbance the wine suffers the better: hence bottling the wine where it's made.

Another trend in an effort to improve the image of Muscadet has been a growth in single vineyard wines, of which the best can be surprisingly full-flavoured and individual. But isn't this rather over-dressing an essentially unsophisticated wine?

A number of useful words on a Muscadet label will give you a strong indication of quality – important in an area where a lot of very dull wine is still being made.

Sèvre et Maine This is the name of the region at the heart of Muscadet production. The quality is higher than ordinary Muscadet and it's worth paying the premium for a wine of greater intensity and depth.

Sur lie See above. This indicates that the wine was kept on its lees until it was bottled.

Mis/mise en bouteille au château (or au domaine) The wine will not have been moved from the cellar before bottling, thus preserving all the advantages of keeping it 'sur lie'.

Other styles of wine made in the Muscadet region are generally less worth buying. They are:

Muscadet AC The basic stuff – and it tends to taste like it.

Gros Plant A VDQS appellation for wine made using the Gros Plant grape. Very tart, acid stuff, possible as a thirst-quencher on a very hot day and not much cheaper than Muscadet.

Drink all these wines from the Muscadet area as young as possible. The 1987 vintage will be in the shops by the late spring and by then it will be the only one to buy. Muscadet Primeur (a white copy of Beaujolais Nouveau) should arrive here by Christmas and will be a good quaffing wine over the Christmas period and into January.

Sweet white wines – forgotten stars

With the growing interest in Sauternes and the high prices that German Trockenbeerenauslese wines always seem to command, it is strange that the sweet white wines of the Loire continue to attract so little attention.

In the valleys of the Layon and Aubance, the Chenin Blanc grape suddenly abandons its rather neutral role as provider of dull dry whites and good sparkling wine and becomes the source of some very fine noble rot sweet wines. The autumn mists here act in the same way as they do in Sauternes – causing a benign fungus on the grapes to shrivel them up, removing the water and leaving just the sweet essence of grape juice.

Four main appellations produce sweet wines. Two – Coteaux du Layon and Coteaux de l'Aubance – produce simple, sweet, fruity wines but without the added extra of the noble rot (except in rare years). But Quarts de Chaume and Bonnezeaux are two tiny pockets of vineyard where the noble rot creates rich, intense, peach-and-apricot wines of great stature and immensely long life. These wines don't really come into their own for as much as 10 or 15 years, but the wait is worth it in great vintages (see overleaf).

Send us **your** views on the report forms at the back of the book.

Back in the main Loire valley, Vouvray and Montlouis, source of dry whites and sparkling wines, also make some intense sweet wines with a honey-like consistency, again with longevity but rarely with noble rot. They are lighter than Quarts de Chaume or Bonnezeaux and just miss that pinnacle of greatness.

SWEET WHITE WINES – VINTAGES

1986 On the whole softer, more quickly maturing wines than 1985, but with plenty of attractive fruit.

1985 An exceptionally fine year with a good deal of noble rot. The wines will need some years before they are ready to drink.

1984 Charming, agreeable wines of comparative lightness. Most will be drinkable within five years, but the few great ones will last up to 15.

1983 Great depth and richness mean that most of the sweet wines will last for anything from 15 to 25 years. Don't drink any before the 1990s.

1982 Soft wines which will be ready for consumption this year or next.

1981 Just coming through a period of dumbness, these wines are beginning to be drinkable in a light sort of way.

1978 Slow-developing vintage that is just starting to show its potential as one for great richness. Worth keeping for some time yet.

1976 Very ripe fruit, full of flavours and complexity. This is a year where the lesser wines are ready to drink now but the greater wines need another five to ten years before they begin to mature.

1975 Lightweight vintage that is well into its maturity.

Older vintages 1969, 1964, 1961 and 1959 are the great long-term vintages of recent years. They're not cheap and are hard to find, but worth buying for future drinking experience (but not for investment).

Red and rosé Loire wines – light and dry

Anjou, Touraine and Sancerre all produce red wines of varying quality. Their one link is their comparative lightness and dryness. They don't have the subtleties of either Bordeaux or Burgundy (although they have some grape varieties in common). Although some Chinon and Bourgueil wines age very well indeed, many tend to be best drunk young. But they are not to be dismissed too lightly, because they fill a gap left by rising Beaujolais and Bordeaux prices for easy-drinking reds that are warm weather wines as well as winter warmers. They are often attractive drunk chilled.

Rosés are more of a mixed bag. The sweetish Rosé d'Anjou is, on the whole, a disaster area, as are such wines as Cabernet d'Anjou. The occasional dry Anjou rosé can be attractive, but avoid the Blush wines that are being made under the Vin de Pays du Jardin de la France label, which are pale imitations of the Blush wines from California (see that section). The best rosés on the Loire are the dry ones from Sancerre and Reuilly (but prices are high – see below).

The three grape varieties that are grown to produce red wines are the

Cabernet Franc (with sometimes a little Cabernet Sauvignon), which makes the best quality reds, the Pinot Noir, which only comes off in good years, and the Gamay, which produces fun, straightforward wines without the real excitement of Beaujolais. Wines made from the Cot grape (the Malbec of Bordeaux) also occasionally put in an appearance.

The Gamay and Cabernet are the staple grapes for rosé wines, while the Pinot Noir makes the rosé in Sancerre and Reuilly.

Where's where in Loire reds and rosés

Sancerre

The reds and rosés of Sancerre, made from the Pinot Noir grape, have in recent years been very fashionable in smart restaurants in Paris and London. Consequently, the prices have shot up. At the moment they don't represent good value at all, even though the 1985 wines have turned out to be very good indeed. A few reds mature for a surprisingly long time.

Chinon and Bourgueil

The most serious Loire reds are made from the Cabernet Franc (with a little Cabernet Sauvignon) in these two towns near Saumur, west of Tours. Chinon produces a lighter wine but with some ageing potential in good years, while Bourgueil makes more austere wine that is not particularly attractive when young, and does need three or four years. St-Nicolas de Bourgueil makes a lighter version of Bourgueil.

Touraine

The Gamay grape is used to produce very enjoyable light wine which goes under the Gamay de Touraine varietal name. The wines have much of the strawberry fruit of the Beaujolais but tend to be a little more attenuated.

Saumur-Champigny

Light, fruity reds from the Cabernet make this tiny area around the town of Saumur a good source of wines. Prices, though, for the better wines, are not particularly cheap.

Anjou

The rosés of Anjou are the wines that have long been the staple production of the area. Slightly sweet wines from the Gamay grape are now being supplemented by somewhat better (and drier) rosés from the Cabernet. Since the appellations are complex, here we give the major styles which appear in the shops:

Cabernet d'Anjou Good quality rosés, generally slightly sweet but with some depth of acidity and tannin.

Rosé d'Anjou The principal appellation of sweet rosés made from the Gamay and other grapes. On the whole, a dull lot.

Rosé de Loire An appellation for dry rosés using the Cabernet grape. Not widely found but worth looking out for.

Anjou also produces good, standard reds from the Cabernet, under the Anjou Rouge appellation.

Other reds of the Loire

Small outposts of red production are dotted in and around the Loire valley. In the south, look for Côtes Roannaises and Côtes du Forez, which are Gamay wines made not far from Beaujolais. Near Saumur, apart from Saumur Rouge, small amounts of fresh Gamay wine are made under the VDQS of Thouarsais.

Red and rosé vintages

1986 A middle-weight vintage, producing wines with some acidity. The rosés should be drunk during 1987/88, but the reds will last for three or four years and some Chinons even longer.

1985 A fine vintage producing some ripe wines from all areas. The Chinon and Bourgueil wines will keep for a while; others (especially rosés) need to be drunk young.

1984 Avoid.

1983 A good vintage with reds at their best. Most rosés are still drinkable – but consume them soon.

1982 Bourgueil reds are still worth drinking. Others are beginning to fade. Rosés should have been drunk.

1981 Anjou Rouge is still worth buying and drinking now. Other wines are on the way down.

Older vintages 1978 and 1976 are the two vintages of Bourgueil and Chinon worth drinking.

Who's who on the Loire

Dry whites

SANCERRE

Jean Vacheron (*Adnams; Eaton Elliot Winebrokers; Hungerford Wine Company*) – also for reds, André Vatan (*Yapp Brothers*), Lucien Crochet, Ch de Thauvenay (*Tanners Wines*), Chavignol Vincent Delaporte (*David Baillie Vintners; Laytons*), Paul Millérioux, Clos du Roy (*Corney & Barrow*), Jean-Max Roger, Le Grand Chemarin (*Davisons*), Clos de la Poussie, Cordier (*Peatling & Cawdron*).

POUILLY FUMÉ

Jean Claude Guyot (*Yapp Brothers*), Ch de Tracy (*Adnams*), Didier Dagueneau (*Lay & Wheeler; La Vigneronne*), de Ladoucette Ch du Nozet

(*J Sainsbury*), Caves St-Vincent Domaine Saget (*Peter Green; Majestic Wine Warehouses*), Michel Bailly, Les Griottes (*Oddbins; Tesco*), Les Bascoins Domaine Masson-Blondelet (*Wines Galore*).

QUINCY, MÉNÉTOU-SALON, REUILLY, ST-POURÇAIN

Quincy Raymond Pipet (*Yapp Brothers*), Quincy Pierre Mardon (*Adnams*), Ménétou-Salon Henri Pellé (*Goedhuis & Co; Wine Society*), Ménétou-Salon Jean Teiller (*Yapp Brothers*), Reuilly Cordier (*Yapp Brothers*), Reuilly Claud Lafond (*Haynes Hanson & Clark*), St-Pourçain Chardonnay (*Yapp Brothers*).

CÔTES DU FOREZ

Les Vignerons Foréziens Gamay (*The Wine Club*)

VOUVRAY/MONTLOUIS

Most producers here make both sweet and dry wines. See under sweet wines for list.

JASNIÈRES

Joël Gigou (*Adnams*).

SAUVIGNON DE TOURAINE

Henri Marionnet, Domaine de la Charmoise (*Richard Harvey*), Confrérie des Vignerons de Oisly-et-Thésée (*Oddbins*), Domaine Octavie (*Majestic Wine Warehouses*).

SAUMUR (STILL WHITE)

Ch de St-Florent Langlois Château (*Alex Findlater*), Albert Besombes Moc-Baril (*Richmond Wine Warehouse*).

SAVENNIÈRES

Domaine des Baumard (*Eldridge Pope/Reynier Wine Library*), Mme Joly Coulée de Serrant and Roche aux Moines (*Hungerford Wine Company*), Yves Soulez Domaine de la Bizolière (*Wine Society; Yapp Brothers*).

MUSCADET

Guy Bossard (*Bibendum; Andrew Mead Wines*), Ch de l'Oiselinière Chéreau-Carré (*Wine Society*), Ch de Chasseloir Chéreau-Carré (*Lorne House Vintners*), Donatien Bahuaud (*Peter Dominic*), Domaine des Dorices Léon Boullault (*Peter Green*), Ch du Cléray Jean Sauvion (*Le Nez Rouge*), Marquis de Goulaine (*Selfridges*), Ch de la Ragotière (*Hedley Wright*), Ch de la Berrière (*Ben Ellis & Associates*), Ch de la Mouchetière (*Safeway*).

Sweet whites

VOUVRAY

Ch de Moncontour (*The Market/Le Provençal*), Gaston Huet (*Adnams*), Prince Poniatowsky Clos Baudoin (*La Vigneronne*), Marc Brédif (*Bow Wine Vaults; Oddbins*), Foreau Clos Naudin (*Adnams*).

MONTLOUIS

G Delétang Montlouis (*Wine Society*), Berger Domaine des Liards (*Lay & Wheeler*).

QUARTS DE CHAUME, BONNEZEAUX, COTEAUX DU LAYON

Domaine des Baumard Coteaux du Layon/Quarts de Chaume (*Eldridge Pope/Reynier Wine Library*), Quarts de Chaume Lalanne Ch de Belle-Rive (*Wine Society*), Quarts de Chaume Ch de Fesles (*Bibendum*), Bonnezeaux René Renou (*Yapp Brothers*), Ch de Gauliers Mme Fourlinnie (*Yapp Brothers*), Domaine des Rochettes G Chauvin Coteaux de l'Aubance (*Prestige Vintners*).

ANJOU BLANC

Les Vins Touchais renowned recently for a rare collection of old vintages of sweet Anjou Blanc (*Adnams; Lay & Wheeler; La Réserve*), Maison Prunier (*La Réserve*).

Reds and Rosés

SANCERRE

Sancerre Rosé and Rouge Vacheron (*Eaton Elliot Winebrokers*), Sancerre Rosé Paul Thomas Chavignol (*Bow Wine Vaults*), Sancerre Rouge Domaine Daulny (*Haynes Hanson & Clark*).

BOURGUEIL, ST-NICOLAS DE BOURGUEIL AND CHINON

Chinon Raymond Desbourdes (*Yapp Brothers*), Bourgueil G Audebert, Domaine de Grand Clos (*Berry Bros & Rudd*), Chinon Charles Joguet (*O W Loeb*), Bourgueil Maître et Viemont (*O W Loeb*), St-Nicolas de Bourgueil J-C Mabilot (*Bibendum; Alex Findlater*), Bourgueil Caslot-Galbrun La Hurolaie (*Eaton Elliot Winebrokers; The Market/Winecellars*), Chinon Couly-Dutheil (*Lay & Wheeler*), Chinon Domaine du Colombier Yves Loisseau (*J Sainsbury*), Chinon Caves du Petit Colombier (*Cadwgan Fine Wine Merchants, The Market/Le Provençal*), St-Nicolas de Bourgueil P Jamet Domaine du Fondis (*Averys*).

TOURAINE

Ch du Petit Thouars (*Goedhuis & Co; Tanners Wines*)

SAUMUR-CHAMPIGNY

Paul Buisse (*Le Nez Rouge*), Domaine Filliatreau (*Yapp Brothers*), Domaine Vinicole de St-Cyr (*Ian G Howe; Pennyloaf Wines*), Saumur-Champigny Ch de Targe (*Alex Findlater; Haynes Hanson & Clark; Lay & Wheeler*).

Best buys from the Loire

DRY WHITES

Sauvignon Vin de Pays du Jardin de la France 1986, Cave des Vignerons de Saumur (*H Allen Smith*)

Touraine Cépage Sauvignon 1985, Cuvée Prestige, Confrérie des Vignerons de Oisly-et-Thésée (*Oddbins*)

Muscadet de Sèvre-et-Maine 1986, Ch de la Galissonnière (*Peter Dominic*)

Muscadet de Sèvre-et-Maine 1985 (*Marks & Spencer*)

Savennières Clos du Papillon 1985, Jean Baumard (*Eldridge Pope/Reynier Wine Libraries*)

Vin de Thouarsais 1985, Cépage Chenin, Michel Gigon (*Yapp Brothers*)

Quincy 1985, Domaine de la Maison Blanche (*Andrew Gordon Wines; Stapylton Fletcher*)

Vouvray 1985, Ch de Moncontour (*The Market/Winecellars*)

SWEET WHITES

Coteaux du Layon (*Peatling & Cawdron*)

Coteaux du Layon, Clos Ste-Catherine, Jean Baumard (*Eldridge Pope/Reynier Wine Libraries*)

Montlouis Demi-Sec, Domaine des Liards (*Yapp Brothers*)

Anjou Moulin Touchais 1959 (*Tanners Wines*)

Bonnezeaux 1981, Domaine la Croix de Mission (*Averys*)

ROSÉS

Sancerre Rosé, Domaine des Godons 1985 (*H Allen Smith*)

Cabernet de Saumur, Cave des Vignerons (*Tesco*)

Sancerre Rosé 1985, Pierre et Alain Dezat (*Alex Findlater*)

REDS

Chinon 1985, Caves du Petit Colombier (*The Market/Winecellars*)

Ch du Petit Thouars 1985, Comte du Petit Thouars (*Bibendum; Tanners Wines*)

Chinon 1985, Domaine du Colombier (*J Sainsbury*)

Cabernet de Touraine, Cuvée Prestige, Confrérie des Vignerons de Oisly-et-Thésée (*Oddbins*)

St-Nicolas de Bourgueil 1985, Paul Buisse (*Le Nez Rouge/Berkmann Wine Cellars*)

Côtes du Forez 1986, Les Vignerons Foréziens (*Bordeaux Direct*)

Specialist stockists

Bibendum; Eldridge Pope; Alex Findlater; Peter Green; Hampshire Wine Co; Ian G Howe; O W Loeb; Nobody Inn; Prestige Vintners; Sherborne Vintners; Yapp Brothers

---

The Wine Development Board is a small organisation with the responsibility of encouraging more people to drink wine. They may be able to supply literature and general promotional material. Contact them at: Five Kings House, Kennet Wharf Lane, Upper Thames Street, London EC4V 3BH; TEL 01-248 5835.

THE MIDI

Of all those French red wines at £1.99 in the shops, it's a fair bet that a large number come from the area known as the Midi. And before readers assume we're about to be snobbish about these wines, let us quickly say that for value for money and sheer drinkability, this part of the south of France is getting better all the time.

Mind you, it's still the land of the wine lake: 40 per cent of all French wine comes from Languedoc and Roussillon, the two ancient regions which follow the coast as it arcs round west of Marseilles as far as the Pyrenees and the Spanish border. Sixty per cent of Midi wine comes from co-operatives – some of which are good, but many more of which are terrible.

Over the past decade, the efforts of enlightened producers and the research work of trained oenologists – carried out in the giant SICAREX Mediterranée station near Montpellier and backed up by money from the French government and the European Commission – have gradually brought about a deep change in the attitude to winemaking – only just in time.

The changes have been forced on producers because less and less of their cheap vin de table was being sold: the French are drinking less wine overall and what they do drink is of better quality.

Good grapes in good places

In the vineyards, the biggest changes have been in the increased attention being paid to the grape varieties used and in lower yields which tend to increase the quality of the harvest. Vineyards on the flat lands are being grubbed up, leaving the better quality, well-drained vineyards on sloping land as the source of more and more of the wine.

Producers on the hillside sites have been encouraged by the creation of new AC and VDQS zones, which tend to push up grape prices, and which certainly improve quality but lessen the yields. At the same time, larger vin de pay areas have led some enterprising producers to experiment with noble grape varieties and they are coming up with some very fine wines.

Quality grape varieties from all over France are being tried out here with much success. In the reds, Cabernet Sauvignon and Syrah, Merlot and Grenache, Cinsault and Mourvèdre are shoring up the firm, tannic but often coarse wines made from the widely planted Carignan. In the whites, Sauvignon and Chardonnay are being tried – both with some success.

The winemaking techniques are improving dramatically as well.

Stainless steel, cold fermentation, white coats and labs are to be seen all over the region in co-operatives and private establishments alike.

There was never really a danger that these southern wines would lack character or distinction. What they needed was reliable quality and fruit and acidity, which is what they're now getting. And what *we* are getting is a whole range of wines – often with names unheard of 10 or 15 years ago – which have risen relatively little in price and are presenting just the right sort of easy tastes.

Where's where in the Midi

The region is now full of appellation areas. Some have been around for a long time, others are so new that the French government's lists haven't caught up with them. Above all, this is the heartland of the vins de pays, areas of superior table wines where official controls ensure reliability, minimum alcohol, decent quality fruit and a value-for-money product.

In this Cook's tour of the south of France, we move from east to west. For availability of the wines, see the Who's who in the Midi section which follows this.

LANGUEDOC (GARD)

Clairette de Bellegarde White wines of an uninspired nature.

Costières du Gard VDQS area near Nîmes which is best for full-bodied reds of a reliable quality. Whites here are dull.

Vin de Pays Vin de Pays du Gard, Côtes du Salavès and Uzège: all are cheap and reasonably cheerful, especially the Gard wines. The very best Vin de Pays are from the Sables du Golfe du Lion (the home of the largest single vineyard in France), owned by Listel and planted on the sands by the sea.

LANGUEDOC (HÉRAULT AND AUDE)

The heartland of the wine lake vineyards now has some pockets where growers are taking a little trouble and making something that is not only inexpensive but reasonably decent at the price. All the best wines seem to come from the slopes away from the flat coastal plain – as might be expected.

Coteaux du Languedoc is the main AC appellation and its best wines are sturdy, simple reds. La Clape is a sub-division, making good rosé and white on chalky soil. St-Chinian VDQS has higher quality, is tough but spicy in a tannic sort of way and worth keeping for a year or two: 1983 is ideal at the moment.

Faugères Soft and full-bodied red AC wines that suddenly became popular in France but are still good value for us.

Fitou Carignan grapes make some well-aged wines in this AC area which will last for three to five years from vintage and are characterised by good ruby-coloured fruit.

Minervois A huge AC area using Carignan and Cinsault in its big, beefy reds. The wines are good value and one or two producers make something that much better (see under the Who's who section below). An area that represents good value.

Blanquette de Limoux Sparkling wine from near Carcassonne (see under Sparkling wines on page 526).

Corbières AC area that makes a large amount of reds by carbonic maceration (which brings out plenty of fruit and colour but requires the wine to be drunk young). Occasional pockets of better quality.

Vins de Pays
There are nearly 45 vin de pays zones in the Hérault and Aude *départements*. The largest production area is Vin de Pays de l'Hérault, which ranges in quality from the pretty ordinary to the superb Cabernet Sauvignon wines of Mas de Daumas Gassac. Other vins de pays in the Aude include the Haute Vallée de l'Aude, the Vallée du Paradis (what a name to sell a wine) and Val d'Orbieu.

ROUSSILLON

Côtes du Roussillon and Côtes du Roussillon Villages
The main area, Côtes du Roussillon, makes good soft reds with plenty of colour from Carignan and Grenache grapes. Interspersed are the better sites of the Villages with slightly higher alcohol but also greater finesse. Collioure is a smaller area for reds.

Vin de Pays Best in Roussillon are Catalan and Pyrénées-Orientales, making large quantities of good-value reds and whites.

VINS DOUX NATURELS

Sweet fortified wines from the Muscat grape are made at Sète (Muscat de Frontignan) and in Roussillon (Muscat de Rivesaltes). Banyuls, right on the Spanish border, specialises in a sweet wine made from the Grenache grape.

Vintages in the Midi

It's rare for vintages to be much affected by the weather. 1986, in fact, was an excellent year with plenty of sunshine bringing in grapes in good condition and comparatively large quantities. Except where indicated under the Where's where section above, most wines are ready to drink when they reach the shops.

Who's who in the Midi

LANGUEDOC (GARD)

Costières du Gard Ch de la Tuilerie (*Wine Growers Association*), Ch Roubaud (*Findlater Mackie Todd*), Domaine St-Louis (*Bordeaux Direct*), Mas de la Louis Perdrix (*Gerard Harris*).

LANGUEDOC (HÉRAULT)

Coteaux du Languedoc Domaine de Lavabre (*Morris & Verdin; Tanners Wines*), Domaine des Tourelles (*Alistair Cameron*), Ch de la Condamine Bertrand (*Stapylton Fletcher*), Domaine de l'Aquirou (*Whynot Wine Warehouses*).

St-Chinian Rouanet (*Waitrose*), Domaine des Jougla (*Stapylton Fletcher*).

Faugères Domaines Fontainilles (*Wine Society*), Cuvée Jules Gaston (*Victoria Wine Co*).

La Clape Ch de Pech-Redon (*Bordeaux Direct*).

Domaine de Mas de Daumas Gassac (*Adnams; Bibendum; J Sainsbury*).

Minervois Ch de Gourgazaud (*J Sainsbury; Tanners Wines*), Domaine de Ste-Eulalie (*Adnams; Lay & Wheeler*), Ch de Pelletier (*The Market/Winecellars*), Cuvée Jean d'Alibert (*Tanners Wines*), Domaine du Pech d'André (*Majestic Wine Warehouses*), Domaine Maris (*Majestic Wine Warehouses*), Domaine de Mayrane (*Marks & Spencer*).

LANGUEDOC (AUDE)

Corbières Ch les Palais (*Victoria Wine Co*), Ch de Montrabech (*Tanners Wines*), Ch des Ollieux (*D Byrne*), Ch de Belle Isle (*The Market/Winecellars*).

Fitou Domaine Mme Parmentier (*Peter Dominic, and others*), Chantovent (*Tanners Wines*), Les Vignerons de France (*Laytons*), Caves de Mont-Tauch (*Berry Bros & Rudd*), Le Carla (*Peter Dominic*).

ROUSSILLON (PYRÉNÉES-ORIENTALES)

Côtes du Rousillon and Côtes du Roussillon Villages Caramany (*Vinimports – tel 0273 540624*), Coteaux Catalans (*Peter Dominic; Tesco*), Ch de Corneilla (*Eldridge Pope*), Bouffet (*Majestic Wine Warehouses*); Félix Laquebrou (*Unwins*), Full French Red Côtes du Roussillon (*Marks & Spencer*).

DESSERT WINES IN LANGUEDOC AND ROUSSILLON

Muscat de Frontignan Aphrodis (*Stapylton Fletcher*), Muscat de Rivesaltes (*Eldridge Pope*).

VINS DE PAYS IN LANGUEDOC AND ROUSSILLON

du Gard (*Peter Dominic; Threshers*).

de l'Hérault Domaine du Chapître (*Adnams; La Vigneronne*), Domaine de St-Macaire (*Waitrose*), Cante-Cigale Syrah (*Waitrose*), Domaine des Lenthéric (*Majestic Wine Warehouses*).

de l'Uzège (*Victoria Wine Co*).

de la Vallée du Paradis (*J Sainsbury*), Val d'Orbieu (*Adnams; Bibendum; Lay & Wheeler; and many others*).

des Coteaux de Salavès (*Peter Dominic*).

de l'Aude Foncalieu Cabernet Sauvignon (*Waitrose*).

Sables du Golfe du Lion Listel (*widely available*).

d'Oc Listel Cabernet Sauvignon and Chardonnay (*Morrisons*), Syrah (*Oddbins; Tesco*).

Pyrénées-Orientales Castel Frères (*Carrefour; Gateway*), St Michael (*Marks & Spencer*).

des Collines de la Moure Abbaye de la Valmagne (*Oddbins*).

Côtes de Thau Syrah (*Eldridge Pope*).

Best buys from the Midi

WHITES

Listel wines
Coteaux du Languedoc, La Clape, Domaine de l'Abbaye de Valfernière (*Bordeaux Direct*)
Minervois, Domaine de Gourgazaud (*Philip Morgan*)

REDS

Faugères, Cuvée Jules Gaston (*Addison Avenue Wine Shop; Victoria Wine Co*)
Full French Red, Côtes du Roussillon (*Marks & Spencer*)
Côtes du Roussillon 1985, Félix Laquebrou (*Unwins*)
Vin de Pays de l'Hérault, Cante-Cigale, Syrah (*Waitrose*)
Listel wines
Cabernet Sauvignon Prestige, Chantovent (*Justerini & Brooks*)
Minervois, Ch de Gourgazaud (*Philip Morgan; J Sainsbury – in magnum*)

Specialist stockists

Bordeaux Direct; Bibendum; Hicks & Don; Ian G Howe; Stapylton Fletcher; Tanners Wines; Taste Shops

PROVENCE

Provence was the first home of the vine in France. It was brought there, probably by the Greeks, long before the Romans moved in and built their aqueducts and arenas, and it has been part of the scene ever since.

That short history lesson is by way of explanation for the casual attitude Provence has had to wine: until recently, only pockets of quality stood out in a sea of rosé, the preferred tipple of the smart set who holidayed on the coast. However, we are delighted to report on the change of vinous fortune for Provence. From producing a few pricey reds and lots of alcoholic rosés, it has become the home of some very exciting winemaking indeed.

The two areas to watch are Coteaux d'Aix-en-Provence and Coteaux des Baux en Provence. Both have attracted some young winemakers who are introducing considerable changes, organic farming methods in some cases, and blending in balanced quantities of Cabernet Sauvignon, Syrah and Mourvèdre into the Cinsault, Grenache and Carignan which are the traditional varieties for the area.

This excitement has rubbed off on to the Côtes de Provence winemakers, the ones who made all that rosé. Here, it's not only reds that are getting better: at last, some decent white wine is coming out of the area, made using all the modern cold fermentation techniques, and with some crisp Sauvignon Blanc fruit introduced into the mix to give the wines clean acidity and a fresh, green taste.

Where does this leave those traditional pockets of quality in Provence? Some – Palette, for example, with Ch Simone its one major estate – are tiny and inevitably pricey. Bandol, though, is bigger, but still expensive. Now it, too, is beginning to lose out in quality comparisons with Coteaux d'Aix-en-Provence and Coteaux des Baux en Provence. Unless, that is, you are interested in some of the old-fashioned, wood-aged rosés of Bandol, which command premium prices and interest in France.

Where's where in Provence

Bellet A tiny area of white wine production in the mountains north of Nice. Little seems to leave the area, although one or two examples are available in Britain.

Côtes de Provence Catch-all appellation that takes in most of southern Provence. Whites, reds and rosés are made. Whites and some of the rosés (by far the bulk of production) are much better than they used to be: dry and on the full side, but some of the better wines now have fruit as well – quite an innovation. Reds, too, are much better, due to the use of noble grape varieties like Syrah and Mourvèdre.

Bandol Traditionally, *the* appellation of Provence, making fine reds and dry whites and rosés. The reds made from the Mourvèdre grape are the most impressive. While the wines are not cheap, they have some unusual, spicy, peppery flavours worth experiencing.

Cassis A dry white wine made from Clairette, Ugni Blanc, Marsanne and Sauvignon grapes. Small production means high prices. Nothing to do with the blackcurrant liqueur.

Coteaux d'Aix-en-Provence This, with Coteaux des Baux en Provence (see below) is the most interesting area of Provence. Mainly reds and rosés, with a few whites – the reds are the best. While the usual southern grape varieties predominate, some enterprising producers are using Cabernet Sauvignon as well.

Coteaux des Baux en Provence AC area producing reds that are more expensive than Aix-en-Provence but are also achieving greater things. The best producers, many of whom employ organic farming methods, use Cabernet Sauvignon and Syrah grapes.

Palette Small appellation making long-lasting whites which tend to offer curiosity value rather than drinkability.

Coteaux Varois A new VDQS zone with large-scale production (30 million bottles) and variable quality, so it pays to seek out good individual producers.

Vins de Pays regions These include the reds and rosés of the Bouches du Rhône. Mont Caume encompasses the lesser offerings from Bandol, plus some Cabernet Sauvignon wines. The Vin de Pays d'Oc region covers Provence and the rest of the Midi.

Vintages in Provence

The quality in vintages varies little in the sunny south of France. 1986 was a typically warm year, with good quality crops making plenty of wine.

White wines – apart from curiosities like Ch Simone – should be drunk young: 1985 wines should be drunk up, with 1986 wines following on fast. Rosés follow the same pattern, apart from some of the Bandol rosés which are designed for ageing.

Reds age much better. For Bandol, the best vintages to drink are 1976, 1978 and 1982, with younger wines needing more maturation. The same is true for Coteaux d'Aix-en-Provence and Coteaux des Baux en Provence, although these wines do age more quickly than Bandol. Côtes de Provence reds need two or three years – drink 1983s now, and start on 1985s.

Who's who in Provence

Bellet Ch de Crémat (*Yapp Brothers*).

Côtes de Provence L'Estandon and Domaine des Hauts de St-Jean (*both from Yapp Brothers*), Domaines Ott (*Harrods*), Ch de Pampelonne (*Christopher Piper Wines*), Vignobles Gasparini, Les Maîtres Vignerons de la Presqu'île de Saint-Tropez (*Berkmann Wine Cellars/Le Nez Rouge*), Saint-André de Figuière (*Morris & Verdin*).

Bandol Moulin des Costes (*Soho Wine Market, 3 Greek Street, London W1*), Domaine Tempier (*Wine Society*), Ch Vannières (*Oddbins*), Mas de la Rouvière (*Yapp Brothers*), Domaine de la Bastide Blanche (*Berkmann Wine Cellars/Le Nez Rouge*), Domaines Ott (*Harrods*).

Cassis Clos Ste-Magdelaine (*Yapp Brothers*), Domaine du Paternel (*Wine Society*).

Coteaux d'Aix-en-Provence Commanderie de la Bargemone (*Barwell and Jones*), Ch de Fonscolombe (*Adnams; Harrods; Tanners Wines*), Domaine de la Crémade (*Peter Dominic*), Ch Vignelaure (*Curzon Wine Company*), Ch de Beaulieu (*Wine Growers Association*), Ch la Coste (*Alex Findlater*).

Stockists given in italic type after wines in this section will be found in the WHERE TO BUY section earlier in the book.

Coteaux des Baux en Provence Domaine de Trévallon (*Yapp Brothers*), Mas de Gourgonnier (*Les Bons Vins Occitans*), Mas du Cellier (*Chesterford Vintners; La Vigneronne*), Mas de la Dame (*Davids of Ashby*), Domaine des Terres Blanches (*Anthony Byrne Fine Wines; George Hill of Loughborough; La Vigneronne*).

Palette Ch Simone (*La Vigneronne; Yapp Brothers*).

Coteaux Varois Domaine de St-Jean (*Ellis Son & Vidler*), Domaine des Chaberts (*High Breck Vintners*), Château St-Estève (*Tanners Wines*).

VINS DE PAYS

Bouches du Rhône Domaine de Boullery (*Wine Growers Association*), Domaine de Temps Perdu (*Berry Bros & Rudd*).

Mont Caume Bunan (*Yapp Brothers*).

Best buys from Provence

WHITES

Coteaux d'Aix-en-Provence, Ch de Fonscolombe (*Adnams; Kershaw's Wine Warehouse; Lay & Wheeler; Tanners Wines*)
Coteaux d'Aix-en-Provence 1986, Ch Beaulieu (*Wine Growers Association*)

REDS

Côtes de Provence 1982, Domaine St-André de Figuière (*Morris & Verdin*)
Coteaux des Baux en Provence 1985, Mas de Gourgonnier, Réserve du Mas (*Les Bons Vins Occitans*)
Côtes de Provence, Domaine Fonscolombe (*Bow Wine Vaults; G E Bromley; and many others*)
Coteaux des Baux en Provence 1983, Mas de la Dame (*Davids of Ashby; Chesterford Vintners*)

Specialist stockists

Les Bons Vins Occitans; Ian G Howe; Le Nez Rouge/Berkmann Wine Cellars; Sherborne Vintners; La Vigneronne; Windrush Wines; Yapp Brothers

THE RHÔNE

The scene is the warm October sunshine outside a medium-sized cellar in the heart of the Côtes du Rhône vineyards. A range of wines made at the cellars is being poured into glasses, sniffed, savoured and, often reluctantly, spat out.

We say reluctantly not just because the idea of actually drinking a glass of wine at 11 o'clock in the morning was appealing, but because the sheer quality and drinkability of the wines made us want to enjoy every aspect down to the final swallow.

The wines – mainly reds, of course, but with the occasional white – were full of fruit, refreshing, rich and powerful, but no longer the hard, tannic and alcoholic monsters that used to be the only thing we could find in the Côtes du Rhône. Here was elegance.

And the price for such paragons of winemaking? Amazingly low – not rock bottom, but all between £3 and £4.

The scene changes to a small cellar in the town of Ampuis, where the vineyards of the Côte Rôtie frown down on to the River Rhône. We are tasting again, more superb wines, deep, tannic, full of the typically Syrah taste of violets and spices, intense and concentrated. We remember discovering these wines some years ago and revelling in the strange aromas and rich tastes, and being able to buy them at very good prices.

Not any more. The price, we ask. Ah, monsieur, I regret that I have none of this wine for sale – it is all sold already, on allocation. And, I regret, monsieur, it was not cheap.

The Rhône discovered

Two scenes which sum up what has happened in the Rhône valley in a remarkably short space of time. While the quality of wines from the Côtes du Rhône, Côtes du Rhône-Villages and the neighbouring appellations like Côtes du Ventoux and Coteaux du Tricastin, Lirac and Côtes du Luberon has been getting better and better, the prices have stayed remarkably constant – a product more of the volumes these vineyards can produce than, necessarily, the magnanimity of the growers.

Sadly, though, the great northern Rhône red wines from Côte Rôtie, Hermitage and Cornas, have been discovered not only by drinkers but by investors who have spotted 'the next thing' after investment in Bordeaux and Burgundy. The producers see that if their wines are regarded as good investments they are probably under-valued, and the consequence has been a rapid rise in prices. They're still terrific wines, but there are no bargains to be had here.

Both these wine areas have one thing in common besides the presence of the River Rhône – their quality. There is a sense of excitement coming from the vineyards of the Rhône valley. It may be the realisation in the northern Rhône vineyards that Hermitage and Côte Rôtie are returning to a pre-eminent place in the pantheon of French wines. It may be the effect the flexibility of investment in new equipment and new approaches is having on the wine producers of the southern Rhône. Or it may be the succession of good vintages – 1985 and 1986 following on 1983, with only the hiccough of 1984.

Whites join in the fun

Whatever it is, the excitement is not confined to red wines – although the Rhône continues to be predominantly a producer of reds. There have been developments in white wines, as well. While many Hermitage whites are still heavy and oxidised, further south, the whites of the Côtes du Rhône, of Côtes du Ventoux, of Côtes du Luberon, of Lirac, the sweet white of Muscat de Beaumes-de-Venise are all proving that even in this Mediterranean heat, new technology and new knowledge can make white wines full of fruit and freshness.

The north–south divide

Traditionally, the Rhône valley vineyards have been divided into two. The northern section, from just south of Vienne to Valence, has vineyards on steep hillsides, mainly in the narrow confines of the Rhône valley as it flows between the eastern outcrops of the Massif Central. The area is dominated by two grape varieties – one widely planted, the other a rare breed indeed.

The Syrah, the only variety for the red wines of the northern Rhône, is the driving force behind the great wines of Hermitage, of Côte Rôtie, of Cornas; and behind the more immediately accessible – and affordable – wines of St-Joseph and Crozes-Hermitage.

While the principal white grape varieties – used in Hermitage and Crozes-Hermitage Blanc and in St-Péray – are the Marsanne and Roussanne – it is to the rare Viognier that experts turn for a unique taste that is found nowhere else. This is the grape variety used to make the whites of Condrieu and Ch Grillet, dry but full of ripe, southern, peachy flavours – and at immense prices because so little is produced. The Viognier is also used to soften the Syrah in Côte Rôtie.

Compared with the northern Rhône, the grape varieties of the southern Rhône are legion. Thirteen permitted grape varieties can be used to produce a Châteauneuf-du-Pape. The same varieties, in differing combinations, turn up all round the flat, sprawling southern Rhône vineyards. They're the varieties of the south of France – the Grenache, Cinsault, Carignan, Mourvèdre are the predominant grapes for the reds; for the whites, it's Clairette and Picpoul, Marsanne, Roussanne and Bourboulenc.

But the southern Rhône red wines now also have increasing amounts of Syrah, acting just as Cabernet Sauvignon does elsewhere in France, as a *cépage améliorateur* – a noble grape variety used to lift the quality of the local wine. And it is the Syrah which is behind much of the fine wine production in the area.

NORTHERN RHÔNE

What's on the label in the northern Rhône

Clairette de Die See the Sparkling wine section on page 528.

Condrieu 35 acres of vineyard produce small quantities of intensely lush white wines from the Viognier grape. Some writers have suggested affinities in taste with a ripe but dry German wine – with the balance poised between rich fruit and acidity.

Cornas Firm red wines made from 100 per cent Syrah in a small vineyard area on steep hillsides south of Hermitage. Unlike Côte Rôtie, no white grapes are used to soften the Syrah, so the wines are almost opaquely tannic when young, but superbly rich in maturity. Small quantities are made – and the price is shooting up.

Côte Rôtie The 'roasted slope' is the most northerly Rhône appellation. It's so called because of its exposure to the sun. The old vineyards that make superb reds from the Syrah grape, with a little white Viognier, are on the steep hillside tumbling down to the River Rhône. New plantings on the top of the hill threaten to dilute the quality.

Crozes-Hermitage The vineyards on the lower slopes and flatter land around the hill of Hermitage (see below). Less intense or punch-packing than Hermitage, it is nevertheless often of good quality with the dry fruit and spicy flavours of Syrah. Whites, made from Marsanne and Roussanne, are improving all the time. Some very good value is to be had from the better producers.

Ch Grillet The smallest French appellation (a mere 7.5 acres) producing a more intense version of Condrieu (see above). Very expensive and difficult to find.

Hermitage The best northern Rhône wines come from the hill above Tain l'Hermitage crowned with a hermit's chapel. Wines whose old reputation as some of the best in France is gradually returning, they are the epitome of the almost inaccessible fruit of young Syrah, softened here with up to 15 per cent of white grapes, which develop into such a rich, powerful yet smooth maturity. White wines are also made in small quantities, mainly traditional in style and with considerable ageing ability.

St-Péray Sparkling wines from the Marsanne and Roussanne grapes, made by the Champagne method. Not very exciting and not often seen in Britain.

St-Joseph A lighter, more delicate version of Hermitage and one which is approachable younger and lasts less time. New vineyards, as with Côte Rôtie, may lower the general quality.

Northern Rhône vintages

1986 A dry, hot summer meant that the red wines all have great intensity of colour and concentration of fruit. Some regard this as a classic Syrah vintage, making reds that will be very long lasting.

1985 Although not one of the very greatest Rhône vintages, it is not far off the quality of the 1983s (see below). There were low quantities in Côte Rôtie. The reds are expected to last, as are white Hermitages. The Viognier whites have a slight lack of acidity because of the intense heat of the autumn. When well made, with some form of temperature control during fermentation, the reds are bursting with powerful Syrah fruit.

1984 Elegance and early maturity are the hallmark of this vintage. Côte Rôtie has lower alcohol and tannin and less concentration than usual, while Hermitage is a middle-range wine. The whites have high acidity – especially those made from the Viognier grape.

1983 An exceptional year, especially for reds, which are concentrated, rich wines lasting for 20 years or more without any difficulty. Hermitage and Côte Rôtie will last very well; Crozes-Hermitage and Cornas will mature in eight to ten years' time. The whites, too, are rich and will last.

1982 Too many grapes and too hot temperatures during fermentation have dogged this vintage. While some wines are fine and will last for 10 to 15 years, others lack structure and their fruit is too 'hot' and jammy. The white Viognier wines are already mature, the white Hermitage should be ready soon.

1981 Careful selection is necessary in the reds for this light year. Good growers, though, made decent wine which is good value. The whites – apart from some Hermitage Blanc – are on the decline and should be drunk soon.

1980 Well-balanced wines, much better than those of northern France, are still maturing. Crozes-Hermitage and St-Joseph should be drunk now, but keep other reds for another year. Most whites have faded.

1979 Medium quality wines, with the best coming from Hermitage. Other reds are lighter and need to be drunk now.

1978 Magnificent wines that are still almost infants. Hermitage and Côte Rôtie won't really be mature until the turn of the century, if then. Other reds will mature sooner, but don't touch them yet. Whites are in fine fettle at the moment.

Earlier vintages 1976, 1972, 1971 are still at their peak, as are the 1969s. Other vintages of the early 1970s need to be bought with care.

Northern Rhône – growers and négociants

Côte Rôtie

Marius Gentaz-Dervieux Long-lasting wines that should go for ten or twelve years before broaching. Look for La Garde, Côte Brune and Viaillère.
Windrush Wines

Guigal A specialist in wood ageing of wines, Guigal keeps his wines in barrel for three years. Look for La Landonne and La Moulieu, also Côte Rôtie Brune et Blonde and white Hermitage. Also owns Vidal-Fleury (see below).
Adnams; Lay & Wheeler; Oddbins; Whynot Wine Warehouses; Wine Society

Jasmin The greatest individual vineyard producer making classic but not heavy wines. Look for La Chevalière d'Ampuis.
Lay & Wheeler; La Vigneronne; Yapp Brothers

Rostaing Deep-flavoured wine that receives two years in cask.
Reid Wines

Vidal-Fleury Now owned by Guigal, this is the largest firm in Côte Rôtie. Long-lasting wines which need at least ten years.
Berkmann Wine Cellars/Le Nez Rouge; La Vigneronne

Hermitage

Chapoutier One of the two big négociants in the region. Makes very traditional wines in Hermitage, Crozes-Hermitage, St-Joseph and Châteauneuf. The white Hermitage Chante Alouette is remarkable.
Adnams; Bibendum; Eldridge Pope; Lay & Wheeler

Chave The greatest of the single vineyard growers. Long-lived reds and whites.
Adnams; Lay & Wheeler; La Vigneronne; Wine Society

Delas Frères Growers and négociants with vineyards in Hermitage, Cornas, Côte Rôtie and Condrieu.
Augustus Barnett shops

Jaboulet Aîné The other big négociant house that's setting the pace for the area. In Hermitage they own La Chapelle for red and Chevalier de Sterimbourg for white. Also make Crozes-Hermitage, St Joseph (La Grande Pompée), Côte Rôtie (Les Jumelles), Tavel, Châteauneuf and the famous Côtes du Rhône, Parallèle 45.
Majestic Wine Warehouses; Oddbins; Tanners Wines; Windrush Wines; Wine Society

Cornas and St-Joseph

Clape One of the finest producers in the Rhône. Deep, long-lasting wines of impenetrable blackness when young. Also makes some sparkling St-Péray.
Adnams; Yapp Brothers

Michel Old-fashioned family holding which needs plenty of time.
La Vigneronne

Bernard Gripa Light-style St-Joseph with only a year's wood ageing but plenty of stalky tannin.
Yapp Brothers

Crozes-Hermitage

Names to look for are Domaine des Clairmonts, Desmeure, Fayolle, Albert Bégot (who makes wine organically), Tardy & Ange, plus the wines of Jaboulet Aîné and Chapoutier.

Condrieu and Ch Grillet

Ch Grillet The single-estate appellation which makes wines that are delicious but rare and difficult to obtain.
Yapp Brothers

Ch du Rozay Young-style wine made mainly in stainless steel with a little wood, although a little traditional wine is made from old vines.
Yapp Brothers

Georges Vernay Some of the best Condrieu, made and sold quickly for freshness.
Eldridge Pope; Majestic Wine Warehouses

Vins de Pays

Vin de Pays les Sables (*Lorne House Vintners*), Vin de Pays de l'Ardèche Syrah (*Tesco*), Vin de Pays des Coteaux de l'Ardèche (*Yapp Brothers*), Vin de Pays des Coteaux de l'Ardèche, Gamay, Cave Co-opérative de St-Désirat (*Bibendum*).

Specialist stockists

For **specialist stockists** of all Rhône wines, see page 403.

SOUTHERN RHÔNE

Plenty of wine – and the quality gets better

The map of the southern Rhône consists of vast tracts of Côtes du Rhône vineyards muddled in with pockets, some large, some much smaller, of areas with their own separate appellations.

Châteauneuf-du-Pape A much abused name that still manages to make some very good wines from quite a large area to the north of Avignon. Big, chewy reds with lots of ripe fruit which mature quite fast and then go down hill slowly. The whites are coming on apace.

Coteaux d'Ardèche An up-and-coming vin de pays area planted with Syrah, Cabernet Sauvignon, Gamay, Merlot and Chardonnay. Some exciting wines from here, some made by Burgundy producers.

Côtes du Luberon A newly established vDQS area in the south of the southern Rhône vineyards. One or two producers are using new technology to make some robust reds and fresh whites and rosés, all very good value.

Côtes du Rhône The basic appellation of the region. Large vineyard areas produce plenty of good basic red wine for quaffing, but, more and more, the quality of serious winemaking is showing through. Producers are important here (see below).

Côtes du Rhône Villages A more closely controlled wine than simple Côtes du Rhône, this comes from specific villages which have better sited vineyards. More flavour and concentration make some of these Villages wines very good. Names to look for: Cairanne, Vacqueyras, Beaumes-de-Venise (yes, they don't just grow Muscat there), Sablet, St-Gervais, Séguret, Valréas, Visan, Laudun (also makes white) and Chusclan (also makes rosé).

Coteaux du Tricastin Fast-maturing reds which should be drunk within two or three years of the harvest. Excellent value, smooth wines which are worth looking for.

Côtes du Ventoux A relatively new appellation which makes light, fresh reds, with a hint of *pétillance*. Delicious drunk slightly chilled.

Côtes du Luberson A newly established vDQS area in the south of the this vDQS area are made using the same grapes as Côtes du Rhône with additional Syrah and Gamay.

Gigondas A less refined version of Châteauneuf, from a village that was until 1971 just another part of the Côtes du Rhône Villages. Southern-tasting wine, ideal for barbecues and rich foods, quite long-lasting, but not terribly subtle. So what's wrong with that? A little on the expensive side for what they are.

Lirac Excellent value wines from south of Châteauneuf. Full, but really fruity reds are generally well made. Rosés are dry and quite powerful.

Rasteau Strange, fortified, sweet red wines which some find very attractive with a lump of ice as an aperitif. There's also a white version.

Tavel Famed rosé, the delightful colour belies the fact that this is strong stuff. Dry but with good fruit, these can be some of the best French rosés.

Southern Rhône vintages

Apart from Châteauneuf and Gigondas, with occasional Côtes du Rhône Villages, southern Rhône wines are not for laying down. Wines earlier than 1978 should certainly have been drunk by now.

1986 Smaller quantity than 1985, with perhaps more acidity and lightness to the wines. Côtes du Rhône is ready to drink now, but Côtes du Rhône Villages will need another few months. Wait three or four years before attempting the more serious wines.

1985 A fine harvest both for quality and quantity was aided by judicious amounts of rain in June and July and fine sunny weather thereafter. Châteauneuf is full of fruit and looks set to mature well. Some modern-style whites and rosés are a little old; the traditional styles (like Tavel and Châteauneuf-du-Pape) are good now.

1984 Light, mid-range wines in both Châteauneuf and Gigondas. They will be drinking well in five or six years' time. The whites, with some acidity, are now very mature. Rosés are fading.

1983 Light-coloured reds in Côtes du Rhône, but elsewhere in Châteauneuf and Lirac the wines will take plenty of time to mature fully. Gigondas is heavier and even slower to develop. Drink Tavel rosé fast.

1982 Many rather flabby, overweight wines were made by careless producers burdened with extraordinary quantities of fruit. Choose carefully. Stick to reds from very good producers, and probably stay with Châteauneuf.

1981 Châteauneuf is beginning to be very drinkable with firm, structured wines. Some Gigondas are a little acid and watery, but there are some good ones to be found as well. A few Côtes du Rhône Villages – those made with Syrah – are still drinkable. Forget about whites and rosés.

1980 What were initially severe, tough wines have begun to mature in Châteauneuf, but they will last well. The same goes for Gigondas. Drink up Côtes du Rhône and Côtes du Rhône Villages. Red Lirac is very good now.

1978 Long-lasting Châteauneuf is still maturing and will keep – lots of fruit and tannin need time to soften together. The same goes for Gigondas. A great year.

Other vintages Try 1972 and 1970 in Châteauneuf.

Who's who in the southern Rhône

Châteauneuf-du-Pape

Different producers specialise in different styles, ranging from light, fresh to heavy, meaty wine.

Light style: Domaine de Mont-Redon (*Eldridge Pope*), Domaine de Beaurenard (*Victoria Wine Co – by order*), Domaine de Nalys (*Windrush Wines*).

Fuller style: Domaine du Vieux Télégraphe (*Adnams; Lay & Wheeler*), Clos des Papes (*Lay & Wheeler*), Domaine Brunel (*J Sainsbury*), Domaine de Cabrières (*Peter Dominic*), Ch des Fines Roches (*Unwins*), Domaine Font de Michelle (*Yapp Brothers*), Jaboulet Aîné Les Cèdres (*Gerard Harris; O W Loeb; Tanners; Wine Society*).

Fullest style: Domaine de Beaucastel (*Adnams; Bibendum; Justerini & Brooks; Lay & Wheeler*), Ch Fortia (*Malmaison Wine Cellars; Oddbins; Edward Sheldon*), Ch Rayas (*Adnams; La Réserve; André Simon Wines; La Vigneronne*), Domaine Chante-Cigale (*Lay & Wheeler*), Domaine de la Solitude (*available only in some hotels and restaurants*).

White Châteauneuf-du-Pape

Domaine de Nalys (*Windrush Wines*), Domaine de Mont-Redon (*Eldridge Pope; Wine Society*), Domaine du Vieux Télégraphe (*Adnams*), Ch de Beaucastel (*Adnams; Bibendum; La Réserve*), Domaine de la Solitude (*available only in some hotels and restaurants*), Ch Fortia (*Selfridges; Edward Sheldon*), Ch Rayas (*O W Loeb*), Jaboulet Aîné les Cèdres (*O W Loeb*).

Gigondas

Domaine de la Fourmone (*Windrush Wines*), Gabriel Meffre (*Wine Society*), Domaine de St-Gayan (*Yapp Brothers*), L'Oustau Fauquet (*Lay & Wheeler*), Domaine de la Longue-Toque (*Barwell & Jones*), Domaine du Grand Montmirail (*Chaplin & Son; Ellis Son & Vidler; Windrush Wines*).

Lirac (red, rosé and white)

Domaine de Ch St-Roch (*Lay & Wheeler*), Domaine de Castel-Oualou (*Vieilleneuve Wines, 27 Northgate, Peebles*), Domaine Maby (*Wine Society; Yapp Brothers*), Philippe Testut (*Stapylton Fletcher*).

Côtes du Luberon

Domaine Val-Joanis New vineyards are producing some good whites, reds and rosés at very good prices (*Harrods; T & W Wines*).

Cellier de Marrenon Good reds capable of some ageing up to four years (*Peter Dominic; Safeway; Stapylton Fletcher*).

Côtes du Rhône

La Serre du Prieur (*Waitrose*), Ch du Grand Moulas (*Adnams; Lay & Wheeler; Tanners*), Jaboulet Aîné Parallèle 45 (*Alex Findlater; Hungerford Wine Company; Lay & Wheeler; O W Loeb; Majestic Wine Warehouses*), Cave des Vignerons de Vacqueyras (*Alex Findlater; Lay & Wheeler; Tanners*), Domaine de l'Espiguette (*Anthony Byrne Fine Wines*), Asda Côtes du Rhône (*Asda*), Cru du Coudoulet (*Bibendum; Seckford Wines; Edward Sheldon; Winecellars Wine Warehouse*), Domaine Rabasse-Charavin (*Berkman Wine Cellars/Le Nez Rouge*).

Côtes du Rhône Villages

Rasteau Cave des Vignerons de Rasteau (*H Allen Smith; The Market/Winecellars Wine Warehouse; Whynot Wine Warehouses*), Visan Domaine de la Cantharide Cuvée de l'Hermite (*Alex Findlater*), Séguret La Fiole du Chevalier d'Elbène Gabriel Meffre (*Bibendum*), Vacqueyras Domaine de la Couroulu Ricard Père (*Berry Bros & Rudd; Christopher Piper Wines*), Vacqueyras Jaboulet Aîné (*Alex Findlater; O W Loeb*), Beaumes-de-Venise Domaine de Coyeux (*Adnams; Prestige Vintners; Windrush Wines*), Vinsobres Domaine du Moulin (*La Réserve*), Sainsbury's Côtes du Rhône Villages (*J Sainsbury*).

Tavel

La Forcadière (*Yapp Brothers*), Caves des Vignerons (*La Vigneronne*), Domaine Maby (*Yapp Brothers*).

Coteaux du Tricastin

Pierre Labaye (*Cachet Wines; Eldridge Pope; Helen Verdcourt Wines*), Les Vignerons d'Ardèche (*Yapp Brothers*), Waitrose Coteaux du Tricastin (*Waitrose*), Sainsbury's Coteaux du Tricastin (*J Sainsbury*).

Côtes du Ventoux

La Vieille Ferme, Domaine des Anges (*Adnams*), Sainsbury's Côtes du Ventoux (*J Sainsbury*).

Muscat de Beaumes-de-Venise

Domaine de Durban (*Gerard Harris; Yapp Brothers*), Séléction Paul Jaboulet Aîné (*O W Loeb; Majestic Wine Warehouses*), Domaine de Coyeux (*Adnams; Windrush Wines*), Cave Co-opérative de Beaumes-de-Venise (*J Sainsbury*), La Vieille Ferme (*Bibendum*).

Vins de Pays

Vin de Pays du Vaucluse (*Tesco*), Vin de Pays de la Principauté d'Orange (*Yapp Brothers*).

Best buys from the Rhône

WHITES

Côtes du Luberon, La Vieille Ferme (*widely available*)
Côtes du Luberon, Ch Val-Joanis (*widely available*)
Côtes du Rhône Blanc 1985, Ch St-Estève (*Barwell and Jones; Alexander Robertson*)

ROSÉ

Lirac La Fermade 1985 (*Yapp Brothers*)

REDS

Côtes du Ventoux, La Vieille Ferme (*widely available*)
Côtes du Rhône, Ch du Grand Moulas 1986 (*Adnams; House of Townend; S H Jones; Tanners Wines*)
Côtes du Rhône Villages, Rasteau 1985, Cuvée de Maître (*Borg Castel*)
Côtes du Ventoux, Domaine des Anges (*widely available*)
Gigondas l'Oustau Fauquet Roger Combe (*G E Bromley; and others*)
Côtes du Rhône, Ch de l'Estagnol (*D Byrne*)
Côtes du Vivarais 1986, Les Caves de la Cévenne Ardéchoise (*Hadleigh Wine Cellars*)
Coteaux Varois, Domaine de St-Estève (*S H Jones*)
Lirac 1981, Les Queyrolles (*Raeburn Fine Wines and Foods*)
Châteauneuf-du-Pape 1980, Domaine de Mont-Redon (*J E Hogg*)

Specialist stockists of Rhône wines

Adnams; Bibendum; Croque-en-Bouche; Peter Green; Ian G Howe; S H Jones; Justerini & Brooks; Lay & Wheeler; O W Loeb; Raeburn Fine Wines and Foods; Sherborne Vintners; Henry Townsend; Helen Verdcourt Wines; La Vigneronne; Yapp Brothers

SAVOIE

Very little wine from Savoie (on the Swiss border) makes its way to British shops. They go in for fresh, crisp whites and light rosés, influenced by Swiss winemakers just across Lake Geneva. Most seems to be drunk at the ski resorts with which the area abounds. The best wine that does find its way here is the sparkling Varichon et Clerc, made by the Champagne method (*Harrods; Waitrose; Wines Galore*), but try also, for curiosity value, the white Apremonts supplied by *Findlater Mackie Todd* and *Majestic Wine Warehouses*.

Best buy from Savoie

Savoie Apremont (*Majestic Wine Warehouses; Marks & Spencer*)

THE SOUTH-WEST OF FRANCE

Getting better known

The rolling hills and secret countryside of the south-west of France are home to the superb foie gras of Gascony, Armagnac brandy and a range of wines whose very existence, in some cases, was unknown until a few years ago, but which offer a wealth of exotic and rare tastes quite unlike other parts of France.

Some of the traditions of the south-western vineyards are more ancient even than those of Bordeaux to the north and west. They supplied much of the wine that left Bordeaux bound for England in the days when the king of England was also Lord of Gascony. The wines of Cahors and Bergerac especially suffered greatly when the vineyards of the Médoc were developed since Bordeaux restricted their passage to the sea.

In the 19th century, much of the South-West suffered from the phylloxera beetle more severely than other parts of France. Whole areas were almost wiped out and forgotten for over three-quarters of a century in some cases. Re-planting really began seriously only in the 1950s and 1960s, and still the area under vine is much smaller than it was in the early 19th century.

The traditions here combine rare local grapes (a few names to conjure with are Gros-Manseng, Mauzac, Pacherenc, Len de l'El, Ondenc, Courbu) with the grapes of Bordeaux. The nearer to Bordeaux (as in Bergerac), the more the grapes of Bordeaux dominate the blend. Down in the Basque country of the Pyrenean foothills, the names and the tastes get stranger and wilder.

Most of the appellations of the South-West are now represented in our shops or on wine merchants' lists. If you're looking for new tastes – or simply bottles to surprise friends – this is the place to go.

BERGERAC

This is an eastward extension of the St-Emilion vineyards of Bordeaux, at the beginning of the Dordogne valley. There are nine different appellations, ranging from dry red through dry white to sweet white. The wines most likely to be found here are Bergerac (red, rosé and dry white), Côtes de Bergerac (red and medium sweet white), Monbazillac (sweet white) and Pécharmant (very fine red).

Vintages in Bergerac

Our advice is to drink the youngest dry whites and rosés – 1985 or 1986 vintages. Ordinary red Bergerac also should be drunk within three years. Côtes de Bergerac red and Pécharmant last longer – vintages to look for are 1982, 1983 and 1985. Sweet Monbazillac is best in warm, ripe years – try the 1983s and keep the 1985s for a couple of years.

Who's who in Bergerac

Ch Belingard, dry white and red (*Barwell and Jones*); Ch la Jaubertie, red and dry white (*Lay & Wheeler; Majestic Wine Warehouses, and many others*); Sainsbury's Bergerac Rouge; Domaine du Grand Jaure Pécharmant (*Haynes Hanson & Clark*); Clos Fontindoule Monbazillac (*La Vigneronne*); Domaine du Haut Pécharmant (*Le Nez Rouge/Berkmann Wine Cellars*); Pierre-Jean Sadoux Côtes de Bergerac (*Sookias & Bertaut*), Ch du Treuil de Nailhac Monbazillac (*Sookias & Bertaut*), Ch de Tiregand Pécharmant (*Sookias & Bertaut*).

CÔTES DE BUZET/CÔTES DE DURAS/ CÔTES DU MARMANDAIS

Three more small regions just over the departmental border from Bordeaux produce wines which have much in common with both Bordeaux and Bergerac. The first two – Buzet and Duras – are AC areas, while Côtes du Marmandais is a VDQS.

Of the three, the best wines certainly come from Buzet. The better reds have some ageing potential, with their jammy fruit and slightly stalky tannin. The most widely available are from the co-operative, but there are also some excellent domaine wines brought in by specialist merchants.

The Côtes de Duras reds made from the Merlot are lighter and are made for early drinking: they're delicious chilled. The dry whites from the Sauvignon (look for the grape name on the label) are typically fresh.

The Côtes du Marmandais makes soft, easy reds for early drinking at good prices. Most wine comes from one or other of the two co-operatives.

The duty-free allowance for wine obtained in the EEC is 5 litres of still table wine per person *plus* 3 litres of still table wine *or* 3 litres of fortified/ sparkling wine *or* 1½ litres of spirits or liqueurs. (See also page 584.)

Who's who in Buzet/Duras/Marmandais

Buzet

Côtes de Buzet, Cuvée Napoléon (*Whynot Wine Warehouses, and others*); Côtes de Buzet, Ch de Padère (*Ian G Howe*); Ch Sauvagnères, Côtes de Buzet (*Sookias & Bertaut*); Sainsbury's Buzet.

Duras

Côtes de Duras, Le Seigneuret red and white (*Waitrose*); Domaine Mau Michau (*Duras Direct*); Côtes de Duras Sauvignon, Les Vignerons des Coteaux de Duras (*Le Nez Rouge/Berkmann Wine Cellars*); Ch la Pilar (*The Market/Winecellars*); Domaine de Durand (*Bibendum*).

Marmandais

Côtes du Marmandais, Cave de Cocumont (*widely available*).

CAHORS

This is one of the wines about which much used to be written and much less drunk. One of the legends told of the 'black wines of Cahors'. We are delighted to explode the myth that these were dark, tannic wines with great longevity. In fact, they resulted from boiled up juice concentrate being added to wine for stability – which doesn't sound like a recipe for fine wine.

Nothing like that appears to happen today. Modern red Cahors ranges from fresh wines which have been made for early drinking to those which are fairly tough and tannic, ideal for rich, spicy foods and some bottle ageing – for as much as 15 to 20 years in some cases.

The grape varieties used here are the Malbec or Auxerrois (to provide the concentration), the Merlot (which softens the Auxerrois and gives extra alcohol) and the Tannat (to provide tannin). The co-operative, Côtes d'Olt, makes much of the wine here but there are also 80 individual growers.

Prices are less cheap now in Cahors than even two or three years ago. The reason is simple – they have become fashionable in France. So don't expect many bargains in Cahors, but do expect some very good wines.

Who's who in Cahors

Clos la Coutale (*Windrush Wines*); Ch de Haute-Serre (*The Wine Society*); Les Côtes d'Olt (*widely available*); Domaine de Mériguet (*Les Amis du Vin*); Domaine de Paillas (*Sookias & Bertaut*); Domaine de Gaudou (*Adnams; The Market/Winecellars*); Ch Didier-Parnac, Rigal et Fils (*H Allen Smith; Bibendum*); Clos Triguedina (*Sookias & Bertaut*); Clos de Gamot (*Sookias & Bertaut*).

FRONTONNAIS

Red and rosé wines are made in this small area to the north of Toulouse. They're excellent value for everyday drinking, although quantities available in this country tend to be small. Drink them young as quaffing wines.

Who's who in Côtes du Frontonnais

Ch Flotis (*Sookias & Bertaut*); Ch Bellevue la Forêt (*Farthinghoe Fine Wine and Food; Le Nez Rouge; Wizard Wines*).

GAILLAC

The slightly sparkling, rather dull Gaillac Perlé is the most common wine seen here. But there are also more interesting still whites and traditional reds, both of which combine a rustic character with reasonably fast maturation. There's also one sparkling wine made by the 'méthode gaillaçoise' (a method which results in fewer bubbles than Champagne), which is well worth seeking out.

Who's who in Gaillac

Jean Cros – for high quality, traditional wines, including the méthode gaillaçoise sparkler (*Sookias & Bertaut*); Cave Co-opérative de Labastide de Lévis (*Peter Dominic*); Domaine de la Gravette (*Majestic Wine Warehouses*); Domaine de Labarthe (*Sookias & Bertaut*).

Please write to tell us about any ideas for features you would like to see in next year's edition or in *Which? Wine Monthly*.

JURANÇON

While much Jurançon is dry and most is drunk along the nearby Atlantic coast at Biarritz, there are still small pockets of the old-fashioned sweet wines, called Jurançon Moelleux, on which this area's reputation used to rest. The corollary is that their rarity value makes these sticky wines expensive – so what's new?

Who's who in Jurançon

Clos Concaillau sweet (*Sookias & Bertaut*); Clos de la Vierge dry (*Sookias & Bertaut*); Cru Lamouroux sweet and medium dry (*La Vigneronne*); Jurançon Brut Caves Vinicoles de Gan (*Lay & Wheeler*).

MADIRAN AND PACHERENC DU VIC-BILH

Heady stuff, these two names. In reality, though, while Madiran is a fine red wine, often dark in colour and tannic (although there are lighter wines around as well), Pacherenc du Vic-Bilh is a straightforward, rather pricey white, most of which is drunk locally. Both come from the Armagnac country of Gascony.

Who's who in Madiran and Pacherenc

Madiran

Ch d'Arricau-Bordes (*Sookias & Bertaut*); Ch de Peyros (*Malmaison Wine Club*); Alain Brumont Domaine Bouscassé (*Bibendum; Sookias & Bertaut*); Cuvée de la Confrérie (*David Baillie Vintners*); Domaine de Teston.

Pacherenc du Vic-Bilh

Domaine du Crampilh (*Sookias & Bertaut*).

LESSER REGIONS OF THE SOUTH-WEST

While there are many more small demarcated wine areas in the South-West, not so many of their products reach our shops. Here is a selection of the better ones which do:

Entraygues et du Fel

A vDQS area on the southern slopes of the Massif Central in the Lot valley. Worth trying: Jean-Marc Viguier (*Sookias & Bertaut*).

Irouléguy

Right on the Spanish border at the western end of the Pyrenees, this makes red, white and rosé. Worth trying: red Irouléguy from the co-operative (*Sookias & Bertaut*).

Marcillac

Deep-coloured reds from a small VDQS area also in the Lot valley. Worth trying: Laurens Teulier (*Sookias & Bertaut; The Wine Club*).

Tursan

Perfumed dry whites and soft reds from the heart of Gascony. Worth trying: Dulucq et Fils (*Sookias & Bertaut*).

VINS DE PAYS OF THE SOUTH-WEST

The most important vins de pays, as far as we are concerned, are: Côtes de Gascogne, Côtes du Tarn, de la Dordogne, des Pyrénées Atlantiques. All make good, everyday drinking wines. The whites (made using high tech equipment) are generally on a higher plain than the reds.

Who's who in the vins de pays of the South-West

Vin de Pays des Pyrénées Atlantiques (*Tanners Wines*); Vin de Pays des Côtes de Gascogne (*Majestic Wine Warehouses; Tanners Wines; Waitrose; and others*); Vin de Pays des Côtes de Thongue cépage Merlot (*Stapylton Fletcher*).

Best buys from the South-West

WHITE WINES

Vin de Pays des Côtes de Gascogne (*widely available*)
Jurançon Sec, Clos Guirouilh (*Alston Wines; Bow Wine Vaults*)
Côtes de Duras Sauvignon 1986, Les Vignerons des Coteaux de Duras (*Le Nez Rouge/Berkmann Wine Cellars*)
Jurançon Moelleux 1983, Domaine Cauhope (*Sookias & Bertaut*)
Côtes du Marmandais white (*Hicks & Don*)

The Wine Standards Board is the trade's disciplinary department and wine watchdog. Their inspectors are responsible for rooting out any malpractices – but they are concerned largely with labelling irregularities. If you have genuine reason to suspect that the wine in a bottle is not what the label claims it is, contact the Board at: 68½ Upper Thames Street, London EC4V 3BJ; TEL 01-236 9512 or contact your local Trading Standards Officer.

WHAT TO BUY

RED WINES

Madiran 1983, Ch d'Arricau-Bordes (*Sookias & Bertaut*)
Côtes de Buzet 1983, Ch de Guéyèze (*Peatling & Cawdron*)
Bergerac 1983, Domaine de Plaisance (*Grape Ideas Wine Warehouse*)
Cahors 1983, Les Côtes d'Olt (*Asda*)
Cahors 1983, Ch St-Didier Parnac (*Great Northern Wine Co; Martinez Fine Wines; and others*)
Cahors 1983, Domaine du Colombie (*Bowlish House Wine Shop*)
Vin de Pays des Coteaux de Quercy, Rigal (*Oddbins*)
Côtes de Buzet, Cuvée Napoléon 1983 (*G Hush; Sebastopol Wines; and others*)

Specialist stockists

Bibendum; Bordeaux Direct; Duras Direct; Andrew Gordon Wines; Ian G Howe; Prestige Vintners; Raeburn Fine Wines and Foods; Sherborne Vintners; Sookias & Bertaut; Stapylton Fletcher; Taste Shops; Wines from Paris

Germany

Wines that lack the BMW image

It has long been something of a puzzle that Germany, with its high reputation for well-crafted consumer goods, especially cars, should apparently have deliberately gone about creating a vinous reputation for producing sugar water at rock-bottom prices.

It's even more puzzling when one remembers – with difficulty sometimes – that Germany also makes some superb white wines, with a balance between sweetness and acidity that is unique anywhere in the world.

But do we see those fine wines? Not without a long and diligent search along the shelves groaning with Liebfraumilch, Piesporter Michelsberg, Niersteiner Gutes Domtal, or strange-looking table wines with fancy names in Gothic lettering that may well contain no German wine at all.

That has been the situation for some years, ever since Liebfraumilch entered our wine-drinking consciousness. At first, it was a style that guaranteed reliable drinking, even if no great excitement, to consumers who were new to wine. But as the marketeers realised that here was a name that sold wine, they began to use it to sell any German wine, however cheap.

And it worked well – until recently. Now a number of factors have combined to put a stop to the Liebfraumilch boom. Small harvests in 1984 and 1985 pushed the cost of grapes up by as much as 150 per cent and reduced their availability. The difficulties of the 1986 vintage (see below under Vintage information) have simply compounded the problem.

At the same time, the 1985 Austrian wine scandal spilled over into Germany when unscrupulous producers were found to be beefing up their home-grown product with fuller Austrian wines.

Both those factors are of a temporary nature. A big harvest will bring prices down, and memories will fade about diethylene glycol. More importantly, and with many more implications for the future of the German wine industry, it seems that British wine drinkers are just that little bit bored with Liebfraumilch and its various associates.

A drop in the ocean

The tidal wave of German wine reaching our shops has ebbed somewhat. A reduction of 6.5 per cent may not sound much but translating it into eight million bottles may help to put it into perspective.

German grapes are costing more, but that price rise has not been reflected in the price in the shops. While our wine merchants are generous chaps, that doesn't mean that they've cut their margins. No, the margin-cutting has taken place in Germany, in a frantic effort to sustain the volumes of wine being sent to Britain. For those with a taste for figures, the average price of a litre of quality wine coming out of German cellars actually fell in 1986 – from 3.46 Deutschmarks in 1985 to 3.29.

It's this short-sighted attitude that has blighted the quality image of German wine in the eyes of British wine drinkers. And, despite the efforts of a handful of dedicated wine shippers, German estate wines – the finest that Germany can produce – are still woefully ignored.

When *Which? Wine Monthly* ran a tasting of German Kabinett wines (see below for German wine terminology) earlier in 1987, we asked for samples from the 1985 vintage – good for Kabinett wines and, we naïvely thought, likely to be the ones in the shops by the spring of 1987. But no: many retailers were still selling the 1983 wines, now sometimes quite mature, and possibly missing some freshness. The reason why they were still selling the 1983 wines was simply that nobody had been buying them.

You can still find sweet wines from the great 1976 vintage at roughly the same price as when they first appeared in this country. Of what other wine-producing country could you say the same? Certainly not France.

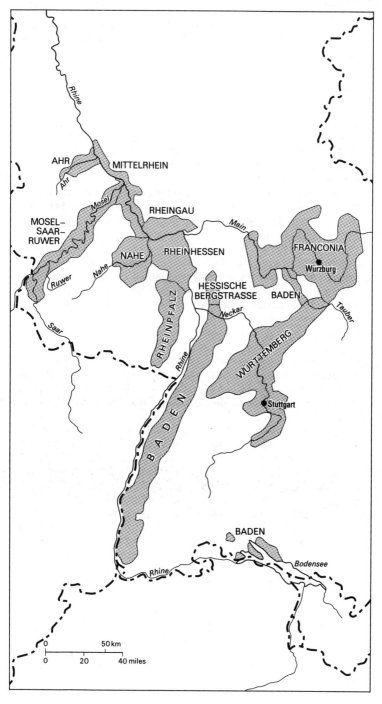

Why don't we buy these fine wines? Because we are drowning in a sea of low-quality German wine that has obliterated the memory of the place German fine wines once had in our estimation.

Tafelwein keeps going

So far, we've been talking about what the Germans call quality wine – yes, Liebfraumilch even at £1.99 a bottle is technically quality wine. However, lurking below that pretty basic quality wine, there's Tafelwein and Landwein, what the French would call Vin de Table and Vin de Pays. There's also the most recent great Germanic contribution to our wine culture – EEC Tafelwein.

Now, if you think Liebfraumilch is getting boring and that some of the cheaper samples are badly made and over-sulphured, wait till you taste Tafelwein. But it's cheap, and at this level it seems that price is much more important than quality.

Sadly, many British wine drinkers seem to agree. So while imports of Liebfraumilch and quality wines fell in 1986, those for Tafelwein actually went up. We suspect that at this level they are hardly regarded as German wines – we certainly hope not, because the association is not a good one. But there they are – all 45 million bottles of them.

The silver lining

But there is possibly a silver lining to all this. The Germans are slowly beginning to realise that it's time they brushed up their image and tried to sell wine that's as good as a BMW and reaches the same market. At the same time, they're also thinking about ways of improving the wine controls.

Various plans have been put forward. One scheme is to insist that wineries which bottle imported wine (ie EEC Tafelwein) should have separate buildings for German and imported wines – in the hope of avoiding another scandal of finding Austrian wine in German bottles. There is also a move to issue a restricted number of paper seals for quality wines – at the moment a producer can print as many 'quality wine' labels as he likes once a single sample has passed the quality control test.

And, at last, there are plans to restrict yields – that would be a revolution in German winemaking, which has always aimed to produce as much wine as possible – and to get the brains in white coats back in the labs to sort out any problems arising from that philosophy. They've realised what the French have known for years – and the Italians have cottoned on to as well – that small yields of high quality grapes produce high quality wines.

While those legal machinations go on, the top producers have decided they must do some promotion of their wines. An organisation calling itself Charta has been set up by some of the best Rheingau producers to make dry wines specifically for drinking with food. They've developed a special bottle with an arched window symbol on it. The wines from the 1985 vintages should be in our shops now, and are worth seeking out.

Not that expensive

The best estate wines – from many of those listed below – may seem expensive if compared with the basic Liebfraumilch style of wine. But in reality – considering the climatic problems associated with making these wines, the infinite care which goes into their vinification and the small amounts of each that are produced – they are still good value, even though, thanks to a falling pound and a mighty Deutschmark, they are by no means as cheap as they were a year ago.

For more everyday drinking, the most exciting area at the moment is Baden. Dominated by its great central co-operative (but with a handful of great estates as well), the region specialises in making fuller-bodied wines than the rest of Germany. They're wines for food, and many of the dry wines are very successful. All are good value.

All over Germany at the moment, wines of the Kabinett quality are well worth looking for. Both the 1983 and 1984 vintages produced excellent easy-drinking wines at this Prädikat level at very good prices. They are certainly the most approachable wines to move on to if you want better things from Germany than Liebfraumilch.

A few definitions

Germany is nothing if not thorough in telling you on the label about the wine inside the bottle (which will be tall and green if it comes from Mosel–Saar–Ruwer and brown from elsewhere, except Franconia which has dumpy green bottles).

1 The label will indicate which category of wine it falls into: Tafelwein, the most basic; Landwein, a sort of German vin de pays; *Qualitätswein bestimmter Anbaugebiete* (QbA), the lowest quality wine level; or, at the top level, *Qualitätswein mit Prädikat* (QmP, which has six sub-divisions). As an indication of what Germans mean by quality wine, 90 per cent of all German wine falls into a quality category. To get real quality, you need to go to the level of QmP wines.

QmP wines are categorised by sweetness: Kabinett (the driest), Spätlese, Auslese, Beerenauslese, Eiswein and Trockenbeerenauslese (the sweetest).

2 Next, the wine region. **Tafelwein** can come from four big districts: Rhein–Mosel, Bayern (Bavaria), Neckar, Oberrhein (basically Baden).

Landwein districts number 15, but since little is sold in Britain you are unlikely to see any on wine merchants' shelves.

Quality wine areas (for QbA and QmP wines) are (from north to south): Ahr, Mittelrhein, Mosel–Saar–Ruwer, Nahe, Rheingau, Rheinhessen, Hessische Bergstrasse, Franken, Württemberg, Rheinpfalz, Baden. In the UK we see wines from all areas except Ahr, Mittelrhein, Hessische Bergstrasse and Württemberg.

3 The label will tell you which sub-region it comes from (*Bereich*), which district (*Grosslage*), which village in that district (*Gemeinde*) or which single vineyard (*Einzellagen*).

Which of these categories is indicated will depend on the quality of the wine. The best wines will have single vineyard names, the most straightforward simply a *Bereich* name.

4 Other information will include:

The AP number given to the wine after it has been tested by a central testing station (useful to know only if something's wrong with the wine).

The degree of dryness (relates to QbA wines only): Trocken (dry), Halbtrocken (less dry), Diabetikerwein (very dry for diabetics) or nothing (for standard styles).

The grape variety: not compulsory, but always included if the *Riesling* (the finest German variety) is predominant. Other grapes you might see are *Müller-Thurgau* (the most widely planted, although the Riesling is coming back into favour), *Silvaner* (in Franconia especially), *Scheurebe* (which produces a highly scented wine), *Kerner* (a stylish grape with some similarity to Riesling), *Spätburgunder* or *Blauer Portugeiser* (if you are looking for a red wine – not often seen in Britain).

The vintage: see below for details of recent vintages.

The producer: if the wine has been estate-bottled the label will bear the term *Erzeugerabfüllung*.

The bottler: if the wine is not estate-bottled it will carry the name of the merchant or shipper who bottled it.

German sparklers

Until 1986, Deutscher Sekt on a label simply meant the wine had German bubbles in it – ie inserted into wine on German territory. Now the wine itself has to be German. The best check for quality is to look for Riesling on the label – that *will* be German. Other Sekts are simply sparkling wines from anywhere – generally Italy – sold under a German producer's name.

Some of the biggest German merchants – Deinhard, Kupferberg, Sichel (of Blue Nun fame) – make sparkling wines. The Deinhard brands are very good. So are some which go under estate names: Schloss Rheingarten, Schloss Böchingen, Fürst von Metternich.

Big harvests – and small

German harvests vary wildly in quantity as well as quality. The early 1980s produced the biggest harvests on record. Most ordinary wines (of QbA and lower Prädikat standard) need to be drunk within 1–2 years or will lose their freshness.

Recent harvests all made some decent wines in the lower categories, but not many in the top very sweet ones.

1986 A mixed bag vintage, with bad weather during the harvest and little of the wine likely to be of QmP standard. However, good acidity suggests that plenty of easy-drinking wines will be available soon.

1985 Excellent quality, especially for the Riesling. As much as 60 per cent reached Prädikat levels (mainly Kabinett). But quantity has been cut by as much as half because of frost in the early part of the year. Drink the Kabinett wines now; keep higher Prädikat wines.

1984 Little but QbA wines were made in a poor year. These should be drunk by now.

1983 A very fine year, with some good wines up to Auslese quality. Buy carefully from the Mosel where not all the wines are good. Keep the top qualities for four or five years, drink the rest.

1982 A year of huge quantities, caused by high rainfall during the harvest. Only QbA wines were produced, and should have been drunk by now.

1981 Some of the Spätlese wines are still worth drinking, but don't keep them for any longer.

1976 The top quality wines from this vintage are German classics. If you find a bottle of Spätlese or above in the QmP wines, buy it and save it for drinking with some appreciative friends.

Who's who in Germany

This selection of German producers includes some of the best estates and also some of the merchants whose wines are regularly seen in Britain.

Affaltrach, Schlosskellerei Estate owners making principally dry or semi-dry wines from vineyards in Wurttemberg and Rheinhessen. *City Cellars*

Anheuser, Weingut Ökonomierat August E Large estate of 60 hectares in the Nahe, making racy wines mainly from the Riesling grape. *Alex Findlater*

Aschrott'sche Erben, Geheimrat High quality estate in Hochheim in the Rheingau. Almost entirely Riesling wines.
Berry Bros & Rudd; O W Loeb

Badischer Winzergenossenschaft, Zentralkellerei A long name for the main co-operative of Baden, making 400 to 500 different wines. High standards for a co-operative.
Oddbins; Waitrose

Balbach Erben, Bürgermeister Anton, Weingut One of the great estates in Nierstein in the Rheinhessen. Modern outlook to winemaking.
Lay & Wheeler; Stapylton Fletcher

Bassermann-Jordan, Weingut Geheimer Rat Dr von Rheinpfalz estate with vineyards in many of the best sites of Deidesheim and Forst. Founded in the 13th century.
Lay & Wheeler

Bergweiler-Prüm Erben, Zach Small Mosel–Saar–Ruwer estate with vineyards in Graach, Bernkastel, Wehlen and Zeltingen–Rachtig.
Alex Findlater

Bischöflichen Weinguter, Verwaltung der Four estates (105 hectares) of ecclesiastical origin in Mosel–Saar–Ruwer, based in the city of Trier. Other ecclesiastical names you will see are Bischöfliche Priesterseminar and Bischöfliche Konvikt.
Lay & Wheeler; Wine Society

Brentano'sche Gutsverwaltung, Baron von Good Rheingau estate, whose holdings of ten hectares include part of Winkeler Hasensprung.
Lay & Wheeler

Breuer, Weingut G Small estate, part of the merchant company of Scholl and Hillebrand (see below). Main holdings are in Rüdesheim in the Rheingau.

Buhl, Weingut Reichsrat von Great Rheinpfalz estate making wines from vineyards in Forst, Deidesheim and Ruppertsberg.
H Allen Smith; Berry Bros & Rudd; Eldridge Pope; O W Loeb

Bürklin-Wolf, Weingut Dr Large estate based at Wachenheim in the Rheinpfalz. Makes very fine wines.
Adnams; Eldridge Pope; Lay & Wheeler; O W Loeb; Wine Society

Castell'sches Domänenamt, Fürstlich Estate owned by the former rulers of the tiny state of Castell in Franconia. Wines made of the Rieslaner grape are a great speciality.
City Cellars; Curzon Wine Company

Crusius, Weingut Hans Family-run estate in the Nahe. Has holdings in the Traiser Bastei and Rotenfels. Very high standards.
George Hill of Loughborough; Lockes

Deinhard & Co Wine merchant and vineyard owner based in Koblenz. Vineyards in Mosel–Saar–Ruwer, Rheingau and Rheinpfalz. Makes good branded wines (Green Label) and sparkling wine (Lila Imperial).
Adnams; Berry Bros & Rudd; Alex Findlater; Haynes Hanson & Clark

Diefenhardt'sches Weingut 12.2-hectare estate in the Rheingau. Vineyards in Eltville, Martinsthal and Rauenthal.
Gerard Harris; Ian G Howe; Peatling & Cawdron

Drathen KG, Ewald Theodor Large-scale exporters of cheap wine. Sell quantities of EEC table wine.
Oddbins; Waitrose

Eltville, Verwaltung der Staatsweingüter The German state's holdings in the Rheingau and Hessische Bergstrasse. 160 hectares in many of the best sites, including all of the walled Steinberg vineyard.
Adnams; Lay & Wheeler

Friedrich-Wilhelm-Gymnasium, Stiftung Staatliches Estate founded by the Jesuits with 45 hectares of vineyard in the Mosel–Saar–Ruwer, based in Trier.
Adnams; Bibendum; Alex Findlater; Lay & Wheeler

Guntrum-Weinkellerei GmbH, Louis Wine merchant and vineyard owner based in the Rheinhessen. Many wines from top vineyards as well as more straightforward ones.
Berry Bros & Rudd; Harrods

Hallgarten GmbH, Arthur Firm of wine exporters selling estate-bottled wines as well as brands and standard wines. Linked with the Pieroth group (see below).
Peter Dominic; Oddbins; Selfridges; Unwins; Victoria Wine Co

Henkell & Co, Sektkellerein Producer of sparkling wine, including Henkell Trocken.
Peter Dominic; Eldridge Pope

Hovel, Weingut von One of the principal estates in the Saar, making classically delicate wines in rare good years.
O W Loeb; Wine Society

Huesgen GmbH, A Firm of wine merchants based in Traben–Trarbach in the Mosel–Saar–Ruwer. Specialises in inexpensive wines.
Les Amis du Vin; Haynes Hanson & Clark

Juliusspital-Weingut Charitable hospital in Würzburg, Franconia, dating from the 16th century. Makes excellent examples of Franconian wines.
O W Loeb

Kesselstatt, Weingut Reichsgraf von Four estates at Graach, Piesport, Kasel and Oberemmel in Mosel–Saar–Ruwer.
Eldridge Pope; O W Loeb

Lang, Weingut Hans Small estate based in the Rheingau. Holdings in Kiedrich and Hattenheim. Lists old vintages.
Harrods

Langenbach Large-scale producers whose wines include Black Tower Liebfraumilch. Now owned by a joint Allied-Lyons and Whitbread company.
Widely available

Loeb GmbH, Sigmund Exporter owned by O W Loeb in London (see WHERE TO BUY section). High quality estate-bottled wines.
O W Loeb

Liegenfelder, Weingut K & H Estate at the northern end of the Rheinpfalz.
Buckingham Wines; City Cellars; Fortnum & Mason; La Vigneronne

Metternich Sektkellerei GmbH, Fürst von Sparkling wine producer. Uses the Metternich name, but not owned by the family.
Arthur Rackhams

Müller GmbH, Rudolf Wine merchant and estate owner. Sells branded wines. Based in Mosel–Saar–Ruwer. Brand is the Bishop of Riesling.
Adnams; Haynes Hanson & Clark; Hungerford Wine Company; Lay & Wheeler

Müller-Scharzhof, Weingut Egon Old Saar estate making fabulous wines in good years.
O W Loeb

Nagler, Weingut Dr Heinrich A small Rüdesheim (Rheingau) estate, still using casks for maturing the wine.
O W Loeb

Niederhausen-Schlossböckelheim, Verwaltung der Staatlichen Weinbaudomänen German state holdings in the Nahe. Some of the best wines from this region.
Lay & Wheeler

Pauly KG, Weingut Otto Mosel–Saar–Ruwer estate, with holdings in Graach and Bernkastel. Good quality.
City Cellars

Pieroth, Weingut Weinkellerei, Ferdinand One of the largest wine merchants in Germany. Specialise in selling QmP wines direct to consumers in their homes by the 16-bottle case. Despite being sold direct, wines are generally expensive for what they are and should really be bought by people who like determined salesmanship in their drawing rooms. Pieroth own a large number of subsidiary companies. Attracted attention during the diethylene glycol affair.

Plettenberg'sche Verwaltung, Reichsgräflich von A large Nahe estate, producing a wide range.
Eldridge Pope; O W Loeb

Prüm, Weingut J J One of the finest Mosel–Saar–Ruwer estates, with holdings all the way along the Middle Mosel.
Bibendum; Wine Society

Reh & Sohn, Franz Large wine merchant with some vineyard holdings in the Mosel–Saar–Ruwer. Mainly export standard wines.
Safeway; J Sainsbury (both sell Reh's boxed wines)

Ress KG, Balthasar Family firm owning vineyards in the central Rheingau, including leaseholding of Schloss Reichhartshausen. Classic Rheingau wines.
Windrush Wines

Richter, Weingut Max Ferd Old-established family business with top quality wines from a 15-hectare estate.
Green's

St Ursula Weingut and Weinkellerei Firm of wine merchants based in Bingen. Make Goldener Oktober branded wines.
Gough Brothers

Scholl & Hillebrand One of the firms in at the founding of the Rheingau Charta group (see above, under The silver lining). Their brand is called Riesling Dry, but they produce a range of fine estate wines.
Berry Bros & Rudd; Alex Findlater; La Vigneronne

Schloss Groenesteyn, Weingut des Reichsfreiherrn von Ritter zu Groenesteyn Estate founded in the 14th century concentrated around Rüdesheim in the Rheingau.
Berry Bros & Rudd; Lay & Wheeler

Schloss Johannisberg Most famous name in the Rheingau making wine from its 35-hectare estate in Johannisberg. Not to be confused with Bereich Johannisberg wines, which can be from anywhere in the Rheingau.
Alex Findlater; Hilbre Wine Company

Schloss Reinhartshausen Large estate of 67 hectares in the Rheingau,

owned by descendants of the German Emperors. Holdings at Erbach.
Hattenheim, Kiedrich, Rauenthal and Rüdesheim.
Berry Bros & Rudd; Eldridge Pope; La Vigneronne

Schloss Schönborn, Domänenweingut Rheingau estate with
vineyards in Oestrich, Winkel, Rüdesheim, Geisenheim, Hochheim,
Hattenheim, Johannisberg and Erbach.
Lay & Wheeler

**Schloss Vollrads, Graf Matuschka-Greiffenclau'sche
Gutserverwaltung** Estate dating from the 12th century, still owned by
the same family. Specialises in dry wines for food. Very fine wines.
Eldridge Pope; Alex Findlater; Reynier Wine Libraries

Schmitt, Weingut Hermann Franz Ancient, family-owned estate in
the Rheinhessen, whose main holdings are at Nierstein.
Kershaw's Wine Warehouse

Schubert'sche Gutsverwaltung, C von Ancient estate, first mentioned
in the 10th century, on the Ruwer, near Trier. Great wines in good
years.
Lay & Wheeler; La Vigneronne

Sichel Söhne GmbH Producers of Blue Nun, but also selling estate
wines.
Widely available

Vila Eden Fine wine arm of St Ursula Weingut (see above). Vineyards
are at Bingen on the Rhine.
Berry Bros & Rudd

Weil, Weingut Dr R Estate with holdings in Kiedrich in the Rheingau.
H Allen Smith; Eldridge Pope; Alex Findlater

Best buys from Germany

Niersteiner Rosengartchen Riesling Kabinett 1985, Friedrich
Wilhelm-Gymnasium (*Henry Townsend*)
Kirchheimer Schwarzerde Gewürztraminer Kabinett 1985, Franz
Nippgen Neuleiningen (*A L Vose; The Wine Schoppen*)
Reiler vom Heissen Stein Kabinett 1985, Rudolf Müller (*Adnams; House
of Townend; S H Jones*)
Rheingau Riesling 1985, Balthasar Ress (*Windrush Wines*)
Forster Rauenthaler Riesling Spätlese 1985 (*Tesco*)

Specialist stockists

*Adnams; H Allen Smith; Berry Bros & Rudd; Bibendum; D Byrne; Curzon
Wine Co; Eldridge Pope; Alex Findlater; Peter Green; Gerard Harris; S H
Jones; Justerini & Brooks; Lay & Wheeler; O W Loeb; Peatling & Cawdron;
Raeburn Fine Wines and Foods; T & W Wines; Henry Townsend; A L Vose;
The Wine Schoppen; The Wine Spot*

Greece

Signs of hope

Last year, we wrote some pretty uncomplimentary things about Greek wines. We touched on the mediocre, oxidised quality of most of both the reds and the whites available here (and there aren't many even of those). We suggested that, apart from the sweet wines of Samos, one or two estates that were trying much harder, and retsina, Greece was a vinous write-off.

Well, it's too early to say that things have changed, but there are a few hopeful signs. One is the arrival of some red wines from Cephalonia (see below). Another is the start of efforts by the Greeks to persuade us to buy their wines (which means that they will have to think about the quality of what they're offering).

Thirdly, a series of controls has been applied to what was seemingly uncontrollable. Since entering the European Community in 1981, Greece has designated regional wines along the lines of the French AC and VDQS rules. There are now 28 of these, and a strange collection some of them make: all eight AC wine areas, for instance, produce only sweet wines. With two exceptions, the Greeks have simply delimited existing areas, but have added regulations about yields, grape varieties and sugar content.

What all this will add up to is hard to say. For now, Greece remains best known for her one unique contribution to viticulture: retsina, produced mainly around Athens. You either love it or hate it. If you love it, some good retsinas are available here and they certainly cut through oily food.

Elsewhere, it is the islands that produce some of the sweet dessert wines, made from the Malvasia and Muscat grapes. Samos makes the best-known Muscats, while Crete has a luscious Malvasia. Sweet red wines are a speciality of the Peloponnese, of which the Mavrodaphne of Patras is most widely known.

And then there are those estate wines. Much attention has recently been focussed on the efforts of Greek tycoon John Carras who has flown in the famous Professor Peynaud from Bordeaux to advise on making a French-style wine in one of the Khalkidhiki peninsulas in northern Greece. Château Carras is the result, made from Bordeaux grape varieties, and a very well made wine it is. The white Domaine Porto Carras, made from Sauvignon grapes, is less successful.

The newcomers to our shops are two wines from the island of Cephalonia, and both prove that native Greek grape varieties can produce some decent wines if only somebody tries. John Calliga's two red wines (Monte Nero, made from Agioritiko grapes, and, especially, the Calliga Ruby – don't be put off by the asymmetrical bottle) are wines that should begin to make us take Greece more seriously.

What's what in Greece

Brand, rather than company, names rule in Greece.

Apelia Full, dry white from Attica.
G E Bromley & Sons

John Calliga Try his red Monte Nero and Calliga Ruby. The white Robola is currently less interesting.
Peter Green, Hicks & Don, Ostlers, Whynot Wine Warehouses

Château Carras This is the top wine produced by the Domaine de Porto Carras. Others, going under the name Côtes de Méliton, are a dry white Blanc de Blancs, Sauvignon, Grand Vin Blanc, Grand Vin Rouge.
Selfridges

Mavrodaphne of Patras Sweet red wine, akin to the Reciotos of Italy, but not as good. A good example is made by the largest Greek wine company, Achaia Clauss.
Peter Dominic

Retsina Metaxas Produced by the firm best known for its brandies. A good example of this style of wine.
Widely available

Retsina Attiki Another good example from Attica.
J Sainsbury

Tsantali Lousy labels hide some tasty wines – there are fresh grapes
there. Try Red Superb, Golden Delicious sweet Samos (no apples),
Mavrodaphne, Naoussa.
Wine Shop (Thurso)

Best buys from Greece

WHITE WINES

Retsina Metaxas (*widely available*)
Mavrodaphne of Patras (*Peter Dominic*)

RED WINE

Ch Carras 1979 (*Selfridges*)
Monte Nero 1981 and Calliga Ruby 1981 (*Peter Green; Hicks & Don;
Ostlers; Selfridges; Whynot Wine Warehouses*)

Specialist stockists
Cumbrian Cellar; Peter Green

Hungary

Losing out

The examples of Hungarian wine that we have tasted over the past
year have (with one exception) fallen into two categories: there are the
slightly sweet reds and medium sweet whites that seem to have had all
personality designed out of them; and there are the occasional flashes
of the exotic tastes that Hungarian wine should have – just to remind
us that the marketing men haven't completely taken over.

Despite the introduction of a range of wines from Hungarian
varietals in the middle of 1986, and the existence of some decent Merlot
and Chardonnay-based wines, the Hungarians have been losing out in
recent years in the competition to attract the good value, good quality,
middle range market. They've lost out particularly to the Bulgarians
who are producing a range of generally excellently made wines from
noble European grape varieties.

The reason lies in the way the wines are made and handled.
Hungarian techniques still haven't caught up with the high standards
of wine hygiene now demanded by consumers in western Europe and
particularly in Britain. That means that what are often good quality

wines suffer during handling and bottling: there's a high rate of faulty bottles and a general loss of the full character of the wine. The biggest-selling Hungarian wine, Bull's Blood, seems to be different with every bottle we taste. Until they improve that aspect of their wines, we must continue to urge caution when buying Hungarian wines.

The taste of Hungary

As so often, a country's wines go with its food. Even Hungary's whites can cut through the spiciness that is a common theme of much Hungarian cooking, and the reds, full and smooth, sometimes slightly sweet and mellow, complement the rich paprika sauces and strong tastes of the meat dishes.

There is one wine – the exception we mentioned above – which keeps Hungary firmly on the world's wine map. That is one of the world's great dessert wines: Tokay. It is still extremely good value for money as well as being a memorable wine: look for the top qualities of sweetness (Tokay Aszu 5 Puttonyos) or, justifiably more expensive, Tokay Aszu Essencia, which is made only from the free-run juice of grapes carrying noble rot.

What's what in Hungary

The Hungarian language is like no other (apart, it seems, from Finnish). Our advice is not to try to pronounce the words but just point – the wine merchant can't pronounce them either. Place names tend to come first, with the suffix 'i', followed by the grape name. This is only a general rule but may be helpful.

Badacsony Quality wine district, producing mainly white wines, on the northern shore of Lake Balaton.

Balaton Wines from Lake Balaton, the Hungarian 'inland sea' which enjoys a favourable micro-climate. Larger area than Badacsony.

Egri Wine from the district of Eger in the north of the country. Source of the red Bull's Blood brand.

Furmint Hungarian white grape variety, making crisp, clean, slightly peppery wines. Can be fresh, but too often dull.

Kadarka Red grape, making a full-bodied, gutsy wine that goes well with meaty stews.

Kisburgundi A light, slightly peppery red, made from the Pinot Noir.

Somló Small wine-growing district to the west of Lake Balaton.

Sopron Wine-growing district on the border with Austria. Much of the wine is red, made either from the Kékfrankos grape or from a Hungarian version of the Gamay.

Tokay The great dessert wine area in the east of Hungary (see above). The top wines will keep for years, the others can be drunk straight away. *Adnams* and *La Vigneronne* have some older vintage Tokay. Some dry whites – Tokay Furmint and Tokay Szamorodni – are also made, but are rather flabby and dull.

Vilány Red-wine-growing district south of Lake Balaton. Some wines made with Pinot Noir (here called Kisburgundi – see above) can be good.

Best buys from Hungary

WHITE WINES

Tokay 5 Puttonyos (*Adnams; Eldridge Pope; Haynes Hanson & Clark; Gerard Harris; Lay & Wheeler; Oddbins; Tanners Wines*)
Somló Furmint (*Peter Dominic*)

RED WINES

Vilány Kisburgundi (*Peter Dominic*)
Hungarian Merlot (*Wines of Westhorpe*)
Hungarian Merlot, Vilány (*Littlewoods shops*)

Specialist stockists

Peter Green; Premier Wines (Ayr); Wines of Westhorpe

India

New wine country

Despite its vast production of table grapes, and the questionable delights of Golconda Ruby (made in Hyderabad from some of those black table grapes), there's only one wine to reach us – and it's surprisingly good.

But it has French technology behind it. Omar Khayyam sparkling wine is the result of a venture by Indian entrepreneur Shyam Chougule with expertise imported from Champagne.

The wine, a more than adequate brut sparkling wine, made using Champagne technology, is not cheap, but it's definitely a wine to start a conversation.

Adnams; Wine Save Cash and Carry (7/8 Whitchurch Lane, Edgware HA8 6JZ).

Israel

At last something vinous has emerged from Israel that's more than pious words and over-oxidised baked wines. While the bulk of Israeli wine production – much of it from the huge Carmel winery – continues to be the unhappy yardstick by which most Israeli production is measured, one winery, just starting out, has proved that the country can produce decent wine – if the vineyard site is right and care is taken in production.

That winery is on the Golan Heights, in a 400-acre vineyard growing on the site of a major battleground of the Yom Kippur war of 1973 – and from which 250 tank carcases had to be removed before planting could take place. They produce wines under the Yarden and Gamla brand names: those available in this country include the white Yarden Mount Hermon White, cold fermented and fruity in the modern tradition; Gamla White, a medium dry wine, also in a modern and fruity style; and varietal wines (by far the most interesting) – Gamla Cabernet Sauvignon and Yarden Sauvignon Blanc. A rosé is also now being made.

While these wines are not cheap, at least they're good, and orthodox Jews will be pleased to learn that they're Kosher.

For the rest, though, Israel continues to bear out our comments of last year: the price is high and the quality uninteresting.

Best buys from Israel

Yarden Sauvignon Blanc 1984 and Gamla Cabernet Sauvignon 1984, Galilee (*both available from Kershaw's Wine Warehouse*)

Specialist stockists

Kershaw's Wine Warehouse; Selfridges; Tesco

Italy

Italian revolution

Italy continues to frustrate its friends and give succour to its enemies. It confounds, excites and nearly always surprises. That may be true of many aspects of Italian life, but it is especially true of wine.

Wine is so much a part of the Italian way of life, that there is a maddening insouciance about the way an Italian producer will present his wines, about the cavalier approach he will have to rules and regulations, and about the matter-of-fact way he will combine tradition and modernity in winemaking.

Tradition and modernity. Those are the two words which provide the clue to the revolution that has been gathering pace in Italy. Nowhere in Europe will you see such modern wineries with such sophisticated equipment. They will be side by side with small, traditional peasant farms or long-established aristocratic estates. Sometimes all three will coalesce, sometimes – more often – they will go their separate ways without a sideways glance at the others.

The revolution in Italian winemaking has meant two things for consumers. One is that a greater range of very fine Italian wines is available than could have been considered at all possible a few years ago. The second is that here (rather like Burgundy in France) the names of producers – those who have taken part in the revolution, rather than those who have stayed behind – have become as important as areas.

Price is important, too. The very best value is to be found among the more expensive wines. By comparison with France, Italy's finest wines are absurdly cheap. The same goes for the middle range wines – those costing between £3 and £5. It's only below £2.50 that poor value starts to set in, with many basic Soaves, Valpolicellas and Chiantis that just don't measure up, so are best avoided.

So be prepared to pay a little more than in the past for Italian wine. The production costs in Italy are the same as in France, but the Italians are taking less profit for themselves than the French. We should be thanking them for that by taking advantage of their generous prices.

The international threat

As well as 'tradition' and 'modernity', two other key words in assessing current Italian wine thinking are 'national' and 'international'.

Apart from New World countries, probably more experimentation is going on in Italy today than anywhere else. Surprisingly, for a nation with such a long history of wine, much of this experimentation is based on copies of French models. There seems to be a distinct feeling that importing the international French grape varieties – Cabernet Sauvignon, Chardonnay, Sauvignon and Merlot in particular – and then putting the wines in new small Bordeaux barrels will produce wines that are better than anything deriving from Italian traditions.

Small Bordeaux barrels – barriques – are the flavour of the year in Italy. Every self-respecting cellar you visit has a little row of brand new barrels surrounded by the huge old 'botti', the big old barrels in which Italian wine has normally been aged.

Inside those barriques – as often as not – will be some Cabernet Sauvignon or Chardonnay, rather than Nebbiolo or Sangiovese. The Italians are in danger of thinking that French is best in the world of wine.

One reason for this, of course, is that the Italians can see the high prices that top French wines command. Then they compare them with the much lower prices their own wines fetch, and reckon the reason is that they are not producing French look-alike wines.

Another reason is that the French have been in the international wine market much longer than the Italians, and French tastes are the yardstick by which the world judges a wine. So rather than give in to the French dominance, the Italians now have to make sure that the gamut of Italian wine tastes becomes as well known as the French.

Italy – White Wines

Chardonnay
Gewürztraminer
Pinot Bianco
Sylvaner
Goldmuskateller
Rhine Riesling
Müller-Thurgau

Picolit
Pinot Grigio
Tocai di Lison
Tocai del Piave

Asti Spumante
Moscato d'Asti
Gavi

Pinot-based
sparkling wines

VAL
D'AOSTA

LOMBARDY

SOUTH TYROL
(ALTO
ADIGE/
TRENTINO)

FRIULI–
VENEZIA–
GIULIA

Bianco di Custoza
Soave
Chardonnay

PIEDMONT

Po

VENETO

LIGURIA

EMILIA–
ROMAGNA

Albana di Romagna

Arno

Galestro
Trebbiano
Vernaccia di San Gimignano

TUSCANY

Verdicchio

MARCHES

UMBRIA

Orvieto

Tiber

LATIUM

ABRUZZI

Est! Est!! Est!!!
Frascati

MOLISE

SARDINIA

CAMPANIA

APULIA

Fiano di Avellino
Greco di Tufo
Lacryma Christi

BASILICATA

CALABRIA

SICILY

Bianco di Alcamo
Moscato di Pantelleria

0   100   200 km

0   50   100 miles

Italy – Red Wines

Barbaresco
Barbera
Barolo
Carema
Dolcetto
Grignolino
Nebbiolo
Spanna

Casteller
Lago di Caldaro
Lagrein
Santa Maddalena
Teroldego

Franciacorta
Oltrepò Pavese
Valtellina

Cabernet/Merlot di Friuli
Cabernet/Merlot di Pramaggiore

VAL D'AOSTA

SOUTH TYROL (ALTO ADIGE/ TRENTINO)

FRIULI–VENEZIA–GIULIA

PIEDMONT

Po

LOMBARDY

VENETO

Bardolino
Raboso
Valpolicella/Recioto di Valpolicella

LIGURIA

EMILIA–ROMAGNA

Lambrusco
Gutturnio dei Colli Piancentini
Sangiovese di Romagna

Arno

TUSCANY

Brunello di Montalcino
Carmignano
Chianti
Rosso di Montalcino
Vino Nobile di Montepulciano

Rosso Conero

MARCHES

UMBRIA

Tiber

Colli del Trasimeno
Torgiano

LATIUM

ABRUZZI

Montepulciano d'Abruzzo

MOLISE

Castel del Monte
Salice Salentino

CAMPANIA

APULIA

SARDINIA

Cannonau

Taurasi

BASILICATA

Aglianico del Vulture

CALABRIA

Cirò

SICILY

0	100	200 km
0	50	100 miles

Increasing variety

Which is where we come in. In Britain we are lucky to have a set of
Italian wine importers who are complete enthusiasts. They have to be,
because the British wine trade, as a whole, still dismisses Italian wine
as something not worth bothering about. But, in shops small and large
around the country, an increasing variety of Italian wines is becoming
available – see the WHERE TO BUY section and right at the end of this
section (under Specialist stockists).

What we should be doing is buying these wines and learning to
appreciate the Italian taste. Get friends who are snobby about Italian
wine to try a glass of something interesting, and they will be back for
more like a shot.

Positive signals

Apart from the trend towards barriques, and the interest in imported
grape varieties – both probably short-term fashions (the Italians are just
as fashion-conscious in wine as they are in clothes) – there are more
long-term trends which give more positive signals about the way
Italian wine is going.

Italy has developed the technology of winemaking to a high degree.
We've already mentioned the modernity of many of the wineries
(cantinas). But while the winemaking was improving at the winery, the
vineyards were being neglected. It is only recently that the picturesque
system of promiscuous cultivation – growing one crop underneath
other vines trained high on pergolas – began to disappear from Italian
vineyards. Now most serious vineyards are single crop. But still the
vineyards turn out enormously high yields, often much too high for
quality. Gradually, the realisation that yields must be restricted is
percolating through Italy: the top producers are already cutting back;
others will surely follow.

At the same time, the grape varieties are being improved. One way
of doing this is to cut down on the high-yielding neutral varieties, like
the white Trebbiano, which only rarely achieves a higher qualitative
assessment than dull (it's the grape variety which produces the base
wine for Cognac in France, where a neutral wine is just what's
needed). They are being replaced by the traditional, low-yielding
varieties – such as the Grechetto in Orvieto (see under Umbria) – which
have much more character and quality.

The other way grape varieties are being improved is by clonal
selection. For instance, in the 1970s many of the new Sangiovese vines
planted in Tuscany to make Chianti were of the prolific, low quality
Sangiovese di Romagna. Now those vines are being replaced by the
superior local clone, the Sangiovese Grosso or Sangioveto, making
smaller quantities of higher quality wine.

Less but better

In a country where wine consumption generally is falling, producers now reckon that the best way they can survive is to answer the increasing demand for better wines – to make less but better wine, which is good news for everyone.

This change can be detected on wine labels. More single vineyard wines are now available in the shops, called Cru, Vigneti or Tenuta. These are wines produced in small quantities, from small-yielding, high quality vineyards, and are often the finest wines that producers can make.

The other tell-tale term on the labels is vino da tavola. This also exemplifies one of the classic contradictions of Italian winemaking. The basic, rot-gut wine of Italy is vino da tavola. But so are some of the very finest wines: the label doesn't distinguish – but the price certainly will.

The growth of what are known as 'super vini da tavola' is a logical extension of the Italian's love for individualism, and the restrictions of the Italian wine laws (see below) which forbid experimentation beyond certain prescribed limits. There are so many anomalies and constraints in the rules that many producers simply ignore them. Many of the finest producers now make a super vino da tavola which goes at the top end of their range above the DOC or DOCG wines which conform with the law.

The Italian wine label

There are three quality designations in Italy:

Vino da tavola This, as we have already seen, can refer to the rock-bottom local wines, or to the finest designer wines from a top producer which do not conform to the DOC or DOCG regulations.

Denominazione di Origine Controllata, DOC for short. This indicates that the wine comes from a specified zone and has been made in accordance with the rules of that zone. It is like the French AC in that it is a guarantee of origin only, not of quality.

The name of the DOC may appear in a number of ways: as a geographical name for a region (Frascati); as the name of a village (Barolo); or it may appear as a grape variety attached to a geographical name (Barbera d'Asti – wines made from the Barbera grape in the town of Asti). It may also appear as a combination of a geographical name and a fantasy name (Oltrepò Pavese Buttafuoco – Oltrepò Pavese the geographical name, Buttafuoco the fantasy name). Occasionally, the name may be sheer fantasy (Lacryma Christi).

Denominazione di Origine Controllata e Garantita, DOCG This is the top Italian controlled quality level. The 'garantita' part of the title means that the wine has been tested by government-appointed officials and conforms to the rules they have set out. It applies currently to only five areas: Barolo, Barbaresco, Brunello di Montalcino, Vino Nobile di Montepulciano and Chianti. All are currently on the market as DOCG, but may also be found as simple DOC where the vintage precedes the year in which DOCG became obligatory for that wine, eg Barolo 1979 DOC, Barolo 1980 DOCG.

The scheme was introduced only in the past few years and has worked, more or less, because the overall quality of wines has risen, even in the enormous area of Chianti.

But, typically Italian, there are rumours that the whole system will be demeaned by the introduction of DOCG zones in areas of pretty mediocre winemaking. Albana di Romagna is likely to get a DOCG – and there are few duller white wines than these. Others not wholly deserving of the scheme may follow. Politics, of course, is at the bottom of it, with wine quality a minor consideration.

At the moment, though, DOCG does mean something, and the DOCG seal (normally placed over the cork) does guarantee that a reasonably high standard has been reached.

Other terms on the label

Abboccato Sweet.

Secco Dry.

Rosato Rosé – you may see either term.

Classico As in Chianti, Valpolicella, Soave and so on; denotes wine from the heart of the delimited area.

Superiore In general, merely signifies extra alcohol. Not necessarily indicative of superior quality.

Riserva (Speciale) Supposed to indicate extra ageing, usually in barrel; more significant in Chianti than Barolo/Barbaresco. Not necessarily an advantage – wines are often kept *too* long in barrel. But the best, richest wines are likely to have been selected in the first place to become Riservas.

VQPRD The EEC's equivalent of DOC.

VSQPRD The EEC's equivalent of DOC for sparkling wine.

Qualitätswein South Tyrolean (Alto Adige) equivalent of DOC.

Consortium seal This indicates that the wine has passed analytical and tasting tests organised by the producers' consortium. Generally not terribly significant, apart from Chianti Classico (Black Cockerel) and Chianti Putto (Cherub).

VIDE (as collar label) This means that the winery belongs to an association of quality producers and that this particular wine has passed genuinely stringest tests.

Once again, it is essential to note the name of the producer, which is the ultimate guarantee of quality. Check also what kind of establishment the wine comes from. **Azienda Agricola** or **Agraria** means that the particular estate makes and bottles its own produce. Words like **Fattoria** (wine-farm, not a factory), **Villa, Castello, Tenuta, Podere, Vigna** or **Vigneto** also indicate that the grapes come from a particular estate or vineyard. **Azienda Vitivinicola** means that the estate grows grapes but also buys grapes in from other growers. An **Azienda** or **Casa Vinicola** makes wine but does not grow grapes. A **Cantina Sociale** is a growers' co-operative.

Vintage chart for Italian wines

	Barolo/ Barbaresco	Amarone/Recioto della Valpolicella	Chianti Classico Riserva (plus Riservas of Rufina & other sub-zones)	Brunello di Montalcino (plus Vino Nobile)
1986	Very good	Excellent	Excellent	Very good
1985	Excellent	Excellent	Excellent	Excellent
1984	Fair to good	Very good	Poor	Fair
1983	Very good	Excellent	Very good	Fair to good
1982	Excellent	Poor	Excellent	Excellent
1981	Mediocre	Fair	Fair to good	Fair to good
1980	Good	Good	Fair	Good
1979	Very good	Very good	Very good	Excellent
1978	Excellent	Excellent	Good	Good
	1977, 1976, 1975 To be avoided 1974, 1971, 1970 All very good to excellent	1977, 1976 Good 1971 Excellent	1977 Good 1976 Poor 1975 Excellent 1971 Excellent 1970 Good	1977, 1971, 1970 Very good 1975, 1964 Excellent

PIEDMONT

This is the region of the big two red wines – Barolo and Barbaresco – and of the satellite red wines also based on the Nebbiolo grape like Ghemme, Gattinara, Spanna and Carema. It's also home to the attractively fruity red Dolcetto and the acid, over-yielding but underrated Barbera. It's also the source of all those delicious moscato-based sweet wines – Asti Spumante, Moscato Spumante, Moscato d'Asti, plus a clutch of dry whites with weird tastes and weird names – Arneis, Gavi, Cortese di Gavi.

Famous reds

Barolo and Barbaresco may be the two famous names of Piedmont, but they're also the most unapproachable, the most undrinkable, and the most expensive. The rules of the DOCG lay down long ageing in wood until all the fruit of the Nebbiolo has disappeared and until the wines taste of tannin and not much else.

This is where the Italian ability to bend rules comes into play. There's now a group of producers (see below for names) who are fermenting their wines very carefully, ageing for the minimum period – and a little less if they can get away with it – and then bottling wine that still has fruit, and in which the glorious truffle-and-violets flavour of the Nebbiolo is brought out. Then you realise how these wines got their reputation.

But they're still expensive – quite rightly so because quantities are small, and great care is taken in their production. If you want the taste of Nebbiolo for less money, try wines like Ghemme, Gattinara or Nebbiolo d'Alba.

The most enjoyable Piedmontese red wine is based on the Dolcetto grape, which produces a really jammy, fruity wine akin to Beaujolais. Like Beaujolais, it's lovely drunk chilled and young.

The workhorse red grape is Barbera, whose name is generally associated with a town, as in Barbera d'Alba or Barbera d'Asti (the same is true of the Nebbiolo and Dolcetto grapes). It makes a heavy, rich, fruited wine with a strong edge of acidity, which tends to need some ageing. Another grape to look out for is Freisa.

The most famous Piedmontese whites are the sweet Asti Spumante and its associate Moscato d'Asti. At their best – and very freshest – they are absolutely delicious and among the most refreshing drinks imaginable on a warm day. Other whites are less exciting: Cortese di Gavi and Gavi dei Gavi which are heavily overpriced, Erbaluce di Caluso and the unusal bone dry Arneis.

Who's who in Piedmont

Ascheri Rich, powerful Barbaresco which still manages to preserve the fruit.
The Market/Winecellars

Felice Bonardi Traditional style of Barbaresco, big and tannic.
Gerry's Wines and Spirits (74 Old Compton Street, London W1); Market Wine House (20 Market Street, Brighton, East Sussex); Terroni & Son (138 Clerkenwell Road, London EC1)

Giacomo Borgogno e Figli Renowned producers of Barolo, specialising in old vintages. Wines: Barbera d'Alba, Barolo, Dolcetto d'Alba.
Adnams; Eldridge Pope; Lay & Wheeler; The Market/Winecellars; Oddbins; Tanners Wines; Wine Growers Association

La Brenta d'Oro Older-style production of Barbarescos which need 20 years before they can be drunk. Wine: Barbaresco Riserva.
Peter Green; Wine Growers Association

Agostino Brugo Good examples of the Nebbiolo in their Ghemme wines.
Eldridge Pope; Lay & Wheeler; Wine Society

Castello di Neive Produce small amounts of fine Barbaresco. Wines: Barbaresco, Barbera d'Alba, Dolcetto d'Alba, Moscato d'Asti.
Bibendum; The Market/Winecellars; Ostlers

Fratelli Cavallotto Own the renowned Bricco Boschis vineyard in Barolo. Wines: Barbera d'Alba, Barolo, Dolcetto d'Alba, Favorita, Grignolino, Nebbiolo.
Cadwgan Fine Wine Merchants; The Market/Winecellars; Ostlers

Ceretto A producer of ripe, fruity, plummy Barolos in a fresher, less traditional style than many. Wines: Barbaresco, Barbera d'Alba, Barolo, Dolcetto d'Alba, Nebbiolo d'Alba. Try Barolo Bricco Roche or Barbaresco Asiy.
Adnams; Berry Bros & Rudd; Wine Society

Pio Cesare Traditional producer making very fine wines. Wines: Barbaresco, Barbera d'Alba, Barolo, Dolcetto d'Alba, Nebbiolo d'Alba, Grignolino.
Adnams; Peter Dominic; Alex Findlater; The Market/Winecellars

Aldo Conterno Makes Monforte d'Alba, Barolo Bussia Soprana and Colonello di Bricco Bussia. Wines: Barbera d'Alba, Barolo, Dolcetto d'Alba.
H Allen Smith

Giacomo Conterno Makes a single-vineyard Barolo Monfortino.
Wines: Barbera d'Alba, Barolo, Dolcetto d'Alba.
Bibendum; The Market/Winecellars; Ostlers; Wine Society

Guiseppe Contratto Specialises in spumante (sparkling wines).
Wines: Asti Spumante, Contratto Brut, Riserva Bacco d'Oro.
G Belloni (128 Albert Street, London NW1); Wine Society

Duca d'Asti Wide-ranging company with a large portfolio of wines.
Wines: Barbaresco, Barbera d'Asti, Barbera del Monferrato, Cortese di
Gavi, Dolcetto di Ovada, Nebbiolo d'Alba, Granduca Brut sparkling.
*Barnes Wine Shop; Berry Bros & Rudd; Eaton Elliot Winebrokers; Wine
Society*

Luigu Ferrando e Figli Producers of pricey Carema Black Label, of
marvellous quality.
Harrods; Ostlers; The Market/Winecellars

Fontanafredda An estate founded by the son of King Victor
Emmanuel II. Make fine spumante as well as accessible Barolo. Wines:
Asti Spumante, Barbaresco, Barbera d'Alba, Barolo, Dolcetto d'Alba,
Brut Spumante Contessa Rosa.
Peter Dominic; Peter Green; The Market/Winecellars

Franco-Fiorina Believers in stainless steel rather than oak, who buy in
grapes and make very good wines. Wines: Barbaresco, Barbera d'Alba,
Barolo, Dolcetto d'Alba, Nebbiolo d'Alba.
Kershaw's Wine Warehouse

Gaja The guru of Piedmont who makes the most expensive and some
of the finest Barbarescos. Wines: Barbaresco, Barbera d'Alba, Dolcetto
d'Alba, Nebbiolo d'Alba, Vinot, Chardonnay, Cabernet Sauvignon.
Adnams; The Market/Winecellars; Windrush Wines

Gancia Major spumante producers. Wines: Asti Spumante, Gancia
Spumante, Gran Reserva Carlo Gancia Brut, Pinot di Pinot.
Widely available

Bruno Giacosa Very fine aged reds, including single vineyard wines.
Wines: Barbaresco, Barbera d'Alba, Barolo, Dolcetto d'Alba,
Grignolino d'Alba, Nebbiolo d'Alba, Arneis.
Barwell and Jones

Marchese di Barolo A long-established firm, recently sold by its
founding family. Wines: Asti Spumante, Barbaresco, Barbera d'Alba,
Barolo, Cortese di Gavi, Dolcetto d'Alba, Freisa d'Alba, Nebbiolo
d'Alba.
Demijohn Wines; Peter Green; Christopher Piper Wines; La Vigneronne

Martini e Rossi Make spumante as well as vermouth. Wines: Asti
Spumante.
Widely available

Luigi Nervi e Italo Produce reasonably quick-maturing Gattinara.
G Belloni (128 Albert Street, London NW1); Lay & Wheeler

Produttori del Barbaresco A small co-operative specialising in top
quality single vineyard Barbaresco. Wines: Barbaresco, Nebbiolo.
Tesco

Alfredo Prunotto Traditional style of wine and single vineyard Barolo.
Wines: Barbaresco, Barbera d'Alba, Barolo, Dolcetto d'Alba, Nebbiolo
d'Alba.
Lay & Wheeler; Wine Society

Terre di Barolo A large co-operative which makes a lighter style of
wine. Wines: Barbera d'Alba, Barolo, Dolcetto d'Alba, Dolcetto di
Diano d'Alba, Nebbiolo d'Alba.
Alex Findlater

Vietti Makes wines for drinking young, as well as some more serious
wines for ageing. Wines: Barbaresco, Barbera d'Alba, Barolo, Dolcetto
d'Alba, Nebbiolo d'Alba, Freisa.
Peter Green; Windrush Wines

Best buys from Piedmont

WHITES

Moscato d'Asti 1985, Fontanafredda (*Valvona & Crolla; Wizard Wine
Warehouses*)
Moscato del Piemonte 1981, Paola Colla (*Ashley Scott*)
(See also sparkling wines on page 529.)

REDS

Barolo 1979, Ascheri (*C A Rookes; The Wine Centre, Worcester*)
Barolo 1982, cru Zonchera, Ceretto (*Master Cellar Wine Warehouse*)
Barbaresco 1980, Giacosa Fratelli (*Barwell and Jones*)
Barbaresco 1978, Ronco (*Millevini*)
Ghemme 1980, Agostino Brugo (*Wine Growers Association; The Wine
Society*)

LOMBARDY

A neglected wine area as far as most of our wine merchants are
concerned. Luckily, some more enterprising souls have gone to the
Oltrepò Pavese (south of the River Po) to find some excellent red wines
made of the local Bonarda or the Piedmontese Barbera. Other red
wines of renown include Franciacorta (made from Cabernet Franc,
Merlot, Barbera and Nebbiolo) and wines from Valtellina which rejoice
in names like Grumello, Inferno and Sassella.

Of the whites, there is a very fine sparkling wine from Ca' del Bosco, and spumantes based on Pinot Nero and Pinot Grigio from Oltrepò Pavese. From around Lake Garda in the north of the region, the white Lugana is similar in style to – and often better than – Soave, while an attractive Chiaretto comes from Riviera del Garda.

Who's who in Lombardy

Ca' del Bosco Producers of very fine Chardonnay-based spumante, also Franciacorta, Wines: Franciacorta Pinot, Franciacorta Rosso, Rosa Ca' del Bosco sparkling.
Harrods; Ostlers; The Market/Winecellars

Castello di Luzzano Make excellent Oltrepò Pavese wines. Wines: Oltrepò Pavese Bonarda, Oltrepò Pavese Barbera, Gutturnio.
The Market/Winecellars

Enologica Valtellinese Very fine Valtellina wines. Wine: Valtellina Superiore.
Wine Growers Association

Longhi-de Carli A Franciacorta producer.
Wine Growers Association

Nera Makes wine in Valtellina. Wines: Sassella, Inferno, Grumello.
The Market/Winecellars; Ostlers

Santi Soave producer who also makes Lugana.
Majestic Wine Warehouses; La Vigneronne; Waitrose

Zenato Producers of Lugana and Riviera del Garda.
H Allen Smith; Arthur Rackhams; Tanners Wines; Wine Growers Association

Best buys from Lombardy

Bonarda Oltrepò Pavese 1985, Fugazza (*The Market/Winecellars; Oddbins*)
Franciacorta Rosso 1984, Longhe-de Carli (*Millevini*)
For sparkling wine best buys from Lombardy, see page 529.

TRENTINO

The wines of this northern region of Italy divide into two distinct areas. The Trentino is the southern part of the Adige Valley, parallel to Lake Garda, and very much part of Italy. The Alto Adige (see below) to the north is very different: a narrow gorge in the valley marks the limit of Italian Mediterranean culture and the beginning of Germanic culture, which stretches from there to the Baltic Sea.

The Trentino is the source of much of the sparkling wine that is bottled by producers in places such as Turin and Milan. It's only recently that local firms have got in on the act, and a few examples are now available in this country (some very good – see under Sparkling wines on page 529).

For still wines, Trentino produces a wide range of wines which are made using modern technology and are labelled varietally. Principal grape varieties used are Riesling Italico, Pinot Bianco, Pinot Grigio, Müller-Thurgau (for whites); Teroldego Rotaliano, Caldero and Schiava for reds. There are also a couple of specialities, the white Nosiola and the red Marzemino.

Who's who in Trentino

Càvit The main Trentino co-operative, making 70 to 77 million litres of wine a year. Quality tends to vary widely; the Chardonnay and Teroldego Rotaliano wines are best. Wines: Casteller, Teroldego Rotaliano, Vicariati (a premium red made from Cabernet Franc and Merlot), Valdadige, Chardonnay, Pinot Grigio.
Victoria Wine Co

Pojer & Sandri Top producers in Trentino, specialising in white wines. Wines: Chardonnay, Müller-Thurgau.
Alex Findlater; The Market/Winecellars

Roberto Zeni Trento winemaker specialising in Teroldego Rotaliano. Wines: Chardonnay, Teroldego Rotaliano.
Berry Bros & Rudd; Tanners Wines; Wine Growers Association

ALTO ADIGE

Popular whites, strange reds

It may be called the Alto Adige officially, but to the locals it's the Südtirol. The white wines of the area have been one of the big Italian success stories over the past three or four years. The reason is both geographical and political. Geographically, the cooler mountain climate of this region in the heart of the Alps produces white wines with natural freshness and fruit that can be lacking further south in the Italian heat. Politically, the wine producers make dry white wines, certainly, but with the fragrant fruitiness that comes from taking Germany and Austria as the model rather than Italy.

The grapes used are a mixture of nationalities: Müller-Thurgau, Sylvaner and Riesling (sometimes called the Rhine Riesling or Riesling Renano to show that it is the true German Riesling), Pinot Grigio and Pinot Bianco, and, increasingly, Sauvignon and Chardonnay. Probably the last two have made the greatest impact. There are also small quantities of the sweet dessert wine made from the Rosenmuskateller grape, a type of Muscat. All wines are labelled varietally.

Reds are a stranger bunch, relying more on local varieties. The most commonly planted is the Vernatsch (Schiavia in Italian), which produces light, bitter-cherry wines, the best of which come from St Magdalen and bear that village's name. Other red grapes grown are Lagrein, Pinot Nero and, more and more, Cabernet Franc and Cabernet Sauvignon.

Increasingly producers are ageing some wines in small new barrels – both white Chardonnay and red Cabernets and Pinot Nero – and producing some top-class wines of an international style and standard.

There has been some concern about the yields from some vineyards, which are extraordinarily high by Italian standards, nearer to German levels. It has been suggested that the high yields decrease the concentration and fruit flavours of the wines, so better producers are cutting down on the yields and producing piercingly fragrant white wines, still at very good prices.

Alto Adige labels can be confusing because they are mainly in German rather than Italian. They may describe the contents as Qualitätswein rather than DOC. Only the small print describing the wine as 'Produce of Italy' will show that it is not from Austria or Germany.

Most of the white wines keep for a couple of years, but not more.

Who's who in the Alto Adige (Südtirol)

Arunda Make brut spumante, one of the finest Italian sparklers, high up in the Alps of the Alto Adige. Wines: Arunda Brut.
H Allen Smith

Josef Brigl Very traditional firm making good whites. Wines: Weissburgunder (Pinot Bianco), Goldmuskateller (dessert wine).
Winchester Wine Company (68 Fairfield Road, Winchester, Hampshire)

Eisacktaler Kellereigenossenschaft (Co-operative of the Isarco Valley) Make wines from vineyards nearest the Austrian border. Wines: Sylvaner, Gewürztraminer, Grüner Veltliner.
Winchester Wine Company (see address above)

J Hofstätter Some of this wide range of wines – especially reds – age remarkably well. Wines: Pinot Grigio, Rhine Riesling, Gewürztraminer, Schiava, Cabernet Sauvignon.
Wine Society

Kettmeir Make the full range of varietal Alto Adige wines.
Vinorio (8 Old Compton Street, London W1)

Alois Lageder Family-owned company making a wide variety of

wines in the Alto Adige. One of the top two of the region. Wines: Chardonnay, Moscato (sweet), Pinot Grigio, Sauvignon, Gewürztraminer (from the village of Tramin, claimed to be the home of this grape), Schiava, Cabernet Franc.
Eldridge Pope; Oddbins; Stapylton Fletcher

Schloss Schwanburg Based in one of the Alto Adige's many old castles, making good quality wines. Wines: Full range of varietals.
Alston Wines

J Tiefenbrunner One of the two top Alto Adige producers, he is proud owner of the highest vineyard in Europe, called Feldmarschal, planted with Müller-Thurgau grapes. Wines: every varietal in Alto Adige, all of very high quality.
Adnams; H Allen Smith; Alex Findlater; Tanners Wines

Viticoltori Alto Adige The main co-operative of the Alto Adige, with very high standards. There are associated co-operatives at St Michael in Eppan and Terlan. Wines: Sauvignon, Gewürztraminer, Rhine Riesling, Chardonnay, Pinot Bianco, Lagrein Dunkel, Cabernet Franc, Schiava.
Les Amis du Vin; Berry Bros & Rudd; Peter Dominic; Tanners Wines; Wine Growers Association

Best buys from the Alto Adige

Chardonnay di Appiano 1983, Viticoltori Alto-Adige (*Peter Green; G Hush; Paul Sanderson Wines*)
Chardonnay Alto Adige 1986 (*J Sainsbury*)
Pinot Grigio 1986, Tiefenbrunner (*Tesco*)

VENETO

Italian wine producers are still having a hard job persuading sceptical British wine drinkers that Soave, Valpolicella and Bardolino do not necessarily taste more of banana skins than of grapes. However, the message is starting to get through because enough retailers are stocking the top wines in these much-abused denominations, revealing the range of tastes that made the wines so attractive in the first place before industrialisation set in.

Many of these wines are from single estates, or crus. Others are the results of careful selection and vinification: Soave tasting of almonds and peachy fruit; Valpolicella that ages to a delicious, rich, bitter-cherry flavour; and Bardolino, almost like rosé in its light, fruity freshness.

The region of Valpolicella also produces the great Reciotos, huge red wines made from partly dried grapes. Deep, rich, bitter-tasting when dry, called Amarone, or smooth and creamy in their sweet version, called Amabile, they are among the finest of Italian red wines. Rarer, and equally exciting, are the sweet white Recioto Soaves, made in the same way.

These are not the only wines from the Veneto. We've just discovered the wines from Bianco di Custoza, a near neighbour of Soave, where the wines are more reliable than run-of-the-mill Soave at only slightly higher prices. Further to the east, there are several DOCs new to us – Colli Berici, south of Vicenza, making a range of varietal wines (Pinot Bianco, Tocai Italiano, Merlot, Pinot Noir); Breganze, to the north of Vicenza, and the Colli Euganaei near Padua, both making a similar range. Further east, in the Valdobbiadene, the white Prosecco produces sparkling wines and the Raboso makes some sturdy reds.

Then there are the vini da tavola. Veneto is a source of some fine super vini da tavola, and the best producers all make one (see below). Many are variations on the theme of Valpolicella or Recioto della Valpolicella, but there are some white ones as well. A few producers (Conte Loredan being the most famous) are working with Cabernet Sauvignon with considerable success.

Who's who in the Veneto

Allegrini Old-fashioned family firm. Excellent Valpolicella and Amarone. Wines: Valpolicella Classico Superiore, Recioto Amarone. *Bordeaux Direct/The Wine Club*

Bertani Traditional family company specialising in old Valpolicella Amarone. Wines: Bardolino, Soave, Valpolicella, Valpolicella Recioto. *G Belloni (128 Albert Street, London NW1); Berry Bros & Rudd*

Bolla Well-established company whose wines are widely available in Britain. Look for single vineyard Soave (Castellaro) and Valpolicella (Jago Bolla). Wines: Soave, Valpolicella, Bardolino, Amarone. *Les Amis du Vin; André Simon Wines*

Boscaini A family firm with sound wines, now also specialising in single vineyard wines. Wines: Soave, Valpolicella, Bardolino, single vineyard Soave (Cantina di Monteleone), single vineyard Valpolicella (Vigneti di Marano) and single vineyard Bardolino (Tenuta Le Canne). Red super vino da tavola, Le Cane. *Wine Growers Association*

Cantina Sociale di Soave Large co-operative dominating the production of good quality Soave. Wines: Bardolino, Soave, Valpolicella; some single vineyard wines. *H Allen Smith*

La Fattoria Based in Lison, home of the best white Tocai of the Veneto. Wines: Tocai di Lison Classico. *The Market/Winecellars; Turl Wine Vaults*

Lamberti Big commercial producer whose wines are widely available. Wines: Bardolino, Lugana, Valpolicella; also sparkling dry wine.
Peter Dominic

Maculan High quality wines from Breganze. Look for sweet white Tercolato. Wines: Breganze Cabernet, Rosato Tercolato.
Alex Findlater; Tanners Wines

Masi One of the best Valpolicella and Soave producers. Also associated with Boscaini (see above). Wines: Bardolino, Soave, Valpolicella, Amarone. Also single vineyard wines (Serego Alighieri is a fine Valpolicella), red super vino da tavola (Campo Fiorín) and white (Masianco).
Adnams; Alex Findlater

Pieropan Often reckoned to be the finest Soave producer. Wines: Soave and Recioto Soave.
Adnams; Bibendum; Bordeaux Direct/The Wine Club

Giuseppe Quintarelli Traditional firm making small amounts of high quality wines. Wines: Valpolicella Recioto Amabile and Amarone.
Adnams; Ashley Scott

Santa Sofia High quality wines from around Lake Garda. Wines: Bianco di Custoza, Soave, Valpolicella, Bardolino.
Eaton Elliot Winebrokers

Santi A medium-sized producer of Soave wines.
Tanners Wines; La Vigneronne

Tedeschi A specialist in Recioto-style wines, and some top quality vini da tavola. Wines: Bianco di Custoza, Soave, Valpolicella, Bardolino, Recioto, Capitel San Rocco super vini da tavola white and red.
Adnams; Bibendum; Wine Growers Association

Venegazzù-Conte Loredan-Gasparini The Loredan family are descendants of Doges of Venice and still sport the Doges' cap of office on their label. Produce some top vini da tavola. Wines: Venegazzù della Casa, Venegazzù Etichetta Nera (Cabernet Sauvignon), Venegazzù Rosso, sparkling Venegazzù Prosecco Brut.
Barnes Wine Shop; Alex Findlater; Majestic Wine Warehouses; Tanners Wines; La Vigneronne

Zenato Make very good whites around Lake Garda, plus Valpolicella. Wines: Soave, Valpolicella, Bianco di Custoza.
H Allen Smith; Arthur Rackhams; Tanners Wines

Stockists given in italic type after wines in this section will be found in the WHERE TO BUY section earlier in the book.

Best buys from the Veneto

WHITES

Bianco di Custoza 1986, Tedeschi (*The Market/Winecellars; and others*)
Chardonnay, Venegazzù della Casa (*Cadwgan Fine Wines; Majestic Wine Warehouses; Millevini*)
Masianco, Masi (*Continental Wine House*)
Soave Classico 1985, Pieropan (*Ostlers; Taste Shops*)
Soave Classico 1986, Zenato (*Arthur Rackhams; Waitrose*)
Bianco San Pietro, Guerrieri-Rizzardi (*Vintage Roots*)

REDS

Le Cane, Boscaini (*Bin Ends; The Market/Winecellars; Wapping Wine Warehouse*)
Valpolicella Castello d'Illasi 1985, Santi (*D Byrne*)

FRIULI–VENEZIA–GIULIA

Quality getting better

About eight or nine years ago, this region seemed poised to outshine the rest of Italy with the quality and reliability of its – mainly varietally labelled – wines.

Then, somehow, the promise was not fulfilled. The whites, which had been so startlingly fresh, started to get soft and flabby; the reds lost their mellowness and became hard-edged. The Alto Adige came up fast from behind and overtook Friuli almost overnight.

So we are glad to report that quality is improving, and that this region in the far north-east of Italy is putting out some very good wines in the lower and middle price ranges. Always buy, though, the most recent vintage of the whites, and don't keep the reds for more than two or three years.

Friuli–Venezia–Giulia is organised in a similar way to the Alto Adige. The wines are labelled mainly varietally, and the three DOC areas to look out for (Collio Goriziano, Colli Orientali del Friuli and Grave del Friuli) permit a range of grape varieties to carry the DOC name.

The whites that can do this are Tocai, Traminer, Pinot Bianco, Pinot Grigio, Riesling Italico, Verduzzo and the new imports of Sauvignon and Riesling Renano (Rhine Riesling). The rare Picolit, making a sweet wine, is less often seen than talked about.

In the reds, Cabernet Franc and Merlot make reliable, good value wines. Also look out for some examples of Pinot Nero (Pinot Noir) and the local Refosco.

Who's who in Friuli–Venezia–Giulia

Collavini Wines from the Collio and Grave del Friuli. Look out for their unusual white Ribolla and red Schioppettino, both local grape varieties. Wines: Varietals from Grave del Friuli and Collio; also a good cheap sparkler, Il Grigio.
Adnams; Bibendum; Haynes Hanson & Clark; Wine Growers Association

Fratelli Pighin New firm which has already established a high reputation. Wines: Varietals from Collio Goriziano and Grave del Friuli; one of the best Picolits.
Epicure Delicatessen (46 West Nile Street, Glasgow); Quality Drinks (Mitcham Road, London SW17)

Best buys from Friuli–Venezia–Giulia

WHITES

Pinot Grigio del Collio 1985, Collavini (*Wine Growers Association*)
Chardonnay di Friuli 1986 (*Marks & Spencer*)
Tocai del Collio, 1985, Pighin (*details from Mondial Wines, 13/14 Nelson Trading Estate, Morden Road, London SW19*)

RED

Cabernet del Collio 1982, Collavini (*Wine Growers Association*)

TUSCANY

DOCG proves its worth

It's not often that a set of Italian regulations actually works, but with Chianti, the most famous wine of Tuscany, it seems that the DOCG guarantee actually stands for something. The quality of basic Chianti is certainly better than it was a few years ago, which is the best test of the system. It has risen in price slightly, but this is probably a better reflection of the true cost of production.

On the other hand, being more suspicious, it may just be that Chianti has had two fine vintages – 1985 and 1986 – and our good opinion of the 1985 basic Chianti is affecting our view before we ever get on to the 1986.

Whatever the reason – and we're not complaining, because the wines are good – Tuscany as a whole and not just Chianti is the most exciting Italian wine area at the moment. It's not just the quality, it's also the innovation that's going on – blending the local red Sangiovese grape with other varieties (principally Cabernet Sauvignon) and ageing the wine in small barrels – often with astounding results. The same experimentation is happening with Chardonnay and even with that much neglected local grape, the Malvasia.

The Tuscans have discovered that Sangiovese Grosso, the standard grape for Chianti, comes in a whole variety of different guises. The latest fashion is for the Sangioveto, which makes some of the best Chiantis in the Chianti Rufina zone north-east of Florence (look out for Frescobaldi's Castello di Nipozzano).

Another interesting trend is a return to the use of the governo, a practice whereby dried grapes were added to the wine after fermentation to speed up the ageing process. It has meant that wines like the Torgaio of Ruffino can reach the shops in the March following the harvest, and have a big, fresh, fruity, grapy taste.

The Chianti region is diffuse so it is not surprising that there are many levels of quality. Basic Chianti DOCG can come from a huge area starting at Pisa on the coast and finishing almost into Umbria at Cortona in the south-east of the region. Within that large zone are smaller areas. Some – like Chianti Classico, Chianti Rufina, Chianti Montalbano, Chianti Colli Senesi – are producing some top wines; others – like Chianti Colline Pisane, Chianti Colli Aretini, Chianti Colli Fiorentini – are the source of the basic flask wine that's consumed locally. You won't always see the name of the zone on the label unless it's Chianti Classico.

Under the new DOCG rules the traditional recipe of Chianti has been modified to cut down on the white grapes and increase the use of noble grape varieties like Cabernet Sauvignon to blend with the principal constituent, Sangiovese. The surplus white Trebbiano grapes have been put to good use: Galestro is the new Tuscan white DOC, making beautifully clean, fresh wines using the most modern technology.

Two DOC zones west of Florence – one red, one white – are worth looking out for. Carmignano makes splendid Chianti, using a certain amount of Cabernet Sauvignon, with Villa di Capezzana and Artimino the most important producers. The white is the long-established Vernaccia di San Gimignano, making wine with a hint of almonds.

In the south of Tuscany, Brunello di Montalcino continues to command high prices even though it sometimes suffers from too much wood. But things may change, and the lesser Rosso di Montalcino DOC is making some very approachable wines. Neighbouring Vino Nobile di Montepulciano has shown considerable improvements in the quality of its reds.

Then there is a clutch of super vini da tavola: Antinori's Tignanello and Solaia and Incisa della Rocchetta's extremely expensive Cabernet Sauvignon Sassicaia and some of the Vinattieris, also 100 per cent Cabernet Sauvignon. Others in this group include Prima Vigna from Castello Vicchiomaggio, Sangioveto di Coltibuono, Palazzo Altesi of Altesino, Ser Niccolò of Serristori, Ghiaie della Furba of Capezzana, Coltassala of Castello di Volpaia, and many others.

Tuscany also makes the incomparable Vin Santo, a sweet

sherry-style but unfortified wine of great character and interest. A few examples are: Villa di Vetrice (*Winecellars*); Frescobaldi (*S H Jones*); Capelli (*Rackhams of Birmingham*); Antinori (*Selfridges*).

Who's who in Tuscany

Altesino Makes some fine Brunello di Montalcino. Wines: Brunello; super vini da tavola: Palazzo Altesi, Alte d'Altesi.
Peter Dominic; The Market/Winecellars

Antinori One of the great names of Chianti. Makes Chianti and fine vini da tavola such as Tignanello, also some of the best Orvieto (see under Umbria). Wines: Chianti Classico, sparkling Brut, Tignanello, Solaia, Galestro.
Adnams; Lay & Wheeler; Majestic Wine Warehouses; Oddbins; Selfridges

Argiano Brunello di Montalcino producer whose cellars are in a spectacular crumbling castle. Wines: Brunello di Montalcino, Rosso di Montalcino.
Peter Dominic

Badia a Coltibuono Top quality Chianti Classico producer. Not cheap. Wines: Chianti Classico Riserva, Chianti Classico; super vino da tavola: Sangioveto di Coltibuono.
Bibendum; Alex Findlater; Gerard Harris

Bigi Large négociant and producer who also makes wines in Umbria (Orvieto). Wines: Vino Nobile di Montepulciano, Chianti.
Barnes Wine Shop; La Vigneronne

Biondi-Santi (Il Greppo) The godfathers of Brunello di Montalcino – they invented it. Their wines command enormous prices, not always justified by the quality.
Harrods; The Market/Winecellars; Tanners Wines

Brolio Medium-weight Chianti from the firm that started modern Chianti in the 19th century. Wines: Chianti Classico.
Kershaw's Wine Warehouse

Castello Vicchiomaggio Fine winemaking, bringing together modern and traditional methods. Wines: Chianti Classico; super vino da tavola: Prima Vigna.
Marks & Spencer; La Vigneronne

Castello di Volpaia Top estate based around a hilltop village. Wines: Chianti Classico; super vini da tavola: Coltassala (Sangiovese), Mammolo (aged in small barrels).
Adnams; Bibendum; Eaton Elliot Winebrokers; The Market/Winecellars; Tanners Wines

Cecchi Producer based in Montepulciano who also makes Chianti. Wines: Vino Nobile di Montepulciano, Chianti Colli Senesi.
Davisons; Alex Findlater; Fullers; Tesco; Threshers

Col d'Orcia Brunello producer now owned by Cinzano. Wines: Brunello di Montalcino.
Barwell and Jones

Conti Serristori The property includes the house where Machiavelli lived in exile. Wines: Chianti Classico, Riserva Machiavelli; super vino da tavola: Ser Niccolò.
Davisons

Fattoria dell'Ugo Traditional-style, family-owned business south-west of Florence. Wines: Chianti Putto
Millevini; Wine Growers Association

Castelgiocondo Large producer of Brunello di Montalcino. A more modern style – with lower prices – than Biondi-Santi (see above). Wines: Brunello di Montalcino, Rosso di Montalcino.
Tanners Wines; Waitrose

Castellare A producer of high quality Chianti Classico. Wines: Chianti Classico; super vino da tavola: I Sodi di San Niccolò.
Harrods; The Market/Winecellars

Castello di Fonterutoli Very traditional Chianti Classico. Wines: Chianti Classico; super vino da tavola: Concerto.
For further information contact Winebank, Winebank House, 178 Ebury Street, London SW1

Castello di San Polo in Rosso Chianti Classico made by one of the best winemakers in Tuscany. Ought to be great, but sometimes disappoints. Wines: Chianti Classico; super vino da tavola: Centinaia.
Eaton Elliot Winebrokers

Fattoria la Querce Top estate producing small quantities of high quality Chianti. Wines: Chianti Classico.
Bin 89 Wine Warehouse

Fattoria Montagliari Top estate making small quantities of Chianti Classico.
Wine Society

Frescobaldi Long-established firm (since the 13th century) producing all their wines from their own estates. Wines: Chianti Rufina (Nipozzano, Montesodi), Chianti Classico, Pomino Chardonnay, sparkling brut, rosé, Galestro, Vin Santo.
Adnams; Alex Findlater; Lay & Wheeler

Isole e Olena Small, high quality Chianti Classico producer. Wines: Chianti Classico; super vino da tavola: Cepparello.
The Market/Winecellars; C A Rookes

Marchesi Incisa della Rocchetta Produce 100 per cent Cabernet Sauvignon Sassacaia. Very expensive. Wines: Sassacaia.
Adnams; Harrods; The Market/Winecellars

Mellini Large producer in Chianti Classico making some single vineyard wines. Wines: Vernaccia di San Gimignano, Chianti Classico, Brunello di Montalcino, single vineyard Chianti (La Selvanella and Granaio); super vino da tavola: I Coltri (Sangiovese and Cabernet Sauvignon).
Selfridges

Pagliarese Make good commercial quality Chianti Classico, and very fine Riservas. Wine: Chianti Classico.
Millevini; Wine Growers Association

Poliziano Producer of Vino Nobile di Montepulciano. Wines: Vino Nobile, Chianti.
Stapylton Fletcher

Rocca della Macie Superb, fruity, good value Chianti Classico, designed to be drunk in two or three years. Wines: Chianti Classico, Chianti Classico Riserva.
Widely available

I L Ruffino Large-scale producer with a very fine Chianti Classico Riserva. Wines: Chianti Classico, Riserva Ducale, Torgaio, Galestro.
Widely available

Tenuta di Capezzana One of the largest producers in the Carmignano DOC, of which this estate was the creator. Wines: Carmignano, Barco Reale; super vino da tavola: Ghiaie della Furba.
Peter Dominic; Alex Findlater

La Torre Good quality Vernaccia di San Gimignano.
Anthony Byrne Fine Wines; Peter Green

Villa Banfi Highly successful firm of Riunite (producers of Lambrusco) have branched into Montalcino with a huge estate mainly designed for sparkling Moscato wines, but also a little red. Wines: Brunello di Montalcino, Rosso di Montalcino, Chianti Classico.
Harrods; The Market/Winecellars; Oddbins; Stapylton Fletcher

Best buys from Tuscany

REDS

Chianti Classico 1985, Rocca delle Macie (*widely available*)
Rosso di Montalcino, Col d'Orcia (*Barwell and Jones; Alexander Robertson*)

Vino Nobile di Montepulciano Riserva 1982, Bigi (*Peter Green; Majestic Wine Warehouses; Morrisons*)

Chianti Classico Riserva 1981, Villa Antinori (*J Sainsbury; Smedley Vintners; Threshers*)

Chianti Classico Riserva 1978, Castell'in Villa (*Turl Wine Vaults; Waitrose*)

Chianti Rufina 1985, Villa Vetrice (*G E Bromley; S H Jones; The Market/Winecellars*)

Carmignano 1985, Tenuta di Capezzana (*Peter Dominic*)

Chianti Putto 1985, Fattoria dell'Ugo (*Tanners Wines*)

Barco Reale, Tenuta di Capezzana (*Helen Verdcourt Wines*)

WHITES

Galestro 1986, Antinori (*Threshers*)

Vinattieri Bianco 1985 (*Hicks & Don*)

EMILIA–ROMAGNA

Fizzy and fun

Emilia–Romagna, to the north-east of Tuscany, is the home of Lambrusco. Most of it is sweet and fizzy – and fun. A few examples are dry and delicious with pasta or rich foods (see Who's who below). Lambrusco with a DOC is better than without.

Some serious reds are also produced in the Colli Piacentini (Piacenza), particularly the Gutturnio. The Sangiovese di Romagna makes standard quality reds. Albana di Romagna makes whites which can be attractive, but the quality varies wildly – and they want to make it DOCG!

Who's who in Emilia–Romagna

Cavacchioli Make top quality dry Lambrusco. Wines: Lambrusco (various DOCs); also white Lambrusco.
Wine Growers Association

Fattoria Paradiso Good quality red Sangiovese wines. Wines: Sangiovese di Romagna, (red) Barbarossa.
Millevini

Pasolini Fruity, good value Sangiovese. Wines: Sangiovese di Romagna, (white) Trebbiano di Romagna.
Gerard Harris; The Market/Le Provençal

Zerioli Producer of Gutturnio. Wines: Gutturnio dei Colli Piacentini.
Haslemere Wine Company (Caxton House, Lower Street, Haslemere, Surrey)

Best buy from Emilia-Romagna
Gutturnio dei Colli Piacentini 1984, Cantine Romagnole (*Valvona & Crolla*)

THE MARCHES

Into the Burgundy bottle

Verdicchio has always been the wine in the peculiar amphora-shaped bottle. Cynics said that was the only noticeable attribute this often dull wine had. Now a few growers have started putting the wine in Burgundy bottles.

Somehow this change of bottling seems to have changed the quality of Verdicchio at the same time. Producers of this popular white wine are forging ahead in the same way as the producers in Tuscany just across the hills.

Verdicchio dei Castelli di Jesi is the standard white DOC of the region (Jesi is a town up in the hills above Ancona). Many claim Verdicchio di Matelica DOC is better, but none seems to find its way out of Italy.

The red of the region, Rosso Cònero, has also suddenly stopped being just another red made from Montepulciano grapes – of which there are so many on Italy's east coast. Again, just as with Verdicchio, producers are suddenly coming out with really exciting wines, some from single vineyards (here they're called Vigneti). They shouldn't be left around too long, though – three to five years is ideal.

Who's who in the Marches

Bianchi Make a delicious Rosso Cònero. Wines: Rosso Cònero, Verdicchio. Brand name is CaSal di Serra.
Majestic Wine Warehouses

Colle del Sole The brand name of the main Verdicchio co-operative. Wines: Colle del Sole, Coste del Molino, Monte Schiavo – all Verdicchio.
Cachet Wines; J E Hogg; Arthur Rackhams; Waitrose

Fazi-Battaglia The inventors of the amphora bottle. Wines: Titulus Verdicchio dei Castelli di Jesi, Rosso Cònero.
Berry Bros & Rudd; Tanners Wines; Wine Society

Fratelli Bucci The pioneer of the Burgundy bottle. Top quality Verdicchio. Wines: Verdicchio dei Castelli di Jesi.
Wine Growers Association

Marchetti Weighty, comparatively long-lasting Rosso Cònero. Wines: Rosso Cònero, Verdicchio.
H Allen Smith

Mecvini Well-balanced Verdicchio from a private producer. Wines: Verdicchio dei Castelli di Jesi.
Barwell and Jones

Umani Ronchi Good quality wines made to a commercial standard; also a single vineyard Verdicchio. Wines: Verdicchio dei Castelli di Jesi, CaSal di Serra, Rosso Cònero.
Augustus Barnett

Best buys from the Marches

WHITES

Verdicchio dei Castelli di Jesi, Bianchi (*Majestic Wine Warehouses*)
Verdicchio dei Castelli di Jesi, CaSal di Serra (*Harrods; Valvona & Crolla*)
Verdicchio dei Castelli di Jesi, Mecvini (*Barwell and Jones; Alexander Robertson*)

REDS

Rosso Cònero, Vigneto San Lorenzo 1981, Bianchi (*The Market/Winecellars*)
Rosso Cònero 1979, Marchetti (*The Market/Winecellars; Tesco*)

UMBRIA

Orvieto comes back

Orvieto used to be the epitome of the dull, flabby, Italian white. Traditionally sold in an abboccato style (which hid the dullness), producers tried to sell a secco (dry) style as well – and failed because they used the dull Trebbiano grape without modern equipment.

Now things are improving. They have rediscovered the Grechetto grape, the traditional white grape of Orvieto, and one major Orvieto producer, Bigi (see below), is working on a 100 per cent Grechetto wine. Look for his single vineyard Vigneto Torricella (dry) and Orzalume (sweet).

Credit must also go to the Tuscan Antinori firm, who own big estates in Orvieto and are installing new equipment and making exciting wine. Their standard Orvietos (sweet as well as dry) are good, and they have a single vineyard Castello della Sala.

The other great entrepreneur in Umbria has been Lungarotti who dominates the Torgiano red DOC near Assisi. Some have claimed to find falling standards in his wines, particularly noting inconsistent bottles of his standard Rubesco di Torgiano, but his single vineyard white and red wines set very high standards.

Elsewhere in Umbria, the Colli del Trasimeno red and white and the Colli Altotiberini red (made using Merlot) and white are good, basic, standard wines; the reds are generally better than the whites.

Who's who in Umbria

Barberani Producer of some top quality Orvieto.
Wine Growers Association

Luigi Bigi Commercial, reliable wines on the one hand and some exciting single vineyard Orvieto on the other. Wines: Orvieto, Vigneto Torricella, Vigneto Orzalume, Colli de Trasimeno (also makes Est! Est!! Est!!! from Latium and Chianti).
Adnams; Bibendum

Lungarotti The creator of the Torgiano DOC and generally regarded as one of Italy's finest winemakers. Wines: Rubesco di Torgiano, Cabernet Sauvignon di Miralduolo, Chardonnay, Solleone (a sherry-like wine).
Adnams; Berry Bros & Rudd; Oddbins; Tanners Wines

Best buys from Umbria

WHITES

Orvieto Secco 1986, Castello della Sala (*Threshers*)
Orvieto Orzalume Abboccato 1985, Bigi (*The Market/Winecellars*)

REDS

Rubesco di Torgiano 1980, Lungarotti (*Cantina Augusto; J E Hogg*)
Rosso Colli Altotiberini, Carlo Polidori (*Marske Mill House*)

LATIUM

Last year, we criticised the quality of the Frascati reaching the shops in Britain. We reckoned that the only place to drink it was where it's made – in the Alban Hills to the east of Rome. Since then, Italian wine shippers have been anxious to prove us wrong . . .

But still Frascati tasted dreadful. It wasn't until this Guide was under way that we came across a wine that, while it didn't set the world on fire, at least tasted of grapes and not of peardrops. So we can recommend one Frascati, plus a top quality vino da tavola and not a

DOC at all, but repeat our warning to steer clear of all the rest. Perhaps next year we will be able to recommend some more.

As for the other major DOC of Latium, the notoriously named Est! Est!! Est!!!, our advice is still to avoid it.

Who's who in Latium

Villa Catone The only Frascati we would recommend is made by Antonio Pulcini. Wines: Frascati Superiore, single vineyard Colle Gaio.
Lay & Wheeler; Tanners Wines; The Market/Winecellars

Bruno Colacicchi Maker of the legendary Torre Ercolana, a blend of Cabernet Franc, Merlot and the local Cesanese. Only about 200 cases made a year, so count your buys in bottles. Wines: Torre Ercolana vino da tavola.
Wine Growers Association

Best buy from Latium

Frascati Colli de Catone (*The Market/Winecellars; Wapping Wine Warehouse*)

THE ABRUZZO AND MOLISE

The land of the Montepulciano

There's only one grape that matters in these two mountainous regions on the east coast level with Rome: the Montepulciano. In the Abruzzo, the DOC is Montepulciano d'Abruzzo, and the wines, at their best, can be rich and elegant; at their least they are full of good, peppery fruit. In Molise, look for the Biferno DOC for bargain reds.

There's also some charming rosato – rosé – wine made with the Montepulciano grape, called Cerasuolo, because of its cherry colour.

The whites – made of the Trebbiano grape – are normally as dull as only that grape can make them. One producer, Valentini, manages something better – but he knows it, and his prices have shot up accordingly.

Who's who in the Abruzzo and Molise

Barone Cornacchia Makes red and very good rosé. Wines: Montepulciano d'Abruzzo, rosé.
The Market/Winecellars

Tenuta del Priore Specialising in Riserva wines, plus a delicious fruity Cerasuolo. Wines: Montepulciano d'Abruzzo, Cerasuolo.
Wine Growers Association

Ramitello Luigi de Majo's organically produced red Biferno is the only wine from this Molise DOC to reach the UK. Wines: Di Majo Norante Biferno.
The Wine Club

Cantina Sociale di Tollo Make widely available vino da tavola. Wines: Montepulciano d'Abruzzo, (red) Colle Secco.
H Allen Smith; Oddbins

Edoardo Valentini Makes one of the few decent Trebbiano wines, as well as Montepulciano. Wines: Montepulciano d'Abruzzo, Trebbiano d'Abruzzo, Cerasuolo.
The Market/Winecellars; Millevini

Best buy from the Abruzzo and Molise

Montepulciano d'Abruzzo Tollo 1982 (*The Market/Winecellars; Valvona & Crolla*)

CAMPANIA

Lacryma Christi gets its DOC

It has been a sad reflection on the quality of the most famous wine of Naples – Lacryma Christi – that until two years ago there was no DOC. Those few producers who made good wine were being pulled down by the many who weren't. We wouldn't say things have improved much yet, but we're more hopeful.

For those who want a white from this region, the Greco di Tufo is a much better bet, and, to an even greater degree, Fiano di Avellino.

There's really only one red that has more than local renown and that's Taurasi. Made from the Aglianico grape (see also Basilicata below), in the hands of Antonio Mastroberardino, the wine has a plummy, almost sweet richness that leaves awe and puzzlement in equal proportions on the faces of those who taste it for the first time.

Who's who in Campania

Mastroberardino A great producer of both white and red wines – at a price. Wines: Fiano di Avellino, Greco di Tufo, Taurasi.
Lay & Wheeler; Millevini; Oddbins; Tanners Wines; Wine Growers Association

Best buy from Campania

Greco di Tufo, Mastroberardino (*Italian Wine Centre; Wine Growers Association*)

PUGLIA (APULIA)

The home of the wine lake

Yes, this is the home of the wine lake. And to look at the vast acres of vineyards on the flat plains stretching for two hundred miles down the heel of Italy, it's hardly surprising that few really good wines emerge. But some producers are making very fine wines and a few – too few – are available in the UK. There's a whole range of DOCs but, as often, the vini da tavola are better.

Who's who in Puglia

Rivera Best known for rosato, but also makes a good red. Wines: Castel del Monte Rosso and Rosato.
For further information contact Mondial Wines (13/14 Nelson Trading Estate, Morden Road, London SW19)

Torre Quarto Run by Belgians, making their best wines from French grapes. Vini da tavola. Wines: Torre Quarto Rosso (made from Malbec), DOC Rosso di Cerignola.
Millevini

Best buy from Puglia

Torre Quarto 1979 (*The Market/Winecellars; Millevini*)

BASILICATA

The forgotten region

A wider variety of wines are made in Basilicata than this small, neglected region's one DOC would suggest. But only one wine is available in Britain – Aglianico del Vulture, a serious, somewhat austere red, thought by some to be the best red from southern Italy.

Who's who in Basilicata

Fratelli d'Angelo Small family company, by far the best producer of Aglianico del Vulture.
Adnams; Lay & Wheeler; The Market/Winecellars; Wine Growers Association

Best buy from Basilicata

Aglianico del Vulture 1982, d'Angelo (*Cantina Augusto; Wine Shop, Caithness; and others*)

CALABRIA

The Greek vineyard

The Greeks called this Enotria, the land of wine. Things may have slipped since then (although that the Greeks watered their wine may say something for its quality), but there are a few characterful wines to be found in the toe of Italy.

Who's who in Calabria

Librandi The only producer of more than local renown, using the Cirò brand name. Wines: Cirò Bianco and Rosso. The red is better and there is a good Riserva.
Wine Growers Association

Best buy from Calabria

Cirò Classico 1977, Librandi (*Wapping Wine Warehouse*)

SICILY

Continuing excitements

There's as much innovation going on in Sicily as anywhere in Italy. Most of it is happening outside the DOC system, which has simply hampered innovation while clinging on to tradition.

So most of Sicily's interesting wines are vini da tavola. They're not of the super vino da tavola type found in Tuscany, which are the top of a range that includes DOC wines. Here they tend to be made instead of DOC wines, and are the main production of the go-ahead companies – brand names are therefore important (see below under Who's who).

Of the DOC wines, Alcamo is one of the more interesting, while Etna tends to be drunk by the holidaymakers on the beaches of Taormina.

Marsala – the cooking wine

Virtually all the Marsala, the fortified wine from the town of the same name in western Sicily, that is sold in this country, is for cooking. It's used in zabaglione, of course, and in a host of other dishes, often produced in Italian restaurants with much flamboyance.

We can be thankful that the flavoured Marsalas seem to be disappearing. If you value your tastebuds, we suggest you steer clear of any remaining examples.

True Marsala can be a delicious aperitif wine or equally successful as a digestif. It shouldn't be ridiculously sweet but have a touch of dryness to stimulate the appetite. There's a range of styles (as in Sherry – see under Spain) from the lightest to the darkest in colour – and the darker styles go well after a meal. The standard style is called Marsala Fine, the next grade up Marsala Superiore, the best Marsala Vergine. The producers mentioned in Who's who all make good examples of the traditional styles.

Who's who in Sicily

Corvo, Duca di Salaparuta Modern winery making modern-tasting, straightforward wines of good quality. Wines: Corvo Bianco and Rosso, Corvo Bianco Colombina Platino.
Augustus Barnett; Millevini

Donnafugata Red and white vini da tavola from an estate owned by the Rallo (Marsala producer) family. Rising stars for quality and character. Wines: Donnafugata Bianco and Rosso.
For further information contact Sunshine Wines (20 Kennet Road, Crayford, Kent)

Pellegrino Old-established Marsala producer. Look for the examples of the Madeira-like Vergine. Wines: Marsala Vergine, Marsala Superiore.
Davisons; Safeway; J Sainsbury; Unwins

Rallo Apart from table wines, also produce a good Vergine (light style) Marsala. Wines: Marsala, DOC Alcamo.
The Market/Winecellars

Rapitalà Make better whites than their DOC would suggest. Wines: Rapitalà Bianco di Alcamo DOC, Rapitalà Rosso.
Luigi Delicatessen (349 Fulham Road, London SW10)

Regaleali The star among Sicilian table wines. Both red and white are top class and good value. Wines: Regaleali Rosso, Regaleali Bianco, Rosso del Conte.
Exmouth Wines (38 Exmouth Market, London EC1); Valvona & Crolla; Waitrose

Samperi Producer of the finest Marsala-style wines. Wines: Vecchio Samperi, Bukkuram (an old moscato wine from the island of Pantelleria near the North African coast).
The Market/Winecellars; Millevini

Settesoli Co-operative making light, fruity wines on the southern coast. Wines: Settesoli Bianco, Rosso, Rosato.
Chiswick Wine Cellar; J E Hogg; Valvona & Crolla

Best buys from Sicily

Regaleali white and red (*widely available*)
Corvo red (*widely available*)
Settesoli white and red (*J E Hogg; Valvona & Crolla*)
Marsala Vecchio Samperi, de Bartoli (*The Market/Winecellars; Millevini; Valvona & Crolla*)

SARDINIA

Iconoclastic wines

One would have thought that Sardinia should, by all the rules, make highly traditional wines with absolutely no commercial value outside the island. Instead, from one ultra-modern winery comes a stream of beautifully crafted wines which would do credit to any part of Italy. The other producers rely on more traditional qualities.

Who's who in Sardinia

Sella e Mosca The only producer worthy of note, whose total production equals that of the whole Côte d'Or of Burgundy, yet makes distinctive wines. Whites: Riveira del Corallo, Vermentino di Alghero, Torbato di Alghero, Terre Bianche; reds: Cannonau di Alghero, Tanca Farra. Dessert wine: Anghelu Ruju.
Lay & Wheeler; Wine Growers Association

Best buy from Sardinia

Cannonau del Parteola 1983, Sella e Mosca (*Albert Wine Wharf Co*)

Specialist stockists of Italian wines

Adnams; H Allen Smith; Bibendum; D Byrne; Cantina Augusto; Continental Wine House; Demijohn Wines; Alex Findlater; Peter Green; J E Hogg; Italian Wine Centre; Lay & Wheeler; The Market/Winecellars; Millevini; Oddbins; Ostlers; Tanners Wines; Valvona & Crolla; Wine Growers Association; The Wine Shop (Caithness); The Wine Society; The Wine Spot; Wines from Paris

Lebanon

Inevitably, any talk of winemaking in strife-ridden Lebanon centres around Serge Hochar and Château Musar. With vineyards on one side of the front line and his winery on the other, it's hardly surprising that he failed to make two vintages – in 1984 and 1985. But in 1986 Serge Hochar's luck returned: despite the constant check points and local 'taxes', the grapes got through, and the wines are reported to be full of fruit, richness and intensity.

Older vintages of the red and white wines have been available here for nearly ten years, but the reds far outshine the whites. There are two reds – Château Musar and a second wine, Cuvée Musar. If that's reminiscent of Bordeaux, Serge Hochar trained in Bordeaux, and the wines themselves have often been likened to a Middle Eastern view of what claret should be. The differences from a classic Bordeaux blend are that although the Cabernet Sauvignon is there (and always predominant), Cinsault and Syrah are also used. The three grapes are blended in varying proportions depending on the year.

Cuvée Musar is made mainly from Cinsault and Syrah, and while lacking the sophistication of the first wine is pleasantly fruity.

Vintages of Château Musar currently available in the UK are 1978, 1979 and 1980, but some merchants have older vintages which are worth seeking out because the wine ages well – up to 20 years or more for good vintages like 1966, 1964 and 1961.

Adnams; H Allen Smith; Les Amis du Vin; Peter Dominic; Alex Findlater; Gerard Harris; Lay & Wheeler; André Simon Wines; Stapylton Fletcher; Tanners Wines; Waitrose

Luxembourg

Very few Luxembourg wines are on sale in Britain. Those few have limited distribution, so the chance to taste these wines from the upper reaches of the Mosel are few and far between.

None of them is of the classically memorable quality of good Mosel from down river in Germany, but they're not to be dismissed either. Luxembourg's quality is high, and most wines made from Luxembourg-grown grapes will be reliable (beware, however, of some sparkling 'Luxembourg' wine which is actually made with Italian grapes and Luxembourg air bubbles).

The best vines are white. They are officially classified, in ascending order of quality, as: marque nationale, vin classé, premier cru or grand premier cru. The only regular producer of Luxembourg wines to reach our shops is the co-operative of Wormeldange.

Grapes on the label

Auxerrois Fairly neutral but pleasant wine which can be quite full and almondy in good years from good sites.

Elbling Light, fresh, crisp wines.

Gewürztraminer Very little is grown, but it makes good, fresh, only slightly spicy wines.

Pinot Gris Little is grown, but it makes full, soft wines.

Riesling Makes flowery wines, with good varietal character, thin in poor years but clean and delicate in better years.

Rivaner The Müller-Thurgau under another name. Makes soft, fruity, sometimes medium dry but often dry wines.

Specialist stockist
Luxembourg Wine Company

New Zealand

Question: which country produces Sauvignon Blanc at a fraction of the price of Sancerre? *Question:* which country's Chardonnay wines are achieving the standards of top-flight Burgundy – but at prices rarely much above £6 a bottle?

No, the answer is not Australia. Australia's climate is too warm to produce either wine in the style of the cool-climate vineyards of the Loire or Burgundy. She has developed her own style – and very good she is at it.

But to get nearer to France, as it were, you have to go to New Zealand. Further south, with a climate made temperate by the cool Pacific and Antarctic Oceans, her vineyards now produce some of the best cool-climate white wines anywhere in the world. We must emphasise the description 'cool-climate', because her wines don't have the ripe, tropical flavours of Australia or California, but the delicate, light, very fruity tastes of France.

And are we buying these paragons of viticulture? Well, more than last year, we're delighted to report, but still not enough. There's a surplus of wine in New Zealand, the prices are very good, and still our wine merchants don't open up their cheque books and sign on the dotted line.

As usual, in 1987 the New Zealand High Commission ran its annual tasting of new releases, both whites and reds. The two major wineries – Cooks and Montana – were present in force, and very good most of their offerings were. But they will surely forgive us for saying that the most interesting wines came from a collection of wineries handled in this country by a hospital pharmacist (she can't earn enough to run a wine-importing business full time), Margaret Harvey. Her company, Fine Wines of New Zealand, brings in wines from Babich, Mission Vineyards, Delegats Vineyards, Matua Valley, Morton Estate and others – all comparatively small, what the Californians would call boutique wineries.

The giants are thinking small as well. Plans are afoot for Montana to export single vineyard wines to go alongside the high quality varietal blended wines they already sell, so watch out for Brancott Estate Fumé Blanc, Kaituna Hills Chardonnay, Brookby Ridge Gewürztraminer, Mount Richmond red and Wairau Valley Cabernet Sauvignon.

The quality of the whites goes ahead by leaps and bounds, but although the reds are more problematic, things are looking up: some Cabernet Sauvignon wines, while not achieving great complexity, are showing real cassis fruit, simple, direct and very drinkable. And the few wines made from the South African Pinotage grape are showing up a good Rhône character, albeit with greater acidity than their French counterparts.

The taste of New Zealand

WHITE WINES

The principal grape variety in terms of acreage is the Müller-Thurgau. Occasionally it is used unblended, but normally it provides the basis of the slightly sweet blends which form the staple part of New Zealand wine production.

More important in terms of quality are the Chardonnay, the Gewürztraminer, the Sauvignon Blanc and the Rhine Riesling. All four produce wines with intense fruit, good acidity and a very pure varietal taste, a result of long, comparatively cool summers and slow ripening. Most of the whites are best drunk young – 1985 is probably the oldest vintage worth considering in 1988.

RED WINES

Cabernet Sauvignon is the best red varietal here, as in so many other wine-producing areas. Again, the tastes are direct, full of fruit and enjoyable when comparatively young (1984/85 are the years to drink now).

New Zealand vintages

1987 A year with a late harvest. Mixed quality for whites, with Müller-Thurgau, Sauvignon and Chardonnay the most successful. Reds should be good.
1986 Low yield but high quality. The whites are excellent, the reds beginning to mature well.
1985 Again a good year. Start drinking reds, drink up the whites.
1984 Whites, once good, may now be a little tired (although some Gewürztraminer and Chardonnay may still be all right). Reds are quite acid.
1982 Reds are the only wines worth drinking now. It was a very good year, and the pricier Cabernet Sauvignons should still be fine.

Where's where in New Zealand

New Zealand's vineyards have shifted their gravity as growers realised where their strength lay. Originally the hot, humid and lush area around Auckland was where the first Yugoslav growers planted their vineyards, but now the best vineyards are at Gisborne and Hawkes Bay on the east coast of North Island, at Marlborough on the northern coast of South Island, and even as far south as Christchurch.

Who's who in New Zealand

Babich Wines (Henderson, Auckland). Descendants of Dalmatian settlers. Their Cabernet Sauvignon, Pinot Noir and Gewürztraminer are regular prize-winners. Wines: Chardonnay, Gewürztraminer, Müller-Thurgau, Pinot Noir, Pinotage, Cabernet Sauvignon.
Les Amis du Vin; Barnes Wine Shop; Alex Findlater; Richard Harvey Wines; Laytons; Ostlers; La Réserve; Wines from Paris

Cloudy Bay Western Australian producer who makes fine, but pricey, Sauvignon Blanc in New Zealand. Wines: Sauvignon Blanc.
Ostlers; La Vigneronne

Collard Brothers (Auckland and Gisborne). Mainly fruity Germanic-style wines, but also some reds and a Chardonnay.
Bibendum

Cooks (Te Kauwhata, North Island). One of the biggest producers, and the best distributed in British shops. Luckily, quality is good as well. Wines: Cooks New Zealand Medium White and Dry White, Chardonnay, Gewürztraminer, Dry Red, Hawkes Bay Cabernet Sauvignon.
Widely available

Delegats Vineyard (Henderson, North Island). Family winery producing award-winning whites, including fine dessert wines. Wines: Chardonnay, Fumé Blanc, Réserve Semillon, Müller-Thurgau Auslese.
Les Amis du Vin; Barnes Wine Shop; Corney & Barrow; Alex Findlater; Ostlers; Windrush Wines

Matua Valley Wines (Auckland and Hawkes Bay). Modern winery in Auckland making some exciting white wines. Wines: Sauvignon Blanc, Cabernet Sauvignon.
H Allen Smith; Barnes Wine Shop; Corney & Barrow; Alex Findlater; Morris & Verdin

Mission Vineyards (Hawkes Bay). As its name suggests, a vineyard run by a religious order. Wines: Semillon Sauvignon Blanc.
H Allen Smith; Peter Dominic (Strand and Eastcheap, London); Alex Findlater

Montana Wines (Gisborne, North Island and Marlborough, South Island). The pioneer of vineyards in the South Island. The experiment has paid off with some good, crisp whites, widely available in British shops. Wines: Gisborne Chardonnay, Sauvignon Blanc, Fumé Blanc, Pinotage, Cabernet Sauvignon.
Widely available

Nobilo (Auckland, North Island). Specialist in red wines. Wines: Riesling/Sylvaner, Chardonnay, Pinotage, Cabernet Sauvignon, Pinot Noir.
Averys of Bristol; Alex Findlater; La Vigneronne

Selaks Wines (Auckland, North Island). One of the longest established New Zealand producers. Wines: Chardonnay, Sauvignon Blanc/Semillon, Rhine Riesling.
Alex Findlater; Oddbins; Ostlers; Wine Society

Te Mata (Hawkes Bay). High-class boutique winery. Wines: Castle Hill Sauvignon Blanc, Elston Chardonnay, Coleraine Cabernet/Merlot.
Curzon Wine Co

Best buys from New Zealand

WHITES

Cooks Dry White (*widely available*)
Montana Sauvignon Blanc 1986 (*widely available*)
Cooks New Zealand Chardonnay 1986 (*Tesco; Waitrose; and others*)

REDS

Cooks Dry Red (*widely available*)
Cookes Hawkes Bay Cabernet Sauvignon 1983 (*Peter Dominic*)

Specialist stockists

Alex Findlater; Selfridges

North Africa

Despite being Muslim countries (which therefore disapprove of alcohol), Algeria, Morocco and Tunisia have a strong wine tradition inherited from the days of French colonial rule. After independence, wine from these countries went to France to disappear in blending vats – some say to Burgundy, but certainly to the south of France. And because of official indifference, the quality of the wines made in the countries themselves – mainly red – did tend to decline.

However, there are now a few signs of improvement: one or two decent ranges of good, robust quaffing wines have turned up in British shops – at competitive prices.

Morocco is the country which has managed to retain a place on world markets most successfully, but in the past year it has been Algeria which has come up with new wines, based on grape varieties from the Rhône and from Bordeaux.

Who's who in North Africa

MOROCCO

Tarik – a red blend of Cinsault, Carignan and Grenache (*Oddbins*).
Sidi Brahim – straight Cinsault and better quality (*contact William Pitters International, Lowgate House, Backbarrow, Ulverston, Cumbria*).

ALGERIA

Wines produced by the state monopoly under a variety of names: Medea Rouge, Coteaux de Zaccar, Dahra, Coteaux de Mascara, and Cuvée du Président, which is regarded as the top wine (*contact Masons, Reed Hall, Holbrook, Ipswich, Suffolk*).
Coteaux de Tiemcen Red Infuriator – a good, basic but powerful red wine (*Peter Dominic*).

Specialist stockist

Vinceremos

Portugal

We are in a small Portuguese manor house in Vinho Verde country. The autumn sun is bright and very warm, but in the cellars below the house the air is cool. The grapes for red Vinho Verde have just come in from the surrounding vineyard and are being pressed in an old mangle before being put into leaky old wooden casts for fermentation. The smell of ripe grapes wafts around the old stone store rooms that are supported by Roman pillars.

A recipe for a wine disaster, you might say. But the previous year's red Vinho Verde, drunk at dinner in the house that night, is beautifully fresh, typically acid and excellent with a plate of bacalhau, the Portuguese dried cod. It wouldn't taste the same elsewhere, of course, but it's none the worse for that.

By contrast, the grapes for white Vinho Verde from this same vineyard go straight to the modern conditions of the local co-operative of Ponte de Lima a mile away. Anybody who has tried their white Vinho Verde will know how crisp, dry, fresh and delicious it can be.

The two faces of Portuguese winemaking are typified here. Traditions die hard in a conservative nation where the modern world has only just begun to impinge; but at the other extreme, some of Portugal's wineries are the most modern in the world – turning out millions of litres of the light rosé wine which put Portugal on the table wine map long before her traditional wines made any impact.

A revolution in the making

So, in the midst of a viticultural scene that often looks as though it hasn't changed since the Moors left the country back in the Middle Ages, there are signs of a vital winemaking revolution in the making.

The changes are coming from two directions. One is the entry of Portugal into the European Community, with all that brings in terms of greatly increased export opportunities. The other is the development of wine tastes new for the Portuguese. The trendy set in Lisbon and Oporto is no longer happy with heavy old reds and whites, but wants the same fresher wine tastes that drinkers throughout Europe are demanding.

It's certainly true that the fresh taste of white Vinho Verde has been the big success story as far as Portuguese wines in British shops are concerned. The theory among marketing men is that Vinho Verde is the wine for drinkers tired of Liebfraumilch. That may be true of the sweeter examples which have been produced until now; but with the greater availability of the – more authentic – dry Vinho Verde, a wine style like no other in the world has emerged.

The same is true of the reds, with which Portugal is more greatly endowed than whites. Traditional Portuguese reds were dry and astringent, aged in cement tanks or wood for as long as it takes any fruit to disappear, and then bottled. That was the way the Portuguese farmer wanted his wine to drink, so that was the way he made it, thank you very much.

The nearest equivalent to this attitude was to be found among older producers of Barolo in Italy. And, just as Barolo producers have begun to change their attitudes to winemaking, cutting down on the wood, cutting out the fermentation with stalks, pips and all, and generally allowing the fruit a chance to emerge – so, in Portugal, fruit is becoming much more important in the taste make-up of a Portuguese red.

There are already good examples of modern red wines in Portugal. The fact that they all seem to be branded, blended wines rather than wines from a demarcated region is typical of the Portuguese approach, where the merchants – the négociants – have bought either grapes or wine and put together their own house wines.

And of course merchants can adapt to modern fashions more quickly than farmers, so many of the branded wines (either with fancy names or under the name Garrafeira – see below for Portuguese wine terms) are much more in the mainstream of modern European winemaking than wines from co-operatives or individual estates.

The merchants may be becoming more modern in some ways but they are still faithful to Portuguese grape varieties. Ones like Cabernet Sauvignon or Chardonnay have made fewer inroads in Portugal than in most other wine-producing countries. The range of native varieties

Portugal

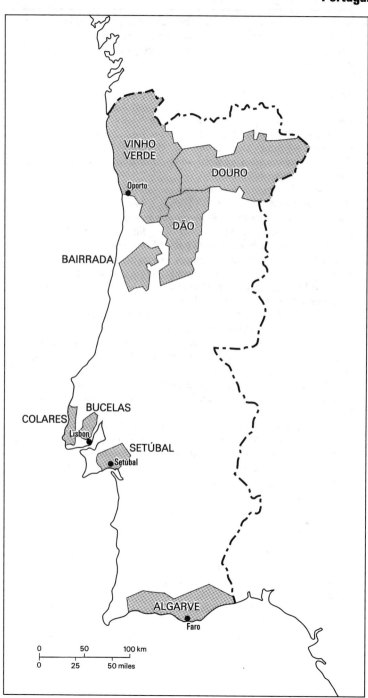

is enormous, and most of their names are utterly forgettable. Luckily, though, their tastes aren't – and we would all be much worse off if Portugal took to imported 'international' grape varieties instead of the home-grown versions.

Vinhos Verdes

Portuguese wine is popularly divided into two distinct categories. There are Vinhos Verdes (no reflection on the colour of the wine but because it is young – a greenhorn of a wine); and there are Vinhos Maduros, wines which are aged (see below). Both categories contain red and white wines.

The best-known wines in this category are Vinhos Verdes from the Minho, the northern province of Portugal. In Britain we only see white Vinhos Verdes, but about half the production is red: very acid and astringent, but fabulous with a plate of sardines or oily food.

The Minho is the most verdant part of Portugal, constantly washed by rains from the Atlantic. The vines, grown in opulent, lush countryside, twirl themselves around trees, posts, pergolas, anything in fact; other crops often grow beneath them because land is so short.

The initial success of Vinho Verde in Britain was as slightly sweet, pétillant, branded white wine. But gradually the truth dawned that true Vinho Verde as drunk in Portugal is bone-dry, with a cooking-apple acidity. A few wines of this style are available in the shops (see Best buys), and are definitely worth snapping up for cool summer drinking.

There are now also some superior estate-bottled Vinhos Verdes: Quinta da Aveleda, Alvarinho (also a grape name), Palacio de Brejoeira.

One other style of wine should also be classed as Vinho Verde. Portuguese rosé, slightly sweet and slightly pétillant, has enjoyed a revival after a couple of years in the doldrums. Some of the brands of Portuguese rosé have been joined by white stablemates, which have a little of the quality of sweetened Vinho Verde.

Drink Vinho Verde as soon as possible: it doesn't keep.

Vinhos Maduros

Where else but in Portugal could you buy red wines – decent, interesting examples, carrying vintages over ten years old and more – for under £4? The range of older vintages still available in our shops continues to amaze and delight. These are the second category of Portuguese wines – the Vinhos Maduros.

Probably, in many cases, if we were presented with young versions of some of these reds, they would be quite undrinkable. They start off inky black and shot through with tannin. Gradually, the tannin wears off, and slight fruit comes through, until eventually a soft, rich, complex wine emerges after, maybe, 15 years.

Sometimes, of course, the fruit never gets a chance, and the dryness remains, simply changing from the dryness of tannic fruit to the dryness of a wine that's too old. This is true of many examples of Dão wines around. But, as well as the branded wines we've already mentioned, some wines from demarcated areas are now much more approachable (see below for a full list). These areas tend to be the newer ones, especially the region of Bairrada which lies to the west of Coimbra in central Portugal. The red grape, the Baga, makes rich, soft wines, with plenty of fruit and not excessive tannin. An area with great potential, whose wines are now in many shops (see Best buys).

The Douro is the second region with potentially good reds. About 40 per cent of this wine is made into Port (see further on), the rest becoming rather fat and oily white or much better red. Indeed, what is often regarded as Portugal's finest wine – Barca Velha, made by Ferreira – is produced here, but only in very good years, and in limited quantities. Another Port producer, Champalimaud, makes a red from Portuguese grape varieties that is Californian in its intensity. Other, cheaper Douro wines are much more disappointing.

Strange system

In the past Dão has been the major area for red wines from Portugal, but a strange system whereby only farmers are allowed to make wine, which they then sell to the merchants and négociants (rather than letting the big companies buy in grapes and use sophisticated equipment to make the wine), has meant that the vast majority of the wine from the area is disappointing. The only Dão which gets round this problem is Grão Vasco from the producers of Mateus Rosé, who control and buy the production of one co-operative.

One small demarcated area on the Atlantic coast is also worth looking for. Colares wines are made from vines grown in sand dunes (so they don't have to be grafted, because the phylloxera louse can't cope with sand). Only a few firms make this wine now: it suffers from Portuguese red astringency and toughness in youth, but matures into an amazingly perfumed wine given many years.

South of the Dão and Bairrada regions are huge areas of flat plains which make up the Alentejo, with pockets of more than local interest, such as the red of Reguengos de Monsaraz, but much of the wine goes into the blending vats of the big merchant houses. The same is true of the Ribatejo, the vineyards of the upper Tagus valley; and as we have already pointed out, those blending vats are the source of some of Portugal's best wines.

South of Lisbon, in the Setúbal peninsula, the firm of J M da Fonseca make a range of branded wines, some of which are generally regarded as Portugal's finest (see below under Who's who).

Few white excitements

Few really exciting Portuguese whites come from south of the Minho with its Vinhos Verdes. Some are made in the Dão and in Bairrada, but there are better wines to be had from other countries.

You have to look again to branded wine producers for some unusual and interesting white wines. João Pires, an associate company of J M da Fonseca, make a 100 per cent dry Muscat wine called after the company (they also make a Chardonnay wine, Caterina, available only in America at the moment). Fonseca also make a long-lived fortified dessert wine, also from Muscat grapes, called Moscatel de Setúbal, full of grapy richness.

What's what in Portugal

Some names that appear on Portuguese labels:
Colheita Vintage
Engarrafado Bottled (by)
Garrafeira A wine merchant's best wines, generally selected after some years in cask and bottle. This will normally be a branded wine, and can be a blend of vintages
Região Demarcada Demarcated region, similar to AC or Italian DOC (see below for list)
Reserva Another term for an older wine but, unlike Garrafeira, one from a demarcated region
Velho (or Velha) Old

Where's where in Portugal

There are ten demarcated regions in Portugal, some of minor significance.
Algarve Reds and whites, both high in alcohol, seen only in the holiday resorts of the Algarve
Bairrada High quality reds from the centre of the country; some whites, mostly made into sparkling wine
Bucelas Dry white wines from near Lisbon, sometimes with a slight prickle
Carcavelos Almost impossible to find this slightly sweet fortified wine, made near Lisbon (buildings cover almost all the vineyards)
Colares Huge red wines from the sand dunes (see above)
Dão Big, tough reds and dry whites
Douro Some very good reds, less interesting whites
Estremadura Red and white wines from just north of Lisbon
Moscatel de Setúbal Fortified dessert wines (see above)
Vinho Verde Largest demarcated region, producing a quarter of all Portugal's wine. Slightly pétillant, crisp, dry whites and acid reds.

Who's who in Portugal

Names of some producers to look for:

Adega Cooperativa de Cantanhede Producer of some excellent Bairrada reds.
Oddbins

Caves Aliança A whole range of good quality wines, from Vinho Verde, Dão, Bairrada and Douro.
Chiswick Wine Cellar; Harrisons (8 Weston Street, Brighton, East Sussex); Wessex Wines

Quinta da Aveleda Producer of a straightforward Vinho Verde (Aveleda) and a superior estate-bottled wine (Quinta da Aveleda).
Augustus Barnett; Peter Dominic

Caves do Barrocão Make reds and sparkling wines in the Bairrada.
Stapylton Fletcher

Borges e Irmão Make the best-selling Vinho Verde, Gatão, but also a drier style and Dão wines.
Victoria Wine Co; Whynot Wine Warehouses

Carvalho, Ribeiro e Ferreira A major table wine producer, specialising in branded and Garrafeira wines of high quality, mainly from the Ribatejo. Brands include Serradayres.
Peter Dominic, Oddbins

Champalimaud Single vineyard Port producer (see under Ports) who also makes some top quality Douro table wines. Names are Cotto Grande Escolha, Quinta do Cotto.
Alex Findlater, Bibendum

Caves Dom Teodosio Garrafeiras under the brand name Casaleiro are huge, peppery and long-lasting.
Arthur Rackhams

J M da Fonseca One of the best wine firms in Portugal. A whole range of branded wines include Camarate, Periquita, Pasmasdos and Garrafeiras. Also the major producer of Moscatel de Setúbal.
H Allen Smith; Waitrose; Whynot Wine Warehouses; Wine Society

João Pires Source of some fine branded red and white wines made in a brand-new, space-age winery. Reds include Tinto da Anfora, whites João Pires. Also make the claret-like Quinta da Bacalhoa, one of the few Cabernet Sauvignon-based wines in Portugal. (Associated company of J M da Fonseca.)
(For Bacalhoa) J Sainsbury; (for other wines) H Allen Smith; Majestic Wine Warehouses; Waitrose; Whynot Wine Warehouses

Sogrape Producers of Mateus Rosé and Mateus White. They also make Grão Vasco Dão wines.
Mateus Rosé and Mateus White widely available. Other wines from: Asda; Davisons; Fullers; Majestic Wine Warehouses; Morrisons

Caves Velhas Sole remaining producer of the Bucelas wines. Also make Dãos and some good Garrafeiras under the Romeira name.
(For Bucelas) Oddbins; (for Garrafeiras) Peter Dominic; Oddbins

Best buys from Portugal

WHITES

João Pires Branco (*Addison Avenue Wine Shop; H Allen Smith; Lockes*)
Vinho Verde, Solar das Boucas (*Stapylton Fletcher*)
Vinho Verde, Casa do Laueiro (*Market Vintners*)
Vinho Verde, Ponte do Lima (*Sherston Wines; Turl Wine Vaults*)

REDS

Periquita 1982, J M da Fonseca (*H Allen Smith; Moffat Wine Shop*)
Aruda (*J Sainsbury*)
Colares 1970, Chitas (*Davids of Ashby*)
Douro 1982, Quinta de Cotto Champalimaud (*Peter Green; Alex Findlater; Lockes*)
Camarate 1980 (*H Allen Smith; Hungerford Wine Co*)
Quinta da Bacalhõa (*J Sainsbury*)
Bairrada, Caves do Barrocão (*Stapylton Fletcher*)
Pasmados 1980, J M da Fonseca (*Sherston Wines*)
Bairrada 1980, Cooperativa Cantanhede (*Snipe Wine Cellars*)
Tinto da Anfora 1982, João Pires (*Waitrose; Whynot Wine Warehouses*)

Specialist stockists

H Allen Smith; Askham Wines; Peter Green; A O L Grilli; Oddbins; Premier Wines (Ayr); La Reserva Wines; Sherston Wine Company

PORT

Change and dissension

It has been a year of change and dissension in what is normally a very traditional trade. The net result is likely to increase confusion for consumers in what is already a complicated branch of wine.

The major change has affected the strict rules governing the way Port is stored before being shipped. Traditionally, the town of Vila Nova da Gaia was the only place where Port could be stored, on the opposite bank of the Douro river to Oporto. Photographs of the Port shippers' lodges halfway up the hillside of Gaia are familiar in books on wine.

New rules say that it is now possible to store and blend the wine up the Douro in the vineyard area and ship direct from there rather than taking the wine to Gaia first. This opens the way up to small producers actually bottling their own wine as single quinta Ports rather than selling to the famous shipping houses. Already one producer, Champalimaud (see under Portuguese table wines above), is bottling his own single quinta Ports in the Douro – and many more should follow.

The effect on the consumer will be to increase the choice – as, for example, domaine-bottling has in Burgundy. It may increase the quality as well – although quality has not been a problem in Port as it has in Burgundy. It will certainly increase the number of names to consider when choosing which Port to buy.

And as if that major change in Port practice were not enough, the Port shippers are busy arguing among themselves about the names to use for styles of Port. Ever since the idea of Late Bottled Vintage Port (see below for Port styles) was introduced, there have been those who argue that LBV – as it was called for short – would be confused with the real Vintage Ports which only came from special, declared years. Until now that has been avoided because LBV vintages have been different from Vintage Port vintages.

But now, the biggest LBV producer, Taylor, has come up with a 1983 LBV and a 1983 Vintage, and the gloves are off, as other producers and the British wine trade accuse Taylor's of creating an element of confusion for customers.

Not only that, but now everybody is arguing about the legal definition of crusted Port, which, for many aficionados of Port, is the most attractive style of Vintage Port, one which can be drunk earlier than true Vintage – and which, importantly, costs much less.

The problem arises because crusted Ports are now being made in a similar way to the big branded LBVs – they are aged in wood for four years and then bottled almost ready for drinking. The word 'crusted' is likely to be used on labels of this style. True crusted is different, because unlike standard LBV (which is freeze-filtered before bottling so that it can never improve in bottle), it will throw a sediment and can certainly improve for some years after bottling.

Back to the basics

After that hothouse of politics and confusion, it's a relief to get back to the Douro vineyards, in some of the most beautiful vineyard scenery anywhere, and remind ourselves of the simplicity of the idea behind Port.

Port derives from wine produced in the Douro demarcated region of Portugal. There are two areas: Douro Beixa, and Douro Alto, further east, up river, which makes the best wines. The wine is made normally, and then the fermentation is stopped, by the addition of brandy, before all the sugar is turned into alcohol.

The whole Port-making process is one of the most strictly controlled in the wine world. Regulations cover the quality of the vineyard, its yield and the amount of wine that that vineyard can produce for Port (the rest going as table wine).

Until now, although it was made in the Douro, the wine has had to be aged and blended in Vila Nova da Gaia. But this is now changing, as we have seen.

Styles of Port

White Port Usually put last in a listing of styles because it has never really taken off. We suggest it should, because it makes a marvellous aperitif, served chilled. It's made from white, rather than red grapes, but fortified in the same way.

Ruby The most basic quality. Youthful, simple wine. Widely available.

Tawny This term has two completely different meanings (more confusion). One is an alternative to ruby, of basic quality. But there are also aged tawnies – 10-year-old, 20-year-old, etc – which are some of the finest Ports available. Tawny Port has a lighter style than a ruby, and is delicious slightly chilled, drunk as an aperitif or after a meal.

Crusted A blend of qualities either from different years or from a single vintage, bottled after three to four years in wood. It matures reasonably quickly in bottle – generally five or six years from bottling (this date should be on the label). It tends to throw a sediment – hence the name. (See also the introduction to the Port section.)

Late Bottled Vintage The poorer man's Vintage Port, kept in wood for four to six years and then bottled. This means it is virtually ready to drink when bottled. The vintage will be on the label, but not the bottling date.

Late Bottled or Vintage Character Similar to Late Bottled Vintage in style, but not necessarily wine from one year.

Single Quinta Port Up until now, this has been wine from one estate made in a year which the shipper doesn't consider quite good enough for a general vintage declaration (see Vintage Port below and vintage information). Bottled and sold after two years, needing some years to mature in bottle. Now single quinta Ports will also come from smaller producers who just produce wine from one vineyard (see above for the new rules).

Vintage The finest of Ports – and the most serious. In style, it's like a very superior ruby. A vintage will be 'declared' only in the best years and bottled after two years in wood. Needs many years to mature, because glass ages wine more slowly than wood. Decant before serving.

The great vintages

1985 Looks like being a great vintage year since the weather was boiling hot right through the summer. The wines were bottled in early 1987.

1983 Well-coloured, aromatic wines. The majority of shippers have declared this vintage. The wines are quite forward and should be ready in the mid-1990s.

1982 Declared by a minority of shippers. The wines are maturing quite fast, full of fruit. Ready by the 1990s.

1980 A longer-lasting vintage. Good quality wines from many of the oldest-established shippers. Ready in the late 1990s. Excellent value for money.

1977 The classic vintage since 1963, much admired. Keep it until the turn of the century.

1975 A light vintage. Drink in the next few years.

1970 Much better than originally considered, this vintage is still underpriced.

1966 We said last year and the year before that, 'historically underrated, absolutely delicious now'. They still are.

1963 Great post-war vintage, best since 1945. Keep those you have and grab any you can. Will keep for years.

In addition to these general vintage years, single quinta Ports (see above) were declared by shippers in 1980, 1972, 1968 and 1967.

Who's who in the Port trade

Churchill Graham Small independent family firm, making extremely good wines. Descendants of the Graham family (see below).
H Allen Smith; Alex Findlater; Lay.& Wheeler; Morris & Verdin; Stapylton Fletcher; Windrush Wines

Cockburn Biggest firm on the British market with Special Reserve. Some good tawnies.
Oddbins; Stapylton Fletcher; Victoria Wine Co

Croft Specialise in LBV and Distinction brands, also Gilbey's Crown Triple Port. Single quinta, Quinta da Roêda.
Bottoms Up; Peter Dominic

Delaforce Owned jointly with Croft, but still managed by the family. His Eminence Choice and Vintage Character as well as lighter vintage styles.
Alex Findlater; André Simon Wines

Dow One of the leading vintage houses. Wines have a dry and nutty style. High quality.
Gerard Harris; Hungerford Wine Company; Lay & Wheeler; Oddbins

Ferreira The leading Portuguese Port house (as opposed to those owned by British families). Some good tawnies. Also produce top quality table wines called Barca Velha (see under table wine section).
Thresher

Fonseca Best-known brand is Bin 27, but also make long-lasting Vintage Ports. Very high reputation.
Alex Findlater; Gerard Harris; Haynes Hanson & Clark; Lay & Wheeler; André Simon Wines

Graham Big, luscious Vintage Ports.
Haynes Hanson & Clark; Lay & Wheeler

Martinez Associated with Cockburn. Producing some really very attractive Ports at good prices.
Adnams; Majestic Wine Warehouses; Wine Society

Noval High quality Ports made in one of the finest Douro vineyards. Late Bottled is their best brand.
Gerard Harris; André Simon Wines; Stapylton Fletcher; Tanners Wines

Offley Forrester One of the most famous names in Port through the activities of Baron Forrester in the 19th century. Now owned by the Italian vermouth house of Martini.
Non-vintage: Army & Navy stores; vintage: more widely available

Rebello Valente Brand name of Robertson Brothers, a small Port house, now owned by Sandeman.
Berry Bros & Rudd; Laytons

Quarles Harris Another small Port house; part of the Symington group which also owns Dow, Graham and Warre.
Berry Bros & Rudd

Sandeman Good value Ports in all styles.
Gough Brothers; Kershaw's Wine Warehouse; Oddbins

Taylor Expensive, top quality Ports. Late Bottled Vintage is widely available. Lighter tawnies of high standard. Single quinta, Quinta de Vargellas.
Haynes Hanson & Clark; Lay & Wheeler; Tanners Wines

Warre Oldest Port house, now jointly owned with Graham and Dow. Brands include Nimrod. Single quinta, Quinta do Bonfim.
Adnams; Haynes Hanson & Clark; Majestic Wine Warehouses

Best buys in Port

The Society's Port, Tawny Character (*The Wine Society*)
Tesco Reserve Tawny Port (*Tesco*)
Fonseca 10-year-old Tawny (*Lay & Wheeler; Ubiquitous Chip*)
Cockburns 10-year-old Tawny (*John Harvey; J Sainsbury*)
Quarles Harris Late Bottled Vintage 1979 (*Haslemere Wine Co, Lower Street, Haslemere, Surrey; Whighams of Ayr, 8 Academy Street, Ayr*)
Dows Vintage Character (*Selfridges; André Simon*)
Martinez Late Bottled Vintage 1981 (*Harrods; Stones of Belgravia*)

Specialist stockists

Bibendum; Berry Bros & Rudd; Classic Wines; Curzon Wine Co; Eldridge Pope; Ellis Son & Vidler; Fine Vintage Wines; Harrods; John Harvey & Sons; Justerini & Brooks; Lay & Wheeler; Nickolls & Perks; Premier Wines (Ayr); Reid Wines; La réserve/College Cellar; Edward Sheldon; Stones of Belgravia; T & W Wines; La Vigneronne; The Wine Society; Peter Wylie Fine Wines

MADEIRA

Madeira is a unique wine. For once, there can be no objection to using that overworked word. No other wine lasts so long with so little apparent change. And, certainly, nowhere else is a wine 'cooked' for six months or more before it can be regarded as the real thing.

Cooking the wine developed, like so many unlikely success stories, by accident. In the 18th century Madeira was shipped regularly round the world: it was highly popular in the southern States of America and it also went down well in the Portuguese colonies and the Far East. It was discovered that the effect of the sun during the long sea voyage made terrific improvements to the wine. Back on Madeira, some bright brains got together and devised a way of reproducing the effect of the sun without sending the wine round the world. So the estufa, the Madeira stove, was born.

For the past century, though, the story of Madeira has been one of gradual decline. First, the effects of the phylloxera louse were particularly severe on this tiny mid-Atlantic island. Then, the vineyards were not replanted with the true Madeira grape varieties (of which more in a moment) but with a range of high-yielding, low quality vines, so wines carrying famous names on the labels were actually made of inferior grapes.

Since 1979, things have looked up. Now 80 per cent of the wine in a bottle of Madeira must be made of the grape indicated on the label.

Those grapes are (from dry to sweet): Sercial, Verdelho, Bual and Malmsey.

Sercial Madeira is a dry wine which makes an excellent aperitif. Verdelho is also an aperitif wine but, being slightly fuller, also goes well with some foods, for instance soups. Both Bual and Malmsey make magnificent after-dinner drinks.

The quality of Madeira available in our shops is improving all the time. Apart from standard ranges, which cost around £5 a bottle, there are older wines and – in small quantities – Madeiras based on soleras which date from the beginning of the 19th century.

Although Madeira is known for its ability to age, it's only the top wines which live up to that reputation. Ordinary Madeiras are wines which are at their best when they are bottled and are not designed to improve beyond that.

Good, basic Madeira is available at most specialist off-licences, priced at just about ruby or Vintage Character Port – remarkable when the very high costs of production are taken into account. But there are shortages of some of the finer Madeiras while producers build up stocks of wines based on the noble grape varieties (which is all they are now allowed to export from Madeira). Recent harvests had been small: 1984 was appalling, while 1985 had high quality but tiny quantities; but luck changed with a good, bumper crop in 1986.

It's certainly worth the effort to search out fine old Madeira. Its complexities, its distinctive, nutty, slightly 'cooked' taste and classic balance between sweetness and dried fruit are well worth savouring.

Who's who in Madeira

Blandy Brothers One of the most famous Madeira companies, which also owns Reid's Hotel, one of the island's top hotels. Wines: Duke of Sussex Sercial, Duke of Cambridge Verdelho, Duke of Cumberland Bual, Duke of Clarence Malmsey.
Peter Dominic; Threshers

Cossart Gordon Producer of classic Madeira, often in a light style. Top quality wines. Wines: Good Company Sercial, Cossart Rainwater, Good Company Bual and Malmsey, Finest Old Malmsey.
Adnams; Berry Bros & Rudd; Ellis Son & Vidler; Lay & Wheeler

Harveys Part of the famous Sherry firm, whose Madeiras are produced for them by Henriques & Henriques. Wines: Very Superior Old Dry Sercial, Royal Solera Verdelho, Old Bual, Old Rich Malmsey.
John Harvey & Son (Pall Mall); Victoria Wine Co; Waitrose

Leacock Rich, deep Madeiras which are balanced by clean fruit. Wines: Leacock St John Reserve Sercial, Verdelho and Bual, Special Reserve Malmsey.
Bordeaux Direct

Lomelino The oldest Portuguese Madeira house. Wines: Imperial Sercial, Verdelho, Old Bual and Rare Old Malmsey.
Russell & McIver

Rutherford & Miles Old company, still family-owned, making very stylish wines. Wines: Old Custom House Sercial, La Reina Verdelho, Old Trinity House Bual, Fine Old Malmsey.
Eldridge Pope; Tanners Wines

Best buys in Madeira

Vintage and vintage solera wines are available from some merchants (see specialist stockists) and are very good value. Of the more widely available wines, here are two best buys:

Blandys Ten-Year-Old Malmsey (*Augustus Barnett Shops; and others*)
Cossart Gordon Duo Centenary Bual (*Ellis Son & Vidler*)

Rumania

Little impression

The overall impact of Rumanian wines on the UK market has barely changed in the past year. The Rumanians just don't seem to be interested in selling their wines here, and on the whole the few wines we have tasted offer little competition with the quality or style of the wines from their neighbour Bulgaria. The company that was established in 1984 to import wines from Rumania still sells them and has increased the selection slightly, but so far the quality doesn't really justify any dedicated search for these rare bottles.

The Rumanians seem best at producing sweetish wines – red as well as white – designed for the Russian market. However, a few wines have risen a little from the general rut. Of the reds, there is a good, fruity Merlot from the Dealul Mare region of the Carpathian mountains and the Minis brand of Cabernet Sauvignon.

Of the whites, look for the medium dry Tirnave made in the Dracula country of Transylvania, a reasonable Laski Riesling, and a wine made from the local grape variety, the Fetească (also called by the German name of Mädchentraube), which is aromatic and grapy. There is also an attractive, sweet white Blanc Murfatlar.

Alex Findlater; Littlewoods; Touchstone Wines (14 Vine Street, Kidderminster, Heref & Worcs); Waitrose

Spain

Spain still has an image problem. Despite the millions of pounds thrown around by the Wines from Spain promotion agency in London to tell consumers about the treats that Spain produces, when it comes to the crunch, most people can only remember Rioja, a couple of producers from Penedès – and Sherry.

What about everything else? The problem is that much of it is still covered by those branded wines – either sold in off-licences or supermarkets – which rejoice in names like Spanish Dry White or Spanish Full-Bodied Red. But we shouldn't blame the supermarket buyers entirely – they are trying to broaden our knowledge (Sainsbury's for instance are selling a good red Jumilla, and Safeways have shown that Valencia can produce quality wine as well as plonk with their Casa lo Alto). And, of course, the specialist importers (see the list at the end of this section) continue to stock wines which in their quality immediately give the lie to any previous misconceptions about Spanish wines.

But it's hard work. Good wines occasionally pop up that sell like hot cakes, but they still don't stick in the mind, so we forget about them and return to Rioja for our regular Spanish wines.

Scant reward

It seems scant reward for all the effort the Spanish are putting into improving their wines at all levels. They have embraced modern winemaking technology as wholeheartedly as many, and in the area of white wine are now able to make a whole range of attractive, modern wines, fruity, nicely acid and clean – quite unlike the tired, oxidised offerings of the past.

In the vineyards, they've begun to experiment with new clones, have improved the types of vine variety planted, and are carefully picking the grapes for white wines so that they are not too ripe. They don't have the German and southern French problem of high yields – Spain's vineyards on parched, poor soil have the lowest yields of anywhere in Europe. But the Spanish government is making a virtue out of this necessity by forbidding irrigation, ensuring vines are widely spaced and carefully pruned.

It's in the areas which have traditionally supplied cheap plonk where these changes have had the most remarkable effect. La Mancha, the high plateau south of Madrid, which contains a third of all Spanish vineyards, has suddenly shown that it can produce those clean, fresh whites and has come up with soft, easy-drinking reds a world apart from the bulk production, most of which gets turned into brandy.

And then there are the smaller areas, largely unexplored except by the specialist importers. Places like Galicia, Ribera del Duero, León, Rueda (apart from one world-class Cabernet Sauvignon wine) have still a long way to go before they become anything like as familiar as similar small areas in France or even Italy.

No rights in Europe

Don't expect Spain's entry into the Common Market to make any changes yet in the price of the wines. France and Italy have made quite sure that it will be a long wait before Spain gets the same rights and privileges under the Common Agricultural Policy. Indeed, she has lost out at first, because she's been made to scrap the rebates to wine companies to export – because that's regarded as a subsidy and against the free market (never mind that there are huge subsidies to peasant farmers in France and Italy to produce wine that's only fit for distillation).

In fact, Spanish wine prices have gone up. In Rioja, especially, the poor 1984 harvest has left the producers paying high prices for grapes and passing them on to the consumer as soon as they can. Despite price rises, there are still plenty of good buys in Rioja, and older wines (when you can find them), the reservas and gran reservas, still provide some of the best value anywhere.

Potential

Spain is still a country of potential as much as achievement in quality wines. Her system of quality wine regions – the Denominación de Origen – is much more a statement of geographical fact than necessarily a reflection of the wine produced. The DOS cover too much of the country (62 per cent of the vineyards against 10 per cent in Italy) to be of any real use to the consumer.

In our minds, Spain has still to achieve quite the image of quality which its better wines deserve. There are still too many preconceptions about Spanish party plonk. And there are still too few memorable names to conjure with.

What's on a Spanish label

As every country, Spain has its own peculiar set of terms to describe the wine inside the bottle. Here are a few of the most common:

Abocado Medium sweet.

Anejado por Aged by.

Año Spain has used terms like 2 año and 3 año which indicate that the wine was bottled in the second (or third) year after the vintage – *not* that it is two or three years old. This term is banned by the Common Market so only older wines will now carry it.

Blanco White.

Bodega Winery.

Brut Dry – generally used for sparkling wines.

Cava A generic term for sparkling wine made by the Champagne method.

Con crianza Means the wine has been aged in wood. Each region has different regulations concerning wood ageing.

Cosecha Harvest.

Cosechero New, fresh – as in Nouveau (see also Nuevo).

Criado por Blended and/or matured by.

Dulce Sweet.

Elaborado por Made/blended/matured by.

Embotellado por Bottled by.

Espumoso Sparkling wine made by any method.

Generoso Fortified or dessert wine.

Gran Reserva Top quality wine aged in the winery for a specified period – the highest quality grading for the finest wines. In Rioja it means two years in wood and three in bottle, or the other way round (ie a minimum of five years in total). Generally used for reds, but can apply to whites or rosés.

Nuevo Young, fresh, fruity wine of the year.

Reserva Good quality red wine, aged (in Rioja) for one year in wood, two in bottle – or the other way round (a minimum of three years). Whites and rosés have different regulations.

Rosado Rosé.

Seco Dry.

Semi-Seco Medium dry.

Sin crianza Without wood ageing.

Tinto Red wine.

Vendimia The gathering of the grapes.

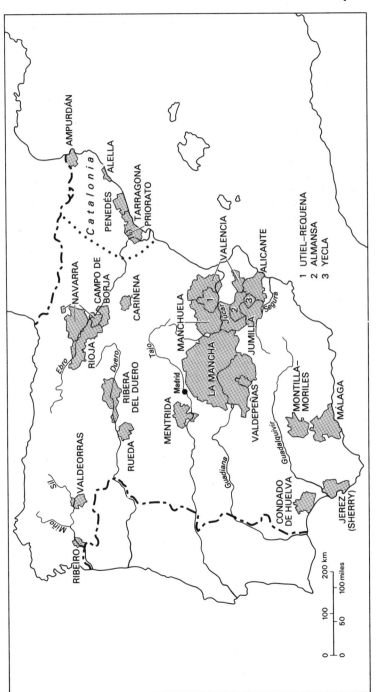

Spain

1 UTIEL–REQUENA
2 ALMANSA
3 YECLA

AMPURDÁN

ALELLA

Catalonia

PENEDÈS

TARRAGONA

PRIORATO

VALENCIA

ALICANTE

NAVARRA

CAMPO DE BORJA

CARIÑENA

MANCHUELA

Ebro

RIOJA

Duero

RIBERA DEL DUERO

Tajo

LA MANCHA

JUMILLA

Júcar

Segura

MADRID

MÉNTRIDA

VALDEPEÑAS

MONTILLA–MORILES

MÁLAGA

VALDEORRAS

RUEDA

Guadiana

Guadalquivir

CONDADO DE HUELVA

JEREZ (SHERRY)

Sil

Miño

RIBEIRO

200 km

100 miles

100

50

0   0

Viña Literally means vineyard, but often used to refer to a wine as part of a brand name.

Vino de mesa Table wine.

Vintages in Spain

1986 Good reds in the north of Spain – Rioja, Navarra, Penedès, but less satisfactory for whites. Further south, a good all-round harvest.

1985 Good generally. Very good in Rioja and Navarra.

1984 Average to good quality, better for whites than reds. Quantities badly down in Rioja.

1983 Good, but not great. Whites have fared better than reds again – especially in Penedès.

1982 A very good year, with some good reds on the way.

1981 Light reds, but very high quality. Some ageing potential in the Reservas.

1980 Variable generally. Very good in La Mancha, good in Rioja, average in Navarra.

1979 Good to average vintage. Rioja and La Mancha good, Navarra average.

1978 Good vintage everywhere. Navarra and La Mancha are very good.

RIOJA

Rioja continues to dominate as the quality wine area of Spain people recognise, and deservedly so for, taken as a whole, Rioja produces the finest table wines in Spain (as distinct from fortified wines). Despite price rises, the region is still able to astonish with the amazingly low prices of her finest wines, and the value for money of her more basic styles.

The reds used to be massive wines, dominated by oak but also capable of emulating Bordeaux and Burgundy. The whites, too, tasted more of oak than fruit but many were oxidised.

As the market has expanded and customers have become more influential, the Rioja bodegas have cut down the oak on the reds – and cut it out completely on the whites. So now we get softer reds but still with some of that enjoyable vanilla-oaky taste, and crisp whites which have flowed straight from stainless steel into bottle.

Don't forget tradition

But in our enthusiasm for modernity, we shouldn't forget that the quality of Rioja was founded on ageing its white wines as well as its reds in wood. In fact it was the typical vanilla flavours of the reds and the properly oxidised scents of the whites which set Rioja apart from other wine regions.

Luckily, a handful of firms – many still run by the founding families, all of them in private hands – have maintained the traditions fast disappearing elsewhere in the world of modern winemaking.

Who's who in Rioja

Bodegas Alavesas Soft, light but concentrated reds made from grapes grown in the Rioja Alavesa. Also a young, deliciously fruity red. Brand name: Solar de Samaniego.
Harrods; Laymont and Shaw

Bodegas Berberana Use of new barrels in maturation gives these a strongly woody dimension, but early bottling means they don't lose their fruit. Bodegas Berberana make Grants of St James's Rioja. Brand name: Berberana.
Peter Dominic; Peter Green; Moreno Wines

Bodegas Beronia Good, soft, oaky reds and fresh whites. Brand name: Beronia.
Alex Findlater; Sherston Wine Company

Bodegas Bilbainas An old-fashioned family firm making wines in the old style. Brand names: Viña Pomal, Viña Zaco.
Moreno Wines; Waters of Coventry

Bodegas Campo Viejo One of the largest bodegas, making reds in a plummy, fruity style. The top wine, Marqués de Villamagna, is very good. Brand names: Marqués de Villamagna, Campo Viejo.
Bibendum; Peter Dominic; Morrisons; David Scatchard; Sherborne Vintners

CVNE (Compañia Vinícole del Norte de España Produce an excellent range of old-style Riojas, including a white called Monopole. The gran reservas and reservas are outstanding. Brand names: Imperial, Monopole.
Berry Bros & Rudd; Peter Dominic; Alex Findlater; Lay & Wheeler; Majestic Wine Warehouses; Tanners Wines

Bodegas El Coto Medium-sized bodega making light, soft, fragrant wines. Brand name: El Coto.
Davisons; Gerard Harris; Le Nez Rouge

Domecq The famous Sherry and brandy producers have established a reputation for good quality Rioja from their own vineyards. Brand name: Domecq Domain.
Peter Green; Whynot Wine Warehouses

Bodegas Faustino Despite the terrible fake dust on the bottles, these are good wines, at all quality levels. The white is in fresh, modern style. Red Reservas are very good. Brand name: Faustino.
Peter Dominic; Peter Green; Sherston Wine Company

Bodegas Franco-Españolas Old-style bodega, now producing fine wines after a poor period in the late 1970s. Brand names: Bordon, Royal.
Peter Green

Bodegas Lagunilla Reliable reds, but a rather dull white. Brand name: Lagunilla.
Peter Dominic

Bodegas Lan Modern producers of good, young wines. The white is fresh, the red fragrant. Brand name: Lan.
Tesco

Bodegas Lopez de Heredia Old-fashioned bodega in the best sense. Virtually everything, including fermentation, is done in wood. The results are glorious whites, more delicate reds. Brand name: Tondonia.
Berry Bros & Rudd; Sherston Wine Company

Bodegas Marqués de Cáceres Pioneer of the new-style whites and softer, modern reds. Still some of the best of their type around. The Reservas age remarkably well for such modernity. Brand name: Marqués de Cáceres.
Widely available

Bodegas Marqués de Murrieta The finest white Riojas, made in the old style and superbly longlasting, the nearest Spain gets to white Burgundy. The reds, less interesting, are still very good and age well. Brand names: Marqués de Murrieta, Ygay.
Peter Dominic; Moreno Wines

Bodegas Marqués de Riscal A bodega that nowadays disappoints despite its fine reputation. Its white is not from Rioja but from Rueda (and none the worse for that), but the red tends to be on the thin side with harsh edges. Brand name: Marqués de Riscal.
Widely available

Bodegas Martinez Lacuesta An old family firm, making fairly standard whites and reds, but some very good reservas. Brand names: Campeador, Reserva Especial.
Moreno Wines

Bodegas Montecillo Ultra-modern bodega that makes very good commercial wines. Brand names: Viña Monty, Viña Cumbrero.
Barwell and Jones; Sherston Wine Company

Bodegas Muga Much better for reds, which are delicate and elegant, than for whites. Traditional methods still in operation. Brand name: Muga.
Bibendum; Eldridge Pope; Peter Green

Bodegas Olarra Brand new bodega making some excellent reds, including a very good gran reserva at a knock-down price. Brand names: Cerro Anon, Anares.
Berry Bros & Rudd; Oddbins; André Simon Wines; Waitrose

Bodegas Federico Paternina Vast, modern bodega but a long-established firm. Make sound, commercial wines, with the red better than the white. Brand names: Banda Azul (red), Banda Dorada (white).
Victoria Wine Co

Bodegas La Rioja Alta A traditionalist producing one of the most reliable ranges in Rioja. Great heights can be reached in the reservas and gran reservas. Brand names: Metropol (white), Viña Alberdi, Viña Arana, Viña Ardanza, Reserva 904.
Adnams; H Allen Smith; Alex Findlater; Lay & Wheeler; J Sainsbury

Bodegas Riojanas The influence of the French founders of this bodega can still be felt in the elegance of the wines. Quite a lot of old-fashioned reds. Brand names: Viña Albina, Monte Real.
Les Amis du Vin; Cullens; Peter Green

Bodegas Unidas Large firm, with American ownership, making reliable wines. The Siglo is sold in a distinctive sacking cover. Brand names: Marqués de Romeral, Siglo, Fuenmayor.
Harrods; Marks & Spencer (for Marqués de Romeral); Selfridges; and many others

Best buys from Rioja

WHITES

Tidón white (*Martinez Fine Wines*)
Marqués de Cáceres Blanco (*widely available*)
Monte Real 1982 (*Majestic Wine Warehouses*)
Marqués de Murrieta Blanco 1982 (*Hilbre Wine Co; Premier Wine Warehouse*)
Muga Blanco 1982 (*Mi Casa Wines*)

REDS

Campo Viejo Reserva 1976 (*Peter Dominic*)
Gran Condal Reserva 1978, Bodegas Rioja Santiago (*Russell & McIver; Waitrose*)
Marqués de Cáceres 1983 (*widely available*)
CVNE Tinto 5 Año 1981 (*Moreno Wines; and others*)
Carta de Plata 1984, Bodegas Berberana (*Curzon Wine Co; Moreno Wines*)

Marqués de Romeral 1981 (*Marks & Spencer*)
Lancorta 1981 (*Bin 89 Wine Warehouse*)
Paternina Banda Azul 1983 (*Chaplin & Sons; Victoria Wine Co*)

CATALONIA AND PENEDÈS

Behind the Costa Brava

Both still wines and sparkling wines are produced here, including some of Spain's best. Penedès, the region inland from the Costa Brava, is the most important Denominación de Origen, but there are others: Ampurdán–Costa Brava, Tarragona, Alella and Priorato. The last two are the source of some good value whites and reds.

The sparkling wine industry here is the biggest in Spain and one of the biggest in Europe. The wines go under the generic name of cava, meaning cellar, and indicating that the wines have their secondary fermentation in the bottle as they do in Champagne. Some of the best producers make good, crisp wines, but there are also quite a few flabby sparklers around made from over-ripe grapes (see Sparkling wines on page 530).

White wines from Penedès should, generally, be drunk young. Look for the 1986 vintage now. The only exceptions to this are some of the wines produced by Torres and Jean León (see below).

Reds also should be drunk younger than they would be from Rioja. Three-year-old wines are at their best, but some wines repay keeping for five or six years – again, those from Torres and Jean León being the best keepers.

Who's who in Catalonia

René Barbier Under the same ownership as the sparkling Conde de Caralt, this estate makes a fresh white and some reliable reds. Wine: Kraliner (dry white).
Whynot Wine Warehouses

Jean León Run by a Spaniard based in California. The influence shows in both his wines, which are 100 per cent varietals. Wines: Chardonnay, Cabernet Sauvignon.
Adnams; Peter Dominic; Alex Findlater; Laymont and Shaw; Majestic Wine Warehouses; Wines from Paris

Masía Bach Best known for its sweet wine which some regard highly, others dislike. Also makes a good red wine, less good dry white. Wines: Masía Bach red, Extrísimo Bach sweet white.
Adnams; Alex Findlater; Wine Society

Raimat Large estate in western Catalonia which makes Cabernet Sauvignon and Chardonnay wines and an excellent blended red. Wine: Raimat Abadía.
André Simon Wines; Victoria Wine Co; Wine Society

Manuel Sancho Best known for both modern and old-style white wines. Wines: Attractively yeasty, rounded white Mont Marçal Añada and oaky, fruity, well-balanced Mont Marçal Blanco Reserva.
Peter Green

Jaume Serra Makes a top Muscat wine.
Sherborne Vintners

Torres The most famous firm in Penedès and probably in Spain. Their reputation is based on the skills of Miguel Torres Jr in blending European grape varieties – Chardonnay, Sauvignon, Gewürztraminer, Muscat, Pinot Noir, Cabernet Sauvignon and Cabernet Franc – with local Spanish varieties to create innovative wines. Wines: Viña Sol (Parellada grapes), Tres Torres (Garnacha and Cariñena), Coronas (Tempranillo and Monastrell), Gran Sangredetoro (Garnacha and Cariñena). The French/Spanish blends are: Gran Viña Sol (Chardonnay and Parellada), Gran Viña Sol Green Label (Parellada and Sauvignon), Viña Esmeralda (Gewürztraminer and Muscat), Viña Magdala (Pinot Noir and Cariñena), Gran Coronas (Cabernet Sauvignon and Tempranillo) and Gran Coronas Black Label (Cabernet Sauvignon and Cabernet Franc).
Widely available

Best buys from Penedès

WHITE WINES

Torres Vinā Sol (*widely available*)
Raimat Chardonnay (*Victoria Wine Co; and others*)
Blanc Cru, Cavas Hill (*H Allen Smith; Hicks & Don*)

RED WINES

Torres reds (*widely available*)
Raimat Cabernet Sauvignon 1983 (*Victoria Wine Co; and others*)
Mont Marçal, Cabernet Sauvignon 1983 (*Arriba Kettle*)

NAVARRA

Navarra has suffered from being right across the river from Rioja – and from not producing such fine wines. Much of her production has been in rosado (rosé) made from the Garnacha grape and frankly only fit for local consumption. Only in the past few years have the producers here recognised that they need to progress in reds and whites to get anywhere in foreign markets.

They've certainly made great progress in the reds – about the whites we are less sure. The planting of the Tempranillo grape (the quality grape of Rioja) has brought much more style and elegance to the reds, some of which are designed for drinking young, others for ageing in the style of reserva wines from Rioja.

Terms in Navarra

Vinos de Crianza Red wines which have spent at least one year in barrel.

Reserva Aged for at least 3 years, one year at least of which must have been in barrel.

Gran Reserva Aged for two years in wood, then three in bottle.

Who's who in Navarra

Bodegas Bardon Owned by Olarra, the Rioja bodega, they produce two young reds and one reserva style. Wines: Togal, Larums, Don Luis.
Wizard Wines

Cenalsa Marketing consortium producing good, modern-style whites, rosés and reds. Wine: Agramont brand.
Tanners Wines

Julián Chivite Fresh, clean, well-made wines. Wines: Gran Feudo range.
Laymont and Shaw: Waitrose

Bodegas Ochoa Lighter-style reds and whites.
Co-operative Stores, Peterborough; Rainbow Superstores (East Anglia)

Señorio de Sarria One of the best producers in the region. A spectacular new-style red, plus oak-aged wines of some class. Wines: Viña Ecoyen, Viña del Perdón, Gran Viña.
H Allen Smith; Peter Green; Majestic Wine Warehouses; Sherston Wine Company; La Vigneronne; Wine Society

Bodegas Villafranca Good, nouveau-style red among others. Wines: Monte Ory brand.
Adnams; H Allen Smith; Hungerford Wine Company; Whynot Wine Warehouses

Best buys from Navarra
Señorio de Sarria 1982 red (*widely available*)
Agramont 1981, Bodegas Cenalsa red (*Moreno Wines; Martinez Fine Wines; La Reserva Wines*)

OTHER REGIONS OF SPAIN

Jumilla – ungrafted vines

Because of the high organic content of the soil in this region inland
from Valencia, phylloxera never struck, so the vines are ungrafted. The
resulting wines are some very rich reds which, when the alcohol is
lowered by early picking, are good drunk young. An area with
potential. Wines: Condestable.
Laymont and Shaw; J Sainsbury

Ribera del Duero – quality in isolation

The reputation of this region has rested on one wine – the legendary
Vega Sicilia, which people have heard of but never drunk. However,
this bodega doesn't quite flourish in isolation. There's a good
co-operative, and a new top quality estate which has just started up
next to Vega Sicilia, both making some very fine reds, so the potential
for this area is considerable.

Bodegas Penalba Lopez Good red wines. Wines: Torremilanos,
Penalba.
Sherborne Vintners; Tanners Wines

Bodegas Pesquera Founded in 1970, this estate makes red wines
which are aged in small Bordeaux barriques for up to two and a half
years. It has received rave notices in the United States.
Adnams

Ribera del Duero Co-operative Old-established but with a newly
enhanced reputation. Wines: Protos red, Ribera Duero red.
Laymont and Shaw

Bodegas Vega Sicilia They say the wine here needs 30 years to reach
its peak. Few get the chance to find out, because this wine, made
mainly from Cabernet Sauvignon, Merlot and Malbec, is available in
tiny quantities at a high price. A second wine, Valbuena, is not much
cheaper. Wines: Vega Sicilia, Valbuena.
Adnams; Peter Dominic; Laymont and Shaw; La Vigneronne

New whites and a classic red from Rueda

Marqués de Riscal white is the best-known wine from this area. It's a
modern-style wine, made for the Rioja bodega by Vinos Blancos de
Castilla.
Widely available

The Bodegas de Crianza de Castilla la Vieja is more of a find. It has used the talents of the Bordeaux-based Professor Peynaud to make a top-class, modern white and an outstanding, oak-aged red (made near Toledo using Cabernet Sauvignon). Wines: Marqués de Griñon red and dry white.
Adnams; H Allen Smith; Corney & Barrow; Tanners Wines

Island in a sea of vines – Valdepeñas

This region lies within the larger *denominación* of La Mancha. Valdepeñas produces some very good reds and less interesting whites at very good prices.

Cosecheros Abastecedores Produce good reds, especially at reserva and gran reserva levels, at amazingly good prices. Wines: Señorío de los Llanos.
Peter Dominic; Alex Findlater; Peter Green; Lay & Wheeler; Laymont and Shaw; André Simon Wines

Bodegas Felix Solis Produce a good red called Viña Albali.
H Allen Smith; Sherborne Vintners

Best buys from Spain's other regions

WHITE WINES

Castillo de Alhambra, La Mancha (*Martinez Fine Wines*)
Reboreda Blanco 1985, Galicia (*Moreno Wines*)
Valdepeñas, Armonioso Vino Joven (*Laymont and Shaw*)

RED WINES

Marqués de Griñon 1984 (*H Allen Smith; Corney & Barrow*)
Gran Colegiata 1982, Reserva, Toro-Zamora (*Sherston Wine Company*)
Sainsbury's Jumilla (*J Sainsbury*)
Palacio de León, Vinos de León (*Moreno Wines; and others*)
Valdepeñas, Señorío de los Llanos, Reserva 1978 (*Peter Dominic; and many others*)

Specialist stockists of Spanish table wines

H Allen Smith; Arriba Kettle; Bottle and Basket; D Byrne; Peter Green; Harrods; George Hill of Loughborough; Laymont and Shaw; Martinez Fine Wine; Mi Casa Wines; Moreno Wines; Premier Wine Warehouse; La Reserva Wines; Paul Sanderson Wines; Sherborne Vintners; Sherston Wine Company; La Vigneronne; The Wine Centre; The Wine Spot

Stockist information has been supplied by the importers of the wine and has not necessarily been checked with the stockists themselves.

SHERRY

When we learnt that Sainsbury's had introduced Manzanilla in
half-bottles, everybody who had been worrying about the future of
Sherry in Britain let out three very relieved cheers. If the largest wine
retailers in the country think it worth their while to sell the driest of all
Sherry styles under their own label and in half-bottles so it can be
drunk at one sitting and not lose its freshness – then we must be
getting back our taste for quality Sherry.

We're delighted to report that those half-bottles have been a great
success. So maybe all the work by that handful of enthusiasts and
retailers who have continued to keep up their Sherry's quality while all
about them were dropping it, hasn't been in vain.

Mind you, we've a long way to go yet. When many off-licences in the
land seem to be in the business of selling stale fino that ought to have
been drunk months ago – and obviously don't care – the Sherry
shippers are still walking up a slippery slope.

And it's going to be fino and Manzanilla – the dry styles of Sherry –
that together will form a principal plank in the salvation of Sherry from
its image as a drink only consumed by maiden aunts in retirement in
Tunbridge Wells (at least they have the good taste to drink it). That and
the superb almacenista Sherries – those produced by small companies
which are then bottled as individual wines by a merchant.

Quality is now the byword, but first there was the era of Rumasa,
when Sherry that was too young was dumped here in complicated and
devious financial transactions. Then there was the problem of Sherry
copies – like Australian, South African, Cyprus and (worst of all)
British. The EEC saw off the word Sherry in association with
Australian and South African fortified wines, but – for shabby political
reasons – failed to do the same with the two worst offenders (in quality
terms), Cyprus and Britain. Be warned: Cyprus Sherry is just about
passable, British Sherry is not.

But even with the Real Thing – from south-west Spain in the Jerez
region of Andalucia – the way that much dry Sherry is still kept too
long on shelves and in warehouses is still giving cause for concern. It's
a delicate white wine which needs care in handling and whose faults
show very clearly. It also needs to be drunk young, and shops haven't
yet got that message.

Last year, our sister publication *Which? Wine Monthly* called for the
date the wine is bottled to be put on the label so that we can know how
fresh the wine is. We would endorse that – and repeat it, because
nothing much has happened. We would also encourage any shipper or
retailer – like Sainsbury's – who brings over half-bottles of fino in small
consignments and sells them fast and fresh.

In the sweeter styles, there are still too many young fino sherries which are sweetened and coloured and then misleadingly labelled amontillado: real amontillado is dry. The continuing success of pale cream (another sweetened fino) shows the power of marketing in this brand-conscious market.

Buying Sherry that's just a little more expensive than the basic prices – going up to £3.50 rather than £3 – will give you an indication of where Sherrry's true quality lies. And buying the drier Sherries from a shop which obviously has a fast stock turnover will help ensure you get fresher bottles.

The Sherry label

Six styles of Sherry are available in the UK:

Manzanilla The driest style of all, applied only to wines made in Sanlúcar de Barrameda by the Atlantic coast. Tasters detect a whiff of sea-salt on the nose and flavour. The wines certainly have a lighter, more pungent flavour than those from Jerez itself. Serve chilled.

Fino The classic dry Sherry. The flor yeast which grows on the wine's surface and protects it from oxidation in the barrel gives the yeasty flavour to this wine. The palate is dry and full of tangy flavour. Serve chilled.

Amontillado True amontillados are aged finos which have taken on an amber colour and nutty taste. They are dry. But much amontillado we see in Britain is sweet and not a patch on the real thing. Real amontillado will probably be labelled dry amontillado or 'amontillado seco', and will be more expensive than commercial sweetened stuff. Worth paying more for it.

Palo Cortado An intermediate style between amontillado and oloroso (see below). Amber-coloured. Should be dry.

Oloroso Wines which have never grown flor. They should not be too sweet, but full of richness and flavour. Most are sweetened, but there are some Old Dry Olorosos around which make good winter aperitifs.

Cream and Pale Cream Marketing man's Sherry. Pale Cream is sweetened fino, Cream is oloroso with extra sweetening.

OTHER TERMS ON THE LABEL

Amoroso A sweetened oloroso style.
Brown A rich dessert Sherry.
Fina A manzanilla fino.
Fino Amontillado A fino which has been left to age in cask under its layer of flor until the flor dies. It is darker in colour than a fino, nuttier and more pungent to taste.
Manzanilla Pasada The manzanilla equivalent of fino amontillado.

Solera The system by which Sherry is matured and prepared for bottling. An individual solera is a series of Sherry butts (barrels) containing wine of similar maturity.

Viejo and Muy Viejo Old and very old. A term used at the discretion of a producer.

Who's who in Sherry

It is a heavily branded product and most major retailers sell an own-label Sherry range. Sometimes, these can be good – it all depends on the quality of the retailer. Our recommendations are indicated in the WHERE TO BUY section under each retailer's entry. Here, we list those producers who sell under their own name.

Barbadillo, Antonio Based in Sanlúcar and recognised as manzanilla specialists, although they handle other styles of Sherry as well. Wines: Manzanilla, Fino de Balbaina, Principe (manzanilla pasada); also a table wine called Castillo de San Diego, made from the same Palomino grapes that are used in Sherry.
Bibendum; Corney & Barrow; Alex Findlater; Laytons; André Simon Wines; La Vigneronne; Windrush Wines

Bobadilla Large company with good value, inexpensive fino.
Peter Green; Moreno Wines

Burdon A range of good value Sherries of commercial character. Wines: Burdon Fino, Golden Oloroso.
Wimbledon Wine Cellars (Gladstone Road, London SW19)

Croft British-owned firm whose main product is a Pale Cream Sherry; plus a range of other styles. Wines: Delicado fino, Palo Cortado, Original Pale Cream.
Peter Dominic

Díez-Merito Firm which makes one of the best older finos. Wine: Don Zoilo very old fino.
Gerard Harris; Moreno Wines; André Simon Wines; La Vigneronne

Domecq One of the largest Sherry bodegas producing a range of top quality wines. Wines: La Ina (fino), Botaina (dry amontillado), Rio Viejo (dry oloroso), plus the less classy Double Century sherries.
Peter Green; Wine Growers Association

Duke of Wellington A very good light fino from Bodegas Internacionales, one of the most spectacular of the modern Jerez bodegas. Other Sherries in the range are less exciting but of good standard.
Whighams of Ayr (8 Academy Street, Ayr)

Findlater Despite being the name of a British wine merchant, this has become a more widely available brand than just an own-label. Wines: Dry Fly, May Fly, River Fly, La Luna, Amontillado Fino Viejo.
Findlater Mackie Todd

Garvey Make superb fino and an equally good range of other styles. Wines: San Patricio fino, Tio Guillermo amontillado, Ochavico dry oloroso, Pale Cream.
Gerard Harris; Majestic Wine Warehouses; Stapylton Fletcher

Gonzalez Byass Large firm with some of the best-known brand names, which always do well in tastings. Wines: Tio Pepe fino, Elegante fino (less expensive), La Concha medium amontillado, San Domingo Pale Cream, Apostoles dry oloroso, Amontillado del Duque Seco (dry).
Widely available; late-bottled Sherries from Oddbins

Harveys The biggest-selling Sherry range in Britain. The top brand is a cream sherry. The quality of the standard range could be much better than it is, but they have also launched a premium range, 1796, which is much more interesting. Wines: Luncheon Dry (fino), Bristol Cream, Bristol Milk, Tico (mixer sherry), 1796 Manzanilla, Fino, Amontillado, Palo Cortado, Oloroso. Harvey's also have a rare range of late-bottled sherries which are available in small quantities and worth looking out for.
Widely available; older Sherries from John Harvey & Sons

Hidalgo Small firm specialising in good quality manzanilla. Wines: La Gitana manzanilla, Jerez Cortado Hidalgo.
Lay & Wheeler; O W Loeb; Tanners Wines (under their own label)

Lustau, Emilio A leading independent company known for its range of almacenista Sherries. Highly recommended. Wines: Main brand is Dry Lustau fino. The almacenista Sherries are known by numbers rather than names.
Peter Green (almacenistas); Hungerford Wine Company; Majestic Wine Warehouses (other Sherries)

Osborne A large, independent company based in Puerto de Santa Maria. Make a top-class fino and a full range of other styles. Notorious in Spain for the use of their bull symbol on hoardings. Wines: Fino Quinta, Coquinero amontillado, Bailen dry oloroso, Osborne Cream.
Peter Green

Sanchez Romate A small, privately owned bodega, mainly concerned with brandy, but also producing a good manzanilla and fino. Wines: Petenara Manzanilla, Marismeno Fino, Don Jose Oloroso, Iberia Cream.
H Allen Smith

Sandeman The same firm as the Port producers with the famous cloaked Don symbol. Wines: Character Amoroso (a medium style), Don Fino, Amontillado, Royal Esmeralda, Old Amoroso, Royal Corregidor, Pale Cream.
Adnams; Bibendum

De Soto A privately owned company which unusually makes wines only from its own vineyards. Wines: Fino Soto, Manzanilla, Amontillado Maravilla, Dry Oloroso, Amontillado Viejo.
Sherston Wine Company

Valdespino Family company producing some good middle-range Sherries which show well in tastings. Wines: Inocente Fino, Tio Diego amontillado.
Caves de la Madeleine; Alex Findlater; André Simon Wines; Wine Society

Williams & Humbert One of the more spectacular bodegas, which suffered under the ownership of the Rumasa conglomerate and has been the subject of a court case over its most famous brand. Wines: Pando fino-amontillado, Dry Sack amontillado, Canasta Cream, A Winter's Tale.
Augustus Barnett shops

Best buys in Sherry

FINOS AND MANZANILLAS

Waitrose Pale Dry Fino (*Waitrose*)
Garvey Fino San Patricio (*widely available*)
Montana Manzanilla, Valdespino (*Cumbrian Cellar; Sherborne Vintners*)
La Gitana Manzanilla, Hidalgo (*Lay & Wheeler; O W Loeb; Tanners Wines*)
Barbadillo Fino de Balbaina (*Corney & Barrow; Oddbins*)
Sainsbury's Manzanilla (*J Sainsbury*)

AMONTILLADOS

Harvey's 1796 Fine Old Amontillado (*Victoria Wine Co*)
Matthew Clarks's Amontillado Fino Very Old Sherry (*Champagne and Caviar Shop; Willoughbys*)
Premium Amontillado, Sanchez Romate (*Tesco*)
Tanners Very Fine Old Sanlucar Amontillado, Hidalgo (*Tanners Wines*)

OLOROSO

Apostoles, Gonzalez Byass (*Oddbins; and others*)

Find the best new wine bargains all year round with our newsletter, *Which? Wine Monthly*, available for just £15 a year from: Dept WG88, Consumers' Association, FREEPOST, Hertford SG14 1YB – no stamp is needed if posted within the UK.

MONTILLA AND MORILES

Heat and alcohol

Despite their similarity to the middle range and cheaper Sherries, these are not in fact fortified wines – they just taste like them. The heat from the sun in the vineyards right in the centre of southern Spain near Córdoba has the effect of pushing up the sugar content of the grapes to such an extent that an effortless 15 or 16 degrees of alcohol is achieved without any aid from brandy.

The word 'montilla' was borrowed by the Jerez Sherry producers and used in the description 'amontillado'. Rather unfairly, the law now forbids Montilla to use its own name in describing its wines, so they are simply labelled 'dry', 'medium' or 'cream'.

Although they don't have the sophistication of top Sherries, the Montilla wines are probably better value at the lower price and quality levels. Most of the Montilla available in the shops is own-label, so the quality varies according to the quality of the stockist.

Moriles produces slightly lighter wines than Montilla, but the style is very similar. Try the two that *Tesco* stock.

Who's who in Montilla and Moriles

Apart from the readily available own-label wines, there are two more classy examples of Montilla.

Bodegas Navarro One of the larger companies in the area. Wines: Navarro Medium, Montilla Dry Solear Especial.
Arriba Kettle

Bodegas Valenzuela Top quality wines. Wine: De Luxe Dry Montilla.
For further information contact D & D Wines (Brook House, Brook Street, Knutsford, Cheshire)

Best buys from Montilla and Moriles
Moriles Solera Fina (*Tesco*)
Montilla Dry, El Capote (*Majestic Wine Warehouses*)

MÁLAGA

Liquid sweetness

Málaga is sweet, fortified wine from the middle of the south coast to the east of Jerez. It is made from a blend of Moscatel and Pedro

Ximenez grapes. At its best, it can be complex, either a sort of cross between old tawny Port and fino Sherry or darker, very nutty and intense. It's best drunk as a dessert wine.

The top quality Málaga is known as Lagrima, simply made from the free-run juice of uncrushed grapes (as in Tokay in Hungary). Other styles are Pajarete (more of an aperitif style), a pale semi-dulce and a darker Moscatel.

Who's who in Málaga

Bodegas Barcelo Family firm making less expensive wines. Wines: Bacarles Solera Vieja, Gran Málaga (very sweet), Lagrima, Gran Vino Sanson (lighter version of Lagrima).
Peter Green; Moreno Wines

Scholtz Hermanos The great name in Málaga, making a whole range of styles. Wines: Solera Scholtz (light brown dessert wine), Seco Añejo (dry), Lagrima.
Alex Findlater; Laymont and Shaw; Majestic Wine Warehouses; Sherston Wine Company.

Best buy from Málaga

Scholtz Hermanos 10-year-old (*Laymont and Shaw*)

Specialist stockists of Spanish fortified wines

Adnams; Arriba Kettle; Cumbrian Cellar; Peter Green; Alex Findlater; Laymont and Shaw; Martinez Fine Wine; Moreno Wines; La Reserva Wines; Paul Sanderson Wines; Selfridges; Sherborne Vintners; Tanners Wines; La Vigneronne; The Wine Society

Switzerland

Swiss wines are rarely seen in this country. That's not because of their quality – which is good – but because the Swiss seem to drink most of what they produce. There must be something about all that mountain air which makes a gnome thirsty, because they manage to import vast quantities of wine as well.

Switzerland's wine production is spread right across the country. While the most famous areas (see below) are in the French-speaking areas north and east of Lake Geneva, the German north-east and the Italian south also have strong winemaking traditions.

The characteristic that binds these different traditions together – apart from the high price of the wines – is the directness of their tastes. There are few complex wines of sophistication, but the tastes are clean and very fresh. Few of the wines take any ageing – one year for the whites and rosés and two for the reds would be about right.

White wine made from the Chasselas – or Fendant – grape (which appears under different names in different cantons – see below) is the most usual taste; but the Sylvaner (here confusingly called the Johannisberger) and the rosé from Neuchâtel (called Œil de Perdrix, or partridge eye) are wines of some character.

In the reds, the most common name is Dôle, a blend of Pinot Noir and Gamay. The same blend also appears as Salvagnin.

What's what in Switzerland

Wines from three principal areas in Switzerland, all French-speaking cantons to the west of the country, are available in Britain.

Valais This canton is the home of Dôle and Fendant. Dôle, at its best, can be akin to a light Burgundy; Fendant, normally a dry white, is made from the Chasselas grape.

Valais producers whose wines are available here are: Alphonse Orsat (*Eldridge Pope; Reynier Wine Libraries*); Provins Valais (*Swiss Centre*).

Vaud The next canton west of the Valais, around the northern shore of Lake Geneva. The same wines are produced: the Pinot Noir/Gamay blend is called Salvagnin but is of a lower quality then Dôle; the Chasselas-based wine is called Dorin.

Testuz is one major producer whose wines are available here. Try the top estate white, Arbalète Dézaley Premier Cru (*Eldridge Pope/ Reynier Wine Libraries*); another, Bernard Bovy, makes a very expensive St-Saphorin la Roche aux Vignes (*Swiss Centre*).

Neuchâtel The third important Swiss production area. More red (from the Pinot Noir) than white is made here, but Chasselas white wines have a pleasant pétillance. Try the wines of Samuel Chatenay (*Eldridge Pope/Reynier Wine Libraries*); also the attractive rosé Œil de Perdrix from the Caves des Coteaux Cortaillod (*Swiss Centre*).

Other areas whose wines are seen in this country:

Ticino, the Italian area, whose Merlot is the best style (Merlot del Ticino, Cantina Sociale Mendrisio, *Swiss Centre*).

Schaffhausen in eastern Switzerland (Steiner Beeriwein Faleberg, a red from Pinot Noir, available from the *Swiss Centre*).

For other wines, there is always a selection at the *Swiss Centre, Leicester Square, London WC2.*

Specialist stockist

A L Vose

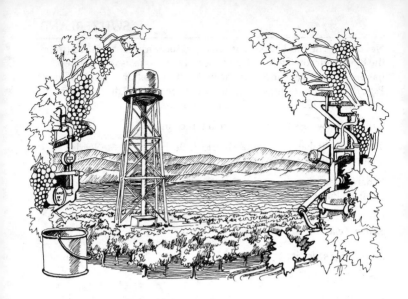

The United States

CALIFORNIA

Things move fast in California. What it took the French centuries to learn, your Californian wine producer works out in a matter of a few years.

In the last edition, we commented on the fact that the days of the huge, oak-filled mouthful of Californian wine were over, and that the new buzz words were elegance and restraint. This year a new word has joined them – blending.

California was the wine area which first perfected varietal wines. Top wineries were proud that their best wines contained 100 per cent Cabernet Sauvignon or Pinot Noir or Chardonnay. While 100 per cent Chardonnay remains (as does Pinot Noir), the lesson of Bordeaux – that Cabernet Sauvignon works better when blended with something softer like Merlot – is being applied more widely out west. So now blends are appearing which may contain 60 per cent Cabernet Sauvignon, plus Merlot, plus Cabernet Franc – just as they do in the Médoc.

But these are not copycat Bordeaux. California has gone well past the days of California Chablis or Claret. There's much more self-confidence in their ability to produce individual styles and their own high quality without referring to Europe. It's more a realisation that Europe was right about blending rather than producing 100 per cent varietals – so follow their example but develop in your own way.

Plant where you like – but will it work?

The same goes for another trend in California – choosing the appropriate site for vines. It seems strange to a European, brought up on strong links between geography and the vine, to realise that in California vines will flourish wherever they are planted. Although areas like the Napa Valley or Sonoma are considered suitable for vines, there has been surprisingly little awareness of which types of vines to plant where.

California's success seems to have been more dominated by the winemaker than the grape grower. There has been much more research into the way a wine is made than the way the grapes are grown – and where.

Until now, that is. It seems as if Californian grape growers have suddenly realised that, for example, Carneros at the southern end of the Napa Valley is good for Pinot Noir; that the southern Napa and Sonoma are better for Chardonnay than further north (because the southern end of those valleys is near cool San Francisco Bay); and conversely that the northern end of the Napa is better for Cabernet Sauvignon, and that the Salinas Valley, south of San Jose and Monterey Bay, is ideal for cooler climate grapes because it is chilled by the breezes off the Pacific Ocean.

Inevitably, the next stage is likely to be a more rigid classification of the California wine-producing areas, perhaps even some form of regulations about which vines to grow where. And if that seems to go against the grain of Californian freedom, they have just legislated about the labelling of sweet dessert wines (see below under the California label section).

Jugs to boutiques

California produces 90 per cent of all the wine made in America, and the range is vast: from the simplest of jug wines – which are, almost literally, bought from the winery by the jugful – to the finest, most serious wines created by skilled, dedicated producers in small, what the Californians call boutique, wineries.

The French – and the Italians and other European producers – have woken up to the excitement of California. Where once it was just Baron Philippe de Rothschild and his enormously expensive Opus One (made in collaboration with Robert Mondavi), now the list of companies from Europe which want a share in the California goodies is lengthening. Moët et Chandon and Bollinger are there making sparkling wine; Antinori from Italy is making his presence felt; J-P Moueix, the creator of Château Pétrus (the most expensive wine in

Bordeaux) is on site, making a fabulous wine called Dominus Cabernet; other Bordeaux and Burgundy producers are rushing out to find vineyards and wineries in which to invest.

Glut of grapes

But there are serious problems in some areas of the California wine industry. The cheaper end of the market is suffering from falling sales and a glut of grapes. It is said that as many as half California's wineries are losing money. The crisis has forced the marketing men to work fast to come up with a way of selling more wine.

They seem to have succeeded on two fronts. One is the creation of coolers – low-alcohol, fruit-flavoured wines, which appeal to younger drinkers who are probably into carbonated fruit drinks and Coca Cola. Coolers are surprisingly refreshing, not too fattening (despite the sugar in the fruit flavour) and very popular on the West Coast – and also now in Britain.

The other product that the California wine industry has created is a superb confidence trick. The major grape gluts are in red grapes, because of the general trend to drink more white wine. So if those grapes are turned into rosé or off-white wines, they, too, will surely appeal to a wider audience.

But don't call them rosé, because that term doesn't sell wine, either: call them Blush or even white Zinfandel – and they sell like hot cakes. So fast, in fact, that producers on the Loire in France, with the problem of what to do with their own rosé wines, have also started calling Rosé d'Anjou Blush and have suddenly found a market where one didn't exist before.

Don't feel the quality, look at the price

At the top quality end, though, things have never been better for us in the UK to try California wines. With the new-found elegance, the greater restraint and sophistication compared with earlier days, there are some very fine wines around.

Even if they were expensive they would be worth trying, but they're not. Prices have been pegged as much as possible for the British market, because California's producers want to see their wines being sold in the world's centre of wine. Compared with French wines of equivalent quality, they're terrific bargains. With the dollar weaker against the pound, things look even better.

The Californian label

Considering the American desire for information and facts, it's not surprising that Californian labels are generally informative and can reveal a great deal about the wine in the bottle: when the grapes were picked, how they were fermented, when the wine was bottled.

There's also a considerable amount on the front label, such as the name of the vendor of the wine: so and so's vineyard. Whether the vendor actually made the wine or just bottled it from wine made elsewhere will be identifiable from the information at the bottom of the label.

The phrases 'estate grown' or 'grown, produced and bottled by' mean that the wine has been made by the vendor from his own grapes. If 'produced and bottled by' appears, he will have bought in the grapes – no bad sign, as many winemakers prefer to leave grape growing to grape growers, as well as wanting to take advantage of the best grapes, wherever they may have been grown. If the phrases are simply 'bottled by' or 'cellared and bottled by', the vendor will have bought in the wine and just matured and bottled it.

There are now new regulations about the labelling of dessert wines, mainly those made from the Johannisberg Riesling grapes, previously described as just Late Harvest whether or not the grape had the noble rot of German Trockenbeerenauslese. Now, there are definite categories of harvesting, depending on the sugar content of the grape – following the German Prädikat (QmP) classification:

Early Harvest equals German Kabinett with a slight sweetness but no noble rot.

Late Harvest equals Auslese.

Select Late Harvest equals Beerenauslese.

Special Select Late Harvest equals Trockenbeerenauslese.

The varietal taste

Despite the interest in blended wines, most top wines in California are still labelled varietally. By law, at least 75 per cent of such a varietal wine must consist of that grape. Below that percentage the wine will be regarded as a blend and will have a brand name (and a description saying which grapes go into the wine).

White grape varieties

Chardonnay The grape variety on which much of California's reputation has been built. This used to make wines that tasted more of new wood than ripe, creamy fruit. Now they're more delicate, but still have the characteristic overtones of tropical fruits.

Sauvignon Blanc (or Fumé Blanc) A grape variety that lends itself well to the current trend for lighter, more acidic wines. Can be full of zing and freshness.

Chenin Blanc Lighter wines are beginning to bring out flavours from this often dull grape that it probably never knew it had. Good, appley acidity is a characteristic.

Johannisberg Riesling Makes wines that are fuller than their German models, so don't have the same delicate balance of acidity and sweetness. But it also produces some marvellous sweet dessert wines (see above for labelling definitions) made from grapes affected by noble rot.

Red grape varieties

Cabernet Sauvignon As much of a success story as Chardonnay in the whites. The fruit can be over-ripe and a touch sweet, but more recent wines have become drier and less heavy. They're tannic when young, but tend to mature more quickly than Cabernet Sauvignon in Bordeaux.

Pinot Noir There are signs at last that California is coming to grips with this elusive Burgundian grape variety. It needs the lighter treatment and less continuous sunshine than much of California provides. But areas like Carneros (a sub-district of the Napa Valley), with its climate affected by the fogs of San Francisco Bay, are well suited to this grape variety.

Merlot Sometimes seen as a straight varietal, when it can be dull or stunning. Best used as a part of a blended wine.

Petit Syrah Makes rather coarse wines which rely on strength rather than character.

Zinfandel California's native grape variety, producing wines that range from the early-maturing (rather like Beaujolais) to the rich, ripe, peppery. Now also used as the basis for the Blush or White Zinfandel wines. An exciting grape that we should learn to appreciate more.

California vintages

1986 California became very excited about this vintage and although enthusiasm has tempered a little, it still looks very good. A cool summer gave a very long ripening period which was good for white grapes if less so for reds (apart from Pinot Noir). Some whites are now arriving, but we will have to wait for the reds.

1985 An outstanding vintage, with low yields and very concentrated grapes after low rainfall. White wines are on the full side, but the concentration has helped the reds to produce some powerful wines.

1984 Whites are on the light, fresh side and are very drinkable at the moment. Reds from this vintage are here now, and they, too, are becoming approachable.

1983 Elegant, restrained whites which will last a while yet. Pinot Noir reds are available and are some of the best yet from that grape variety. Other reds will keep for a few years.

1982 The whites are now well matured, some past their best. Chardonnays will still keep. The Cabernet Sauvignons are now mature, although they will get even better in 1988. Pinot Noir and Zinfandels are mature.

1981 All the whites should be drunk now – except Chardonnays, which are still very good. Reds, too, are approaching a decline.

1980 Whites should have been drunk, except for top Chardonnay, but reds will continue to mature, especially Cabernet Sauvignons.

1978 Drink up the Cabernet Sauvignons and Chardonnays. Other wines will probably be quite old. Some top wines will continue to improve.

1977 and before Only top Cabernet Sauvignons from 1974, 1973, 1971 and 1970 are likely to last. Other wines should be approached with caution – if you find any, that is.

Where's where in California

As vineyards in California mature, so different areas emerge as good at different wine styles. Certain areas produce outstanding wines, others are better at jug wines. California is slowly getting round to organising a geographical appellation system. For the time being, here are some areas whose wines seem to have consistency and quality.

Mendocino County The northernmost wine-growing region. Sub-regions are Anderson Valley, Ukiah Valley, Potter and Redwood Valleys.

Monterey County A cool area inland from Monterey Bay. Sub-regions are Arroyo Secco, Carmel Valley, Greenfield, The Pinnacles, Salinas Valley.

Napa Valley The biggest quality wine area. Sub-regions include Calistoga, Carneros, Chiles Valley, Stag's Leap, Silverado Trail, Pope Valley, Mount Veeder, Yountville, Oakville, St Helena and Spring Mountain, Rutherford Bench.

San Joaquin The Central Valley, which produces large quantities of jug wines from the biggest vineyard area in California.

San Luis Obispo Up-and-coming area. Sub-regions include Paso Robles, Edna Valley, Shandon.

Santa Barbara To the north of Los Angeles. Sub-regions are Santa Maria and Santa Ynez.

Santa Clara Vineyard area south of San Francisco. Sub-regions are Hecker Pass and Santa Cruz.

Sonoma County between Napa and the ocean north of San Francisco, and approaching Napa in fame and quality. Sub-regions are: Sonoma Valley, Kenwood, Russian River Valley, Dry Creek, Alexander Valley, Knight's Valley.

Who's who in California

Acacia In Carneros, Napa Valley. Has only been making wine for nine years, but already the quality is high. Wines: Chardonnay, Pinot Noir.
Les Amis du Vin (Pinot Noir); Bibendum; Alex Findlater (Chardonnay); Ostlers; Whynot Wine Warehouses (Pinot Noir)

Almadén Range of standard varietals from one of the largest California producers. Wines: Chardonnay, Chenin Blanc, Cabernet Sauvignon, Zinfandel.
Bentalls of Kingston, Surrey; Chaplin & Son; Gerry's Wines and Spirits (74 Old Compton Street, London W1); White Hart Liquor Store (115 White Hart Lane, London SW13)

Beaulieu One of the pioneering wineries of the Napa Valley. Still makes very fine wines. Wines: Chardonnay, Pinot Noir, Cabernet Sauvignon (top wine is called Georges de Latour Private Reserve Cabernet – pricey but outstanding).
Tylers (6/7 Motcomb Street, London SW1); La Vigneronne

Beringer Vineyards Medium-sized producer of sound varietals but no excitement. Wines: Chardonnay, Cabernet Sauvignon, Fumé Blanc, Riesling.
Victoria Wine Co

Buena Vista Sonoma winery under German ownership. Wines: Fumé Blanc, Zinfandel, Spiceling (an atrociously named blend of Riesling and Gewürztraminer).
Les Amis du Vin

Calera Small winery inland from the Salinas Valley. Very good Pinot Noir. Wines: Jensen Vineyard Pinot Noir, Zinfandel.
Adnams; La Vigneronne

Chalone Vineyards Another winery that has made top-class Pinot Noir, also Chardonnay. Wines: Chardonnay, Pinot Blanc, Pinot Noir.
Adnams; Les Amis du Vin; La Vigneronne

Ch Montelena Small producer making superb (and expensive) Chardonnay and Cabernet Sauvignon in Calistoga, Napa. Wines: Chardonnay, Cabernet Sauvignon.
Les Amis du Vin; Ostlers

Ch St Jean White wine producer specialising in noble-rot Rieslings.
Wines: Robert Young Vineyard Chardonnay, Riesling.
Eldridge Pope; La Vigneronne

Clos du Bois Northern Sonoma producer with vineyards in Alexander
Valley and Dry Creek, making very good Merlot and Chardonnay.
Wines: Sauvignon Blanc, Chardonnay, Pinot Noir, Cabernet
Sauvignon, Merlot.
*Les Amis du Vin; Peter Dominic; Majestic Wine Warehouses; Oddbins; La
Vigneronne*

Clos du Val Wines made by a Frenchman whose father was manager
of Ch Lafite in Bordeaux. The influence shows, even in the Burgundian
Pinot Noir. Wines: Merlot, Chardonnay, Zinfandel, Pinot Noir,
Cabernet Sauvignon.
Alex Findlater; Ostlers; Reid Wines

Conn Creek Elegant Cabernet Sauvignons from this St Helena, Napa
winery. Wines: Chardonnay, Zinfandel, Cabernet Sauvignon.
Lay & Wheeler; Windrush Wines

Cuvaison Top quality producer in the Napa Valley. Wines: Cabernet
Sauvignon, Chardonnay, Zinfandel.
Barnes Wine Shop; Anthony Byrne Fine Wines; Ostlers; Windrush Wines

Diamond Creek Minute quantities of top-class single vineyard
Cabernet Sauvignons in the Napa Valley.
Windrush Wines

Dry Creek Vineyards Good whites, especially the Fumé Blanc. Wines:
Fumé Blanc, Chenin Blanc.
Les Amis du Vin

Edna Valley Vineyards Producer of rich, full-flavoured Chardonnay.
Les Amis du Vin; La Vigneronne

Fetzer Vineyards Good, middle-range wines, especially blended
wines. Good value too. Wines: Premium red and white, Cabernet
Sauvignon, Chardonnay.
Alex Findlater; Majestic Wine Warehouses; Ostlers; Wizard Wines

Firestone Vineyard Famous for its big, rich wines from the Santa Ynez
Valley. Wines: Chardonnay, Cabernet Sauvignon, Merlot.
*Les Amis du Vin; Peter Dominic; Alex Findlater; Ostlers; J Sainsbury;
La Vigneronne; Whynot Wine Warehouses*

Freemark Abbey Well-established producer of expensive, high quality
Cabernet Sauvignon and Chardonnay.
La Vigneronne

Grgich Hills Cellar Big wines from Rutherford, Napa. Wines: Chardonnay, Fumé Blanc.
Eldridge Pope

Hanzell Vineyards Old-established winery in Sonoma which has now a high reputation, particularly for its Pinot Noir. Wines: Chardonnay, Pinot Noir.
Windrush Wines

Heitz Wine Cellars Famous small producer of top quality single vineyard wines. Wines: Martha's Vineyard Cabernet, Bella Oaks Cabernet, Chardonnay.
Les Amis du Vin; Bibendum; La Vigneronne

Iron Horse Light, often austere wines from Sonoma. Wines: Cabernet Sauvignon, Chardonnay.
Les Amis du Vin

Jekel Vineyard Monterey County winery with vineyards in Arroyo Secco. Wines: Cabernet Sauvignon, Riesling.
Bordeaux Direct; Alex Findlater

Jordan Winery Expensive winery making expensive Cabernet Sauvignon (blended with Merlot) and Chardonnay.
Curzon Wine Company; Peter Green; Lay & Wheeler

Paul Masson Bulk producer of the carafe wines whose containers now house more cut flowers than any other wine bottle. Wines: Varietal wines under the Pinnacles name, as well as the red, white and rosé carafes.
Peter Dominic; Oddbins

Mayacamas Vineyards Tiny producer in the Napa of top quality Chardonnay and Cabernet Sauvignon. They need ageing for a long time. Wines: Chardonnay, Cabernet Sauvignon.
La Vigneronne

Robert Mondavi Winery Often described as the guru of Californian winemaking, Robert Mondavi and his family make some of the best, most reliable wines in the State. Co-producer of the expensive Opus One with Philippe de Rothschild of Bordeaux. What Mondavi does this year, others follow next. Wines: Fumé Blanc, Chardonnay, Cabernet Sauvignon, Riesling.
Adnams; Les Amis du Vin; Peter Dominic; Alex Findlater; Majestic Wine Warehouses; Oddbins; La Vigneronne

The Monterey Vineyard Part of the Seagram empire which also owns Paul Masson. Make a range of inexpensive blended wines. Wines: Classic brand range of wines.
Rodney Densem Wines; Alex Findlater; Harrods; Kershaw's Wine Warehouse; Selfridges

Monticello Cellars Southern Napa producer of distinguished Chardonnay. The winery house is modelled on Jefferson's house in Virginia.
Oddbins; Ostlers; La Vigneronne

Joseph Phelps Vineyard Reliable wines from most varietals, many to a very high standard, particularly Chardonnay. Wines: Riesling, Gewürztraminer, Chardonnay, Cabernet Sauvignon.
Adnams; Les Amis du Vin

Ridge Vineyards Single vineyard wines from Santa Cruz, with a reputation for longevity. Wines: Zinfandel, Cabernet Sauvignon, Montebello Cabernet (high reputation, but scarce).
Adnams; Bibendum; Peter Green; La Vigneronne

Schramsberg Vineyards Napa Valley producer of top quality (and expensive) sparkling wines made by the Champagne method. Wines: Blanc de Blancs, Blanc de Noirs.
Les Amis du Vin; La Vigneronne

Simi Winery Small winery in Sonoma making some superb Chardonnay. Wines: Sauvignon, Alexander Valley Chardonnay.
Corney & Barrow

Stag's Leap Wine Cellars Small producer of top quality Chardonnay and Cabernet Sauvignon. Worth the high price. Make a second wine – in the style of Bordeaux châteaux – called Hawk Crest. Wines: Chardonnay, Cabernet Sauvignon, Merlot.
Lay & Wheeler; Windrush Wines

Stelzner Napa Valley producer of complex Cabernet Sauvignon.
Great American Wine Co; Ostlers; Wizard Wines

Sterling Vineyard Another part of the Seagram empire, with a spectacular winery in the northern Napa Valley. Wines: Diamond Mountain Ranch wines; Cabernet Sauvignon.
For further information contact De Ville & Co (17 Dacre Street, London SW1)

Tjisseling Dutch-owned winery in Mendocino, making wines in a full, open style. Wines: Chardonnay, Cabernet Sauvignon.
Alex Findlater; Ostlers; Wizard Wines

Trefethen Vineyards Good value wines of high quality. The blended wines are very reliable. Wines: Chardonnay, Pinot Noir, Cabernet Sauvignon, Eshcol branded wine (red and white).
Adnams; Les Amis du Vin; Alex Findlater; Oddbins; La Vigneronne

Wente Brothers Large-scale producer of middle-range wines. Good, reliable quality, with some good, aged Zinfandels. Wines: Sauvignon Blanc, Chardonnay, Riesling, Cabernet Sauvignon, Zinfandel.
Connolly's; Davisons; Peter Green

Mark West Vineyards Elegant, light wines from the Russian River Valley. Wines: Chardonnay, late harvest Riesling.
Les Amis du Vin; La Vigneronne

ZD Wines Good quality wines made from grapes bought in from other vineyards. Wines: Chardonnay, Pinot Noir.
Barnes Wine Shop; Great American Wine Co; Ostlers; Wizard Wines

Best buys from California

WHITE WINES

Fetzer Premium White (*Ostlers*)
Geoffrey Roberts California White (*Les Amis du Vin; Cullens*)
Clos du Bois Chardonnay 1985 (*D Byrne; Peter Dominic; Oddbins*)
Robert Mondavi Fumé Blanc 1984 (*Peter Dominic; Oddbins*)

RED WINES

Zinfandel 1980, Wente Brothers (*Rodney Densem Wines; Matthew Gloag & Son*)
Fetzer North Coast Zinfandel 1984 (*Waitrose*)
Firestone Merlot 1983 (*Majestic Wine Warehouses; J Sainsbury*)
Fetzer Premium Red (*Great American Food and Wine; Ostlers*)
Geoffrey Roberts California Red (*Les Amis du Vin; Cullens*)
Eschcol Red (*Les Amis du Vin; La Vigneronne*)

Specialist stockists

Adnams; Les Amis du Vin; Barnes Wine Shop; Farthinghoe Fine Wine and Food; Great American Food and Wine; Ostlers; Reid Wines; Selfridges; T & W Wines; La Vigneronne; Windrush Wines

NEW YORK STATE

Still only a few wines from New York State are available here. Well-made, flavoursome and with higher acidity than most West Coast whites, the Chardonnay is particularly good. The sparkling wine is more interesting than outstanding.

Best buys from New York State

Gold Seal Chardonnay 1982
Gold Seal Blanc de Blancs NV
Both available from: Great American Wine Co; Ostlers; Wizard Wines

California and North–West U.S.A.

NORTH-WEST USA

Every year, new developments bring more and more exciting wines from the Pacific North-West States of Oregon and Washington, with some interesting sniffs from Idaho.

This is the wine production region which has the greatest natural chance of achieving the light, elegant sophisticated wines that California is now making with the aid of modern technology. It is the cool climate grape varieties which respond to a slow ripening season and aren't affected by the Pacific fogs and breezes that have the greatest potential. The area has been especially successful in making some outstanding Pinot Noir (probably the best Pinot Noir wines outside Burgundy). Light Chardonnays are also very good.

The wines from the North-West have – like those from California – become very good value for money as prices have been held, the dollar has swung in their favour and Burgundy has rocketed in price. Prices are not cheap, though, since they come from relatively small production areas and are available only in limited quantities in this country, but they are well worth searching out.

The taste of the North-West

As with California, varietal wines are the principal quality wines. But here, the wine must contain 90 per cent of that variety (although Cabernet Sauvignon needs only 75 per cent, to encourage a 'Bordeaux' blend with Merlot and Cabernet Franc).

The principal Oregon regions are Willamette Valley, Umpqua Valley and Rogue Valley. Neither Washington nor Idaho has area designations yet.

Pinot Noir This is the flagship grape of the North-West. Pale in colour, the wines have a complexity of flavours and a perfumed aroma combined with relatively low alcohol.

Chardonnay Low alcohol and quite high acidity again make very sophisticated wines at their best, but quality can be variable. Oregon makes the best Chardonnays.

Gewürztraminer Much more successful than in California, producing some fine, dry wines and a few late-harvest sweet wines in Idaho.

Cabernet and Merlot Some fine wines from Washington. Not successful in the cooler climate of Oregon.

Who's who in the North-West

OREGON

Alpine Vineyards Family-owned vineyard in Willamette Valley, making small quantities of wine. Wines: Chardonnay, Pinot Noir, Riesling.

The Eyrie Vineyards Pioneer Oregon vineyard that has won medals in France for its Pinot Noir. Wines: Pinot Gris, Pinot Noir.

Elk Cove Small-scale family business making delicious Pinot Noir. Wines: Chardonnay, Riesling, Pinot Noir.

Knudsen Erath Oregon's largest producer, also making sparkling wine. Wine: Pinot Noir.

Tualatin Top quality Chardonnay and consistent Pinot Noir.

All these wines from Oregon are available from Windrush Wines, except those from Knudsen Erath, which are stocked by Ostlers and Wizard Wines.

WASHINGTON STATE

Columbia Formerly known as Associated Vintners, this has a high reputation for white wines. Wines: Gewürztraminer, Chardonnay, Cabernet Sauvignon.

Snoqualmie Unpronounceable winery making good whites, especially the Semillon.

IDAHO

Louis Facelli Elegant Chardonnay from a new winery.

Ste Chapelle Largest producer in the State, with good Riesling, Gewürztraminer and top Chardonnay.

The stockist for all these wines from Washington State and Idaho is Windrush Wines.

Best buys from the North-West

WHITES
Chardonnay 1983, Tualatin (*Windrush Wines*)
Pinot Gris 1984, The Eyrie Vineyards (*Windrush Wines*)

RED
Pinot Noir 1983, Tualatin (*Windrush Wines*)

Specialist stockists
Askham Wines; Curzon Wine Co; Great American Food and Wine; Peter Green; Windrush Wines

USSR

When the Beatles wrote 'Back in the USSR' they probably weren't thinking of Soviet wine. But back in the USSR is really the only place where this wine is suitably drunk. Wine consumption is being encouraged by the Soviet government as a way of cutting down vodka consumption. What they seem to like there is anything – red, white, sparkling – as long as it's sweet.

Pockets of good winemaking exist in this, the third largest producer of wine in the world. Georgian wine is reputed to be excellent. In Britain, the best place to find examples of these products is at the *Russian Shop, 278 High Holborn, London WC1.*

Yugoslavia

Yugoslavia doesn't just make Laski Riesling, although we would be forgiven for thinking so, because that's the only Yugoslav wine with any wide distribution.

No, she makes much better, more individual wines than that. A few years ago, a tasting in London displayed to an awed audience 80 Yugoslav wines, most of them in theory available here, and – apart from each shipper's Laski Riesling – almost unknown.

They still remain unknown. A few firms take the trouble to import a range of wines from Yugoslavia and they do have limited distribution. But it is reckoned that nearly 95 per cent of all Yugoslav wine that gets brought into this country is Laski Riesling.

As an alternative to Liebfraumilch – which is how it has been billed – it really doesn't seem to have much going for it. The sugar-water fruitiness of the German wine at its worst is preferable to the flabby, coarse, often over-sulphured wine that comes from the Laski Riesling grape. Alarmingly, the Laski Rieslings have now been joined by a sweet red wine called Amselfelder.

To more cheerful thoughts: it is worth rewarding the efforts of the brave few who are bringing us some good Yugoslav wines. As elsewhere in Eastern Europe, French grape varieties have made inroads into Yugoslav vineyards: Cabernet Sauvignon, Merlot, Pinot

Noir, Sauvignon, Gewürztraminer. The Cabernet Sauvignon is less successful than it is in Bulgaria, but the Merlot makes some very good wines.

White wines made in Slovenia from the Sauvignon, the Gewürztraminer and the Rhine Riesling (as distinct from the Laski) are lively with good, fresh acidity, reminiscent in a somewhat coarser way of the Italian Alto Adige. They tend sometimes to be softened and sweetened for the UK market (as in Grants of St James's varietals) – which is a pity.

Of native Yugoslav varieties, the most famous and interesting are the red wines made from the Vranac grape (the word means 'black stallion') in Montenegro – rich, robust and dark in colour (this wine will improve with some ageing). The white Zilavka from Herzegovina is a steely dry wine.

What's what in Yugoslavia

The Yugoslav label has some terms which may be unfamiliar as well as the names of French grape varieties.

Beli Burgundec The Pinot Blanc grape.

Fruška Gora Quality white wine area of Serbia.

Faros A red wine from Hvar, with high acidity but a soft, slightly sweet finish.

Gamé The Gamay grape.

Modri Burgundec The Pinot Noir grape.

Strem (Stremski Karlovci) Formerly called Carlowitz, this area once famous for reds now makes some good whites as well. Traminer and Sauvignon are worth looking out for.

Best buys from Yugoslavia
Milion Merlot (red) (*Old Compton Wines, 64 Old Compton Street, London W1; Waitrose*)
Montenegro Vranac (red) (*Old Compton Wines*)

Specialist stockist of Yugoslav wines
The Wine Spot

Zimbabwe

Old Southern Rhodesia hands will know that there has been a small wine industry in the land for many years. And now a small selection of the wines has arrived in Britain. They are possibly more of a curiosity than something to rush out to buy, but the quality is very acceptable – and you could certainly put the wines in blind tastings with devastating effect.

Who's who in Zimbabwe

Flame Lily Brand name for wines from Philips Central Cellars of Harare. Wines: Dry white, Medium white, Premium white and red. *For further information contact Vinceremos (see WHERE TO BUY section).*

Specialist stockist

Vinceremos

Sparkling wines

Here we give a recommended selection of the main styles of sparkling wines available in Britain. The vast majority of these wines are made in the same way as Champagne with the second fermentation in the bottle in which the wine is eventually sold: the only exceptions are sweeter wines like the Italian spumantes and some from southern France.

AUSTRALIA

Early endeavours in top quality sparkling winemaking are encouraging:
Hardy's Grand Reserve, from South Australia (*H Allen Smith*)
Yellowglen Brut, from Victoria (*Ostlers*)
Rosemount Chardonnay Brut, from New South Wales (*Premier Wine Warehouse; Sherston Wine Company*)
Seaview Brut and Grande Cuvée, from South Australia (*Oddbins*)

FRANCE

Details of **Champagne** will be found separately on page 359.

ALSACE

Alsace's sparkling wines are called Crémant d'Alsace. Unlike Champagne, where the term Crémant means a lower pressure and hence fewer bubbles, in Alsace it simply means a straightforward Champagne method sparkling wine. The wines are good and not cheap.

Who's who in Alsace

Crémant d'Alsace, Dopff et Irion Cuvée Extra (*Eldridge Pope; Hungerford Wine Company*)
Crémant d'Alsace, Dopff au Moulin (*Lay & Wheeler*)

Crémant d'Alsace, Louis Gisselbrecht (*Christopher Piper Wines*)
Crémant d'Alsace Rosé, René Schmidt (*Ellis Son & Vidler*)
Crémant d'Alsace, Marc Kreydenweiss (*La Vigneronne*)
Crémant d'Alsace, Wolfberger Cuvée (Eguisheim Co-operative)
(*Wines from Paris*)

BLANQUETTE DE LIMOUX

With a claim to have been sparkling even before Champagne, these are some of the most attractive and enjoyable sparkling wines that France produces. They come from the South-West near Carcassonne and all the brands available are dry.

Who's who in Blanquette de Limoux

Blanquette de Limoux, Cuvée Alderic (*Ellis Son & Vidler; Matthew Gloag & Son*)
Blanquette de Limoux, Fleur de Lys (*Christopher & Co; Waitrose*)
Blanquette de Limoux, Domaine de Treilhes (*Wine Growers Association*)
Blanquette de Limoux, Ets Salasar (*Hungerford Wine Company; Morris & Verdin*)

BURGUNDY

Burgundy seems an unlikely source of sparkling wine when everything they can produce would seem allotted to the still wine vats. But Aligoté and Gamay grapes make good sparklers which go under the name either of Bourgogne Mousseux or, better, Crémant de Bourgogne.

Who's who in Burgundy

WHITE

Crémant de Bourgogne, Caves de Bailly (*Majestic Wine Warehouses*)
Crémant de Bourgogne, Chandesais (*Eldridge Pope/Reynier Wine Libraries*)
Paul Robin Blanc de Blancs (*Tanners Wines*)
Crémant de Bourgogne Blanc de Blancs, Caves des Vignerons de Mancey (*La Vigneronne*)
Blanc de Blancs, Dominique Charnay (*Windrush Wines*)
St Michael Sparkling Burgundy (*Marks & Spencer*)

RED AND ROSÉ

Crémant de Bourgogne Rosé, Bailly (*Majestic Wine Warehouses; Waitrose*)
Chanson Père et Fils, Red (*Tanners Wines*)
Prosper Maufoux, Red (*Harrods*)

SAUMUR

The major source of sparkling wine on the Loire is the town of Saumur, whose cellars carved out of chalk cliffs are reminiscent of Champagne – so reminiscent, in fact, that many Champagne houses have bought up companies in Saumur. Quality is high, even if some of the wines lack great individuality. Wines labelled Crémant will have followed more stringent rules of production. Rosés wines are made as well as Blanc de Blancs.

Who's who in Saumur

La Grande Marque (*Adnams; Tanners Wines*)
Bouvet-Ladubay (*Davisons; Whynot Wine Warehouses*)
Gratien et Meyer (*Peter Dominic*)
Langlois Château (*Alex Findlater; Oddbins; André Simon Wines*)
De Neuville (*Eldridge Pope*)
Veuve Amiot (*Threshers*)
Sainsbury's Sparkling Saumur
Tesco's Sparkling Saumur

VOUVRAY AND MONTLOUIS

Further up the Loire, the town of Vouvray also has a tradition of sparkling wine production – again in cellars carved out of chalk. Wines tend to be fuller than in Saumur, and some producers also make a medium sweet style. On the southern banks of the Loire, opposite Vouvray, Montlouis produces sparkling wines in a similar style.

Who's who in Vouvray

Aigle d'Or, Prince Poniatowski (*Hungerford Wine Company; La Vigneronne*)
Marc Brédif (*Oddbins*)
Foreau Clos Naudin (*O W Loeb*)
Huet Brut (*Averys; The Wine Society*)
Daniel Jarry (*Yapp Brothers*)
Prince Poniatowski (*La Vigneronne*)
Roger Félicien Brou (*Majestic Wine Warehouses*)

Who's who in Montlouis

Berger Brut and Demi-Sec (*Lay & Wheeler; Yapp Brothers*).

OTHER FRENCH SPARKLING WINES

Clairette de Die Tradition: a sweet Muscat-based sparkler from the Alps (*Waitrose*)
Clairette de Die Tradition Demi-Sec, Archard-Vincent (*Yapp Brothers*)
Brut de Listel: simple straightforward sparkling wine (*Rodney Densem Wines; Ellis Son & Vidler; Matthew Gloag & Son; Kershaw's Wine Warehouse; C A Rookes*)
Varichon et Clerc Blanc de Blancs, produced in Seyssel in Savoy (*Harrods; Waitrose*)
Vin de Bugey Blanc de Blancs, made east of Lyons (*The Wine Society*)
Vin Sauvage Brut, made in Gascony in the Armagnac country (*Bibendum*)
Diane de Poitiers, Chardonnay Brut, made in Haut-Poitou (*Adnams*)
Diane de Poitiers, Chardonnay Blanc de Blancs (*Stapylton Fletcher*)
Crémant de Loire, Gratien & Meyer (*Peter Dominic*)
Crémant de Loire, Marcel Neau (*Majestic Wine Warehouses*)
Blanc Foussy de Touraine (*Victoria Wine Co*)
Ryman Brut, made at Ch de la Jaubertie in Bergerac (*Wines from Paris*)

GERMANY

The best German sparklers are made from the Riesling grape. Regulations which came into force in early 1986 stipulate that all sparkling wine labelled Deutscher Sekt will now consist of German wine as well as German bubbles (only the bubbles needed to be German before then). Any wine labelled simply Sekt will consist of Italian or French wine or a blend plus German air.

Who's who in Germany

Deinhard Lila Imperial (*Eaton Elliot Winebrokers*)
Deinhard Sparkling Mosel (*Gerard Harris*)
Schloss Vollrads Sekt (*Eldridge Pope*)
Burgeff Rheingau Riesling (*Oddbins*)

The duty-free allowance for wine obtained in the EEC is 5 litres of still table wine per person *plus* 3 litres of still table wine *or* 3 litres of fortified/sparkling wine *or* 1½ litres of spirits or liqueurs. (See also page 584.)

INDIA

Some surprisingly good sparkling wine – if expensive – is made in
Maharashtra State, near Bombay.
Omar Khayyam (*Adnams*)

ITALY

The most familiar sparkling wine from Italy is sweet and based on the
Moscato grape. It appears under the name Asti Spumante or the
slightly cheaper but often better quality Moscato d'Asti or Moscato
Spumante. It needs to be very fresh and young to give its delicious
honey and fruit taste.

Italy is also making more serious dry sparkling wines, some of very
high quality. Some use the classic Champagne blend of Pinot Noir and
Chardonnay, others go for local grapes like Prosecco from the Veneto.

For details of Lambrusco, see page 454.

Who's who in Italian sparkling wines

ASTI SPUMANTE AND MOSCATO SPARKLERS

Gancia Spumante (*Davisons; Peter Dominic; J E Hogg*)
St Michael Asti Spumante (*Marks & Spencer*)
Asti Spumante Martini (*Chaplin & Son; Gerard Harris; Tanners Wines*)
Asti Spumante Fontanafredda (*Seymour Ramsey; La Vigneronne*)
Asti Spumante Calamandrina (*Wine Growers Association*)
Asti Spumante, Cinzano (*Peter Dominic*)
Cora Asti Spumante (*G Belloni, 128 Albert Street, London NW1*)
Gallo d'Oro, Duca d'Asti (*Eaton Elliot Winebrokers; Waitrose*)
St Michael Moscato Frizzante (fewer bubbles than standard Spumante)
(*Marks & Spencer*)

DRY SPARKLING WINES

Arunda Extra Brut (*H Allen Smith*)
Brut Pinot Oltrepò Pavese, Villa Banfi (*George Hill of Loughborough;
Ostlers*)
Ca' del Bosco, Franciacorta (*The Market/Winecellars; Ostlers*)
Contessa Rosa Fontanafredda (*Augustus Barnett; The Market/Winecellars*)
Ferrari Gran Spumante Brut (also rosé) (*Wine Growers Association*)
Frescobaldi Brut (*Christopher & Co*)
Pinot di Pinot, Gancia (*Cesari Wines & Spirits, 97–99 Westminster Bridge
Road, London SE1; Chiswick Wine Cellar; Valvona & Crolla*)

Prosecco Spumante Venegazzù (*Augustus Barnett; Italian Continental Stores, 42 Vicarage Road, Maidenhead, Berks; Majestic Wine Warehouses; Whynot Wine Warehouses*)
Santa Sofia Brut (*Eaton Elliot Winebrokers*)

LUXEMBOURG

Luxembourg's small wine industry produces some good, Champagne method sparklers.
Bernard Massard (*Eldridge Pope*)

SPAIN

The generic name of Champagne method sparkling wines is cava. The centre of production is in Catalonia in the Penedès area west of Barcelona. The taste is peppery and quite full, and the wines need to be drunk young or the fruit tends to fade. They actually work better with food than without.

Who's who in Spain

Castellblanch Brut Zero (*Waitrose*)
Cavas Mestres (*Laymont and Shaw*)
Codorníu Premier Cuvée (*Victoria Wine Co*)
Freixenet Cordon Negro (*André Simon Wines; Tanners Wines; Whynot Wine Warehouses*)
Sainsbury's Spanish Cava
Tesco Cava
Delamonte Brut, Cava (*H Allen Smith*)
Cavas Manuel Sancho, Mont Marçal (*Arriba Kettle*)
Raimat Chardonnay (*Victoria Wine Co*)

The Wine Development Board is a small organisation with the responsibility of encouraging more people to drink wine. They may be able to supply literature and general promotional material. Contact them at: Five Kings House, Kennet Wharf Lane, Upper Thames Street, London EC4V 3BH; TEL 01-248 5835.

USA

Of the many American sparkling wines, few are available here. Some are cheap and reasonably cheerful, one is pricier than most standard Champagnes. All, except one, come from California.

Who's who in American sparklers

Domaine Chandon, the California arm of the giant Moët et Chandon Champagne house – some critics say they make better wine than the French (*Adnams*)

Paul Masson Brut (*Safeway*)

Schramsberg Blanc de Blancs and Blanc de Noirs (*Adnams; Les Amis du Vin; La Vigneronne*)

Iron Horse (*Les Amis du Vin*)

Gold Seal, New York State (*Great American Wine Company*)

Organic wines

Most of today's wine producers use a bewildering array of chemical treatments in the vineyard and the winery. Each year, in the cause of agriculture, 1lb of pure chemical substance is deliberately applied to the surface of the planet for each human being on it – most of it in the western nations. During every growing season, a vine can receive as many as 12–14 applications of herbicides, fungicides and pesticides, depending on the position of the vineyard and the climatic conditions.

In the winery, another 20 additives are permitted to improve the taste, colour and clarity. The absence of any information about these chemicals and additives on the labels of bottles means that consumers have no idea what – apart from grapes – was used in making the wine inside. The scandals in Austria, Germany and Italy have shown what can happen when chemicals finally take over from the produce of the vine.

Against this background, producers in France, Germany, Italy and England have gone back to basics. They are producing what in the UK are called organic wines. In France, where they call them 'vins biologiques', production is organised according either to the Lemaire-Boucher system or to the rules of the Fédération Européenne des Syndicats d'Agrobiologistes. Both organisations foster a general philosophy of production backed up by a strictly enforced régime of regulations.

What organic means is that the emphasis is transferred from the use of chemical assistance back to good husbandry and the choice of natural fertilisers to help regulate the equilibrium of the soil. In the vineyard, grapes are left undoused by fungicide sprays. This allows the grape's natural yeasts to be used in fermentation rather than the artificial yeasts needed if the grapes have been sprayed with chemicals. In the winery, although sulphur can still be added to keep the wine clean and free from disease, its use is carefully regulated and amounts are well below EEC regulations. Other chemicals and additives are not used. Filtration of the wine is minimal, so you can expect more sediment in an organic wine than in a conventional one.

Many of the producers of organic wines are small estates, where the wines can be more or less hand-made. But that is not an essential to the production of these wines. The largest vineyard in France, that of Listel in the Salins du Midi, is run on organic lines, as are the big Rhône estates of Ch de Beaucastel and La Vieille Ferme. In the Muscadet region, Alsace and Bordeaux many estates produce organic wines – about 150 in all.

Outside France, producers using organic methods include the Pagliarese and Castellare estates in Tuscany; the Fugazza sisters in Lombardy (Oltrepò Pavese and Gutturnio); and Guerrieri-Rizzardi in the Veneto, as well as Tiefenbrunner in the Alto Adige.

In Germany, although some producers do use organic methods, their wines are still rather primitive and not seen outside their immediate locality. In England, the Avalon vineyard in Somerset makes organic wines.

Proponents of organic wines say that their products taste more natural. They show themselves more directly, come clearer into focus, taste richer and more complex. Of course, just as the virtues appear more clearly, so the warts cannot be hidden either, and some bad organic wines (none of those available in the UK) sell simply because they are biologically produced.

The people who produce organic wines prefer not to take the risks associated with the headlong use of concentrations made possible by chemical sophistication. They keep control of things, ensuring that their products are safe and often more individualistic, complete and tasty. After all, super-refinement in food products is no longer as positively regarded as it once was; organic wines are the vinous counterpart to Real Food.

Below we list merchants whose entries appear in the WHERE TO BUY section and who stock at least some organically produced wines. Those firms specialising entirely in organic wines are indicated with an 'O'.

Addison Avenue Wine Shop
Adnams
Les Amis du Vin
BH Wines
Bibendum
Bin 89 Wine Warehouse
Les Bons Vins Occitans (O)
Bordeaux Direct
Anthony Byrne Fine Wines
Cachet Wines
Champagne de Villages
Chaplin & Sons
Continental Wine House
Rodney Densem Wines
CCG Edwards (O)
GM Vintners
Goedhuis & Company
Le Gourmet Gascon (O)
Great Northern Wine Company
Peter Green
Gerard Harris
George Hill of Loughborough

Ian G Howe
Jeroboams
Kershaw's Wine Warehouse
Kurtz & Chan Wines
Marske Mill House
Martinez Fine Wine
Morris & Verdin
Le Nez Rouge/Berkmann Wine Cellars
Ostlers
Oxford & Cambridge Fine Wine Co
Peatling & Cawdron
Stephen Porter Wines
Arthur Rackhams
Raeburn Fine Wines and Foods
Rattlers Wine Warehouse
C A Rookes
Sebastopol Wines
Edward Sheldon
André Simon
Sookias & Bertaut
Tanners Wines
Taste Shops

House of Townend
Helen Verdcourt Wines
Vinceremos
La Vigneronne
Vintage Roots (O)
The Wine Case Place

The Wine Schoppen
The Wine Spot
Wines Galore
Wines from Paris
Yapp Brothers
Yorkshire Fine Wines

Pudding wines

Merchants with a particularly wide range of sweet dessert wines include:

Barnes Wine Shop
Bowlish House Wine Shop
Curzon Wine Co
Eldridge Pope
Corney & Barrow
Farthinghoe Fine Wine and Food
Alex Findlater
Andrew Gordon Wines
Peter Green
Gerard Harris

J E Hogg
Hungerford Wine Company
Nobody Inn
Raeburn Fine Wines and Foods
Edward Sheldon
Tanners Wines
Henry Townsend
La Vigneronne
Peter Wylie Fine Wines

Old and rare wines

Specialist stockists include:

Barts Cellars
Eldridge Pope
Ben Ellis & Associates
Farr Vintners
Fine Vintage Wines
Hungerford Wine Company
Justerini & Brooks
Kurtz & Chan Wines

Nickolls & Perks
Reid Wines
La Réserve/College Cellar
Stones of Belgravia
T & W Wines
Philip Tite Fine Wines
La Vigneronne
Peter Wylie Fine Wines

Special bottle sizes

Half-bottles

Although you may find odd half-bottles at many merchants, the following stockists make a point of carrying a good number. It's a practice we think every merchant should adopt.

Adnams
Berry Bros & Rudd
Eldridge Pope
Great Northern Wine Company
Peter Green
Ingletons Wines
Jeroboams
S H Jones
Lay & Wheeler

Le Nez Rouge/Berkmann Wine Cellars
Nobody Inn
Christopher Piper Wines
Raeburn Fine Wines and Foods
Edward Sheldon
T & W Wines
Tanners Wines
La Vigneronne
Peter Wylie Fine Wines

Large bottles

For celebrations or for finer wines which age well in larger bottles, you may find the following stockists' lists particularly rewarding:

Berry Bros & Rudd
Champagne and Caviar Shop
Peter Green
Gerard Harris
Hungerford Wine Company
Jeroboams
Kurtz & Chan Wines

Lay & Wheeler
Edward Sheldon
Stones of Belgravia
T & W Wines
Peter Wylie Fine Wines
Yorkshire Fine Wines

Part III

Wine away from home

Britain's top 50 wine bars

How to spot a restaurant winner

English vineyards open to the public

Britain's top fifty wine bars

Every town seems to have its wine bar. The majority, we are sad to report, serve up poor wines, often as the accompaniment to equally depressing food.

But all is not lost. We have discovered a number of exciting wine bars which offer a sensibly chosen range of wines to suit all pockets. Here we present our top fifty, some familiar from last year, some newcomers to our gallery of the élite. All have been singled out on the strength of their wines, not on their food or atmosphere – although generally all three are of similar quality.

LONDON

Albertine

1 Wood Lane, W12   TEL 01-743 9593

OPEN Mon–Fri 11–3, 5.30–11   CLOSED Sat, Sun, public holidays
CREDIT CARDS Access, Amex, Diners   UNDERGROUND Shepherd's Bush
WHEELCHAIR ACCESS Yes, not to lavatories   VEGETARIAN DISHES At least
two daily

Handy for Shepherd's Bush media types, with an interesting menu and a list of good wines, helpfully annotated. About a dozen by the glass, including Chanut Frères' white and red house wines (£4.90/90p),

539

Muscadet sur Lie 1986, Sauvion (£5.60/£1.05) and Dolcetto d'Alba 1985, Fontanafredda (£5.75/£1.10). Even more in half-bottle: Mondavi Fumé Blanc 1984 (£5.40), Ch Bel-Air 1982 (£4.50). After that, choose from Gisselbrecht Alsace (Riesling 1985, Grande Réserve, £7.50), Duboeuf's Juliénas 1985 (£7.95), Crozes-Hermitage 1983, Michel Bernard (£6.70), Wiltinger Scharzberg Riesling Kabinett 1983, Huesgen (£6.40), or Dão Cardeal Reserva 1974, Caves Dom Teodósio (£6.25). George Goulet Brut non-vintage Champagne is £14.65; for £2 more you can try the 1982 Rosé version. Taylor's Ports by the glass.

L'Autre

5B Shepherd Street, W1   TEL 01-499 4680

OPEN 12–3, 5.30–11   CLOSED Sat L, Sun, most public holidays
CREDIT CARDS Access, Visa   UNDERGROUND Green Park, Hyde Park Corner
WHEELCHAIR ACCESS Impossible   VEGETARIAN DISHES Usually

Outside tables and fine glasses make this Shepherd Market wine bar a popular spot. As well as offering a good selection of wines by the glass, they have a 'happy two hours' (5.30–7.30) when sparklers are reduced in price: Fontal Champagne drops from £14.50 to £11.95, Blanquette de Limoux from £9.25 to £7.75. The three dozen wines include Côtes de Provence Rosé from the Vignerons de St-Tropez (£6.75/£1.40); the splendid Bollini Chardonnay 1985 and Cabernet Sauvignon 1982 (£6.95) made in Italy by a New Zealander; Côtes-du-Rhône, Domaine Ste-Anne 1983 (£6.95/£1.40); Léon Beyer Gewürztraminer 1984 (£8.95); Sauvignon de St-Bris 1985 (£7.50); Siglo Rioja 1983 (£5.95/£1.30); and Wehlener Sonnenuhr Spätlese 1982, Hammes-Scherr (£8.95). House French red and white are £4.95 (£1 the glass). Varied and imaginative food, much of it fishy, some of it Mexican.

Balls Brothers

2/3 Old Change Court, St Paul's Churchyard, EC4	TEL 01-248 8697
6/8 Cheapside, EC2	TEL 01-248 2708
42 Threadneedle Street, EC2	TEL 01-628 3850
Bucklersbury House, Cannon Street, EC4	TEL 01-248 7557
Great Eastern Hotel, Liverpool Street, EC2	TEL 01-626 7919
Laurence Pountney Hill, EC2	TEL 01-283 2947
Moor House, London Wall, EC2	TEL 01-628 3944
St Mary at Hill, EC3	TEL 01-626 0321
Fish Restaurant and Wine Bar, Hay Galleria, Tooley Street, SE1	TEL 01-407 4301

OPEN Mon–Fri 11–3, 5–8   CLOSED Sat, Sun, public holidays
CREDIT CARDS All accepted   VEGETARIAN DISHES Sandwiches; others with prior notice

Balls Brothers wine bars stick to the successful formula of offering their own good wines at reasonable prices in rather staid, mostly City, surroundings. The most attractive are probably the clubby Edwardian bar in the Great Eastern Hotel, the atmospheric two-floor bar in Threadneedle Street, and the St Paul's Churchyard bar with outside tables. There are ten routine wines by the glass. Others to consider include Muscadet, Fief de la Brie 1985 (£6.30); Ch du Grand Moulas 1985, Côtes du Rhône (£6.15); seven clarets from La Tour Michèle (£5.40/£1.10) to Ch Camensac 1976 (£19.50); Gaillac Perlé (£4.90); and Lindeman's Chardonnay 1986 (£7.50). The list still lacks most producers' names, thus making it impossible to evaluate, for example, the German and Burgundy sections. Useful range of Sherries and Ports, and gently marked-up Champagne (Laurent Perrier Rosé, £18.90).

Bleeding Heart

Bleeding Heart Yard, Hatton Garden, EC1   TEL 01-242 8238

OPEN Mon–Fri 12–3, 6–11   CLOSED Sat, Sun, public holidays
CREDIT CARDS Access, Amex, Diners, Visa   UNDERGROUND Chancery Lane, Farringdon   WHEELCHAIR ACCESS Possible   VEGETARIAN DISHES Good selection

This Dickensian wine bar off Greville Street (between Hatton Garden and Saffron Hill) is hard to find but worth the effort. Prices are fairly high, but there are some decent wines by the glass, from house red and white (95p) to Georges Duboeuf Beaujolais 1985 (£1.65). The main list of about 100 bins covers the French classic regions: Ch Bel-Air 1982 (£8.75); Volnay Tête de Cuvée Comtes Lafon 1980 (£22.50); Chablis 1985, Jean-Marc Brocard (£12.95). Further afield there's Montana Marlborough Sauvignon and Chardonnay, both 1985 (£7.95); Rosemount Chardonnay 1985 (£8.50); Portuguese Camarate 1980 (£7.25); and California Monterey Classic Red 1985 (£7.25). Half-bottles include Bourgogne Pinot Noir 1983, Domaine Parent (£6.95). The food has a French accent.

Boos

1 Glentworth Street, Marylebone Road, NW1   TEL 01-935 3827

OPEN Mon–Fri 11.30–3, 5.30–8   CLOSED Sat, Sun, public holidays, 3 weeks Sept, 2 weeks Chr   CREDIT CARDS Access, Amex, Diners
UNDERGROUND Baker Street   WHEELCHAIR ACCESS Not possible
VEGETARIAN DISHES Some

The Roses' cellar remains popular: at times it feels like a neighbourhood club. It's not just the pleasant atmosphere and home-cooked food which draw people back, however. The wine list is still not greedily priced and it contains many interesting bottles – most of them French. House wines, sensibly sold by bottle, half-litre or glass, include Willm's Alsace Pinot Blanc (£7.25/£6.45/£1.70) and Penedès Grand Civet 1984 (£5.95/£5.25/£1.50). Nine Alsace wines get the French white section off to a stunning start, reinforced by Condrieu, Ch du Rozay 1985 (£23.75). The French reds include serious clarets: from Ch Citran 1978 (£10.50) to Ch Margaux 1978 (£52) with a tempting Ch Cheval Blanc 1971 (£38) in between. The Australian section has been augmented by Hardy's Padthaway Chardonnay 1985 (£9.75). Aperitifs include white Port, good Sherries and Madeira; and Morris of Rutherglen's superb Liqueur Muscat (£1.50) would round things off nicely.

Bow Wine Vaults

10 Bow Churchyard, EC4   TEL 01-248 1121

OPEN Mon–Fri 11.30–3, 5–7   CLOSED Sat, Sun, public holidays
CREDIT CARDS Access, Diners, Visa   UNDERGROUND Mansion House
WHEELCHAIR ACCESS Yes, but not to lavatories   VEGETARIAN DISHES Yes

The Vaults near Cheapside house a complex of wine merchant (see the WHERE TO BUY section), cellars, restaurant, private dining-rooms and two wine bars. Check the blackboard for special offers: perhaps Lirac, Domaine Tour des Chênes 1984, Andreo (£6.75/£1.25); Lucien Tempé Alsace Pinot Blanc 1985 (£6.50/£1.20); or Quincy 1985, Pierre Mardon (£8.35/£1.45). Once into the main list, you are spoilt for choice: distinguished Loires and red and white Burgundies; six Alsace bins, including Willm's delicious Gewürztraminer 1985 (£8.55); Rothbury Estate Semillon 1985 (£9.55); Sancerre Chavignol Rouge 1985, Paul Thomas (£9) – sensibly served chilled as it would be at home; impressive clarets and Rhônes (Ch Les Ormes de Pez 1980, £14.15; Côte Rôtie, Brune et Blonde 1980, Guigal, £14.80). Decent Champagnes, too, and sonorous Ports back to 1945 Martinez (£97.70). Food varies in style, depending on where you find a perch.

Cork & Bottle

OPEN Mon–Sat 11–3, 5.30–11   Sun 12 noon–2, 7–10.30 (closed Sun lunchtime March/April–Sept)   CLOSED 25 & 26 Dec, 1 Jan   CREDIT CARDS Amex, Diners, Visa   UNDERGROUND Leicester Square   WHEELCHAIR ACCESS Not possible   VEGETARIAN DISHES Several salads and hot dishes

Leicester Square's most civilised watering-hole, Don Hewitson's crowded basement bar suffers only from its popularity. The owner's enthusiasms keep the list and special offers changing, so that one month you might be bewitched by 20 Spanish wines, another it could be Beaujolais, and most of the time Listel Gris de Gris will be loudly featured. Quality is always high, the Australian and New Zealand sections are irresistible, and the many wines sold by the quarter-bottle-sized glass allow you to taste your way painlessly round the wine world. A few chosen almost at random: Pinot Blanc d'Alsace 1985, Boeckel (£6.95/£1.85); Orlando Chardonnay 1986 (£7.50/£1.85); Ch Respide 1983, Graves (£8.50); Provençal Carte Noire Rosé 1985 (£7.50); Torres Gran Viña Sol 1985 (£6.95); Italian Chardonnay 1985, Bollini (£7.50); Selaks Sauvignon-Semillon 1986 (£10.95); Clos du Bois Merlot 1984 (£9.95). And that's ignoring the sparklers, the Australian liqueur Muscats . . . Impossible to keep up with the man, despite the informative, opinionated list. The jazz is good, the special events are fun, the food is excellent. What a pity so many people know and love it. (See also Methuselah's and Shampers.)

Davys of London

Most branches are closed Sat, Sun and public holidays; many close about 8 pm on weekday evenings.

Arch 9 Arch 9, Old Seacoal Lane, EC4	TEL 01-248 8991
Bangers 2–12 Wilson Street, EC2	TEL 01-377 6326
Bishop of Norwich 91–93 Moorgate, EC2	TEL 01-920 0857
Bishop's Parlour 91–93 Moorgate, EC2	·TEL 01-588 2581
Boot & Flogger 10–20 Redcross Way, SE1	TEL 01-407 1184
Bottlescrue 53–60 Holborn Viaduct, EC1	TEL 01-248 2157
Bung Hole 57 High Holborn, WC1	TEL 01-242 4318
Burgundy Bens 102/108 Clerkenwell Road, EC1	TEL 01-251 3783
Champagne Charlies 325 Essex Road, Islington N1	TEL 01-226 4078
Chopper Lump 10C Hanover Square, W1	TEL 01-499 7569
City Boot 7 Moorfields High Walk, EC2	TEL 01-588 4766
City Flogger 120 Fenchurch Street, EC3	TEL 01-623 3251
City FOB Lower Thames Street, EC3	TEL 01-621 0619
City Pipe Foster Lane, EC2	TEL 01-606 2110
City Vaults 2 St Martins-le-Grand, EC1	TEL 01-606 6721
Colonel Jaspers 161 Greenwich High Road, SE10	TEL 01-853 0585
Colonel Jaspers 190 City Road, EC1	TEL 01-608 0925
The Cooperage 48–50 Tooley Street, SE1	TEL 01-403 5775
Crusting Pipe 27 The Market, Covent Garden, WC2	TEL 01-836 1415
Davys Wine Vaults 161 Greenwich High Road, SE10	TEL 01-858 7204
Grape Shots 2/3 Artillery Passage, E1	TEL 01-247 8215
The Guinea Butt New City Court, SE1	TEL 01-407 2829
Gyngle Boy 27 Spring Street, W2	TEL 01-723 3351
The Habit Fiery Court, 65 Crutched Friars, EC3	TEL 01-481 1137
Lees Bag 4 Great Portland Street, W1	TEL 01-636 5287
Mother Bunch's Seacoal Lane, EC4	TEL 01-236 5317
The Pulpit 63 Worship Street, EC2	TEL 01-377 1754
Segar & Snuff Parlour 27A The Market, Covent Garden, WC2	TEL 01-836 8345
Shotberries 167 Queen Victoria Street, EC4	TEL 01-329 4759

Skinkers 42 Tooley Street, SE1	TEL	01-407 9189
The Spittoon 15–17 Long Lane, EC1	TEL	01-726 8858
Tappit-Hen 5 William IV Street, WC2	TEL	01-836 9839
Tapster 3 Brewers Green, Buckingham Gate, SW1	TEL	01-222 0561
Udder Place Wine Rooms Russia Court, Russia Row, 1–6 Milk Street, EC2	TEL	01-600 2165
The Vineyard International House, St Katharine's Way, E1	TEL	01-480 6680
Wines Galore 161 Greenwich High Road, SE10	TEL	01-858 6014
Wine Shop 151 Borough High Street, SE1	TEL	01-407 1484

Davys wine bars proliferate relentlessly – there are about 40 of them, most in the City, the rest mainly in London, with a few country outposts. Their success is no accident. As well as the atmospheric decor, rich in sawdusty floors, casks and candles – to say nothing of the eccentric locations – they benefit from John Davy's astuteness as a wine merchant. Special offers are always worth considering, but otherwise the basic list of three dozen wines is thoroughly reliable and reasonably priced. Wines by glass as well as bottle include: French 'Ordnary' No 1 red or white (£4.95/£1.30); fresh and flowery hock (£5.25/£1.40); Bordeaux Sauvignon 1986 (£5.95/£1.50); and Davy's Rioja 1981 (£5.95/£1.50). Other bottles worth a second glance include sparkling Savoie Blanc de Blancs (£8.95); Davy's White Burgundy (Montagny, Premier Cru AC, £9.95); Beaujolais Brouilly 1986, Clos de Briante (£7.95); and Ch Talbot 1980 (£13.95). There are always fine Ports and Sherries by glass and bottle, and if you wish to fly high, summon a bottle from the list of fine claret, Burgundy and Port available at the Boot & Flogger (24 hours' notice required). The 'bill of fare' never tastes as interesting as it sounds.

Draycott's

114 Draycott Avenue, SW3   TEL   01-584 5359

OPEN Mon–Sat 11.30–3, 5.30–11   Sun 12–2, 7–10.30   CLOSED 25 & 26 Dec
CREDIT CARDS All accepted   UNDERGROUND South Kensington, Sloane Square   WHEELCHAIR ACCESS Yes   VEGETARIAN DISHES Selection available

The Ebury Wine Company's Yuppie branch at Brompton Cross (see also below) is still packing its enlarged premises with devotees of its 19 Champagnes: for example, the house one from Boizel (£14.50/£3); Champagne Palmer Rosé (£18.50); Georges Gardet 1976 (£21). Kirs, Bucks Fizz and Bellinis too, of course. There are about three dozen wines, well chosen, carefully annotated and relatively gently priced: house Blanc de Blancs (£5.50/£1.50); Chardonnay di Appiano 1986 (£8/£2.20); Ch de Fayolle, Côtes de Bergerac 1985 (£6.80/£1.80); Sancerre, Cuvée Les Baronnes 1986, H Bourgeois (£11.50); Torres Gran Coronas 1983 (£9.50). Imaginative food; Sunday brunch with newspapers.

Drinks

21 Abingdon Road, W8   TEL 01-937 6504

OPEN Mon–Sat 11.30–3, 5.30–11   Sun 12 noon–2   CLOSED Public holidays, 25
& 26 Dec, Easter   CREDIT CARDS Access, Amex, Diners, Visa
UNDERGROUND High Street Kensington   WHEELCHAIR ACCESS Possible
VEGETARIAN DISHES Limited

A comfortable wine bar just off Kensington High Street, whose
proprietor also owns Hambledon vineyard. Thus the house white is
Hambledon (mainly Chardonnay, £5.25/£1.75), the same price as the
Chantovent red. Even with 20cl glasses, prices are no bargain – take
friends and share a bottle: Muscadet sur Lie 1985 (£6.85/£2.35);
Domaine d'Ormessan 1983, Vin de Pays d'Oc (£6.25/£2.35). The list,
although carelessly annotated, is worth exploring: Mâcon-Clessé 1983,
Jean Thévenet (£9.65); Alsace Pinot Blanc 1984, Gisselbrecht (£6.85); De
Bortoli Fumé Blanc 1984 (£7.45); Ch Segonzac 1982 (£10.95); Torres
Gran Coronas 1982 (£8.75). Interesting menu and considerate service.

Ebury Wine Bar

139 Ebury Street, SW1   TEL 01-730 5447

OPEN Mon–Sat 11–3, 5.30–11   Sun 12 noon–2, 7–10.30   CLOSED 24 & 25
Dec   CREDIT CARDS Access, Amex, Diners, Visa   UNDERGROUND Victoria,
Sloane Square   WHEELCHAIR ACCESS No   VEGETARIAN DISHES Very limited
selection

The Ebury Wine Company owns this bar and Draycott's (*qv*), which are
both stocked with fine examples of the wares. About 20 wines by the
glass include Gisselbrecht's Pinot d'Alsace 1984 (£7.50/£1.60);
Chardonnay di Appiano DOC 1985 (£8/£1.70); Côtes du Rhône, Cuvée
Personnelle Pascal 1980 (£8.20/£1.70); and Ch Bonnet 1983
(£9.20/£1.90); as well as the French house wines (£5.50/£1.20).
Elsewhere on the list, consider Sauvignon de St-Bris 1985, Sorin
(£8.50); Sancerre Les Baronnes 1984, H Bourgeois, either rosé or red
(£11.50); Clos du Bois Chardonnay 1984 (£10.90) from California; and
the delicious Monbazillac, Ch de Septy 1980 (£8.50). Various Sherries,
Ports and Madeiras (Cossart Gordon Sercial, £1.90), and a long
blackboard list of Champagnes. Imaginative food.

The Greenhouse

16–17 Royal Exchange, EC3   TEL 01-236 7077

OPEN Mon–Fri 11.30–3, 5–8   CLOSED Sat, Sun, public holidays
CREDIT CARDS Not accepted   UNDERGROUND Bank
WHEELCHAIR ACCESS Impossible   VEGETARIAN DISHES Not provided (menu
mainly fish)

The City's smallest, most elegant wine bar, run by wine merchants Green's (see the WHERE TO BUY section), has survived the Big Bang with a reasonable increase in prices during the past year. If you can afford them, you will enjoy the Floquet Brut Réserve Champagne (£15/£3) or Krug 1979 (£53.50). The few other wines by the glass include the delicious Brauneberger Juffer Riesling Spätlese 1985, M F Richter (£9.40/£2) and Pinot Grigio, Santa Margherita 1986 (£9/£2). Clos du Marquis 1981, the second wine of Ch Léoville-Las-Cases is £17; otherwise stick to the good Sherries, Ports and Madeiras by the glass (Graham's Malvedos 1976, £30/£5). Smoked salmon or crab sandwiches are favourites (£2.50).

Hoults

20 Bellevue Road, SW17   TEL 01-767 1858

OPEN Every day 12–2.30, 5.30–11 CLOSED 24–31 Dec
CREDIT CARDS Access, Amex, Visa UNDERGROUND Balham
WHEELCHAIR ACCESS Possible VEGETARIAN DISHES Good selection

This trendy wine bar and restaurant overlooking Wandsworth Common are attached to a wine warehouse which produces some interesting finds for the list. Ten wines by the glass include Gisselbrecht's Pinot Noir 1985 (£6.50/£1.30); Cannonau 1982, Sella & Mosca (£5.75/£1.15); and Bernkastler Badstube Riesling QbA 1985, Deinhard (£6.95/£1.40). Others to consider might include Champigny Rouge 1985, Bouvet-Ladubay (£6.95); Rosemount Hunter Valley Chardonnay 1985 (£7.50); Ch Fourcas-Hosten 1979 (£10.95); and Recioto della Valpolicella Amarone 1979 of Masi (£10.50). The Champagnes include the delicious George Goulet Extra Quality Rosé Brut 1982 (£17.95); the Sherries are from Lustau, the Ports from Taylors (Atlantic Tawny, £10.50/£2.10; Quinta de Vargellas 1974, £19.75/£3.95). Smart food at appropriate prices.

Just Williams

6 Battersea Rise, SW11   TEL 01-228 9980

OPEN Mon–Sat 12–3, 5.30–11 (Sat 6.30–11) Sun 7–10.30 CLOSED Sun L, Chr, Easter Day CREDIT CARDS Access, Amex, Visa BR STATION Clapham Junction WHEELCHAIR ACCESS One small step down to bar; lavatories impossible VEGETARIAN DISHES A couple each day

One of Battersea's more endearing spots, with a patio for summer evenings, Just Williams has an impressive, thoughtfully compiled wine list. As well as basic house red and white (£4.50/80p), there are five others at £4.95/95p, including Côtes du Rhône Villages 1984 and Muscadet sur Lie 1985, Rémy Pannier. Further afield, and still excellent value for money, are Bulgarian Sakar Mountain Cabernet 1976 (£5.65), Portuguese Camarate 1980 da Fonseca (£5.65) and Portuguese dry

Muscat 1985, João Pires (£5.35). Add to those a dozen impressive clarets and the same number of Burgundies (many in useful half-bottles), and you will understand the temptations. Try the François Paquet Beaujolais (Morgon, Les Rigottes 1985, £8.50) or Cabernet de Saumur Rosé 1985 (£4.95). Good bistro cooking – more adventurous in the adjacent restaurant, Pollyanna's.

Methuselah's

29 Victoria Street, SW1   TEL 01-222 0424

OPEN Mon–Fri 11.30–3, 5.30–11   CLOSED Sat, Sun, public holidays
CREDIT CARDS All accepted   UNDERGROUND St James's Park, Victoria
WHEELCHAIR ACCESS Not possible   VEGETARIAN DISHES Good selection

The Victoria member of the Hewitson stable (see under Cork & Bottle) is almost as crowded at lunchtime, more peaceful in the evening. The same varied and interesting wine list at reasonable prices is supplemented by special offers and seasonal events. Imaginative buffet, and two ground-floor restaurants.

Le Métro

28 Basil Street, SW3   TEL 01-589 6286

OPEN Mon–Fri 7.30 am–11 pm   Sat 7.30 am–6 pm   Sun 8 am–11 am
CLOSED Sat & Sun evenings, public holidays   CREDIT CARDS Amex, Visa
UNDERGROUND Knightsbridge   WHEELCHAIR ACCESS Difficult, only from the
rear; lavatories impossible   VEGETARIAN DISHES Some

Handy for Harrods, this terribly smart basement (related to the Capital Hotel) has a suitably French feel to it, and the wine list lingers lovingly in the classic French regions: ten fine Loires (Sauvignon de Cheverny 1985, Cazin, £7.20); Louis Jadot Burgundies (Beaune Chouacheux 1980, £18); Alsace wines from seven shippers; a still Champagne, Coteaux Champenois Denois (£11.65); and of course distinguished clarets (Ch Lynch-Bages 1980, £16.50). As well as several of the listed wines by the glass (Muscadet-sur-Lie, Clos des Barillères 1986, £6.25/£1.40), there is a Cruover machine with ten exciting bottles on tap: a summer visit offered five 1979 clarets (from £3.50 a glass) and five fine rosés (Bourgogne de Marsannay, £1.95). The food is suitably elegant. (Note that Sunday morning is alcohol-free breakfast time.)

Odette's

130 Regent's Park Road, NW1   TEL 01-586 5486

OPEN 12–3, 5.30–11   CLOSED Sun, public holidays, 10 days Chr
CREDIT CARDS All accepted   UNDERGROUND Chalk Farm
WHEELCHAIR ACCESS Impossible   VEGETARIAN DISHES One or two

Primrose Hill offers few bargains, but this attractive wine bar beneath a busy restaurant has several wines at last year's prices, now seeming much more acceptable. They quote too many split vintages, too few producers, but even so, there are some fine wines to choose from: for example, Rolly Gassmann's Gewürztraminer 1984 (£8.75); Berberana Gran Reserva Rioja 1975 (£9.50); Châteauneuf-du-Pape, Ch de Beaucastel 1980 (£16.50); and about 20 good Bordeaux (Ch Potensac 1982, £11.50; Ch Cantemerle 1966, £44). The basic French house wines are £4.70/£1; the Champagnes run from the house non-vintage at £17.50 to the rare Bollinger Vieilles Vignes Blanc de Noirs 1980 at £70.

192

192 Kensington Park Road, W11　　　　　　　　TEL 01-229 0482

OPEN Mon–Sat 12.30–3, 5.30–11　Sun 1–3　CLOSED Sun evening, Chr–New Year's Day, some public holidays　CREDIT CARDS Access, Amex, Visa UNDERGROUND Ladbroke Grove, Notting Hill Gate WHEELCHAIR ACCESS Yes, not to lavatories　VEGETARIAN DISHES Salads only

This smart wine bar/restaurant continues to offer intelligently chosen wines on a clear list, with one from each section available by the glass. The house selection includes Corney & Barrow's house red from Lebègue (£5.85/£1.20), Costamour Costières du Gard 1986 (£7.50/£1.55) and Rosé de Provence Carte Noire 1986 from Les Maîtres Vignerons de St-Tropez (£8/£1.55). The good Bordeaux include the 'clairet' Ch Thieuley 1983 (£9.50) and among the Burgundies is the excellent Bourgogne Pinot Noir 1984 from Jacques Parent (£12). Others which catch the eye include the Australian McLaren Vale Cabernet Sauvignon 1983 (£6.50/£1.30); Georges Duboeuf 'flower label' Beaujolais-Villages 1986 (£8.75/£1.80); João Pires' delicious Moscato Branco 1986 (£6.50); and Marqués de Griñon Cabernet Sauvignon 1983 (£13.50/£2.50) – near-infanticide but worth a glass to see whether you want to lay some down. Various cocktails and Champagnes (Delamotte Brut reduced to £13 between 5.30 and 7.30), and decent fruit juices. Inventive menu.

The Pavilion

Finsbury Circus Gardens, Finsbury Circus, EC2　　　TEL 01-628 8224

OPEN Mon–Fri 11.30–3, 5–8　CLOSED Sat, Sun, public holidays CREDIT CARDS Access, Amex, Visa　UNDERGROUND/BR STATIONS Moorgate, Liverpool Street　WHEELCHAIR ACCESS Impossible VEGETARIAN DISHES Salads

The former clubhouse for the bowling-green feels pleasantly rustic on a summer's day in the City, though there's nothing rustic or simple about David Gilmour's impressive range of wines. Every two months he chooses a theme for the wines on offer by the glass (region or grape, say), so that regulars need not become bored. A recent Loire theme

offered Touraine Cabernet, Domaine de la Châtoire 1983 (£6.70/£1.75)
from the co-operative at Oisly-et-Thésée, the Domaine's white wine,
Sauvignon Blanc 1985 (£6.85/£1.80) and Marc Brédif Vouvray 1983
(£7.60/£2). French house wines cost £5.50/£1.45, and there's a good
range of Sherries, Ports and Madeiras as well. Gilmour's persuasive
annotations introduce the mainly French list effectively: consider the
seven Champagnes (the house Ailerons et Baie Brut, £15.50); Rully
1983, Jean Daux (£9.75); Mas de Daumas Gassac Rosé 1986 (£7.95);
Cornas 1980, Jaboulet Aîné (£11.75); some useful 1982 clarets (Ch La
Terrasse, £6.50); and Ladoix 1980, Chevalier (Côte de Beaune, £11).
Spain, Germany, California and Australia have a brief look-in
(Balgownie Cabernet Sauvignon 1983, £10.70). There are several
half-bottles. Small wonder that the place is crowded out: go early or be
patient. Don't miss the fruit cake.

Reynier at Fleet Lane

29 Fleet Lane, Old Bailey, EC1   TEL 01-236 0552

OPEN Mon–Fri 11.30–3, 5–7.30   CLOSED Sat, Sun, public holidays
CREDIT CARDS Access, Visa   UNDERGROUND St Paul's, Blackfriars
WHEELCHAIR ACCESS Not possible   VEGETARIAN DISHES Not available (see
below)

On the analogy of a 'restaurant with rooms', this is a 'wine shop with
tables'. You choose – with sound advice – from the 700 or so items on
the impressive Eldridge Pope/Reynier list at off-sales prices, and then
go down to the clubbily stylish cellar bar to enjoy your find along with
help-yourself pâtés, cheeses, fruit and coffee (£5). The list, with its
strong French bias, is worth leisurely study. Note particularly the sixty
or so halves: the house Champagne (£4.88); Muscat les Amandiers 1983
Dopff & Irion (£3.13); Ch Feytit-Clinet 1982 (£5.41); and the Chairman's
delicious late-bottled Port (£3.24). Full bottles range from Chenin du
Jardin de la France (£2.31) through fine Australians and Californians
and superb Bordeaux – even Ch Lafite 1975 (£103.50). Beware of City
cigars, a hazard in the tiny cellar.

Shampers

4 Kingly Street, W1   TEL 01-437 1692

OPEN Mon–Fri 11–3, 5.30–11   Sat 11–3   CLOSED Sat evening, Sun, Easter,
25 & 26 Dec   CREDIT CARDS All accepted   UNDERGROUND Oxford Circus,
Piccadilly Circus   WHEELCHAIR ACCESS Yes, but not to lavatories
VEGETARIAN DISHES Varied selection

A cheerful relative of the Cork & Bottle (see above) with the endearing
family trait of boundless enthusiasm and the same varied and
interesting wine list at reasonable prices. Watch out for the special
offers and events throughout the year. Imaginative self-service buffet,

still well stocked late in the evening. Stick to the ground floor rather than the basement if you are unsure of foot.

Whittington's

21 College Hill, EC4	TEL 01-248 5855

OPEN Mon–Fri 11.30–3, 5–7.30 CLOSED Sat, Sun CREDIT CARDS All accepted UNDERGROUND Cannon Street WHEELCHAIR ACCESS No VEGETARIAN DISHES Selection of salads

These ancient cellars – owned before the Great Fire by the legendary Dick himself – are noisily popular at lunchtime. As well as substantial snacks, there are various wines by the glass (Belair Sauvignon 1986, £6.25/£1.20) and about 40 others which include some decent mature claret (Ch La Gravière 1978, £13.50); Mâcon Chardonnay 1986, Caves Co-opératives (£11.15); Berberana Rioja Gran Reserva 1978 (£9.50); and Seppelt Black Label Shiraz 1982 (£10.75). Casual annotation and alternative vintages make it difficult to judge the quality of several of the wines: ask to see the bottle before you choose. House Champagne is £13.50, Perrier-Jouët 1979, £22.

OUT OF LONDON

BILLERICAY Essex

Webber's

2 Western Road	TEL (0277) 656581

OPEN 11.30–2.30, 6–10.30 (Mon from 7, Fri & Sat to 11) CLOSED Sun, public holiday L, 1 week Chr, last week July, first week Aug CREDIT CARDS All accepted WHEELCHAIR ACCESS Possible with help VEGETARIAN DISHES Good selection

This split-level wine bar near the station reflects the enthusiasm of its proprietors, with an impressive list of some 250 wines – many of them available by the glass (thanks to a Canadian Wine Machine), an off-sales department, special events and tastings, and home-cooked food so popular that they now take bookings. House wines include Geoffrey Roberts Reserve red and white from California (£5.85/£1.14) and the Tuscan Bianca Santa Fina dry white (£5.65/£1.10); house claret is from Teltscher (£6.35/£1.23). Otherwise browse through the up-to-date computerised list with its succinct tasting notes: Ch Chicane 1981, Graves (£9.85); Trois Mouline Sauvignon Sec, Sarjeant (£6.45/£1.25); Ch de Grand Moulas 1985, Rhône (£6.65); Domaine Chante-Cigale 1980, Sabon-Favier (£11.75); Saumur-Champigny 1984, Hospices de Saumur (£6.85); St-Véran 1985, Loron (£7.95); Ch La

Jaubertie, red 1982, white 1984 (each £6.95); Pinot Grigio 1986 Lageder (£7.45); Los Llanos Gran Reserva 1975 (£6.85); and so one could go on. The splendid Burgundies and California wines deserve careful study, as does the page of Champagnes (Joly Brut, £14.95). Don't miss the two dozen half-bottles (Mondavi Pinot Noir 1981, £6.45) and the decent aperitifs and Ports.

CHESTER Cheshire

Watergates

11 Watergate Street   TEL (0244) 20515

OPEN Mon 10.30–3   Tue–Sun 10.30–3, 5.30–11   CLOSED 25 & 26 Dec, 1 Jan
CREDIT CARDS All accepted except Diners   WHEELCHAIR ACCESS Difficult
VEGETARIAN DISHES Possible

One of Chester's finest medieval crypts now houses a wine bar and restaurant run jointly by Whynot Wine Warehouses and Boddingtons (see WHERE TO BUY section). A Cruover machine allows them to offer fine wines by the glass. More mundanely, there are 11 house wines at £6 and under with a 12.5cl glass costing £1, double that £2: Côtes de Buzet (£6), Vinho Verde (£5.50), Coteaux de l'Ardèche (£5.25) – a few details of vintages and shippers would be helpful. About 20 'specially selected' wines have lively tasting notes and careful annotations: they include Australian De Bortoli Chardonnay 1985 (£8.20), good mature claret in the shape of Ch Peyraud 1982 (£7.25), and the excellent house Champagne from Pierre Moncuit (£11). The main list ranges from French country wines (Côtes du Marmandais, £5.80) through fine clarets and Burgundies (Savigny-lès-Beaune 1982, Louis Latour, £14.50) to Portugal (João Pires' Tinto da Anfora 1982, £7.10), to Spain for several Torres wines, and to the New World (New Zealand's Cooks medium white and red, £6.25). Afternoon tea and Sunday brunch as well as food at more predictable times.

CHOBHAM Surrey

Racoons

1 Bagshot Road   ·   TEL (099 05) 8491

OPEN Tue–Fri 12 noon–2.30, 7–10.30   Sat 7–10.30   CLOSED Sun, Mon, public holidays   CREDIT CARDS Access, Diners, Visa   WHEELCHAIR ACCESS Yes, but not to lavatories   VEGETARIAN DISHES Some

The Wale family offer about 80 wines at ungrasping prices in their cheerful wine bar. House wines (from £4.95/£1) include a Languedoc, a white Bergerac and a Corbières. Higher flyers might consider, among the whites, Ch Cruzeau 1983, Graves (£8.85), a couple of 1985 Alsace Gewürztraminers or Tiefenbrunner Chardonnay 1986 (£8.05). The reds include an impressive range of 1983 cru Beaujolais (Fleurie, Ch de Fleurie, £11.05), a quartet of Riojas from Bodegas Beronia in the Rioja Alta, and some petit château Bordeaux (Ch Garraud 1979, £11.10). You must eat as well as drink on Friday and Saturday evenings – no hardship.

CIRENCESTER Gloucestershire

Shepherd's

Fleece Hotel, Market Place   TEL (0285) 68507

OPEN Mon–Sat 10.30–2.30, 7–11   Sun 10.30–2.30, 7–10.30   CLOSED 25 Dec
CREDIT CARDS All accepted   WHEELCHAIR ACCESS Yes
VEGETARIAN DISHES Reasonable selection

A comfortable, wood-panelled wine bar in an old coaching-inn, with a tasty menu and some well-chosen wines. By the glass, there's house claret, Burgundy and Sauvignon (£6.30/£1.05), and Fonseca-Guimaraens 1967 Port (£2.50). The list still sports too many alternative vintages and too few shippers' names, but those that are there are impressive: Fleurie, Ch de Fleurie 1985, Loron (£8.75), a delicious cru Beaujolais; Ch Potensac 1980 (£8.50); Wolf Blass Black Label Cabernet Sauvignon 1981 (£11.25); Montagny 1978, Delorme (£11.25). And a special note on the list to say how proud they were to buy at the Hospices de Beaune auction in 1981 Meursault Genevrières (of that year), Baudot (£19.75).

CLACTON-ON-SEA Essex

Nookes & Crannies

1 Carnarvon Road   TEL (0255) 426572

OPEN Mon–Sat 12–2.30, 7–12 (Sun 12 noon–2, 7–10.30)   CLOSED 25 & 26 Dec,
1 Jan   CREDIT CARDS Access, Amex, Visa   WHEELCHAIR ACCESS Yes
VEGETARIAN DISHES Some

The Starrs, in their wine bar near the sea, offer home-cooked food, special wine dinners and tastings, and an intelligently composed list of over 70 wines (22 of them available by the glass). Instead of house wines, they elect two 'wines of the week' so that regulars can work painlessly through the list. The helpful tasting notes might guide you to the Muscadet-sur-Lie 1986, Domaine de la Jousselinière (£5.95), Merchant Vintners' Claret de Maré (£5.25/£1.05), Cahors 1977, Les Côtes d'Ott (£6.50), or Torres Gran Coronas 1981 (£7.25). Blanquette de Limoux Brut still shines amongst the sparklers (£7.75).

CONGLETON Cheshire

Odd Fellows

20 Rood Hill   TEL (0260) 270243

OPEN Mon–Sat 12–2.30, 6.45–11   Sun 7–10.30   CLOSED Public holidays
(except Good Fri), 25–28 Dec   CREDIT CARD Amex
WHEELCHAIR ACCESS Difficult   VEGETARIAN DISHES Wide selection

All sounds merry and bright in this multi-level wine bar and bistro,
with a fountain in the courtyard and fondue bourguignonne at
lunchtime in the wine bar. The facetious list may not be to everyone's
taste but the 150 or so wines it describes have been chosen with care
(and split vintages are a thing of the past). The house red and white
wines are Boutinot's Cuvée Jean Paul (£5.75 litres/85p) with 'oddities'
also by the glass: Glühwein (winter only, 95p), Sangria (summer only,
90p) and all three colours of Lambrusco (80p). Turning to more serious
things, note the quartet of Alsace wines from the excellent Turckheim
co-operative (Pinot Blanc 1985, £6.35); Mâcon-Clessé 1985, Dépagneux
(£9.10); Rully Rouge 1983, Pierre Cogny (£12.65); the enormous dry
Graves, Ch Torteau-Chollet 1984 (£8.45); and the sound selection of
clarets, from Tanners Claret (NV) (£6.95) to Ch Talbot 1978 (£21.95). The
Rhône, the Loire and South-West France are equally worth study:
Provence appears rather arbitrarily in the South-West, but the elegant
Domaine de Trévallon 1984 red wine made from Cabernet Sauvignon
and Syrah (£11.50) would impress anywhere. The large Italian section
is adventurous: for example, Arneis di Montebertotto 1985, Castella di
Neive (£12.95), a 'rediscovered' Piedmontese grape. The New World
features too, of course: don't miss the New Zealand Cloudy Bay
Sauvignon Blanc 1986 (£11.95), one of the very best. There is more,
much more . . .

CROYDON Greater London

Pearls

34 Surrey Street   TEL 01-686 0586

OPEN Mon–Fri 12–3, 5.30–11   Sat 7–11   CLOSED Sat L, Sun, public holidays,
25 & 26 Dec   CREDIT CARDS All accepted
WHEELCHAIR ACCESS Impossible   VEGETARIAN DISHES Good selection

Pearls is a rather smart wine bar underneath its parent restaurant,
called 34 Surrey Street. House wines are Georges Duboeuf white and
red (£5.25/£1) and Fetzer white and red (£5.50/£1.10). Thirty California
wines include Fetzer Fumé Blanc 1985 (£7.95); Acacia Pinot Noir St
Claire Vineyard 1982 (£20); and three blush wines (White Zinfandel,
Bel Arbres 1986, £8.95). The European section is less adventurous, but
note the two wines from Châteauneuf-du-Pape, Clos de l'Oratoire:

white 1985 (£17.50) and red 1981 (£15.95). Sauvignon, Domaine de la Chaignée is £6.50, and an interesting red Graves, Ch du Cruzeau 1982, £11.50; a decent list of Champagnes. The menu (snacks at lunchtime only) also has a transatlantic accent.

EDINBURGH

Doric Tavern

15 Market Street   TEL 031-225 1084

OPEN Mon–Wed 12 noon–1, Thur–Sat 12 noon–2   Sun 6.30–11
  CLOSED 25 Dec, 1 Jan   CREDIT CARDS Access, Amex, Visa
WHEELCHAIR ACCESS Impossible   VEGETARIAN DISHES Always some

This cheerfully informal first-floor wine bar near Waverley station offers well-cooked, imaginative food and an interesting wine list. House wines include André Simon claret (£5.60/£1.05), Bulgarian Chardonnay (£5.40/£1) and Algerian Rosé, Coteaux de Mascara 1983 (£5.40/£1). Despite this strong international statement, the real strength of the list lies in France: consider Ch Chasse-Spleen 1979 (£14.10); Ch de Fuissé 1984, Domaine Vincent (£6.10 half-bottle); Mâcon-Villages Laforêt 1985, Drouhin (£8.60). Ranging further afield, you can find Portuguese Colares 1981 (£6.10), red Marqués de Cáceres Rioja 1981 (£6.55), and even Japanese saké (£7.95/£2.25 flask). Don't miss the bin-ends which make the Doric worth a considerable detour, and don't neglect the impressive list of single malts.

Handsel's Wine Bar

22 Stafford Street   TEL 031-225 5521

OPEN Mon–Sat 10–11   CLOSED Sun   CREDIT CARDS Access, Amex, Diners,
Visa   WHEELCHAIR ACCESS Yes, but not to lavatories
VEGETARIAN DISHES Only on request (not on menu)

One of Edinburgh's best new restaurants has a stylish wine bar on its ground floor – already very popular, and worth booking if you want to have lunch. Open all day, for coffee and tea as well as lunch and dinner (no alcohol between 10 and 11 am), it offers a limited but imaginative menu and about 40 wines, half of them by the glass (with the option of choosing also from the restaurant list). Few thrills, but some worthwhile bottles at West End prices: Sauvignon de St-Bris 1985 (£8); Gewürztraminer 1985, Heim (£8.35); Torres Gran Viña Sol 1985 (£5.80/£1.40); Ch Canteloup 1983 (£6.50/£1.55); Caves Velhas Garrafeira 1974 (£6.20/£1.50); and Penfold's Shiraz Cabernet 1983, Dalwood (£7.50).

Prices are correct to the best of our knowledge in summer 1987.

Whighams Wine Cellars

13 Hope Street   TEL 031-225 8674

OPEN 11 am–midnight (Fri to 1 am)   CLOSED Sun, 25 & 26 Dec, 1 Jan
CREDIT CARD Visa   WHEELCHAIR ACCESS Impossible
VEGETARIAN DISHES Several

A popular and civilised semi-basement just off Princes Street (at the
West End), offering interesting wines from a list more helpfully
annotated than previously but still showing too many alternative
vintages. About half of the 45 wines are available by the glass:
Nathaniel Johnston Special Reserve Claret (£5.25/£1.05), Muscadet,
Domaine des Dorices 1985 (£6.25/£1.20), Marqués de Cáceres red Rioja
1982 (£6.25/£1.20) and Barancourt Champagne Brut (£15.50/£2.95).
Delicious food.

EPWORTH Humberside

The Epworth Tap

9–11 Market Place   TEL (0427) 873333

OPEN Tue–Sat 7.30–12   CLOSED All lunchtimes, Sun, Mon, 1st 2 weeks Aug,
25 Dec–1 Jan   CREDIT CARD Access   WHEELCHAIR ACCESS Yes, but not to
lavatories   VEGETARIAN DISHES Occasionally on menu, special dishes by
arrangement

The cottagey exterior hides a power-house of wine expertise and
enthusiasm. John Wynne's list is constantly changing, chosen from
good suppliers, with wines offered when they are ready to drink, and
modestly marked up. As we went to press, the house wines included
Colombard 1985 from the Plaimont co-operative (£5.95/95p), a 1983
Côtes du Ventoux from Jaboulet (£5.95/£1) and Señorio de los Llanos
Reserva 1981 (£5.95/£1). The clarets ready for current enjoyment
include Ch Méaume 1983 (£8.95) and Ch Feytit-Clinet 1981 (£10.95),
with Ch Pichon-Lalande 1978 (£30) for higher flyers. The impressive
list of Burgundies starts with Hautes Côtes de Beaune 1983 from the
co-operative (£7.95) and goes on to, for example, the grand cru
Mazis-Chambertin 1982, Rousseau (£20). Consider too the fine Rhônes
from Jaboulet, Chave and Clape; the 1985 cru Beaujolais; the serious
Australians – from Brown Brothers Shiraz 1983 (£7.50) to Penfold's
Grange Hermitage, Bin 95 1979 (£45); the Barberas and Barbarescos
from Gaja; the 1983 Chablis from, for example, Durup, Michel and Pic;
the New Zealand Delegat's Chardonnay 1985 (£10.50); and the
delicious Maximin-Grünhäuser wines from von Schubert in the Ruwer.
There are decent half-bottles – and many other areas to explore: by the
time of your visit, there will certainly be yet more discoveries to make.
Good home cooking: best to book.

ETON Berkshire

Eton Wine Bar

82/83 High Street   TEL (075 38) 54921

OPEN Mon–Sat 12–3, 6–11   Sun 12–2.30, 7–10.30   CLOSED 5 days Chr, Easter
Sun   CREDIT CARDS Access, Visa   WHEELCHAIR ACCESS Possible
VEGETARIAN DISHES Good selection

The Gilbey family, well known as importers of wine, may become
equally noted for running a very efficient wine bar where most of the
prices are *lower* than they were a year ago. This makes it worth
persisting with their system of listing wines by style and price, which
puts, for example, amongst the 'dry whites', Ménétou-Salon 1986, H
Pellé (£9.15) cheek by jowl with St-Véran, Domaine des Dimes 1986,
Chanut Frères (£9.25). Red wines run from Vin de Pays de l'Ardèche,
Domaine de Bournet 1985 (£5.70) to Ch Marquis de Terme 1982 (£21.45)
with such worthwhile stations en route as Givry 1983 Cellier aux
Moines, Thénard (£11.25) and Ch Le Crock 1983 (£13). There are a few
German exceptions to the French list (Erdener Treppchen Riesling
Spätlese 1981, Otto Beiser, £7.50), and the aperitifs include the
excellent Barbadillo Sherries, as well as Pineau des Charentes (£1.35).
Chanut house wines are £5.25 a bottle, £1.15 a glass. Interesting food.

EXETER Devon

Bottlescrue Bills

White Hart Hotel, South Street   TEL (0392) 37511

OPEN Mon–Sat 12–2.30, 7–11   CLOSED Sun, public holidays
CREDIT CARDS All accepted   WHEELCHAIR ACCESS Yes
VEGETARIAN DISHES With notice

This attractive 14th-century inn with a sunlit courtyard is a link in John
Davy's chain (see under Davys in the London section) with the
advantage of a summer barbecue. Look out for the blackboard specials
which supplement the reliable, ungreedily priced basic list: French
'Ordnary' red and white (£4.95/£1.25 large glass), Davy's Rioja 1981
(£5.50/£1.40) and the delicious house hock (£5.15/£1.35). Ports,
Sherries, Madeiras and Champagnes are a special feature (Fine Old
Tawny, £8.50/£1.25).

Find the best new wine bargains all year round with our newsletter, *Which?*
Wine Monthly, available for just £15 a year from: Dept WG88, Consumers'
Association, FREEPOST, Hertford SG14 1YB – no stamp is needed if posted
within the UK.

HARROGATE North Yorkshire

William & Victoria

6 Cold Bath Road   TEL (0423) 506883

OPEN Mon–Sat 12 noon–3, 6.30–11   CLOSED Sun, Chr
CREDIT CARD Access   WHEELCHAIR ACCESS No
VEGETARIAN DISHES Available

Harrogate's oldest established wine bar – Will and Vic's to its regulars –
is deservedly popular for good Yorkshire food and an imaginative
selection of wine, particularly strong in French bottles. House wines
include Loron red and dry white (£4.95/90p), and after that you are
spoilt for choice: Ch La Terrasse 1983 (£6.75); Côtes du Ventoux, La
Vieille Ferme 1985, Perrin (£5.95); house Burgundy 1985 from Raoul
Clerget (£8.50); Touraine Sauvignon, Domaine Octavie 1986, Barbeillon
(£6.10); Gewürztraminer 1985, Pfaffenheim (£7.50). Outside France,
consider Torres Gran Coronas 1982 at a reasonable £8.75; Brown
Brothers' Dry Muscat Blanc 1986 (£7.75); Galilee Cabernet Sauvignon
1984, Gamla Vineyards (£8.05); and even the Rothschild-Mondavi
sensation, Opus One 1982 (£46). Pudding wines include Ch de Malle
1981, Grand Cru Sauternes (£8.90 for a half-bottle); and Champagnes
range from house Camuset Brut at £12.95 to Krug 1979 at £47.50. Look
out for blackboard specials.

HUNGERFORD Berkshire

The Galloping Crayfish

Courtyard, 24 High Street   TEL (0488) 84008

OPEN Mon–Sun 11.30–2.30 (2 Sun), 6–11   CREDIT CARDS Access, Visa
WHEELCHAIR ACCESS Yes   VEGETARIAN DISHES 2 dishes always available

Behind the Hungerford Wine Company (see the WHERE TO BUY
section), in a prettily revamped courtyard, is Nick Davies' newest
venture, a bistro/wine bar with outstandingly good food and an
impressive range of wines from the company, 20 of them on tap,
thanks to a Wine Machine (Canada's answer to the Cruover). Glasses
are quarter-bottle size: recent offerings have included João Pires Dry
Muscat 1986 (£6.95/£1.75); Hardy's Chenin Blanc 1985, Captain's
Selection (£6.95/£1.75); Côtes de Duras, Domaine de Laulan, red, white
and rosé, from Gilbert Geoffroy (£1.99); Torres Chilean Sauvignon
Blanc 1986 (£8.95/£2.25); Ch Musar 1980 (£9.50/£2.75); and Richebourg
1980, Domaine de la Romanée-Conti (£85/£21.25) – two takers as we
went to press. Drop in for morning coffee, afternoon tea, a glass of
wine, a snack or a full meal. A few tables in the courtyard.

INVERNESS Highland

Brookes

75 Castle Street   TEL (0463) 225662

OPEN Mon–Fri 11.30–3, 5–11 (late licence to 1 am Thur & Fri)   Sat
11.30–11.45   CLOSED Sun, local holidays, 25 & 26 Dec, Jan 1–7
CREDIT CARDS Not accepted   WHEELCHAIR ACCESS Yes, not to lavatories
VEGETARIAN DISHES Several

Brookes, a well-run wine bar beside the castle, celebrated its fifth
birthday in 1987 with an even more interesting list of little-known and
reasonably priced wines: note that their glasses hold a quarter-bottle.
The 'everyday' list of two dozen wines includes Cépage Colombard
1985 from the Plaimont co-operative (£5.50/£1.60); Tricastin 1984
Producteurs Réunis Ardéchois (£5.75/£1.65) and a dry German
sparkling wine, Ockfener Bockstein Sekt Trocken (£7.95/£1.90 'per
flute'). Whites worth considering include the dry Ch Doisy-Daëne 1983
(£10) from a house better known for its Barsac; Saumur, Domaine
Filliatreau 1985 (£7.50); and Château Tahbilk Marsanne 1984 (£8.50)
from Australia. Interesting reds include the impressive page of clarets
(Ch Cissac 1981, £12.75); Chorey-lès-Beaune 1984, Tollot-Beaut
(£12.50); Dão Grão Vasco Reserva 1978 (£7.25); and the Australian St
Hubert's Cabernet Sauvignon 1982 from Yarra Valley (£13.75). And
among the other attractions are Buck's Fizz by the jug, continental
beers, a non-smoking area and sympathetic treatment of vegetarians
and children.

LLANGOLLEN Clwyd

Gales

18 Bridge Street   TEL (0978) 860089

OPEN (June–July) Every day 12–2, 6–10.15   CLOSED (Aug–May) Sun, Mon,
Chr and New Year   CREDIT CARDS Not accepted
WHEELCHAIR ACCESS Difficult   VEGETARIAN DISHES Limited selection

Gales is a small wine bar but its list is impressive and the cellar well
stocked with wines for current or future drinking (or wholesale
purchase). House wines include Salavert Cuvée André Côtes du
Ventoux 1985 (£4.40/80p) and Cuvée Philippe white (£4.40/80p). Rich
pickings thereafter include Ch Haut-Marbuzet 1979 (£13.95); Vouvray
1983, Ackerman (£5.50); Gewürztraminer Réserve 1983, Boeckel
(£7.95); Torres Gran Coronas Black Label 1978 (£13.95); João Pires
Moscato Branco 1985 (£5.80); and Ch Musar 1980 (£7.90). Given a day's
notice you could indulge from the cellar with Ch Margaux 1957
(£31.65); Vosne-Romanée 1971, Jules Regnier (£12.65); Dom Pérignon

1976 (£42.17); or any of the three dozen Ports going back to Martinez 1958 (£18.50). Well-cooked food and B&B if you like sleeping where you drink.

MIDDLEWICH Cheshire

Tempters

11 Wheelock Street   TEL (060 684) 5175

OPEN Tue–Sat 7–10.30   CLOSED L, Sun, Mon, Chr–New Year, 1 week mid-Mar, 2 weeks mid-Oct   CREDIT CARDS Access, Visa
WHEELCHAIR ACCESS Difficult   VEGETARIAN DISHES By prior arrangement

Tempters is still tempting, so expect to find most people eating as well as drinking, with tables fully booked at weekends. The wine list continues to improve in both range and helpfulness. The five dullish wines offered by the glass (from 85p) encourage you to venture further: perhaps Bulgarian Cabernet Sauvignon (£5.15), or Ch du Grand Moulas, Côtes du Rhône 1985, Ryckwaert (£7.45) or California Firestone Merlot 1981 (£11.40). Attractive whites include Sauvignon Trois Mouline, Sarjeant (£6.95), English Adgestone 1983 (£7.30), Rully Blanc 1983, Cogny (£13.60) and Oppenheimer Krotenbrunnen Spätlese 1982, Deinhard (£7.95). Reasonable Sherries and Ports by the glass (Taylor's 10-year-old tawny, £1.10).

NORWICH Norfolk

Skippers

18 Bedford Street   TEL (0603) 622836

OPEN Mon–Fri 12.30–2.30   Fri, Sat, Mon 7–10   CLOSED Sun, public holidays, 25 & 26 Dec   CREDIT CARDS All accepted
WHEELCHAIR ACCESS Impossible   VEGETARIAN DISHES Some, more with notice

Skippers was in a state of flux as we went to press, with a juggling of directors and a change in operation: the wine bar is to be more like a 'real' wine bar, the shop will specialise even more in fine wines, and the first floor will house a restaurant with decent and frequently changed wines. Their enormous list is too tempting to ignore, but it would be foolish to give specific details. Go along for yourself and find out whether the mature clarets are still well chosen and modestly priced (with the option of having older vintages – 1945 or 1961, say – brought in from the shop); whether the Alsace wines are Gisselbrecht and the Beaujolais Duboeuf; whether the local Magdelen Rivaner and Auxerrois 1984 are still available by the glass at £1; whether the Champagnes still include George Goulet and Salon Le Mesnil 1976; and whether the Ports still go back to 1870. Let's hope you can still get a glass of Garvey's Sherry and Grand Vernaux house red or white.

OXFORD Oxfordshire

The Crypt

Frewin Court, off Cornmarket   TEL (0865) 251000

OPEN Mon–Sat 11.30–2.30, 6–10.30 (Fri 6–11, Sat 7–11)   CLOSED Sun, public holidays   CREDIT CARDS All accepted   WHEELCHAIR ACCESS Impossible   VEGETARIAN DISHES Some available

These 'wine and steak vaults' follow John Davy's attractive formula (see under Davys in the London section): Victorian atmosphere, sawdust floors, wine paraphernalia. The wine list is the standard reliable three dozen, sensibly chosen and priced, from French 'Ordnary' red or white (£4.85/85p) to Ch Moulinet 1980 (£11.50). Look out for blackboard special offers, and don't neglect the excellent Port, Sherry and Madeira from the wood. The food formula is less attractive, but adequate.

ROSSETT Clwyd

Churton's Wine & Food Bar

Machine House, Chester Road   TEL (0244) 570163

OPEN Mon–Sat 12 noon–2, 7–10   CLOSED Sun, public holidays, 24 Dec–2/3 Jan   CREDIT CARDS Access, Amex, Diners, Visa
WHEELCHAIR ACCESS With assistance   VEGETARIAN DISHES A selection

The Churton family's comfortably converted barn remains popular for exceptionally good food and a thoughtfully compiled list of interesting wines. With fewer split vintages and more shippers' names for Italian and German bottles, all would be perfection. The names that *do* appear are winners, and happily most straddle the great divide: the list groups wines under £8.50 in one section, those over that price in another. Alsace offers Boeckel (Pinot Blanc 1985, £6.60; Gewürztraminer Vendange Tardive 1983, £16.50). Rhône and Beaujolais come from Salavert (for whom Churtons are the UK agents): Côtes du Rhône, Blanc Goutte d'Orée 1985 (£5.30); Brouilly 1985 (£8.10); Côte Rôtie 1984 (£13.30). The Marcilly Burgundies include Bourgogne Aligoté 1986 (£7.95) and Monthélie 1983 (£11.25). The cheaper clarets include as house claret Ch La Croix-Millorit 1979 (£6.25/£1.20) and Ch La Garde 1978 (£8.45); while the more expensive section lists 18 temptations (Ch du Paradis 1982, £10.95, and Ch Malescot-St-Exupéry 1979, £15). Elsewhere you will find two vintages of the Lebanese Château Musar, Marqués de Cáceres white Rioja 1985 (£5.60), various Australian Rosemount Estates wines, and Montaudon Champagnes. There is an adjacent delicatessen and wine shop.

ROSS-ON-WYE Hereford & Worcester

The Wine Bar

24 High Street   TEL (0989) 67717

OPEN Mon–Sat 11–2.30, 7–11 Sun (public holidays only) 7–10.30
CLOSED Sun (except public holiday evenings), 25 & 26 Dec, 1st 2 weeks Feb
CREDIT CARDS None accepted WHEELCHAIR ACCESS Yes, but not to
lavatories VEGETARIAN DISHES Always several

The Bennets' cheerful wine bar in a 17th-century building lurks behind
a beamed coffee shop. The food is imaginative, the wine list
interesting, with helpful tasting notes. House Bordeaux Blanc de
Blancs and Côtes du Roussillon cost £4.15/80p, and most other prices
are equally restrained: Ch Méaume 1983 (£6.95); Crozes-Hermitage
1985, Paul Jaboulet (£7.50); Pinot d'Alsace 1985, Pfaffenheim (£5.75);
Chardonnay 1985, Tiefenbrunner (£6.80); Marqués de Griñon Seco
1985 (white, £6.45); and the local product, Three Choirs
Muller-Thürgau/Reichensteiner 1984 (£5.50). A useful dozen
half-bottles include Ch de Veyres 1982, Sauternes (£3.60).

SOUTHEND-ON-SEA Essex

The Pipe of Port

84 High Street   TEL (0702) 614606

OPEN Mon–Fri 11–2.30, 6–11 (Sat 7–11) CLOSED Sun, public holidays
CREDIT CARDS Access, Diners, Visa WHEELCHAIR ACCESS Impossible
VEGETARIAN DISHES Some

The Pipe may look old-fashioned, with its sawdusty floor and vast
barrels, but as we went to press it was having a Cruover machine
installed so that fine wines can be served by the glass: keep us posted.
House wines are from Loron (£4.75/£1.20) and Rudolf Müller
(£5/£1.30); others by the glass include Campillo Rioja (£5.40/£1.40) and
Varichon et Clerc's sparkling Blanc de Blancs (£8.60/£2.20). Thereafter,
you can opt for French country wines (Gamay du Haut-Poitou 1985,
£6.50), Davy's non-vintage house claret (£5.50) or hit the highspots
with, for example, Ch Fourcas-Hosten 1978 (£16.95) or Volnay 1983,
Jaffelin (£20.15). Don't miss the bin-ends at the bar, or the convenient
half-bottles of Don Zoilo Fino (£5.15) – or even the decadent-sounding
pint jug of vintage-character Port (£8.10). The food has an English
accent.

Please let us know if you agree or disagree with our choice of Britain's top
50 wine bars.

SOUTHWOLD Suffolk

The Crown

High Street   TEL (0502) 722275

OPEN Mon–Sat 10.30–2.30, 6–11   Sun 12 noon–2, 7–10.30
CREDIT CARDS Access, Amex, Visa   WHEELCHAIR ACCESS Yes
VEGETARIAN DISHES Some

An old-fashioned seaside resort with an inn that offers comfortable
beds, good food and distinguished wines seems almost too much to
hope for. But it does exist, and Southwold's Crown also throws in
concerts and special events, many of them wine-related. And a
Cruover machine which allows them to serve 18 carefully chosen wines
by glass as well as bottle: with over 250 bins on the Adnams' list (see
the WHERE TO BUY section), the choice understandably changes
monthly. Recently it included Tiefenbrunner Pinot Blanc 1985
(£6.25/£1.25); Australian Moss Wood Estate Chardonnay 1985
(£12.40/£3.10) from Margaret River; Rully Rouge 1982, Cogny
(£10.20/£2.55); Bonnes Mares 1976, Domaine Joseph Drouhin
(£26/£6.50); and Adnams' Coaster 10-year-old Tawny Port from
Taylor's (£12.30/£1.55). The 20-page list takes some digesting,
especially since Simon Loftus's notes are well worth absorbing *before*
the wine: for example, there are 40 clarets, with a general note on each
vintage as well as specific details of each wine, from house Bordeaux
Rouge 1984, Pierre Coste (£6.05) to Ch Latour 1961 (£170), with
worthwhile petits as well as grands châteaux in between. The rest is a
roster of admirable producers in every area, and the mark-ups gentle
on the whole. A special offer provides three glasses of wine for £5 to go
with the menu (a rosé, a red or white, and a pudding wine).

STAMFORD Lincolnshire

The George at Stamford

                                                   TEL (0780) 55171

OPEN Mon–Sat 11–3, 6–11   Sun 6.30–10.30   CREDIT CARDS All accepted
WHEELCHAIR ACCESS Limited   VEGETARIAN DISHES Yes

The Garden Lounge of this old coaching-inn makes an unexpectedly
green and pleasant wine bar with a generous buffet and inventive hot
dishes. Ivo Vannocci, Poste Hotels' director, has chosen about 20
first-rate Italian wines, all of which are now available by glass as well as
bottle (thanks to the installation of Canada's answer to the Cruover):
Gold Muskateller Atesino 1985, Lageder (£6.85/£1.40); Soave Col
Baraca 1985, Masi (£8.50/£1.70); Rosso Cònero, Enzo Marcella (specially
bottled for the George, £6.55/£1.25); Serego Alighieri 1983, Masi
(£8.95/£1.80); and Moscato d'Asti 1985, Fontanafredda (£7.90/£1.60).

Others on offer by the glass include Ch Lynch-Bages 1979 (£4.20).
Garden loungers may also choose from the hotel's main list, which has
rewarding tasting notes.

TAUNTON Somerset

Porters

49 East Reach   TEL (0823) 256688

OPEN Mon–Fri 12 noon–2.30, 7–11   Sat 7–11   CLOSED Sun
CREDIT CARDS Access, Visa   WHEELCHAIR ACCESS Possible
VEGETARIAN DISHES Selection available

Unpretentious, friendly, with newspapers on sticks and occasional live
pianists, Porters is attracting local support, not least for its interesting
menu and reasonably priced wines. The list, though rather hit and
miss as to vintages and shippers, has its heart in the right place. There
are about 70 wines, starting with French house (£5/90p), lingering
further in France with, for example, good basic Mâcon Rouge 1983,
Loron (£6.40) as well as the more ambitious Ch Picque Caillou 1979,
Graves (£10.25), in reds, and Dopff & Irion Alsace wines and
Savennières, Clos du Papillon 1985 (£7.75) among the whites. Others
of interest include Sonoma Valley Zinfandel 1983 (£9.85) and the
excellent local dry white from Staplecombe (£5.80).

THAXTED Essex

The Cuckoo

36 Town Street   TEL (0371) 830482

OPEN Tue–Sat 12–2.30, 7–11   Sun 12–2, 7–10.30   CLOSED Mon, 1–2 weeks
Jan   CREDIT CARDS Access, Diners, Visa   WHEELCHAIR ACCESS Difficult, not
to lavatories   VEGETARIAN DISHES Several

This pretty village is lucky in its small wine bar, which could serve as a
model to many: about 60 well-chosen wines are carefully listed with
helpful tasting notes – and ungrasping prices. House wines include
Fleur de Lys dry white and Barton & Guestier's Partager red (£4/80p);
and others also by the glass: Torres Viña Sol 1985 (£5.45/£1.05); Franzia
California Cabernet Sauvignon (£5.20/£1). The half-dozen clarets have
decent bottle-age (there is now a vintage chart on the list to help
waverers decide): Ch Puy-Barbe 1979 (£5.80); Ch Clos-des-Jacobins
1978 (£17.80). Other interesting ideas include Ménétou-Salon
Sauvignon 1985, Jacky Rat (£8.30); Winkeler Hasensprung Riesling
Auslese 1976, Nagler (£12.50); Brown Brothers Semillon 1984 (£9.60);
Syrah de Pays de l'Ardèche 1986 (£5.95); and Chinon, La Baronnie
Madeleine 1978 (£8.95) – rare to see a Chinon of this age outside
growers' own cellars. Home-cooked snacks in the bar.

How to spot a restaurant winner

The appearance of a restaurant wine list is often a good clue to the quality of the wines. JAMES AINSWORTH *gives some guidance on how to spot the clues.*

For a surprising number of restaurants, even in the late Eighties, wine is still something of an afterthought, a necessary evil whose only saving grace is that it can be marked up to pay not just for itself, but also for half the wages and some of the food.

For a few restaurateurs, it is a consuming hobby. Handwritten lists, maps, summaries, introductions, asterisks, and a fabulous range of bottles and halves from all over the world at knock-down prices, are all part of a Messianic zeal to convert doubters to the cause. For some reason this religious fervour seems to be at its height in Scotland: **La Potinière** in Gullane and the **Peat Inn** in Fife are among the best places to worship.

In between these extremes are lots of other troupers who wear their hearts on their wine lists. Some lists amount to no more than a scruffy bit of paper. While there is an outside chance that a genuinely good list will be short, and so well used that it becomes dog-eared from enthusiastic custom, in most cases it will warn that the buying is likely to have been as slap-happy as the presentation. The best plan is to test it out with a glass of house wine before committing any real money.

But smart, printed lists are not *ipso facto* any better. The trouble with these is that they cost a lot to produce, and are too rigid to respond to the new discoveries and changing vintages that make wine interesting. They are typified by entries such as 'Beaujolais 1984/85/86' to cover any eventuality. The wines are controlled by the merchant, who is likely to send along any old Beaujolais, and poorly managed by the restaurateur, who probably doesn't notice what he's selling anyway. So wherever you see a printed list, always ask for up-to-the-minute details, and check the label carefully before the bottle is opened.

I wish I had a pound for every time I had come across a bald wine list, usually in an Italian restaurant, which said something like 'Barolo, £16' or 'Chianti, £9'. There are some brilliant Italian wines but if the restaurant is too arrogant or unthinking to provide the necessary information, how do you know whether this Barolo, or this Chianti, is one of them? The solution is to get them to bring out all the bottles so that you can have a look. The ensuing circus will either make or break the evening.

But this business of having to make the best of a poor list is fortunately on the wane. News filters through to restaurants slowly, but it generally gets there in the end. One simple indicator of this is Antipodean wine. The home drinker will by now have become used to Australian wine as a regular tipple: the quality is good, the price is right, the shops are full of it. Over the past year, the number of restaurants with a token Aussie has increased considerably. New Zealand wines, on the other hand, which have been in the shops for a much shorter time, are barely making a mark in restaurants. Give them another year, possibly two, and they will pop up more frequently, as the foodies begin to catch on.

The supremacy of the Totally French List (TFL) is being increasingly eroded. The **Cedar Restaurant** of the Evesham Hotel takes a swipe at it by not listing a single French (or German) wine at all. Yet it still offers plenty of choice (from thirty countries), and relies on the New World to keep up the quality.

Nevertheless, it will take a lot of chipping away at the TFL before it ever looks like being toppled. And indeed why should it be, when it is so easy to fulfil all the conditions of a good wine list without looking any further? The most common problems with a TFL, though, are a reverential treatment of the major communes, top châteaux and great vintages of Bordeaux, and a willingness to list high-priced Burgundies. But we know, and restaurateurs ought to know, that there are some extremely good buys among the petits châteaux, and plenty of alternatives to Burgundy, more directly in the case of whites, indirectly, in the sense of being able to partner most dishes equally well, in the case of reds. If the list does not explore these possibilities, you can take it as a sure sign that the restaurant hopes to sell on fancy names and prices, and should proceed cautiously.

Big names are just the ticket for those who go to restaurants for comfort and reassurance, but the more enterprising customer who looks to the four principal second-tier regions of France will often be rewarded with the best value under £10.

Alsace is still a bargain area: even if '83s and '85s are marked up high, there are the humble '84s, which in many cases go better with food anyway.

The Rhône is dominated on many lists by Jaboulet, but his cheaper labels – Parallèle 45, Côtes du Ventoux, for instance – are dependable. There is some Vacqueyras and Gigondas about, but not much. Côtes du Rhône is also good value, depending on the producer. Restaurateurs are unlikely to list youthful, fruity reds from the Ardèche unless they have *some* interest in wine, so if you see one it a) will augur well for the rest of the collection, and b) should be a reasonable buy in its own right.

The Loire can be hit and miss. A few restaurants (**RSJ** for one) specialise in it, but by no means all of them can rustle up a decent Muscadet. Chenin Blanc is one of the Loire's chief problems, another is that we don't drink much rosé, so that leaves Pouilly and Sancerre centre stage. If prima donna prices are asked for these, see if there's a red. If not, you're left with Sauvignon, and there's no excuse for it not being young and fresh.

Restaurants adopt one of three approaches to Provence. The first is to ignore it altogether. The second, equally wrong, is to list Ch Simone, a Bellet and some Domaines Ott, which are the most expensive ones they can find. The correct procedure is to accept that there are decent and relatively inexpensive wines from Coteaux d'Aix-en-Provence, Côtes de Provence, Salins du Midi and others. Domaine de Trévallon is the fashionable one, but it's a hefty Cabernet so would respond well if vintages could be cellared for a little longer.

The best value French wines should be vins de pays, but restaurants haven't taken them on board as enthusiastically as supermarkets and wine warehouses. The reason, I suspect, is that the mark-up (even at 100 per cent) is too low. With a whole case sale, a warehouse can make sufficient profit, but in a restaurant, where a bottle is drunk between perhaps two, and priced at less than £5 on the list, it simply doesn't pay its way. The restaurateur applies the same reasoning to them as he does to the classic French regions, which results in only the better-known, and more expensive, wines appearing, of which the decidedly youthful Mas de Daumas Gassac is a prime example.

A similar philosophy applies to Italy and Spain. In an attempt to get away from anonymous Trebbiano and Sangiovese or Soave and Valpolicella, a typical restaurateur will jump straight for Tignanello and Sassicaia or Gaja and Lungarotti. These are fine, and more than welcome, but there are still gaps in the middle price range which need to be plugged. Some Veneto and Alto Adige wines are surfacing, but not enough, and a Piedmontese Barbera is still a rare bird.

As for Spain, the top places want to show off their Vega Sicilia, and most restaurants stock a couple of Reserva Riojas. The other regions still have a hard time of it, but Torres is making a big push to supply all the best restaurants, convinced that somewhere among the dozen or more grape varieties they handle there is one that will go with whatever is on the menu.

That, of course, is the key to success: bringing wine and food into contact with each other. At its most obvious, there's not much point in having pages of mature claret in a fish restaurant; but there is a lot of territory to explore concerning the interaction of food and drink, to increase our enjoyment of the ensemble. A start has been made by some restaurants – **L'Escargot** was perhaps the first and now has a few disciples – in grouping the wines by style rather than by region: **Brown & Boswell** and **Bowlish House** are two that do it this way. It helps to pick out, at a glance, a robust red wine for a garlicky steak or winter casserole.

But there are signs that more interesting developments are on the way. Menus are being streamlined. The set menu with a small choice continues to consolidate its lead over the large carte; some, for example **Clarke's**, have done away with choice, John Tovey at **Miller Howe** all but gave it up years ago, most boarding houses have never even heard of it. This gives the restaurateur a chance to offer a particular wine by the glass which he feels will bring out the best in both it and the food. Spread over an evening the wastage should be minimal. (Keeping wine either under nitrogen or a vacuum allows more room for manoeuvre, but the machines don't come cheap.)

A first-class example of this in operation can be seen at the **Village Restaurant** in Ramsbottom. For a start the list is impressive, arranged by grape variety, and would deserve its Bottle award in *The Good Food Guide* if it did nothing else. But since there is no choice on the menu (you eat the food or you don't), three wines are chosen to accompany its different stages. The system is informal, and flexible enough to allow suggestions from the customer, which is a strength. This is just one example, and in its infancy, but as a project it takes the idea of relating food and drink more seriously than most, and at the same time makes it more fun.

Details of restaurants with interesting wine lists referred to in the text:

La Potinière, Main Street, Gullane, Lothian TEL (0620) 843214

The Peat Inn, Peat Inn, Fife TEL (033 484) 206

Cedar Restaurant, Evesham Hotel, Cooper's Lane, Evesham, Hereford & Worcester TEL (0386) 49111

RSJ, 13A Coin Street, London SE1 TEL 01-928 4554

L'Escargot, 48 Greek Street, London W1 TEL 01-437 2679

Brown & Boswell, 28 High Street, Wallingford, Oxfordshire
TEL (0491) 34078

Bowlish House, Wells Road, Shepton Mallet, Somerset
TEL (0749) 2022

Clarke's, 124 Kensington Church Street, London W8 TEL 01-221 9225

Miller Howe, Rayrigg Road, Windermere, Cumbria TEL (096 62) 2536

Village Restaurant, 18 Market Place, Ramsbottom, Lancashire
TEL (070 682) 5070

This is only a short selection of restaurants with good wine lists. For much more detail, we suggest that you refer to *The Good Food Guide 1988*, available from bookshops or from *Consumers' Association, Castlemead, Gascoyne Way, Hertford SG14 1LH* (£10.95, postage and packing free).

English vineyards open to the public

ENGLAND

AVON

Avonwood (1 acre)
Dr J D Minors, Seawalls Road,
Sneyd Park, Bristol
(0272) 686635
VA VS

BERKSHIRE

Ascot (3 acres)
Col A R Robertson, Ascot Farm,
Winkfield Road, Ascot
(0990) 23563
V CP WTF VS M

The Holt (1½ acres)
Brigadier W G R Turner CBE,
Woolton Hill, Newbury
(0635) 253680
VA

Joyous Garde (2½ acres)
D T Dulake, Crazies Hill, Wargrave
(073 522) 2102
VA OD WTF VS

Thames Valley (17 acres)
J S E Leighton, Stanlake Park,
Twyford
(0734) 340176
CP/BA VA

Westbury (12½ acres)
B H Theobald, Westbury Farm,
Purley on Thames, Nr Reading
(073 57) 3123
CP VA WTC VS M

BUCKINGHAMSHIRE

Wickenden (4 acres)
R H Lock, Wickenden, Cliveden
Road, Taplow
(0628) 29455
CP/BA VA WTC VS S

CAMBRIDGESHIRE

Chilford Hundred Vineyard
(18 acres)
S Alper, Chilford Hall, Balsham
Road, Linton, Nr Cambridge
(0223) 892641
CP/BA OD VA WTC M VS

The Isle of Ely (2½ acres)
Messrs Reeve-Goring, Twentypence
Road, Wilburton
(0353) 740799
V VA VS

DEVON

Beenleigh Manor (1 acre)
A K Wilson-Gough, Beenleigh
Manor, Harbertonford, Totnes
(080423) 4738
VA

Highfield (1 acre)
Ian & Jennifer Fraser, Long Drag,
Tiverton
(0884) 256362
V VA OD VS WTF M

Loddiswell (4 acres)
R H Sampson, Lilwell, Loddiswell,
Kingsbridge
(0548) 550221
V CP OD VA WTC VS

Whitmoore House (2 acres)
Richard and Ann Trussell, Ashill,
Cullompton
(0884) 40145
VA WTF CP/BA VS M

Whitstone (1½ acres)
George and Laura Barclay, Bovey
Tracey, Nr Newton Abbot
(0626) 832280
OD VA WTF VS

Yearlstone (2 acres)
Miss G Pearkes, Chilton, Bickleigh,
Tiverton
(088 45) 450
VA OD VS WTF

ESSEX

Nevards (1 acre)
W Hudson, Boxted, Colchester
(0206) 230 306
VA

GLOUCESTERSHIRE

St Anne's (2 acres)
A V & B R Edwards, Wain House,
Oxenhall, Newent
(098 982) 313
CP/BA WTF V VS

Tapestry Wines (3 acres)
D M Jones, The Vineyard, Wells
Farm, Apperley
(045 278) 435
V CP VS

Three Choirs (20 acres)
T W Day, Rhyle House, Welsh House
Lane, Newent
(053 185) 223/555
V CP/BA OD VA WTF VS S

HAMPSHIRE

Aldermoor (5 acres)
M F & W A Baerselman, Aldermoors,
Picket Hill, Ringwood
(04254) 2912
V VA CP WTF

Beaulieu (6 acres)
The Hon Ralph Montagu, John
Montagu Buildings, Beaulieu,
Nr Brockenhurst
(0590) 612345
VA CP VS

Broadley (1 acre)
D H Brown, Broadley Farm, Mead
End, Sway
(0590) 682310
V BA

Holly Bush (4 acres)
C & E Landells, Holly Bush Farm
(A337), Brockenhurst
(0590) 23054
V CP

Lymington (6 acres)
C W & M M R Sentance, Wainsford
Road, Pennington, Lymington
(0590) 72112
V WTC VS

Meon Valley (8 acres)
C J Hartley, Hillgrove, Swanmore,
Southampton
(0489) 877435
VA CP OD VS WTF

HEREFORD & WORCESTER

Astley (4½ acres)
R M Bache, The Crundels, Astley,
Stourport-on-Severn
(02993) 2907
CP VA VS

Broadfield (10 acres)
Mr & Mrs K R H James, Broadfield
Court Estate, Bodenham
(056 884) 483/275
CP/VA OD/VA WTC VS S

Croft Castle Vineyard (1½ acres)
The Hon Mrs F Uhlman, Croft Castle,
Nr Leominster
(056 885) 560
V CP VS

HERTFORDSHIRE

Frithsden (2.5 acres)
Peter and Anne Latchford,
Frithsden, Nr Hemel Hempstead
(0442) 57902
CP/VA WTF VA VS

ISLE OF WIGHT

Adgestone (9 acres)
K C Barlow (and others), Upper
Road, Adgestone, Sandown
(0983) 402503
VA WTF VS

Barton Manor (5½ acres)
Mr & Mrs A H Goddard,
Whippingham, East Cowes
(0983) 292835
CP OD WTC VS S

Cranmore (12 acres)
V J Hui, Solent Road, Cranmore,
Nr Yarmouth
(0983) 761414
VA WTC

Hamstead (4 acres)
T J Munt, Hamstead Vineyard,
Yarmouth
(0983) 760463
VA OD VS WTC

Morton Manor (1¾ acres)
J A J Trzebski, Morton Manor
Vineyard, Brading
(0983) 406168
V V/BA WTC CP/BA M S VS

KENT

Bardingley (2 acres)
B Turner, Babylon Lane,
Hawkenbury, Staplehurst
(0580) 892264
V VS WTC

Biddenden (18 acres)
R A Barnes, Little Whatmans,
Biddenden
(0580) 291726
V CP WTF VS S

Chiddingstone (6½ acres)
J M & D Quirk, Vexour Farm,
Chiddingstone, Edenbridge
(0892) 870277
VA OD

Conghurst (¾ acre)
Miss J Helen Bridgwater, Conghurst
Oast, Conghurst Lane, Hawkhurst
(05805) 2634
WTF VA VS

Elham Valley (3 acres)
Mrs J V Allen & Mr P W Warden,
Breach, Barham
(0227) 831266
VA WTC VS OD

Harbledown & Chaucer (2 acres)
A G Fisher & L C W Rea, Isabel Mead
Farm, Upper Harbledown,
Canterbury
(0227) 463913
WTC V

Harbourne (2½ acres)
L S Williams,
Vineyard: High Halden,
Nr Tenterden
Winery & Wine Shop: Wittersham,
Nr Tenterden
(07977) 420
V VA VS WTF

Ightham (3 acres)
J M B & K R Corfe, Ivy Hatch,
Nr Sevenoaks
(0732) 810348
VA

Lamberhurst (55 acres)
K McAlpine, Ridge Farm,
Lamberhurst, Nr Tunbridge Wells
(0892) 890844 & 890286
CP/VA V OD CP WTF VS S M

Leeds Castle (2¾ acres)
Leeds Castle Foundation, Leeds
Castle, Maidstone
(0622) 65400
CP OD VA S VS

Penshurst (12 acres)
D E Westphal, Grove Road,
Penshurst
(0892) 870255
CP/BA WTF V VS OD M/S

St Nicholas of Ash (2 acres)
J G Wilkinson, Moat Lane, Ash,
Canterbury
(0304) 812670
CP/BA WTF V VS S

Staple (7 acres)
W T Ash, Church Farm, Staple,
Canterbury
(0304) 812571
CP/BA V VA WTC OD VS

Tenterden (12 acres)
W Garner & D Todd, Spots Farm,
Small Hythe, Tenterden
(05806) 3033
V CP WTF VS M

Three Corners (1½ acres)
Lt Col C S Galbraith, Beacon Lane,
Woodnesborough
(0304) 812025
V A

NORFOLK

Elmham Park (7 acres)
R S Don, Elmham House, Dereham
(036 281) 571 or 363
CP VA WTF

Heywood (2 acres)
R C Aikman, Heywood, Holly Farm,
The Heywood, Diss
(0379) 2461 & 01-340 9635
OD VA

Lexham Hall (8 acres)
W R B Foster and Partners, Lexham
Hall, Nr Litcham, Kings Lynn
(0328) 701288
CP/BA OD VA WTF VS

Pulham (6 acres)
P W Cook, Mill Lane, Pulham
Market, Diss
(037 976) 342 and 672
CP VA WTC VS

NOTTINGHAMSHIRE

Eglantine (3⅓ acres)
A M & V Skuriat, Ash Lane, Costock,
Nr Loughborough
(050 982) 2386
VA OD WTF VS

OXFORDSHIRE

Bothy (3 acres)
R & D B Fisher, Bothy Cottage,
Frilford Heath, Abingdon
(0491) 681484
VA VS WTF

Chiltern Valley (3 acres)
D J Ealand, Old Luxters Farm,
Hambleden, Nr Henley
(049163) 330
VA OD WTF

SOMERSET

Brympton D'Evercy (1 acre)
Charles E B Clive-Ponsonby-Fane,
Yeovil
(093 586) 2528
V CP VS S

Castle Cary (4 acres)
Mr & Mrs P C Woosnam Mills,
Honeywick House, Castle Cary
(0963) 50323
V VS WTF

Cheddar Valley (3 acres)
N A & P K McDonald, Stoneleys,
Hillside, Axbridge
(0934) 732280
CP/BA WTF V VS

Coxley (4 acres)
W Austin, Church Farm, Coxley,
Nr Wells
(0749) 73854
CP OD WTF V VS S/M

H R H Vineyard (& English Basket
Centre) (8 acres)
Nigel Hector, Alastair Reid, Derek
Hector, The Willows, Curload, Stoke
St Gregory, Taunton
(0823 69) 418
V VS

Pilton Manor (6½ acres)
N de M Godden, Pilton Manor,
Shepton Mallet
(074 989) 325
CP OD WTF V VA VS WTC M/S

Spring Farm (12 acres)
Mr & Mrs T Rees, Moorlynch,
Bridgwater
(0458) 210393
CP/BA V WTF VS S

Staplecombe (4 acres)
M M Cursham, Burlands Farm,
Staplegrove, Taunton
(082 345) 217
VA WTF

Whatley Vineyard & Herb Garden
(4 acres)
M J E Witt, Old Rectory, Whatley,
Nr Frome
(037 384) 467
V CP VS WTC S

Wootton (6 acres)
C L B Gillespie, North Wootton,
Shepton Mallet
(074 989) 359
V CP VS

Wraxall (5½ acres)
A S Holmes and Partners, Shepton
Mallet
(074 986) 486 and 331
V VA CP/BA WTC VS

SUFFOLK

Brandeston Priory (6½ acres)
H P B Dow, The Priory, Brandeston,
Woodbridge
(072 882) 462
V WTF CP VS

Broadwater (3½ acres)
A W & S F Stocker, Broadwater,
Framlingham
(0728) 723645
CP VA V WTF VS

Bruisyard (10 acres)
Mr & Mrs I H Berwick, Church Road,
Bruisyard, Saxmundham
(072 875) 281
CP/BA WTF V VS

Chickering (2½ acres)
P H Day, Chickering Hall, Hoxne,
Eye
(037 975) 227
V A

Willow Grange (1 acre)
W A Sibley, Street Farm, Crowfield,
Nr Ipswich
(044 979) 234
CP/BA WTC VA OD VS

SUSSEX

Berwick Glebe (2 acres)
Jane Broster & Doreen Birks,
Frensham Cottage, Berwick,
Nr Polegate
(0323) 870361
VA VS WTC

Bookers (5 acres)
J M & R V Pratt, Foxhole Lane,
Bolney
(044 482) 575
VA VS

Breaky Bottom (4 acres)
Peter Hall, Northease, Lewes
(0273) 476427
V WTF CP VA VS M

Carr Taylor (21 acres)
David and Linda Carr Taylor,
Westfield, Hastings
(0424) 752501
V CP/BA WTF VA VS S/M

Chilsdown (10½ acres)
Ian Paget, The Old Station House,
Singleton, Chichester
(0243 63) 398
V CP/BA OD VS WTF

Ditchling (5 acres)
David & Ann Mills, Claycroft, Beacon
Road, Ditchling, Hassocks
(079 18) 2634
V VS WTF

Downers (7 acres)
Commander & Mrs E G Downer,
Downers, Clappers Lane, Fulking,
Henfield
(079 156) 484
V VS WTF VA S

English Wine Centre (1 acre)
Christopher & Lucy Ann, Drusillas
Corner, Alfriston
(0323) 870532
CP M V S OD VA VS WTF

Five Chimneys (5 acres)
W Russell, Hadlow Down, Uckfield
(082 581) 3159/2541
VA OD

Flexerne (5 acres)
Peter & Brenda Smith, Fletching
Common, Newick
(082 572) 2548
VA

Hooksway (3 acres)
S R Moore, c/o Lares, Bepton Road,
Midhurst
(073 081) 3317
VA VS WTF

Leeford (25 acres)
J P Sax, Leeford Vineyard,
Whattlington, Battle
(04246) 3183
WTF VA VS

Lurgashall (Winery only)
Virginia & Jerome Schooler,
Windfallwood, Lurgashall,
Nr Petworth
(0428 78) 292 or 654
CP/BA WTF VA VS

Lyminster (1½ acres)
J & V Rankin, Lyminster Road,
Nr Arundel
(0903) 882587 (wine shop) and
883393 (vineyard)
V VA WTF VS

Nutbourne Manor (14 acres)
J J Sanger, Nutbourne Manor,
Nr Pulborough
(07983) 3554
OD V VS WTC

Rock Lodge (4 acres)
Norman Cowderoy, Scaynes Hill
(044 486) 224
WTC VS S

St George's (20 acres)
Gay Biddlecombe, Waldron,
Heathfield
(043 53) 2156
M/S V VA CP WTF OD VS

Seymours (2 acres)
Mr & Mrs H McMullen, Forest Road,
Horsham
(0403) 52397
CP/BA VA OD VS WTF

Steyning (3 acres)
Joyce Elsden, Nash Hotel, Ashurst
Road, Steyning
(0903) 814988
CP/BA VA VS WTC S

Swiftsden House (3½ acres)
William & Moira Gammell, Swiftsden
House, Hurst Green
(058 086) 287
VA VS WTF

WILTSHIRE

Chalkhill (6½ acres)
D Mann, Knowle Farm,
Bowerchalke, Salisbury
(0722) 780451
VA WTF

Elms Cross (3 acres)
A R Shaw, Elms Cross,
Bradford-on-Avon
(022 16) 6917
V VS

Fonthill (6 acres)
C P M Craig-McFeeley &
J F Edginton, The Old Rectory,
Fonthill Gifford, Tisbury
(0747) 870231/89365
VA VS WTF

Sherston Earl (3 acres)
Norman Sellers, Sherston,
Malmesbury
(0666) 840716
V VS WTF

Stitchcombe (5 acres)
N Thompson, Stitchcombe,
Nr Marlborough
(0672) 52297
V CP OD VA VS S

Tytherley (1¼ acres)
J R M Donald, Mallards,
West Tytherley, Salisbury
(0794) 40644
VA VS WTC

WALES

GLAMORGAN

Croffta (3 acres)
J L M Bevan, Groes-Faen, Pontyclun
(0443) 223876
VA VS WTC

GWENT

Tintern Parva (4 acres)
Martin & Gay Rogers, Parva Farm,
Tintern, Nr Chepstow
(029 18) 636
CP VS V WTF

CHANNEL ISLANDS

La Mare (6 acres)
R H and A M Blayney, St Mary,
Jersey
(0534) 81491
CP/BA V WTC VS M (Light)

Serving and storing wine

Serving wine

Temperature Port, and medium-bodied and heavier reds, need to be served warm enough for their aromas to evaporate; chilling white, rosé, light red, sweet or sparkling wines in the fridge for a couple of hours adds to their freshness, while chilling any poor wine will help disguise its defects. A good, full-bodied white such as a California or Australian Chardonnay, a fine white Burgundy or a fino Sherry needs less chilling – just an hour in the fridge is enough, or the aromas will not be released.

If you're caught short of cold wine, ten minutes in the freezer will certainly do the wine no harm – but beware of lollipops in broken bottles. In desperation, for a not particularly fine wine, ice cubes are the other obvious solution – though it's a shame to water down a *good* wine. Once your bottle is cool, good alternatives to the ice bucket are the widely available plastic insulating sleeves, and insulated portable bottle-bags useful for picnics.

It's more difficult to warm up a bottle of red instantly without overheating parts of the bottle and risking spoiling the wine's aromas. Be gentle. Pour it into a warm, not hot, decanter, or, better still, just wait for it to warm up in the glass – cupping in your hands will help.

Glasses To taste a wine at its best and to catch all the aromas, use a glass that curves in at the upper edges and is big enough to hold a reasonable amount. The thinner and finer the glass, the finer the wine will taste: experiment and see. Any engraving, and particularly smokiness or colour in the glass, will of course make it impossible to inspect the wine's colour properly. Filling the glass just half to two-thirds full leaves an air-space into which the aromas can evaporate and remain trapped until sniffed out. It also leaves scope to swirl the wine around the glass without putting table cloth or carpet at risk. Nowadays the flat coupe-shaped Champagne glasses are fortunately less common: they are hopeless, allowing expensive bubbles to escape in a flash from their enormous surface. Best are the tall, thin Champagne flutes, with only a tiny surface area, but there's nothing wrong with using an ordinary large wine glass for Champagne and other sparkling wines. For Sherry, use a copita – a tulip-shaped glass – and avoid the narrow-waisted Elgin glass.

Opening Remove the foil or plastic capsule completely, or cut it well underneath the bottle lip, so that it cannot possibly come into contact with the wine: this would be just messy with modern aluminium foil or plastic, potentially poisonous in the long term if it's the old-fashioned lead variety! If the cork won't budge, hold the neck for a minute or so under fairly hot running water and try again. For corks that drop into the bottle, there's a long spindly-legged plastic gadget called a 'Decorker'; you may have to resort to a coffee filter or a sieve if you make unacceptable quantities of cork crumbs.

Champagne corks Twist the bottle by holding it firmly at the base: don't twist the cork or it may break. Hold the top firmly and be careful where you point the bottle: people have lost eyes through flying corks. If the mushroom top breaks off as you twist the bottle, carefully use a corkscrew. Always disturb the bottle as little as possible beforehand, and keep a glass on hand to catch accidental fountains.

Checking the quality Pour some for *yourself* first to check that it is sound before serving your guests; and don't forget to check subsequent bottles. There may be a difference between two bottles of a quite simple wine, so make sure that any wine connossieurs among your guests have finished up the dregs of one bottle in their glass before serving them from the next; they may be deeply shocked if you mix bottles, especially of different wines! Non-winos will think this nonsense – so just top them up.

Unfinished bottles Still wines can just be recorked, or poured into a smaller bottle for better keeping. Special clamp tops are available for stopping half-drunk Champagnes or sparkling wines.

Please write to tell us about any ideas for features you would like to see in next year's edition or in *Which? Wine Monthly*.

Storing wine

Few people are fortunate enough today to own a cellar. It is possible to buy air-conditioned/chilled cabinets storing a considerable number of bottles. Those with neither cellar nor cabinet should choose a spot in the house where there is least risk of vibration (away from scampering feet) and where the temperature is fairly constant (away from central heating and water pipes, and away from outer walls). Wine will mature more quickly in a warm place, and may spoil or re-ferment if suddenly exposed to heat-wave conditions. Very cold conditions may cause more solids to be deposited in the bottle, though most medium to low-priced wines are now chilled before bottling to forestall this risk. Avoid these extremes and temperature fluctuations, and you should have no problems. The bottles should lie on their sides, to keep the corks moist. Dried-up corks let air into the bottle and are also difficult to remove. It takes some time, however, for a properly capsuled bottle to come to any harm.

For the cellared few, the main problem can be dampness, which can obscure and rot the labels. The best answer is plastic bottle sleeves, or Clingfilm, or spraying the labels with hair spray! And beware of introducing rare, cellar-blackened bottles without washing them carefully. One wine expert we know has cellar walls, bottles and labels sprouting slowly with healthy (and harmless) black cellar mould, and some of the labels are already hard to read – all the results of one aged bottle of Champagne from a French cellar.

Decanting

There are no hard and fast rules about whether to decant or not. It's a favourite subject for argument in the wine magazines – especially in the letters columns. But a general consensus does emerge about when it can be an advantage.

• When a bottle of wine has a sediment in the bottom, decanting is essential unless you want to end up with the last glasses full of unpleasant black sluge.

• Strong red wines, which may have spent some time in wood before bottling – Barolo, some Portuguese reds, Gran Reserva Rioja or Rhônes, for example – will benefit from some decanting, especially if they are quite young.

• Conversely, old vintages of any wine will suffer positive harm if decanted – the remains of the fruit will combine with oxygen and the whole delicious fragrance of mature wine will disappear.

- The only reason for decanting everyday reds will be to get rid of some of the sulphury smells that may still linger in the bottle. A few minutes in a glass will achieve the same effect.

- Some whites – particularly those which have been in wood and are still quite young – will benefit from an hour in a decanter before serving. Make sure the decanter is cool before pouring the wine in and then keep it in a cool place or in the fridge.

The only time when care needs to be taken over decanting is when the wine has thrown a sediment and the purpose of decanting is to leave this in the bottle and the clear wine in the decanter. Before decanting, stand the bottle upright for two or three days to allow the deposit to collect in the bottom. Draw the cork and pour the wine carefully into the decanter. If the bottle is dusty from the cellar, a light shining through from below will help identify when the sediment reaches the neck of the bottle. If you're at all worried about letting the sediment pass into the decanter, despite all your efforts, a coffee filter paper should solve the problem.

How the law can help you

If you buy a bottle that is bad or isn't what the label says it is, the law offers you some protection and redress. Barrister JENI McCALLION *sets out just what the law can do to assist you.*

In the eyes of the Law, if not the connoisseur, wine is any liquor obtained from the alcoholic fermentation of fresh grapes or the must of fresh grapes. Wine can, of course, be made from other fruits or vegetables, but in this case an indication of the type of fruit or vegetable used must appear on the label immediately before the word wine: Apple wine or Elderberry wine, for example.

There are a number of laws which protect you when you buy and drink wine. Civil laws cover things like getting a bottle of Burgundy when you ask for a bottle of Bordeaux. It's generally necessary to enforce your civil rights through court action if necessary. Criminal offences include selling adulterated wine and false or misleading labelling – and are matters for your local trading standards department. Some things may infringe both the Criminal and Civil law. So if the pickled remains of a snail drop into your glass as you drain the last of your bottle of Châteauneuf-du-Pape, and you are violently ill as a result, the seller may be guilty of a criminal offence, under the Food Act, and you might also be able to sue the seller or the manufacturer for damages.

Here are some of the things that you might need to know:

1 *You notice a bottle of 'de-alcoholised' wine on sale in your local off-licence. This seems to be a bit of a contradiction in terms – is it legal?*

Yes. As long as the product is made from fresh grapes or fresh grape must and has been fermented, the fact that the alcohol is then removed doesn't prevent it from being called wine. The term 'non-alcoholic wine', on the other hand, should be used only to describe a drink made from unfermented grape juice which is intended exclusively for communion or sacramental use – and it must be clearly labelled as such. You're unlikely to find this in your local supermarket.

2 *You see a very attractive wine offer in a magazine. A delivery time of 28 days is given and you send off your order, along with a cheque for the full amount. Your cheque is cashed, but six weeks later you're still waiting for the wine to arrive. What should you do?*

Write to the company concerned giving them an ultimatum – either they deliver within the next, say, 14 days, or you will consider the order cancelled. If you get your wine within the specified time, all well and good; if not, you should write to the advertising manager at the publication in which the advertisement appeared. The advertising manager should see that your complaint is investigated. Your legal rights when buying goods by mail order are the same as those when buying from a shop. So if the company fail to deliver the goods, you are entitled to your money back, plus any additional cost in getting the same wine elsewhere.

3 *You buy a bottle of inexpensive red wine at a local supermarket. It tastes like vinegar and is quite undrinkable.*

It's usually true that you get what you pay for – and there's a world of difference between a good bottle of St-Emilion and a litre of vin de table. Leaving aside the finer distinctions that exist between a good and a mediocre bottle of wine, the Law says that wine must be of 'merchantable quality' and that it must be 'fit for human consumption'. So even the cheapest plonk must be drinkable – but you can't reasonably expect the same standard from a bottle of cheap sparkling wine as from a much more expensive vintage Champagne.

4 *You buy a bottle of wine which, when opened, turns out to be way past its best. What can you do?*

Not much, apart from putting it in the boeuf bourguignonne. Unlike some foods, the law doesn't insist that wine bottles be labelled with a 'sell by' or 'best before' date.

5 *You buy a bottle of wine and share it with friends. The next day all who indulged are violently ill – suggesting that the wine may have been contaminated.*

It is a criminal offence to sell or to offer for sale any food or drink which is intended for human consumption, but which is unfit. If you suffer as a result, inform your local trading standards department who will consider bringing a prosecution. As the actual buyer of the wine, you are entitled to redress for a breach of contract. Until recently, the unfortunate consumer who suffered injury as a result of faulty goods, but didn't actually buy them, could only get compensation if he or she could prove negligence. The Consumer Protection Act 1987 should make things easier. Under this Act, your friends wouldn't have to prove negligence, only that the wine was defective and that they were ill as a result.

6 *You're looking for something festive to take to a special celebration. The Champagne is a bit pricey, but you notice a bottle of 'German Champagne' at a price you can afford.*

The Courts have decided on a number of occasions that the word 'Champagne' can be given only to wine which originates in the Champagne district of France – so you shouldn't see German, Spanish or Australian Champagne around. The same goes for 'Champagne Perry' or 'Champagne Cider'. The term 'méthode champenoise' is now on its way out as well, following pressure from Champagne producers. So although you will still see 'méthode champenoise' on bottles of Saumur or Spanish Cava for a while, producers of sparkling wine made by the Champagne method will have to dream up a new term to distinguish their product from cheaper sparkling wines. American producers sometimes use the phrase 'wine fermented in this bottle'.

7 *You buy a bottle of '1868 Vintage Port' at auction, but you subsequently discover that it's really an injudicious mixture of supermarket vintage character Port and Lambrusco-style home brew. What can you do?*

Deliberately setting out to fake something (be it a bottle of vintage Port or a Constable painting) and then passing it off as the real thing, is fraud and the seller will be liable to criminal prosecution. But in sales by auction (as opposed to buying from a wine merchant), any undertaking as to merchantable quality or conformity with description or sample can be excluded. It's also worth noting that your rights are generally against the seller rather than the auctioneer, which could make it difficult to get redress if the wine does happen to be faulty in some way (although, as we suggest in the section on buying wine at auction, most auction houses will help in negotiations with the seller).

8 *You go to a restaurant and order a bottle of house red. You are disappointed to find that it yields only five glasses of wine, instead of the usual six. You inspect the bottle, and find that it is labelled as having 70cl instead of the 75cl that you are familiar with. You note that the wine list makes no mention of the bottle size.*

70cl bottles of wine are now illegal in the EEC, but the phasing-out period runs until 31 December 1988. So, at the moment, it's still legal to sell 70cl bottles – and there is no legal obligation on a restaurant or shop to state the bottle size.

9 *You're having a quick lunch-time drink at a local wine bar, so you order by the glass, rather than the bottle. Your second glass of house white is noticeably smaller than the first, but you're charged exactly the same. Is it legal?*

Unfortunately, the Law is extremely slack on wine glass measurements. At the moment, there are no standard quantities for wine, unlike those for beer and spirits. There is, however, a purely voluntary code which says, among other things, that quantities of wine should be given alongside prices, and that no bar or restaurant should sell wine by the glass in more than two measures and that the difference between these two measures should be at least two fluid ounces (or 50ml). However, few wine bars or restaurants seem to follow this voluntary code.

10 *You order a bottle of 1978 Chablis Premier Cru at a local restaurant. The waiter brings the bottle to your table, and allows you a cursory glance before opening it. When you taste the wine, you realise immediately that you're drinking a lesser quality 1977 Petit Chablis. What should you do?*

Strictly speaking, the fact that you had an opportunity to inspect the label before the bottle was opened might weaken your legal position and your right to insist on getting exactly what you ordered. But in most cases, a bar or restaurant should exchange without too much hassle. If you proceed to consume the whole bottle before noticing the difference, you can't then complain and reasonably expect to get your original order.

11 *What do you do if you think you've been over-charged for a bottle of wine?*

A restaurant must display a menu and a wine list outside, or immediately inside the entrance. Wine lists containing six or fewer items must state the price (inclusive of VAT) for each wine available. Establishments with a larger selection must show at least six items, but they don't have to display a comprehensive list. You should always check your bill carefully and query anything which doesn't add up.

Sour grapes? – how to complain

The Criminal Laws mentioned above are usually enforced by public authorities. So if you've been sold a bottle of wine which contains something unpleasant or positively harmful to health, you should report the matter to the environmental health department of your local authority. False or misleading descriptions are a matter for the trading standards department of your local authority. If you want to bring a civil action for damages, you should seek legal advice.

Buying wine abroad

You may just be making a day trip to Boulogne or Calais, or you may be taking your car on a touring holiday in France, Italy, Spain or Germany. Either way, you may well be wondering whether it's worth bringing wine back with you, and what the rules are.

A surprising number of wine merchants in this Guide started life with a load of cases of wine in the back of their estate car. It was the cheapest and easiest way to find new producers and even discover new areas which could form the basis for their business. However, most people aren't in it for the career, but simply to provide some pleasurable memories during the coming winter months back home.

As a guide to bringing wine back from holiday we've compiled advice on how and where to buy, and have put together some hints on how to deal with the paperwork required by HM Customs and Excise. (Don't forget that wine can be bought direct from the grower in England and Wales – see the list of English vineyards on page 569 for those which sell to the public.)

How to buy wine

You can buy wine easily enough at any shop or supermarket – and often the range will be sufficiently large or interesting to provide all you want. Some chains of supermarkets have an enormous range of wines, most of which are unobtainable in the UK: Auchan in France is a good example, as are many of the out-of-town mega-stores in northern Italy.

Much more fun, though, is buying at the vineyard. Throughout the wine-growing areas, producers large and small are happy to sell their wine to the passing public, with signs to attract them: Visite des Caves or Dégustation in France; Flaschenwein in Germany; Degustazione in Italy. They tend to be open during the morning and afternoon – but generally firmly closed at lunchtime. Some have proper tasting rooms where you can taste before you buy, while in others, less organised, you may even be invited into the cellar or the house.

To find the good producers in any area is a question of trial and error. But there are certain clues. The best organised places, with large coach parks outside, may be the easiest to cope with, but they will often be well-known co-operatives or large merchant houses, so perhaps less fun. Rough tracks and faded signs may well lead to greater and more interesting discoveries.

Another way to find good producers is to study the wine list in the local restaurants. In the more famous wine towns, you will also come across tasting shops or cellars run by the equivalent of the local chamber of commerce, and wine 'libraries' or enoteca in Italy. Here you can taste the wines, possibly buy and certainly get directions to the producer whose wines you like.

Beware of instant enthusiasms. Professional wine buyers never make decisions to buy at the first encounter. They take samples back to the UK to taste in the cold light of a November morning, far away from the warm hospitality of the French vigneron. You can't do that – but you can buy a couple of bottles to try that evening and then go back if you like the wine. Try and think of drinking it at home, and not on the hotel terrace in the evening sun.

If possible, ask to try more than one wine – different vintages and styles are often to be had. Comparing new and older vintages will give you an idea of how the wine will develop with time. Do not, though, expect grand or old bottles to be opened unless you come recommended, or can convince the grower that you plan to buy a fair amount of his wine.

If you think you've just discovered the wine find of the year from an unknown area, ask yourself why the British wine trade – which has a sharp eye for new wines and new areas – hasn't come across it before. It may be of course that, as in parts of Germany and all over Switzerland and Austria, the locals are too thirsty for their own wine to let any go for export.

Is it cheaper? Of course, because the Chancellor isn't getting his cut. The amateur importer is avoiding the taxes and, if he buys well, can also cut out the wine merchant's transportation costs, overheads and profits. This means that mid-rank wines will be half the UK price, and less special ones even more of a bargain. But because of the risk of disappointment with your holiday favourite vin very ordinaire once you get home, it's often better to buy fewer bottles of more expensive wines. Anyway, the duty on a bottle of first-growth claret is the same as the local co-operative's basic plonk. That means that if you are going over the duty-free allowance the cost of a cheap bottle of wine could double by the time you get it home.

Where to buy wine

While it's the smaller producers who often offer the best hunting ground for the amateur wine buyer, don't necessarily expect the grand estates to welcome you with open arms. Especially in Bordeaux, the château owners can be – not surprisingly – distinctly offhand to a casual passer-by who bowls up in a battered old car wanting to buy a couple of cases of an old vintage.

But elsewhere, even the most famous are surprisingly happy to receive visitors. In Alsace, for instance, companies such as Hugel open tasting shops throughout the day. In most of the Loire – even in pricey

Sancerre – there are Salles de Dégustation. In Champagne, all the big houses are highly organised with visits, tastings and opportunities to buy.

In Burgundy it is more difficult. While the négociants generally run tasting rooms and expect visitors, the small growers often don't want to have to deal with strangers. If you plan to tour in Burgundy, it's best to come armed with introductions from your wine merchant.

Further south in France, things can be disorganised, but always pretty friendly. Producers in Châteauneuf-du-Pape and Provence and larger producers in Côtes du Rhône can cope better than those, say, in Languedoc and Roussillon. Everywhere, the co-operatives are ready to receive visitors.

In Italy, areas like Tuscany, the Veneto (Soave and Valpolicella) and around Rome are best organised for visitors, but most Italians will be happy to see you. In Spain, the bodegas in Rioja, the Cava producers of Penedès and the Sherry producers have good arrangements for tasting and buying. In Portugal, although some of the Port producers receive visitors at their lodges in Oporto, it's best to make appointments beforehand.

Germany and Austria are both well organised for visitors. Even the top producers in Germany have tasting rooms, and are surprisingly happy to sell their finest wines on the spot over the counter. Some producers run very enjoyable restaurants as part of the facilities – and in Austria, the producers in the Vienna woods sell all their wine at the heurige (taverns) in the city's suburbs.

Further afield, California producers are mostly well geared up for tastings and sales, and in areas like Napa Valley and Sonoma, it's possible to do very serious winery crawls if you feel so inclined. In Australia and New Zealand, distances are the problem, but once at a winery, your efforts are likely to be rewarded.

Getting wine back home

After the fun comes the hard part – the transportation and the paperwork.

Most people bring their wine home in the back of their car. A car boot is one of the least congenial places for wine. It is subjected to heat, jolting and vibration, and possibly odours of petrol and oil. If it must go in the boot, pack it in a stout cardboard box with plenty of newspaper. Position the box so that it won't have to be moved every time you shift a suitcase, if possible away from the sun and engine heat and covered with something else in an attempt to keep the temperature even. It does not matter if the bottles are upright: the corks won't dry out in the time involved. When you have got the bottles home, store them in normal conditions for at least a month to let them recover from the journey.

If you are returning home by air, carry the bottles securely packed in hand luggage, not in suitcases which will go in the aircraft hold. The combination of airport baggage handlers and reduced pressure in flight almost guarantees disaster.

The paperwork

The EEC duty-free allowance system permits the import of five litres of wine per person from another EEC country (now including Spain, Greece and Portugal as well as France, Italy and Germany but not Switzerland or Austria). Then you have a choice as to whether you bring three litres more of wine, *or* spirits *or* fortified wine.

If all your wine is bought in the EEC (*not* in duty-free shops), the allowance is thus eight litres per adult (under-18s don't count). This works out at 10.5 75cl bottles each, or 21 for a couple. If you are close to the limit, check the capacity of the bottles: if they contain 70cl (this applies generally only to Germany), the allowance goes up past 11 bottles.

The duty-free allowance from non-EEC countries is wine to a maximum value of £32. If you buy the wine in duty-free shops the maximum you can import is two litres of fortified and/or sparkling wine plus two litres of still table wine.

The problems start if you have more than the allowance. You will need to declare what you are bringing in and pay duty and VAT on the amount of wine over the allowance. Remember that while duty is flat rate (£1.12 per litre on still wine, £1.86 per litre on sparkling wine and £1.94 on fortified wine), VAT is 15 per cent of value, so it's worth treating your most expensive wines as the duty-free allowance. Remember that VAT is also charged on the duty. (The duty payable on wine imported from non-EEC countries is £1.34 per litre on still wine, £2.09 per litre on fortified wine and £2.13 per litre on sparkling – likewise with VAT to be added on.)

In order to work out the VAT, the Customs will need to know how much the wine cost, so you will need to keep receipts. If you don't, they will assume the wine is expensive (especially if it's from France).

Importations of wine over £200 in basic cost should be entered on c10 or c12 forms which you can obtain in advance from a British port. If you are buying more than 60 litres, you need to get a VA form declaring the wine fit for human consumption. To avoid customs duty (which is different from excise), you will need a T2 form from the French port.

When buying in France, you can avoid paying VAT in France (higher than in the UK) by going to the local tax office near the vineyard to get the sale registered as an export from France. Give this form to French customs as you leave.

Find out more about wine

For those smitten with fascination for wine, plenty of things are happening – organised and happily disorganised – to help you find out more. They include wine clubs up and down the country which either sell wine (often specialising in one area) or organise wine tastings. Or there are special wine courses, many run by the top people in the wine trade, where you can learn more intensively. And there are also holidays to wine regions where, apart from learning, you can meet some of the friendliest people – wine producers – and see some beautiful parts of the world.

WINE CLUBS

The Alsace Club of Great Britain
Martin Mistlin, 41 Kingsend, Ruislip HA4 7DD   TEL 01-427 9944 (daytime)
Joining fee £5. President Hugh Johnson. Tutored tastings and dinners (mostly in London), annual trip to Alsace.

Les Amis du Vin
19 Charlotte Street, London W1P 1HB   TEL 01-636 4020
Membership £15. Discounts: five per cent off all wines, ten per cent off unmixed cases, free delivery for 2+ cases or over £75. Priority booking for tastings. Regular newsletter. Members can buy wines at club prices at any Cullens stores on production of membership card. Regular special offers. (See also WHERE TO BUY section.)

Cofradia Riojana
66 Pinner Green, Pinner HA5 2AB   TEL 01-427 9944 (daytime)
Contact Martin Mistlin
Membership £11.50 (includes society medallion). No annual subscription. Tastings and dinners featuring wines from Rioja and other regions of Spain.

Connoisseur Wine Club
57 Cambridge Street, London SW1V 4PS   TEL 01-834 4101
Unit 28, Dreadnought Trading Estate, Bridport, Dorset DT6 5AG
TEL (0308) 25906

Membership free. Organisers Edward Hicks (London) and Andrew Bell (Bridport). President Prince Rupert Löwenstein. Free tastings in London and Bridport, tutored by one of the vice-presidents, who include Jean-Claude Fourman of Joseph Perrier and Jacques Parent of Burgundy. Monthly newsletter, wine list four times a year, plus bin-end offers. Free delivery in England and Wales, discounts on gift delivery service called Speedifizz.

Coonawarra Club

Mike McCarthy (secretary), 224 Minard Road, Catford, London SE6 1NJ   TEL 01-828 2216 (work), 01-698 2504 (home)
This club was set up by Mike McCarthy, who also runs the Zinfandel Club (see below). Membership £5, renewal £2 per annum. Tastings of Australian wines, sometimes tutored. Occasional dinners with appropriate wines.

Gallo Nero Wine Club

Martin Mistlin, 41 Kingsend, Ruislip HA4 7DD   TEL 01-427 9944 (daytime)
Annual subscription £5 single, £7.50 double. President The Hon Rocco Forte. Tastings, dinners, occasional visits to Chianti Classico vineyards and a stay in Florence. In addition the club plans occasional events featuring wines from other regions.

Howells of Bristol Limited Bin Club

Creswicke House, 9 Small Street, Bristol, Avon BS1 1DB
TEL (0272) 277641   TELEX 449443 (CRES HO)
This club, run by Tim Hood, specialises in 'the laying down of wines under ideal conditions so that our customers can buy wines at opening prices, gradually build up a cellar and then enjoy drinking their wines at a later date when they are properly mature.' It is particularly popular with expatriates wanting to accumulate a wine cellar while they are abroad, but UK residents are also welcome. Membership £15, plus a monthly subscription (min £30). You receive a Cellar Book on joining and a storage charge is made, which covers insurance (currently 17p per case per month). Offers are made twice a year in the spring and autumn and, in addition, en primeur offers of new vintages of clarets and Ports. The regular offers give notes on each wine and recommended ready for drinking dates. Statements of account are sent with the spring and autumn offers, showing the amount of credit accumulated and offering advance credit calculated at three times the monthly contributions.

International Wine & Food Society

108 Old Brompton Road, London SW7 3RA   TEL 01-370 0909
Director Hugo Dunn-Meynell. Enrolment fee £4.60. Membership £16 single, £22 joint, £8.70 young members (under 25). President Michael

Broadbent MW. London HQ with library and worldwide contacts.
Regional branches organise dinners, tastings, lectures, visits. Annual
journal *World Gastronomy* free of charge.

Lay & Wheeler

6 Culver Street West, Colchester, Essex CO1 1JA   TEL (0206) 67261
A series of popular wine workshops held in the Colchester Garrison
Officers' Club each involving distinguished speakers, tasting and cold
supper. During 1987 Peter Sichel presented the wines of Châteaux
Palmer and d'Angludet, and Jean Eugène and Xavier Borie the wines
from Châteaux Ducru-Beaucaillou, Grand-Puy-Lacoste and
Haut-Batailley; while Jean Hugel lectured on his Alsace wines.
Monthly mini-workshops are held at their Gosbecks Road Wine
Market in Colchester.

Lincoln Wine Society

12 Mainwaring Road, Lincoln, Lincolnshire LN2 4BL
TEL (0522) 42077
Chairman Christine Austin. Monthly talk and tasting sessions. Fine
Wine evenings (with dinner included) held three times a year. Three
newsletters a year. Membership £5 annually (£8 joint membership).

Malmaison Wine Club

28 Midland Road, London NW1 2AD   TEL 01-388 5086
Membership £5 per annum. Discount: five per cent. Tastings, special
events, special offers.

Methuselah's

29 Victoria Street, London SW1H 0EU   TEL 01-222 0424/3550
Annual subscription £15. Tutored tastings held every second Monday.
Various discounts and priority bookings for events. Two-course dinner
with coffee at £7.50 a head available after tastings. Part of Don
Hewitson's Cork & Bottle wine bar chain (see under WINE BARS).

Le Nez Rouge Wine Club

Berkmann Wine Cellars, 12 Brewery Road, London N7 9NH
TEL 01-609 4711
Manager Philip MacGregor. Life membership costs either a case of club
wine or a case of wine plus £10. Special offers, regular tastings (tutored
and blind), dinners. Club magazine twice a year. (See also WHERE TO
BUY section.)

North East Wine Tasting Society

Terry Douglas (Secretary), 3 Bemersyde Drive, Jesmond,
Newcastle-upon-Tyne, Tyne & Wear NE2 2HC   TEL 091-281 4769
Monthly tastings held in Newcastle, some of them tutored. Annual
membership £10.

Northern Wine Appreciation Group

D M Hunter, 21 Dartmouth Avenue, Almondbury, Huddersfield, West Yorkshire HD5 8UR   TEL (0484) 531228
Weekly meetings in West Yorkshire from September to June, 'to taste, assess and extend the members' experience of wine and food'. The relationship of food to wine leads to the planning and development of the meals which form part of the group's activities. Tastings are supplemented by tastings at merchants.

Helen Verdcourt Wines

Spring Cottage, Kimbers Lane, Maidenhead, Berkshire SL6 2QP
TEL (0628) 25577
Two local clubs meet monthly, one in Maidenhead, the other in Englefield Green, for tastings tutored by Helen Verdcourt. Other clubs meet occasionally. No membership fees, tastings charged at cost. (See also WHERE TO BUY section and WINE TOURS.)

La Vigneronne

105 Old Brompton Road, London SW7 3LE   TEL 01-589 6113
The tutored tastings of fine and rare wines held every Monday and Thursday (and occasionally on Wednesdays) are very popular. No membership fee. (See also WHERE TO BUY section.)

Vintner Wine Club

Winefare House, 5 High Road, Byfleet, Surrey KT14 7QF
TEL (09323) 51585
Initial enrolment fee and annual membership £12. President Derek Cooper, manager David Cartwright, club contributor Maggie McNie MW, owned by Arthur Rackhams. Quarterly newsletter. Comprehensive list of 300 wines and individual tasting notes. Members can get a discount on single bottles at every Arthur Rackhams. Gastronomic programme of monthly tutored tastings and dinners in West End and Surrey restaurants. La Grande Taste – weekend members' tastings at Arthur Rackhams. The Vintner Festival at the Savoy Hotel (London) every October. (See also Arthur Rackhams in the WHERE TO BUY section.)

The Wine Club

New Aquitaine House, Paddock Road, Reading, Berkshire RG4 0JY   TEL (0734) 481713
Also known as The Sunday Times Wine Club. Mail order only. President Hugh Johnson, Secretary Hilary Penrose. Annotated list, tastings, tours, Vintage Festival, and a lively quarterly journal, *Wine Times*. Tours vary from long weekends to six-day tours of other European wine-growing regions. (See also Bordeaux Direct in the WHERE TO BUY section.)

The Wine & Dine Society

Gail Wright, 173 Denmark Hill, London SE5 8DX   TEL 01-274 9484
Anyone who asks is put on the mailing list. Weekly London tastings of
food and wine, plus tours of wine regions. Annual subscription £5.

Wine Mine Club

Peter Dominic, Vintner House, River Way, Harlow, Essex
CM20 2EA   TEL (0279) 416291
Membership £5 per annum (on receipt of which you will receive a £5
wine voucher to spend in any Peter Dominic shop). The club provides
a basic information service, organises tastings, makes special offers (eg
en primeur claret and Port) and distributes a quarterly newsletter.
They have recently introduced a wine list exclusive to club members.
(See also Peter Dominic in the WHERE TO BUY section.)

The Wine Society

Gunnels Wood Road, Stevenage, Hertfordshire SG1 2BG
TEL (0438) 314161; ORDER OFFICE (0438) 728701 or 01-349 3296;
TELEX 826072 (IECWS)
53 Bolsover Street, London W1P 7HL   TEL 01-387 4681
See WHERE TO BUY section.

The Winery

4 Clifton Road, Maida Vale, London W9 1FF   TEL 01-286 6475
Manager James Whitehead. Now part of Les Amis du Vin (see WHERE
TO BUY section), The Winery does however retain its own identity, an
attractive part of which are special wine tastings organised by Isabelle
Plevin.

The Winetasters

P N Beardwood (Secretary), 44 Claremont Road, London
W13 0DG   TEL 01-997 1252
Annual subscription £3 (£1.50 if you live more than 50 miles from
London). Non-profit-making club which organises tastings, seminars,
dinners and tours (next major tour in 1989). The club grew out of the
Schoolmasters' Wine Club.

Zinfandel Club

Mike McCarthy (Secretary), 224 Minard Road, Catford, London
SE6 1NJ   TEL 01-828 2216 (work), 01-698 2504 (home)
Membership fee £5. Sporadic meetings to taste California wines,
sometimes tutored. Occasional dinners with appropriate wines.

WINE COURSES

David Baillie Vintners School of Wine

The Sign of the Lucky Horseshoe, 86 Longbrook Street, Exeter, Devon
EX4 6AP   TEL (0392) 221345
This West-country wine merchant (see WHERE TO BUY section) plans to
repeat its School of Wine course in 1988. The course is run two or three
times a year, and comprises six three-hour evening sessions of tastings
and lectures given by experienced members of the Wine Trade, with an
optional exam at the end, leading (for those who pass) to a Certificate
from the David Baillie School of Wine. Cost in 1987, £75.

Christie's Wine Course

63 Old Brompton Road, London SW7 3JS   TEL 01-581 3933
Principals Michael Broadbent MW and Steven Spurrier, secretary
Caroline de Lane Lea. Christie's run two wine courses: Part 1 is an
introduction to wine tasting through the principal wines of France and
is run four to five times a year; Part 2 consists of specialised tastings of
Burgundy, Bordeaux, Port and Madeira, and is run once or twice a
year. Both courses take place on five consecutive Tuesday evenings,
lasting roughly two hours, for 45 students. Discussion and tasting are
conducted by top wine experts (in 1987 the roll included Michael
Broadbent MW, Serena Sutcliffe MW, David Peppercorn MW, Pamela
Vandyke Price and Steven Spurrier). Part 1 costs £100 and Part 2 £125,
but the latter can be taken as five separate evenings, each at £30 (the fee
for Part 2 may increase by the beginning of 1988). Occasional single
tasting evenings.

Ecole du Vin, Château Loudenne, Bordeaux

Valerie Sargent, Ecole du Vin, IDV Vintner House, Harlow, Essex
CM20 2EA   TEL (0279) 26801
Six-day courses (starting on Monday) are held for a dozen students five
times a year at Gilbey's Ch Loudenne, under the direction of Charles
Eve MW. Accommodation and cuisine of very high standard in the
château. Aimed at the public and professionals in the trade, the
lectures and tastings cover all aspects of viticulture and vinification.
Visits are arranged to other Bordeaux areas and châteaux. Cost (in
1987) £795, exclusive of travel to France.

German Wine Academy, Kloster Eberbach

German Wine Information Service, 31 Brechin Place, London
SW7 4QD   TEL 01-244 7558
Arranges in-house courses and lectures for interested trade groups.

German Wine Academy, PO Box 1705, 6500 Mainz, Federal Republic of Germany

A 12th-century monastery houses these seminars (given in English), including lectures by experts, vineyard visits and tastings. The basic seven-day course (DM 1,740 in 1987) is offered six times a year between May and September and follow-up courses are also organised.

Leith's School of Food and Wine

21 St Alban's Grove, London W8 5BP   TEL 01-229 0177

Some of Leith's wine courses are for students of the School only, as part of their food and wine studies. However, at least two are available to others: five two-hour evening sessions starting on 12 and 16 February 1988, leading to the Leith's Certificate (if you pass the exam, that is); and a ten-session course (also two-hour evening sessions), starting on 12 January 1988, leading to Leith's Advanced Certificate of Wine, examined by Leith's Master of Wine, Richard Harvey. This is roughly analogous to the Wine and Spirit Education Trust's Higher Certificate, without the sessions on licensing and labelling laws, and with particular stress on tasting. Cost £120 and £200 respectively. Other courses, such as specialist evenings, are also sometimes available.

Sotheby's

Wine Evenings with Sotheby's, 34–35 New Bond Street, London W1A 2AA   TEL 01-493 8080

Organiser Jane Swallow (Wine Department). A series of six evenings, tutored by experts (Christian de Billy – Pol Roger Champagne, Val Brown – 1983 Red Burgundies, Nick Davies – Ch Larmande, were among the names in 1987) on 'Some of the world's great or unusual wines'. A relaxed atmosphere is encouraged by an aperitif at 6.45 pm, with the tasting running from 7 pm to 8.30 pm. The course cost £140 in 1987 (individual evenings £25–£30). If you already subscribe to Sotheby's wine catalogues, there is a discount of 15 per cent. Other major tastings in 1987 included the London Wine Trade Fair and Vinexpo in Bordeaux.

Tante Marie School of Cookery

Woodham House, Carlton Road, Woking, Surrey GU21 4HF
TEL (048 62) 26957

Conal Gregory MW, MP, organises wine appreciation courses, generally during autumn and winter, on three weekday evenings (lasting two hours), aimed at those with little previous knowledge and including tutored tastings.

WINE TOURS

Abreu Travel Agency

109 Westbourne Grove, London W2 4UL   TEL 01-229 9905
This travel agency organises an eight-day tour of the Portuguese wine
areas, with appropriate visits and tastings. There were four departure
dates in 1987: 31 May, 20 and 27 September, and 11 October and cost
£369. Three departure dates are currently being planned for 1988, also
in May, September and October.

The Alsace Club of Great Britain

See under WINE CLUBS.

Australian Tourist Commission

Heathcoat House, 20 Savile Row, London W1X 1AE   TEL 01-434 4371
The Tourist Commission can provide information on tours and wine
routes available through Australian travel firms, from a half-day in
McLaren Vale to seven days in Hunter Valley at a riding lodge.

Blackheath Wine Trails

13 Blackheath Village, London SE3 9LD   TEL 01-463 0012
In 1987, eight tours were offered: northern Portugal, Burgundy and
Beaujolais, Champagne, Central and Eastern Loire, Madrid and Rioja,
Seville and Jerez, Tuscany, and the Madeira Wine Festival, ranging
from four to eight days. All were air/coach (except Champagne which
was ferry/coach).

Brittany Ferries

The Brittany Centre, Wharf Road, Portsmouth, Hampshire PO2 8RU
TEL (0705) 827701
In 1987 Brittany Ferries ran two Wine Workshops, one to the Loire
Valley and the other to the Champagne area; the four-day coach tours
offer plenty of opportunity to buy and taste on both tours. Cost in 1987
was £169 (including ferry return with cabins, coach, three nights' hotel
accommodation, most meals and entrance fees to relevant wine
museums).

Thomas Cook

PO Box 36, Thorpe Wood, Peterborough, Cambridgeshire PE3 6SD
TEL (0733) 63200
In May and September 1988 Thomas Cook will be running a 7-night
coach tour of the Loire Valley including several wine tastings and
château visits.

DER Travel Service

18 Conduit Street, London W1R 9TD   TEL 01-408 0111
As well as Rhine and Mosel cruises with no special emphasis on wine,
DER arranges accommodation in German hotels, guest houses or
apartments, some of them in wine-growing areas: with your own car
you would be free to visit vineyards. For summer 1988 there are plans
for a special holiday to the Rheingau for wine lovers.

English vineyards

Many English vineyards are open to the public offering guided tours,
tastings and sales. For further information see the ENGLISH
VINEYARDS section.

Eurocamp

28 Princess Street, Knutsford, Cheshire WA16 6BG
TEL (0565) 3844
Eurocamp arrange self-drive camping and caravan holidays at 115 sites
in Europe, many of which are 'almost among the grapes – and the
more well-known grapes at that'. These include the Gironde, Saumur,
Meursault, Bergerac, Cahors and the Mosel.

European Canal Cruises

79 Winchester Road, Romsey, Hampshire SO51 8JB
TEL (0794) 51442
The *Duchess Anne*, a luxury barge-yacht, takes eight people for a week
in Brittany and the Pays de la Loire, with a mini-bus and bicycles on
hand for excursions. The *Royal Cognac* spends a week exploring the
Charente, with appropriate visits. It sleeps nine and has available a
mini-bus (for trips to Bordeaux, for instance) and bicycles. Cost in 1987
for either tour was £680 (£520 in July and August).

Francophiles

Ron and Jenny Farmer, 66 Great Brockeridge, Westbury-on-Trym,
Bristol, Avon BS9 3UA   TEL (0272) 621975
The Farmers offer France 'lovingly packaged' on their personally
accompanied holidays of discovery in the wine-growing regions. Their
customers are 'not usual coach holiday travellers' who appreciate
in-depth, unhurried visits and structured tastings. In 1988 they offer
Heritage of Burgundy, Portrait of Alsace, Loire Valley and 'Vive le
Beaujolais', plus general interest holidays with wine appeal.

Gallo Nero Wine Club

See under WINE CLUBS.

KD German Rhine Line

G A Clubb Rhine Cruise Agency, 28 South Street, Epsom, Surrey
KT18 7PF   TEL (037 27) 42033
In 1987, a week-long cruise left from Cologne, visited vineyards on the
Rhine, the Mosel and in Alsace, and included lectures and tutored
tastings by Dr Hans Ambrosi, Director of the Eltville State Vineyards.
This 'floating wine seminar' ended in Basle. Cost in 1987 £762 plus
travel to Cologne and from Basle.

Moswin Tours

PO Box 8, Oadby, Leicester, Leicestershire LE2 5WX
TEL (0533) 719922 (ABTA No 32053)
Moswin Tours specialise in tours of the Mosel, but offer tours to other
German wine areas. Wine seminars (either as part of a tour or
completely separate) and wine gourmet tours can also be arranged for
interested groups. Visits to vineyards, tastings, good restaurants and
hotels. Wine tours for private parties are tailor-made with a special
booklet. Tours range from four to fifteen days; coach and air travel.
Holidays staying with a wine-farmer can be arranged.

Rosecourt Fine Wine

Wine Warehouse, Unit 1/2 Osborne's Court, Olney, Buckinghamshire
MK46 4AA   TEL (023 471) 3077
(Previously known as Connaught House). Specialised education tours
related to the growers in France, Germany and Austria. Details
available from early 1988.

Special Interest Tours

1 Cank Street, Leicester, Leicestershire LE1 5GX   TEL (0533) 531373
Coach tours (with convenient joining points: Leicester, Birmingham,
Coventry, Sheffield, London etc) visit French wine regions for five, six
and seven day tours, which include tastings.

Helen Verdcourt Wine Tours

Spring Cottage, Kimbers Lane, Maidenhead, Berkshire SL6 2QP
TEL (0628) 25577
A 22-day round the-world trip to the Australian vineyards is the tour
on offer for 1988. Places to be limited to a maximum of 30 people. Final
details and price had yet to be finalised as we went to press.

Victour

Tourist Office, Victoria House, Melbourne Place, Strand, London
WC2B 4LG   TEL 01-836 2656
The Victoria Tourism Commission produces a good wine and food
guide to Victoria with helpful notes on wineries and ideas for self-drive
visits. They also have details of various rail and coach tours. (See also
Australian Tourist Commission in this section.)

Vintage Wine Tours

8 Belmont, Lansdown Road, Bath, Avon BA1 5DZ
TEL (0225) 315834/315659 (ABTA No 42060)
Concentrates efforts on designing tours for groups (approx 24 people) and will 'custom make' tours to any destination, including gourmet meals, sightseeing excursions and any special requirements. A brochure is available to spark off ideas.

Wessex Continental Travel

124 North Road East, Plymouth Devon, PL4 6AH
TEL (0752) 228333/225572
The Wine Tour programme has been devised and will be presented by Helen Gillespie-Peck. Regions on offer in 1987 were the Dordogne, Alsace and Champagne, Burgundy, Bordeaux, Spain, Italian northern vineyards, Portugal and California.

The Wine Club

See under WINE CLUBS.

The Wine & Dine Society

See under WINE CLUBS.

The Winetasters

See under WINE CLUBS.

World Wine Tours

4 Dorchester Road, Drayton St Leonard, Oxfordshire OX9 8BH
TEL (0865) 891919
World Wine Tours organise a wide-ranging series of tours, most of which are led by Masters of Wine. In 1987, 16 tours of 4–9 days were offered to 11 regions (Alsace, Bordeaux, Burgundy, Champagne, the Loire Valley, Napa Valley, Piedmont, Portugal, the Rhône Valley, Rioja, Tuscany). Tours in 1988 are likely to run from February–October and plans are being made to add Madeira and Germany to the regions on offer. In addition to these tours, Liz and Martin Holliss devise tours and short breaks for individuals, couples and groups. World Wine Tours are also the exclusive agents in the UK for courses, tours and seminars at L'Ecole de Bordeaux.

Wine bookshelf

Wine books continue to pour off the presses. This is a selection of those published during the past two years which we have found the most interesting.

General

The Wine Companion – Hugh Johnson (Mitchell Beazley, £14.95)
A complete revision of the widest-ranging guide to wine regions of the world and the producers who work in them. Essential reference.

Webster's Wine Guide (1988 edition) – edited by Oz Clarke (Webster's, £8.95)
A guide to the price you should expect to pay for wine at merchants and in the supermarkets, coupled with brief articles on the state of the market in the production regions. Now in paperback format.

Pocket Wine Book (1988 edition) – Hugh Johnson (Mitchell Beazley, £4.95)
The annual update of the book most wine merchants stick in their pockets when they travel or even when they meet customers.

Christie's Wine Companion – edited by Patrick Matthews (Webb and Bower/Michael Joseph, £14.95)
A series of essays from top wine writers and experts as well as enthusiastic amateurs, ranging round the world of wine. The enjoyment to be had from the quality of the writing is as great as the interest to be found in the information.

Liquid Gold, Dessert Wines of the World – Stephen Brook (Constable, £14.95)
The first book ever devoted entirely to sweet wines the world over (although it devotes most detail to France and Germany). Well written, with good producer profiles and a detailed study of the way the wines are made.

André Simon, Gourmet and Wine Lover – Patrick Morrah (Constable, £10.95)
A biography of the founder of the International Wine and Food Society and guru of today's generation of wine writers.

The World Atlas of Wine – Hugh Johnson (Mitchell Beazley, £22.50)
A revision of the best-selling book which now includes greater detail on the New World wine areas as well as Italy and Spain.

Vines, Grapes and Wines – Jancis Robinson (Mitchell Beazley, £16.95)
A book that goes back to origins – the vine – exploring the character of
each vine and the types of wine it produces. Beautiful line drawings.

Anatomy of the Wine Trade – Simon Loftus (Sidgwick & Jackson, £5.95)
A series of essays on characters and aspects of the wine trade – both in
the vineyards and in Britain. Elegant writing and some interesting
insights.

Wine: Lore, Legends and Traditions – Pamela Vandyke Price (Hamlyn,
£8.95)
The truth behind the tales and myths of wine reveals some
fascinatingly useless information. It's the sort of book that repays
constant dipping.

The Cellar Book – Hugh Johnson (Mitchell Beazley, £16.95)
Facts and information combine with plenty of space for keeping details
of what's in the cellar (if you don't drink it first).

The Illustrated Guide to Wine – Chris Foulkes (W H Smith, £5.95)
The gift for the wine beginner, this book will definitely stimulate the
enthusiasm to drink widely and with a catholic taste.

Specialist

AUSTRALIA

Complete Book of Australian Wine – Len Evans (J M Dent & Sons, £25)
Complete is the word – every winery, small and large, is there with
tasting notes and technical information galore.

FRANCE – GENERAL

French Wine Atlas – Hubrecht Duijker and Hugh Johnson (Mitchell
Beazley, £16.95)
A complete and well-written guide to visiting French vineyards: route
maps, lists of producers, where to eat and drink, where to stay, places
of interest. To read at home as well as to take with you.

The Pocket Book of French Regional Wines – Roger Voss (Mitchell Beazley,
£4.95)
May we modestly recommend this new guide (in the familiar Pocket
Book format) to the wines and producers of all the regions of France
apart from Bordeaux, Burgundy and Champagne? Tasting information
and vintage reports, plus detailed information on all the AC and VDQS
areas of France.

The Wines of France – Serena Sutcliffe (Futura, £2.95)
An up-to-date view of the wines being made in France today. Vintage
information as well as descriptions of the different vineyard areas.

The Wine Lovers' Guide to France – Michael Busselle (Michael Joseph, £14.95)
Beautiful photographs of the vineyard areas, but also useful information for tours and visits (including details from *Michelin* maps).

Eperon's French Wine Tour – Arthur Eperon (Pan, £6.95)
A tour of French vineyards, with maps, information on where to stay and eat, a description of the wines and advice on where to taste and buy them.

FRANCE – BORDEAUX

Pocket Guide to the Wines of Bordeaux – David Peppercorn (Mitchell Beazley, £4.95)
Following the standard Pocket Book style, this covers the whole of Bordeaux with a tightly written guide to the main areas and estates. Tasting notes include ones on recent vintages.

The Wines of Bordeaux (revised edition) – Edmund Penning-Rowsell (Penguin, £12.95)
Anybody who knows how comprehensive and useful previous editions of this guide to Bordeaux were will definitely want to buy this new edition.

FRANCE – BURGUNDY

Pocket Guide to the Wines of Burgundy – Serena Sutcliffe (Mitchell Beazley, £4.95)
A guide to the minefield of Burgundy, based on the Pocket Book formula, with directory-style entries for producers and villages. Plenty of opinions, too.

FRANCE – CHAMPAGNE

Champagne – Tom Stevenson (Sotheby's, £19.95)
An authoritative guide to everything there is to know about Champagne – the producers, the villages, the history, the taste, the vintages, how to drink and store Champagne.

GERMANY

Atlas of German Wines – Hugh Johnson and Ian Jamieson (Mitchell Beazley, £14.95)
A guide to the German vineyards, with listings of all the different estate names and regions. Good for touring (if a bit big) and for reference.

ITALY

Life Beyond Lambrusco – Nicolas Belfrage (Sidgwick & Jackson, £7.95)
Full of information on Italian wines with easy cross-referencing and plenty of background. Wines and producers are described, the main styles are analysed and what each area produces is listed.

WINE BOOKSHELF

NEW ZEALAND

The Wines and Vineyards of New Zealand – Mike Cooper (Hodder & Stoughton, £14.95)
Everything you want to know about New Zealand's wines, plus some beautiful photography.

PORTUGAL – PORT

Rich, Rare and Red – Ben Howkins (Christopher Helm/Wine Appreciation Society, £5.95)
A revised edition of this guide to Port which first appeared five years ago. History, geography, plus profiles of the Port houses and anecdotes from someone closely connected with the Port wine trade.

SPAIN

The Wine and Food of Spain – Jan Read and Maite Manjon (Weidenfeld and Nicolson, £12.95)
The top experts on Spanish food and wine cover the country, looking at different regions, their wine, the local cuisine. Includes information on restaurants and hotels.

SPARKLING WINES

Pocket Guide to Champagne and Sparkling Wines – Jane MacQuitty (Mitchell Beazley, £4.95)
Exhaustive guide to the sparkling wines of the world – from New Zealand to Oregon and Champagne to Chile. Directory-style entries in the Pocket Book format.

Index

This index covers the WHAT TO BUY section only. Names from the lists of 'Who's Who' in each country have been indexed only if they also appear in the main text. Maps have not been indexed.

Report to the Editor *Which? Wine Guide*

This report is

a new recommendation   ☐
a comment on existing entry   ☐   *please tick as appropriate*

name of establishment

address

tel no:

please continue overleaf

date of most recent visit
_____

signed
_____

I am not connected directly or indirectly with the management or
proprietors

name   *in block letters, please*
_____

address
_____
_____

Report to the Editor *Which? Wine Guide*

This report is

a new recommendation ☐

a comment on existing entry ☐   *please tick as appropriate*

name of establishment

address

tel no:

please continue overleaf

date of most recent visit
_____

signed
_____

I am not connected directly or indirectly with the management or proprietors

name   *in block letters, please*
_____

address
_____
_____

Send to: Which? Wine Guide, Freepost, London WC2N 4BR
(please note: no postage required within UK)

Report to the Editor *Which? Wine Guide*

This report is

a new recommendation ☐
a comment on existing entry ☐ *please tick as appropriate*

name of establishment

address

tel no:

please continue overleaf

date of most recent visit
_____

signed
_____

I am not connected directly or indirectly with the management or proprietors

name   *in block letters, please*
_____

address
_____

_____

Send to: Which? Wine Guide, Freepost, London WC2N 4BR
(please note: no postage required within UK)

Report to the Editor *Which? Wine Guide*

This report is

a new recommendation ☐
a comment on existing entry ☐ *please tick as appropriate*

name of establishment
_____

address
_____

tel no:
_____

please continue overleaf

date of most recent visit
_____

signed
_____

I am not connected directly or indirectly with the management or
proprietors

name   *in block letters, please*
_____

address
_____

_____

Send to: Which? Wine Guide, Freepost, London WC2N 4BR
(please note: no postage required within UK)

Report to the Editor *Which? Wine Guide*

This report is

a new recommendation ☐
a comment on existing entry ☐   *please tick as appropriate*

name of establishment

_____

address

_____

tel no:

_____

please continue overleaf

date of most recent visit
_____

signed
_____

I am not connected directly or indirectly with the management or proprietors

name   *in block letters, please*
_____

address
_____

_____

Send to: Which? Wine Guide, Freepost, London WC2N 4BR
(please note: no postage required within UK)

Report to the Editor *Which? Wine Guide*

This report is

a new recommendation   ☐

a comment on existing entry   ☐   *please tick as appropriate*

name of establishment

_____

address

_____

tel no:

_____

please continue overleaf

date of most recent visit
_____

signed
_____

I am not connected directly or indirectly with the management or proprietors

name   *in block letters, please*
_____

address
_____

_____

Send to: Which? Wine Guide, Freepost, London WC2N 4BR
(please note: no postage required within UK)

Report to the Editor *Which? Wine Guide*

This report is

a new recommendation ☐
a comment on existing entry ☐ *please tick as appropriate*

name of establishment

address

tel no:

please continue overleaf

date of most recent visit

signed

I am not connected directly or indirectly with the management or proprietors

name _in block letters, please_

address

Send to: Which? Wine Guide, Freepost, London WC2N 4BR
(please note: no postage required within UK)

Report to the Editor *Which? Wine Guide*

This report is

a new recommendation   ☐
a comment on existing entry   ☐   *please tick as appropriate*

name of establishment

_____

address

_____

tel no:

_____

please continue overleaf

date of most recent visit
_____

signed
_____

I am not connected directly or indirectly with the management or proprietors

name   *in block letters, please*
_____

address
_____
_____

Send to: Which? Wine Guide, Freepost, London WC2N 4BR
(please note: no postage required within UK)